BORDERLINE PERSONALITY DISORDER: TREATMENT AND MANAGEMENT

National Clinical Practice Guideline Number 78

National Collaborating Centre for Mental Health
commissioned by the

National Institute for Health
& Clinical Excellence

published by
The British Psychological Society and The Royal College of Psychiatrists

British Library Cataloguing-in-Publication Data

A catalogue record for this book is available from the British Library.

ISBN: 978-1-85433-477-0

Printed in Great Britain by Stanley L. Hunt (Printers) Ltd.

Additional material: data CD-Rom created by Pixl8 (www.pixl8.co.uk)

developed by   National Collaborating Centre for Mental Health
Royal College of Psychiatrists' Research and Training Unit
4th Floor, Standon House
21 Mansell Street
London
E1 8AA
www.nccmh.org.uk

commissioned by   National Institute for Health and Clinical Excellence
MidCity Place, 71 High Holborn
London
WC1V 6NA
www.nice.org.uk

published by   The British Psychological Society
St Andrews House
48 Princess Road East
Leicester
LE1 7DR
www.bps.org.uk

and

The Royal College of Psychiatrists
17 Belgrave Square
London
SW1X 8PG
www.rcpsych.ac.uk

The British Psychological Society

RC PSYCH
ROYAL COLLEGE OF PSYCHIATRISTS

CONTENTS

GUIDELINE DEVELOPMENT GROUP MEMBERS   **6**

ACKNOWLEDGEMENTS   **9**

1. PREFACE   **10**
1.1   National guideline   10
1.2   The national borderline personality disorder guideline   13

2. BORDERLINE PERSONALITY DISORDER   **15**
2.1   The disorder   15
2.2   Diagnosis   17
2.3   Epidemiology   20
2.4   Aetiology   21
2.5   Treatment and management   25
2.6   Multi-agency perspective   32
2.7   Young people   34
2.8   The experience of service users, and families and carers   35
2.9   Economic impact   35

3. METHODS USED TO DEVELOP THIS GUIDELINE   **38**
3.1   Overview   38
3.2   The Scope   38
3.3   The Guideline Development Group   39
3.4   Clinical questions   41
3.5   Systematic clinical literature review   42
3.6   Health economics review strategies   55
3.7   Stakeholder contributions   58
3.8   Validation of this guideline   58

4. EXPERIENCE OF CARE   **59**
4.1   Introduction   59
4.2   Personal accounts   59
4.3   Review of the qualitative literature   81
4.4   Family and carer experience   93
4.5   Summary of themes   96
4.6   Clinical practice recommendations   99

5. **PSYCHOLOGICAL AND PSYCHOSOCIAL TREATMENTS IN THE MANAGEMENT OF BORDERLINE PERSONALITY DISORDER** **101**
 5.1 Introduction 101
 5.2 Arts therapies 115
 5.3 Brief psychological interventions 117
 5.4 Complementary therapies 124
 5.5 Individual psychological therapies 126
 5.6 Combination therapy 144
 5.7 Psychological therapy programmes 153
 5.8 Therapeutic communities 175
 5.9 Data by outcome 188
 5.10 Overall clinical summary 204
 5.11 Overall summary of economic evidence 206
 5.12 Clinical practice recommendations 207
 5.13 Research recommendations 208

6. **PHARMACOLOGICAL AND OTHER PHYSICAL TREATMENTS IN THE MANAGEMENT OF BORDERLINE PERSONALITY DISORDER** **211**
 6.1 Introduction 211
 6.2 Anticonvulsants and lithium 218
 6.3 Antipsychotics 230
 6.4 Antidepressants 246
 6.5 Omega-3 fatty acids 254
 6.6 Naloxone 257
 6.7 Effect of treatment on symptoms 260
 6.8 Effect of treatment on general functioning and other outcomes 278
 6.9 Effect of treatment on acceptability/tolerability outcomes 283
 6.10 Summary of clinical evidence review 296
 6.11 Health economic evidence 296
 6.12 Clinical practice recommendations 297
 6.13 Research recommendation 297

7. **MANAGEMENT OF CRISES** **298**
 7.1 Introduction 298
 7.2 Current practice 298
 7.3 Reviewing the evidence base 299
 7.4 General management of crises 299
 7.5 Pharmacological management of crises 301
 7.6 Management of insomnia 303

8. THE CONFIGURATION AND ORGANISATION OF SERVICES   305
8.1   Introduction   305
8.2   The role of specialist services   306
8.3   Risk factors for suicide in people with borderline
        personality disorder   310
8.4   The role of inpatient services   320
8.5   Care pathway   324
8.6   Research recommendation   342
8.7   Special considerations for people with learning disabilities   342
8.8   Special considerations for people from black and
        minority ethnic groups   345

9. YOUNG PEOPLE WITH BORDERLINE PERSONALITY DISORDER   346
9.1   Introduction   346
9.2   Diagnosis   348
9.3   Stability of the diagnosis of borderline personality
        disorder in young people   349
9.4   Suicide risk in young people with borderline
        personality disorder   358
9.5   Assessment   363
9.6   Treatment   365
9.7   Service configuration   366
9.8   Suggested care pathway for young people with
        borderline personality disorder   366
9.9   Overall clinical summary   376
9.10 Clinical practice recommendations   377

10. SUMMARY OF RECOMMENDATIONS   378
11. APPENDICES   393
12. REFERENCES   519
13. ABBREVIATIONS   552

GUIDELINE DEVELOPMENT GROUP MEMBERS

Professor Peter Tyrer (Chair, Guideline Development Group)
Professor of Community Psychiatry, Imperial College, London

Dr Tim Kendall (Facilitator, Guideline Development Group)
Joint Director, The National Collaborating Centre for Mental Health
Deputy Director, Royal College of Psychiatrists' Research and Training Unit
Consultant Psychiatrist and Medical Director, Sheffield Health and
Social Care Foundation Trust

Professor Anthony Bateman
Consultant Psychiatrist, Barnet, Enfield, and Haringey Mental Health NHS Trust
Visiting Professor, University College London

Ms Linda Bayliss (2008)
Research Assistant, The National Collaborating Centre for Mental Health

Professor Nick Bouras
Professor Emeritus of Psychiatry, Health Service and Population Research
Department, Institute of Psychiatry, King's College London
Honorary Consultant Psychiatrist, South London and Maudsley NHS Foundation Trust

Ms Rachel Burbeck
Systematic Reviewer, The National Collaborating Centre for Mental Health

Ms Jenifer Clarke-Moore (2006–2007)
Consultant Nurse, Gwent Healthcare NHS Trust

Ms Elizabeth Costigan (2007)
Project Manager, The National Collaborating Centre for Mental Health

Dr Mike Crawford
Reader in Mental Health Services Research, Imperial College London
Honorary Consultant Psychiatrist Central & North West London NHS Foundation Trust

Ms Victoria Green
Representing service user and family/carer interests

Dr Rex Haigh
Consultant Psychiatrist, Berkshire Healthcare NHS Foundation Trust

Ms Sarah Hopkins (2007–2008)
Project Manager, The National Collaborating Centre for Mental Health

Mrs Farheen Jeeva (2007–2008)
Health Economist, The National Collaborating Centre for Mental Health

Ms Katherine Leggett (2008–2009)
Project Manager, The National Collaborating Centre for Mental Health

Mr Dennis Lines
Representing service user and family/carer interests

Dr Ifigeneia Mavranezouli (2008)
Senior Health Economist, The National Collaborating Centre for Mental Health

Dr David Moore
General Practitioner, Nottinghamshire County Teaching Primary Care Trust

Dr Paul Moran
Clinical Senior Lecturer, Institute of Psychiatry, King's College London
Honorary Consultant Psychiatrist, South London and Maudsley NHS
Foundation Trust

Professor Glenys Parry
Professor of Applied Psychological Therapies, Centre for Psychological Services
Research, University of Sheffield
Consultant Clinical Psychologist, Sheffield Health and Social Care
Foundation Trust

Mrs Carol Paton
Chief Pharmacist, Oxleas NHS Foundation Trust

Dr Mark Sampson
Clinical Psychologist, Manchester Mental Health and Social Care Trust

Ms Poonam Sood (2006–2007)
Research Assistant, The National Collaborating Centre for Mental Health

Ms Sarah Stockton
Senior Information Scientist, The National Collaborating Centre for Mental
Health

Dr Michaela Swales
Consultant Clinical Psychologist, North Wales NHS Trust and Bangor University

Guideline development group members

Dr Clare Taylor
Editor, The National Collaborating Centre for Mental Health

Dr Angela Wolff
Representing service user and family/carer interests

Mr Loukas Xaplanteris (2006–2007)
Health Economist, The National Collaborating Centre for Mental Health

ACKNOWLEDGEMENTS

The Borderline Personality Disorder Guideline Development Group and the National Collaborating Centre for Mental Health (NCCMH) review team would like to thank the following people:

Those who acted as advisers on specialist topics or have contributed to the process by meeting with the Guideline Development Group:

Dr Andrew Cotgrove,
Cheshire and Wirral Partnership NHS Trust

Professor Kate Davidson,
University of Glasgow

Ms Jane Dudley,
South West London and St George's Mental Health NHS Trust and The British Association of Art Therapy

Professor Edzard Ernst,
Peninsula Medical School

Professor Roger Mulder,
University of Otago

Professor John Oldham,
The Menninger Clinic

Professor Kenneth Silk,
University of Michigan Health System

Professor Paul Soloff,
University of Pittsburgh

Dr Alison Wood,
Bolton Salford and Trafford Mental Health NHS Trust

Those who contributed personal accounts of their experiences of borderline personality disorder that have been included in this guideline.

1.   PREFACE

This guideline has been developed to advise on the treatment and management of borderline personality disorder. The guideline recommendations have been developed by a multidisciplinary team of healthcare professionals, service users, a carer and guideline methodologists after careful consideration of the best available evidence. It is intended that the guideline will be useful to clinicians and service commissioners in providing and planning high-quality care for people with borderline personality disorder while also emphasising the importance of the experience of care for them and their families or carers (see Appendix 1 for more details on the scope of the guideline).

Although the evidence base is rapidly expanding, there are a number of major gaps, and future revisions of this guideline will incorporate new scientific evidence as it develops. The guideline makes a number of research recommendations specifically to address gaps in the evidence base. In the meantime, it is hoped that the guideline will assist clinicians, people with borderline personality disorder and their families/carers by identifying the merits of particular treatment approaches where the evidence from research and clinical experience exists.

1.1   NATIONAL GUIDELINE

1.1.1   What are clinical practice guidelines?

Clinical practice guidelines are 'systematically developed statements that assist clinicians and patients in making decisions about appropriate treatment for specific conditions' (Mann, 1996). They are derived from the best available research evidence, using predetermined and systematic methods to identify and evaluate the evidence relating to the specific condition in question. Where evidence is lacking, the guidelines incorporate statements and recommendations based upon the consensus statements developed by the Guideline Development Group (GDG).

Clinical guidelines are intended to improve the process and outcomes of healthcare in a number of different ways. They can:

- provide up-to-date evidence-based recommendations for the treatment and management of conditions and disorders by healthcare professionals
- be used as the basis to set standards to assess the practice of healthcare professionals
- form the basis for education and training of healthcare professionals
- assist service users and their families or carers in making informed decisions about their treatment and care
- improve communication between healthcare professionals, service users and their families or carers
- help identify priority areas for further research.

1.1.2 Uses and limitations of clinical guidelines

Guidelines are not a substitute for professional knowledge and clinical judgement. They can be limited in their usefulness and applicability by a number of different factors: the availability of high-quality research evidence, the quality of the methodology used in the development of the guideline, the generalisability of research findings and the uniqueness of individuals with borderline personality disorder.

Although the quality of research in this field is variable, the methodology used here reflects current international understanding on the appropriate practice for guideline development (AGREE: Appraisal of Guidelines for Research and Evaluation Instrument; www.agreetrust.org; AGREE Collaboration [2003]), ensuring the collection and selection of the best research evidence available and the systematic generation of treatment recommendations applicable to the majority of people with these disorders and situations. However, there will always be some service users for whom clinical guideline recommendations are not appropriate and situations in which the recommendations are not readily applicable. This guideline does not, therefore, override the individual responsibility of healthcare professionals to make appropriate decisions in the circumstances of the individual, in consultation with the person with borderline personality disorder or their family/carer.

In addition to the clinical evidence, cost-effectiveness information, where available, is taken into account in the generation of statements and recommendations of the clinical guidelines. While national guidelines are concerned with clinical and cost effectiveness, issues of affordability and implementation costs are to be determined by the National Health Service (NHS).

In using guidelines, it is important to remember that the absence of empirical evidence for the effectiveness of a particular intervention is not the same as evidence for ineffectiveness. In addition, of particular relevance in mental health, evidence-based treatments are often delivered within the context of an overall treatment programme including a range of activities, the purpose of which may be to help engage the person and to provide an appropriate context for the delivery of specific interventions. It is important to maintain and enhance the service context in which these interventions are delivered; otherwise the specific benefits of effective interventions will be lost. Indeed, the importance of organising care in order to support and encourage a good therapeutic relationship is at times as important as the specific treatments offered.

1.1.3 Why develop national guidelines?

The National Institute for Health and Clinical Excellence (NICE) was established as a Special Health Authority for England and Wales in 1999, with a remit to provide a single source of authoritative and reliable guidance for patients, professionals and the public. NICE guidance aims to improve standards of care, to diminish unacceptable variations in the provision and quality of care across the NHS and to ensure that the health service is patient centred. All guidance is developed in a transparent and collaborative manner using the best available evidence and involving all relevant stakeholders.

NICE generates guidance in a number of different ways, three of which are relevant here. First, national guidance is produced by the Technology Appraisal Committee to give robust advice about a particular treatment, intervention, procedure or other health technology. Second, NICE commissions public health intervention guidance focused on types of activity (interventions) that help to reduce people's risk of developing a disease or condition or help to promote or maintain a healthy lifestyle. Third, NICE commissions the production of national clinical practice guidelines focused upon the overall treatment and management of a specific condition. To enable this latter development, NICE has established seven National Collaborating Centres in conjunction with a range of professional organisations involved in healthcare.

1.1.4   The National Collaborating Centre for Mental Health

This guideline has been commissioned by NICE and developed within the National Collaborating Centre for Mental Health (NCCMH). The NCCMH is a collaboration of the professional organisations involved in the field of mental health, national patient and carer organisations, a number of academic institutions and NICE. The NCCMH is funded by NICE and is led by a partnership between the Royal College of Psychiatrists' research and training unit and the British Psychological Society's equivalent unit (Centre for Outcomes Research and Effectiveness).

1.1.5   From national guidelines to local protocols

Once a national guideline has been published and disseminated, local healthcare groups will be expected to produce a plan and identify resources for implementation, along with appropriate timetables. Subsequently, a multidisciplinary group involving commissioners of healthcare, primary care and specialist mental health professionals, service users and families/carers should undertake the translation of the implementation plan into local protocols taking into account both the recommendations set out in this guideline and the priorities set in the National Service Framework (NSF) for Mental Health and related documentation. The nature and pace of the local plan will reflect local healthcare needs and the nature of existing services and existing local therapeutic expertise and experience; full implementation may take a considerable time, especially where substantial training needs are identified.

1.1.6   Auditing the implementation of guideline

This guideline identifies key areas of clinical practice and service delivery for local and national audit. Although the generation of audit standards is an important and necessary step in the implementation of this guidance, a more broadly based implementation strategy will be developed. Nevertheless, it should be noted that the Care Quality Commission will monitor the extent to which Primary Care Trusts, trusts responsible for mental health and social care and Health Authorities have implemented these guidelines.

1.2 THE NATIONAL BORDERLINE PERSONALITY DISORDER GUIDELINE

1.2.1 Who has developed this guideline?

The GDG was convened by the NCCMH and supported by funding from NICE. The GDG included two service users and a carer, and professionals from psychiatry, clinical psychology, general practice, nursing, psychiatric pharmacy and child and adolescent mental health services (CAMHS).

Staff from the NCCMH provided leadership and support throughout the process of guideline development, undertaking systematic searches, information retrieval, appraisal and systematic review of the evidence. Members of the GDG received training in the process of guideline development from NCCMH staff, and the service users and carer received training and support from the NICE Patient and Public Involvement Programme. The NICE Guidelines Technical Adviser provided advice and assistance regarding aspects of the guideline development process.

All GDG members made formal declarations of interest at the outset, which were updated at every GDG meeting. The GDG met a total of 17 times throughout the process of guideline development. It met as a whole, but key topics were led by a national expert in the relevant topic. The GDG was supported by the NCCMH technical team, with additional expert advice from special advisers where needed. The group oversaw the production and synthesis of research evidence before presentation. All statements and recommendations in this guideline have been generated and agreed by the whole GDG.

1.2.2 For whom is this guideline intended?

This guideline will be relevant for adults and young people with borderline personality disorder.

The guideline covers the care provided by primary, community, secondary, tertiary and other healthcare professionals who have direct contact with, and make decisions concerning, the care of adults and young people with borderline personality disorder.

The guideline will also be relevant to the work, but will not cover the practice, of those in:

● occupational health services
● social services
● forensic services
● the independent sector.

The experience of borderline personality disorder can affect the whole family and often the community. The guideline recognises the role of both in the treatment and support of people with borderline personality disorder.

1.2.3   Specific aims of this guideline

The guideline makes recommendations for the treatment and management of borderline personality disorder. It aims to:

- evaluate the role of specific psychosocial interventions in the treatment of borderline personality disorder
- evaluate the role of specific pharmacological interventions in the treatment of borderline personality disorder
- integrate the above to provide best-practice advice on the care of individuals with a diagnosis of borderline personality disorder
- promote the implementation of best clinical practice through the development of recommendations tailored to the requirements of the NHS in England and Wales.

1.2.4   The structure of this guideline

The guideline is divided into chapters, each covering a set of related topics. The first three chapters provide an introduction to guidelines, the topic of borderline personality disorder and to the methods used to develop guidelines. Chapters 4 to 9 provide the evidence that underpins the recommendations.

Each evidence chapter begins with a general introduction to the topic that sets the recommendations in context. Depending on the nature of the evidence, narrative reviews or meta-analyses were conducted, and the structure of the chapters varies accordingly. Where appropriate, details about current practice, the evidence base and any research limitations are provided. Where meta-analyses were conducted, information is given about both the interventions included and the studies considered for review. Clinical summaries are then used to summarise the evidence presented. Finally, recommendations related to each topic are presented at the end of each chapter. On the CD-ROM (see Text box 1 for details), full details about the included studies can be found in Appendix 16. Where meta-analyses were conducted, the data are presented using forest plots in Appendix 17 and the full GRADE evidence profiles can be found in Appendix 18.

Text box 1: Appendices on CD-ROM

Content	Appendix
Study characteristics tables	Appendix 16
Forest plots	Appendix 17
GRADE evidence profiles	Appendix 18

2. BORDERLINE PERSONALITY DISORDER

2.1   THE DISORDER

The term 'borderline personality' was proposed in the United States by Adolph Stern in 1938 (most other personality disorders were first described in Europe). Stern described a group of patients who 'fit frankly neither into the psychotic nor into the psychoneurotic group' and introduced the term 'borderline' to describe what he observed because it 'bordered' on other conditions.

The term 'borderline personality organisation' was introduced by Otto Kernberg (1975) to refer to a consistent pattern of functioning and behaviour characterised by instability and reflecting a disturbed psychological self-organisation. Whatever the purported underlying psychological structures, the cluster of symptoms and behaviour associated with borderline personality were becoming more widely recognised, and included striking fluctuations from periods of confidence to times of absolute despair, markedly unstable self-image, rapid changes in mood, with fears of abandonment and rejection, and a strong tendency towards suicidal thinking and self-harm. Transient psychotic symptoms, including brief delusions and hallucinations, may also be present. The characteristics that now define borderline personality disorder were described by Gunderson and Kolb in 1978 and have since been incorporated into contemporary psychiatric classifications (see Section 2.2).

Either as a result of its position on the 'border' of other conditions, or as a result of conceptual confusion, borderline personality disorder is often diagnostically comorbid with depression and anxiety, eating disorders such as bulimia, post-traumatic stress disorder (PTSD), substance misuse disorders and bipolar disorder (with which it is also sometimes clinically confused). An overlap with psychotic disorders can also be considerable. In extreme cases people can experience both visual and auditory hallucinations and clear delusions, but these are usually brief and linked to times of extreme emotional instability, and thereby can be distinguished from the core symptoms of schizophrenia and other related disorders (Links *et al.*, 1989).

The level of comorbidity is so great that it is uncommon to see an individual with 'pure' borderline personality disorder (Fyer *et al.*, 1988a). Because of this considerable overlap with other disorders, many have suggested that borderline personality disorder should not be classified as a personality disorder; rather it should be classified with the mood disorders or with disorders of identity. Its association with past trauma and the manifest similarities with PTSD have led some to suggest that borderline personality disorder should be regarded as a form of delayed PTSD (Yen & Shea, 2001). Despite these concerns, borderline personality disorder is a more uniform category than other personality disorders and is probably the most widely researched of the personality disorders. While some people with borderline personality disorder come from stable and caring families, deprivation and instability in

15

relationships are likely to promote borderline personality development and should be the focus of preventive strategies.

It is important to note that borderline personality disorder should not be confused with so-called 'borderline intelligence' which is a wholly distinct and unrelated concept. Nevertheless, borderline personality characteristics (notably self-harm) are sometimes present in people with significant learning disabilities and can be prominent (Alexander & Cooray, 2003).

The course of borderline personality disorder is very variable. Most people show symptoms in late adolescence or early adult life, although some may not come to the attention of psychiatric services until much later. The outcome, at least in those who have received treatment or formal psychiatric assessment, is much better than was originally thought, with at least 50% of people improving sufficiently to not meet the criteria for borderline personality disorder 5 to 10 years after first diagnosis (Zanarini *et al.*, 2003). It is not known to what extent this is a consequence of treatment – evidence suggests that a significant proportion of improvement is spontaneous and accompanied by greater maturity and self-reflection.

There is some controversy over the possible age of onset of borderline personality disorder. Many believe that it cannot, or perhaps should not, be diagnosed in people under 18 years of age while the personality is still forming (although diagnosis is possible in the *Diagnostic and Statistical Manual of Mental Disorders*, 4th edition [DSM-IV; APA, 1994] based on the same criteria as adults with additional caveats). Nevertheless, borderline symptoms and characteristics are often identifiable at a much earlier age, and sometimes early in adolescence (Bradley *et al.*, 2005a). More attention is now being paid to its early manifestations in adolescent groups (see Section 2.7).

Borderline personality disorder is associated with significant impairment, especially in relation to the capacity to sustain stable relationships as a result of personal and emotional instability. For many the severity of symptoms and behaviours that characterise borderline personality disorder correlate with the severity of personal, social and occupational impairments. However, this is not always the case, and some people with what appears to be, in other ways, marked borderline personality disorder may be able to function at very high levels in their careers (Stone, 1993). Many, but not all, people with borderline personality disorder recurrently harm themselves, usually to provide relief from intolerable distress, which for many can lead to significant physical impairment and disability. Moreover, suicide is still common in people with borderline personality disorder and may occur several years after the first presentation of symptoms (Paris & Zweig-Frank, 2001).

Although the prognosis of borderline personality disorder is relatively good, with most people not meeting the criteria for diagnosis after 5 years, it is important to note that a minority of people have persistent symptoms until late in life. Recurrent self-harm may occasionally be a problem in the elderly and the possibility that this may be because of borderline personality disorder should be considered in such circumstances. However, the prevalence of the condition in the elderly is much lower than in the young and one of the encouraging features about remission from the condition is that it is much less often followed by relapse than is the case with most other psychiatric disorders.

Comorbidities

Borderline personality disorder is a heterogeneous condition and its symptoms overlap considerably with depressive, schizophrenic, impulsive, dissociative and identity disorders. This overlap is also linked to comorbidity and in clinical practice it is sometimes difficult to determine if the presenting symptoms are those of borderline personality disorder or a related comorbid condition. The main differences between the core symptoms of borderline personality disorder and other conditions are that the symptoms of borderline personality disorder undergo greater fluctuation and variability: psychotic and paranoid symptoms are transient, depressive symptoms change dramatically over a short period, suicidal ideas may be intense and unbearable but only for a short time, doubts about identity may occur but are short-lived, and disturbances in the continuity of self-experiences are unstable. For each of the equivalent comorbid disorders there is much greater consistency of these symptoms.

2.2   DIAGNOSIS

Borderline personality disorder is one of the most contentious of all the personality disorder subtypes. The reliability and validity of the diagnostic criteria have been criticised, and the utility of the construct itself has been called into question (Tyrer, 1999). Moreover, it is unclear how satisfactorily clinical or research diagnoses actually capture the experiences of people identified as personality disordered (Ramon *et al.*, 2001). There is a large literature showing that borderline personality disorder overlaps considerably with other categories of personality disorder, with 'pure' borderline personality disorder only occurring in 3 to 10% of cases (Pfohl *et al.*, 1986). The extent of overlap in research studies is particularly great with other so-called cluster B personality disorders (histrionic, narcissistic and antisocial). In addition, there is considerable overlap between borderline personality disorder and mood and anxiety disorders (Tyrer *et al.*, 1997; Zanarini *et al.*, 1998).

This guideline uses the DSM-IV diagnostic criteria for borderline personality disorder (APA, 1994), which are listed in Table 1. According to DSM-IV, the key features of borderline personality disorder are instability of interpersonal relationships, self-image and affect, combined with marked impulsivity beginning in early adulthood.

A stand-alone category of borderline personality disorder does not exist within the *International Classification of Diseases*, 10th revision (ICD-10; World Health Organization, 1992), although there is an equivalent category of disorder termed 'emotionally unstable personality disorder, borderline type' (F 60.31), which is characterised by instability in emotions, self-image and relationships. The ICD-10 category does not include brief quasi-psychotic features (criterion 9 of the DSM-IV category). Comparisons of DSM and ICD criteria when applied to the same group of patients have shown that there is little agreement between the two systems. For example, in a study of 52 outpatients diagnosed using both systems, less than a third of participants received the same primary personality disorder diagnosis (Zimmerman, 1994). Further modifications in the ICD and DSM are required to promote convergence between the

Table 1: DSM-IV criteria for borderline personality disorder (APA, 1994)

	A pervasive pattern of instability of interpersonal relationships, self-image and affects, and marked impulsivity beginning by early adulthood and present in a variety of contexts, as indicated by five (or more) of the following:
1.	Frantic efforts to avoid real or imagined abandonment. Note: Do not include suicidal or self-mutilating behaviour covered in Criterion 5.
2.	A pattern of unstable and intense interpersonal relationships characterised by alternating between extremes of idealisation and devaluation.
3.	Identity disturbance: markedly and persistently unstable self-image or sense of self.
4.	Impulsivity in at least two areas that are potentially self-damaging (for example, spending, sex, substance abuse, reckless driving, binge eating). Note: Do not include suicidal or self-mutilating behaviour covered in Criterion 5.
5.	Recurrent suicidal behaviour, gestures, or threats, or self-mutilating behaviour.
6.	Affective instability due to a marked reactivity of mood (for example, intense episodic dysphoria, irritability, or anxiety usually lasting a few hours and only rarely more than a few days).
7.	Chronic feelings of emptiness.
8.	Inappropriate, intense anger or difficulty controlling anger (for example, frequent displays of temper, constant anger, recurrent physical fights).
9.	Transient, stress-related paranoid ideation or severe dissociative symptoms.

two classifications, although greater convergence is unlikely to resolve the problems inherent in the current concept of personality disorder.

The reliability of diagnostic assessment for personality disorder has been considerably improved by the introduction of standardised interview schedules. However, no single schedule has emerged as the 'gold standard' as each has its own set of advantages and disadvantages, with excessive length of interview time being a problem common to many of the schedules. (The main instruments available for assessing borderline personality disorder are listed in Table 2.) When used by a properly trained rater, all of the schedules allow for a reliable diagnosis of borderline personality disorder to be made. Nevertheless, the level of agreement between interview schedules remains at best moderate (Zimmerman, 1994). In addition, clinical and research methods for diagnosing personality disorders diverge. Westen (1997) has found that

Table 2: The main instruments available for the assessment of borderline personality disorder

Diagnostic Interview for DSM-IV Personality Disorders (DIPD-IV) (Zanarini, 1983)
Structured Clinical Interview for DSM-IV Personality Disorders (SCID-II) (First *et al.*, 1997)
Structured Interview for DSM-IV Personality (SIDP-IV) (Pfohl *et al.*, 1997)
International Personality Disorder Examination (IPDE) (Loranger *et al.*, 1996)
Personality Assessment Schedule (PAS) (Tyrer *et al.*, 1979)
Standardised Assessment of Personality (SAP) (Mann *et al.*, 1999)

although current instruments primarily rely on direct questions derived from DSM-IV, clinicians tend to find direct questions only marginally useful when assessing for the presence of personality disorders. Instead, clinicians are inclined to arrive at the diagnosis of personality disorder by listening to patients describe interpersonal interactions and observing their behaviour (Westen, 1997).

Currently, outside specialist treatment settings, there is still a heavy reliance on the diagnosis of borderline personality disorder being made following an unstructured clinical assessment. However, there are potential pitfalls in this approach. First, agreement among clinicians' diagnoses of personality disorder has been shown to be poor (Mellsop *et al.*, 1982). Second, the presence of acute mental or physical illness can influence the assessment of personality. The presence of affective and anxiety disorders, psychosis, or substance use disorder, or the occurrence of an acute medical or surgical condition can all mimic symptoms of borderline personality disorder; a primary diagnosis of borderline personality disorder should only be made in the absence of mental or physical illness. It is also preferable for clinicians to obtain an informant account of the individual's personality before definitively arriving at a diagnosis of borderline personality disorder.

All personality disorders have been defined by their stability over time. Indeed, ICD and DSM definitions of personality disorders describe them as having an enduring pattern of characteristics. However, until recently, there was a paucity of longitudinal research into personality disorders to support the notion of borderline personality disorder as a stable construct. Reviews of the subject published over the past 10 years hinted at considerable variation in stability estimates (Grilo *et al.*, 2000). Recent prospective studies have shown that a significant number of individuals initially diagnosed with borderline personality disorder will not consistently remain at diagnostic threshold, even over comparatively short periods of time (Shea *et al.*, 2002). It seems that while individual differences in personality disorder features appear to be relatively stable (Lenzenweger, 1999), the number of criteria present can fluctuate considerably over time. Given the many problems associated with the diagnosis of borderline personality disorder, it seems clear that reclassification is urgently needed and this is likely to happen with the publication of DSM-V (Tyrer, 1999).

2.3 EPIDEMIOLOGY

2.3.1 Prevalence

Although borderline personality disorder is a condition that is thought to occur globally (Pinto *et al.*, 2000), there has been little epidemiological research into the disorder outside the Western world. Only three methodologically rigorous surveys have examined the community prevalence of borderline personality disorder. Coid and colleagues (2006) reported that the weighted prevalence of borderline personality disorder in a random sample of 626 British householders was 0.7%. Samuels and colleagues (2002) found that in a random sample of 742 American householders the weighted prevalence of borderline personality disorder was 0.5%. Torgersen and colleagues (2001) reported a prevalence of 0.7% in a Norwegian survey of 2,053 community residents. Despite methodological differences between these studies, there is remarkable concordance in their prevalence estimates, the median prevalence of borderline personality disorder across the three studies being 0.7%. Only Torgersen and colleagues' 2001 study provides detailed information about the sociodemographic correlates of borderline personality disorder. In this study, there was a significant link between borderline personality disorder and younger age, living in a city centre and not living with a partner. Interestingly, the assumption that borderline personality disorder is over-represented among women was not supported by the data.

In primary care, the prevalence of borderline personality disorder ranges from 4 to 6% of primary attenders (Moran *et al.*, 2000; Gross *et al.*, 2002). Compared with those without personality disorder, people with borderline personality disorder are more likely to visit their GP frequently and to report psychosocial impairment. In spite of this, borderline personality disorder appears to be under-recognised by GPs (Moran *et al.*, 2001).

In mental healthcare settings, the prevalence of all personality disorder subtypes is high, with many studies reporting a figure in excess of 50% of the sampled population. Borderline personality disorder is generally the most prevalent category of personality disorder in non-forensic mental healthcare settings. In community samples the prevalence of the disorder is roughly equal male to female, whereas in services there is a clear preponderance of women, who are more likely to seek treatment. It follows that the majority of people diagnosed with personality disorder, most of whom will have borderline personality disorder, will be women.

Borderline personality disorder is particularly common among people who are drug and/or alcohol dependent, and within drug and alcohol services there will be more men with a diagnosis of borderline personality disorder than women. Borderline personality disorder is also more common in those with an eating disorder (Zanarini *et al.*, 1998), and also among people presenting with chronic self-harming behaviour (Linehan *et al.*, 1991).

2.3.2   The impact of borderline personality disorder

Many people who have at one time been given the diagnosis of borderline personality disorder are able to move on to live a fulfilling life. However, during the course of the disorder people can have significant problems which mean that they require a large amount of support from services and from those around them. The functional impairment associated with borderline personality disorder appears to be a relatively enduring feature of the disorder (Skodol *et al.*, 2005). Studies of clinical populations have shown that people with borderline personality disorder experience significantly greater impairment in their work, social relationships and leisure compared with those with depression (Skodol *et al.*, 2002). However, studies of selected samples of people with borderline personality disorder have shown that symptomatic improvement can occur to the extent that a number of people will no longer meet the criteria for borderline personality disorder and that the prognosis may be better than has previously been recognised (Zanarini *et al.*, 2003).

People with borderline personality disorder may engage in a variety of destructive and impulsive behaviours including self-harm, eating problems and excessive use of alcohol and illicit substances. Self-harming behaviour in borderline personality disorder is associated with a variety of different meanings for the person, including relief from acute distress and feelings, such as emptiness and anger, and to reconnect with feelings after a period of dissociation. As a result of the frequency with which they self-harm, people with borderline personality disorder are at increased risk of suicide (Cheng *et al.*, 1997), with 60 to 70% attempting suicide at some point in their life (Oldham, 2006). The rate of completed suicide in people with borderline personality disorder has been estimated to be approximately 10% (Oldham, 2006). A well-documented association exists between borderline personality disorder and depression (Skodol *et al.*, 1999; Zanarini *et al.*, 1998), and the combination of the two conditions has been shown to increase the number and seriousness of suicide attempts (Soloff *et al.*, 2000).

2.4   AETIOLOGY

The causes of borderline personality disorder are complex and remain uncertain. No current model has been advanced that is able to integrate all of the available evidence. The following may all be contributing factors: genetics and constitutional vulnerabilities; neurophysiological and neurobiological dysfunctions of emotional regulation and stress; psychosocial histories of childhood maltreatment and abuse; and disorganisation of aspects of the affiliative behavioural system, most particularly the attachment system.

2.4.1   Genetics

Twin studies suggest that the heritability factor for borderline personality disorder is 0.69 (Torgersen *et al.*, 2000), but it is likely that traits related to impulsive aggression and mood dysregulation, rather than borderline personality disorder itself, are transmitted in families. Current evidence suggests that the genetic influence on personality disorder generally, not specifically borderline personality disorder, acts both individually and in combination with anomalous environmental factors (White *et al.*, 2003; Caspi *et al.*, 2002; Caspi *et al.*, 2003). More recent studies of heritability suggest that the heritability factor for cluster C disorders lies within the range 27 to 35% (Reichborn-Kjennerud *et al.*, 2007) suggesting that genetic factors play a less important role than previously thought.

2.4.2   Neurotransmitters

Regulation of emotional states is a core problem in borderline personality disorder. Neurotransmitters have been implicated in the regulation of impulses, aggression and affect. Serotonin has been the most extensively studied of these, and it has been shown that there is an inverse relationship between serotonin levels and levels of aggression. Reduced serotonergic activity may inhibit a person's ability to modulate or control destructive urges, although the causal pathway remains unclear. Reduced 5-HT 1A receptor-mediated responses in women with borderline personality disorder and a history of prolonged child abuse have been noted (Rinne *et al.*, 2000), suggesting the possibility that environmental factors might mediate the link between 5-HT and aggression.

Limited evidence exists for the role of catecholamines (norepinephrine and dopamine neurotransmitters) in the dysregulation of affect. People with borderline personality disorder have lower plasma-free methoxyhydroxyphenylglycol (a metabolite of noradrenaline), compared with controls without borderline personality disorder, but the finding disappears when aggression scores are controlled (Coccaro *et al.*, 2003). The effects produced on administering amphetamines to people with borderline personality disorder suggest that such people are uniquely sensitive and demonstrate greater behavioural sensitivity than control subjects (Schulz *et al.*, 1985).

Other neurotransmitters and neuromodulators implicated in the phenomenology of borderline personality disorder include acetylcholine (Steinberg *et al.*, 1997), vasopressin (Coccaro *et al.*, 1998), cholesterol (Atmaca *et al.*, 2002) and fatty acids (Zanarini & Frankenburg, 2003), along with the hypothalamic-pituitary adrenal axis (Rinne *et al.*, 2002).

2.4.3   Neurobiology

Evidence of structural and functional deficit in brain areas central to affect regulation, attention and self-control, and executive function have been described in borderline personality disorder. Areas include the amygdala (Rusch *et al.*, 2003), hippocampus (Tebartz van Elst *et al.*, 2003) and orbitofrontal regions (Stein *et al.*, 1993; Kunert *et al.*, 2003; De la Fuente *et al.*, 1997). Most studies are performed without emotional stimulation, however recent studies under conditions of emotional challenge suggest similar findings. People with borderline personality disorder show increased activity in the dorsolateral prefrontal cortex and in the cuneus, and a reduction in activity in the right anterior cingulate (Schmahl *et al.*, 2003). Greater activation of the amygdale while viewing emotionally aversive images (Herpertz *et al.*, 2001) or emotional faces (Donegan *et al.*, 2003) has also been described.

2.4.4 Psychosocial factors

Family studies have identified a number of factors that may be important in the development of borderline personality disorder, for example a history of mood disorders and substance misuse in other family members. Recent evidence also suggests that neglect, including supervision neglect, and emotional under-involvement by caregivers are important. Prospective studies in children have shown that parental emotional under-involvement contributes to a child's difficulties in socialising and perhaps to a risk for suicide attempts (Johnson *et al.*, 2002). People with borderline personality disorder (at least while symptomatic), significantly more often than people without the disorder, see their mother as distant or overprotective, and their relationship with her conflictual, while the father is perceived as less involved and more distant. This suggests that problems with both parents are more likely to be the common pathogenic influence in this group rather than problems with either parent alone. While these findings should be replicated with those who have recovered from borderline personality disorder, the general point about biparental difficulties being important in the genesis of borderline personality disorder is given further support from studies of abuse.

Physical, sexual and emotional abuse can all occur in a family context and high rates are reported in people with borderline personality disorder (Johnson *et al.*, 1999a). Zanarini reported that 84% of people with borderline personality disorder retrospectively described experience of biparental neglect and emotional abuse before the age of 18, with emotional denial of their experiences by their caregivers as a predictor of borderline personality disorder (Zanarini *et al.*, 2000). This suggests that these parents were unable to take the experience of the child into account in the context of family interactions. Abuse alone is neither necessary nor sufficient for the development of borderline personality disorder and predisposing factors and contextual features of the parent-child relationship are likely to be mediating factors in its development. Caregiver response to the abuse may be more important than the abuse itself in long-term outcomes (Horwitz *et al.*, 2001). A family environment that discourages coherent discourse about a child's perspective on the world is unlikely to facilitate successful adjustment following trauma. Thus the critical factor is the family environment. Studies that have examined the family context of childhood trauma in borderline personality disorder tend to see the unstable, non-nurturing family environment as the key social mediator of abuse (Bradley *et al.*, 2005b) and personality dysfunction (Zweig-Frank & Paris, 1991).

Few of the studies point to how the features of parenting and family environment create a vulnerability for borderline personality disorder, but they are likely to be part of a disrupted attachment or affiliative system that affects the development of social cognition, which is considered to be impaired in borderline personality disorder (Fonagy & Bateman, 2007).

2.4.5   Attachment process

The literature on the relationship between attachment processes and the emergence of borderline personality disorder is broad and varies. For example, some studies suggest that people are made more vulnerable to the highly stressful psychosocial experiences discussed above by early inadequate mirroring and disorganised attachment. This is likely to be associated with a more general failure in families such as neglect, rejection, excessive control, unsupportive relationships, incoherence and confusion. While the relationship of diagnosis of borderline personality disorder and specific attachment category is not obvious, borderline personality disorder is strongly associated with insecure attachment (6 to 8% of patients with borderline personality disorder are coded as secure) and there are indications of disorganisation (unresolved attachment and inability to classify category of attachment) in interviews, and fearful avoidant and preoccupied attachment in questionnaire studies (Levy, 2005). Early attachment insecurity is a relatively stable characteristic of any individual, particularly in conjunction with subsequent negative life events (94%) (Hamilton, 2000; Waters *et al.*, 2000; Weinfield *et al.*, 2000). Given evidence of the continuity of attachment from early childhood, at least in adverse environments, and the two longitudinal studies following children from infancy to early adulthood (which reported associations between insecure attachment in early adulthood and borderline personality disorder symptoms [Lyons-Ruth *et al.*, 2005]), childhood attachment may indeed be an important factor in the development of borderline personality disorder. Fonagy and colleagues (2003) suggest that adverse effects arising from insecure and/or disorganised attachment relationships, which may have been disrupted for many reasons, are mediated via a failure in development of mentalising capacity – a social cognitive capacity relating to understanding and interpreting one's own and others' actions as meaningful on the basis of formulating what is going on in one's own and the other person's mind.

This formulation overlaps with the importance of the invalidating family environment suggested by Linehan (1993) as a factor in the genesis of borderline personality disorder and further developed by Fruzzetti and colleagues (2003; 2005). Fruzzetti and colleagues report that parental invalidation, in part defined as the undermining of self-perceptions of internal states and therefore anti-mentalising, is not only associated with the young person's reports of family distress, and their own distress and psychological problems, but also with aspects of social cognition, namely the ability to identify and label emotion in themselves and others. Along with other aspects contributing to the complex interaction described as invalidating, there is a systematic undermining of a person's experience of their own mind by that of another. There is a failure to encourage the person to discriminate between their feelings and experiences and those of the caregiver, thereby undermining the development of a robust mentalising capacity.

2.4.6   Conclusion

Individuals constitutionally vulnerable and/or exposed to influences that undermine the development of social cognitive capacities, such as neglect in early relationships, develop with an impaired ability both to represent and to modulate affect and effortfully control attentional capacity. These factors, with or without further trauma, exemplified by severe neglect, abuse and other forms of maltreatment, may cause changes in the neural mechanisms of arousal and lead to structural and functional changes in the developing brain. Unless adequate remedial measures are taken, borderline personality may develop.

2.5   TREATMENT AND MANAGEMENT

2.5.1   Current configuration of services

General adult mental health services in England and Wales offer varying levels of service provision for people with personality disorder. England and Wales have a health service in which personality disorder services are considered to be an integral part. As the decision to expand services to include the treatment of personality disorder was only made in 2003 the development of these services remains patchy and, in some areas, rudimentary. Although these services are for personality disorder generally, most users seeking services are likely to have a diagnosis of borderline personality disorder and this is anticipated in the service provision.

The programme in England includes the development of innovative psychosocial approaches to treatment, national service pilot projects and a workforce and training programme. The long-term plan is to develop capacity for specific personality services in all parts of the country.

2.5.2   Pharmacological treatment

Comorbid mental illness, particularly depression, bipolar disorder, PTSD, substance misuse disorder and psychosis are more common in people with borderline personality disorder than in the general population; lifetime prevalence of at least one comorbid mental illness approaches 100% for this group (Bender *et al.*, 2001). In addition, many of the trait- and state-related symptoms of borderline personality disorder (including affective instability, transient stress-related psychotic symptoms, suicidal and self-harming behaviours, and impulsivity) are similar in quality to those of many types of mental illness and could intuitively be expected to respond to drug treatment.

25

The use of antidepressants, mood stabilisers and antipsychotics is common in clinical practice. One large study of prescribing practice in the US found that 10% of people with borderline personality disorder had been prescribed an antipsychotic at some point during their contact with services, 27% a mood stabiliser, 35% an anxiolytic and 61% an antidepressant (Bender *et al.*, 2001); the lifetime prescribing rate for antidepressants was double that for patients with major depression. There are no published UK-based studies of prescribing practice, but given that people with borderline personality disorder tend to seek treatment, there is no reason to suspect that the prevalence of prescribing of psychotropic medication differs from that in the US. Such treatment is often initiated during periods of crisis and the placebo response rate in this context is high; the crisis is usually time limited and can be expected to resolve itself irrespective of drug treatment.

Often the prescribed drug is continued in an attempt to protect against further transient, stress-related symptoms and when these occur, another drug from a different class is likely to be added (Tyrer, 2002; Paris, 2002; Sanderson *et al.*, 2002). A longitudinal study found that 75% of participants with borderline personality disorder were prescribed combinations of drugs at some point (Zanarini *et al.*, 2003). Those who have repeated crisis admissions to hospital may be prescribed multiple psychotropic drugs in combination with a range of medicines for minor physical complaints. Adherence to medication in the medium term is often poor and the frequency with which prescriptions are altered makes it difficult to see which drug, if any, has helped and how.

The psychotropic drugs that are commonly prescribed are all associated with clinically significant side effects. For example, antipsychotic drugs may lead to considerable weight gain (Theisen *et al.*, 2001), both compounding problems with self-esteem and increasing the risk of serious physical pathology such as diabetes and cardiovascular disease (Mackin *et al.*, 2005). Lithium can cause hypothyroidism and is a very toxic drug in overdose; valproate can lead to weight gain and is a major human teratogen (Wyszynski *et al.*, 2005); and selective serotonin re-uptake inhibitors (SSRIs) can cause unpleasant discontinuation symptoms if they are not taken consistently (Fava, 2006). The balance of risks and benefits of psychotropic drugs is generally even more unfavourable in adolescents and young adults: the risks associated with SSRIs, which have been associated with treatment-emergent suicidal ideation in young people (Hammad *et al.*, 2006), may outweigh the benefits (Whittington *et al.*, 2004), and valproate may increase the risk of young women developing polycystic ovaries (NICE, 2006a; NICE, 2007a).

No psychotropic drug is specifically licensed for the management of borderline personality disorder, although some have broad product licences that cover individual symptoms or symptom clusters. Where there is a diagnosis of comorbid depression, psychosis or bipolar disorder, the use of antidepressants, antipsychotics and mood stabilisers respectively would be within their licensed indications. Where there are depressive or psychotic symptoms, or affective instability, that fall short of diagnostic criteria for mental illness, the use of psychotropic drugs is largely unlicensed or 'off-label'. Prescribing off-label places additional responsibilities on the prescriber and may increase liability if there are adverse effects (Baldwin, 2007). As a minimum, off-label prescribing should be consistent with a respected body of medical opinion (Bolam test) and be able to withstand logical analysis (House of Lords, 1997). The Royal College of Psychiatrists recommends that the patient be informed that the drug prescribed is not licensed for the indication it is being used for, and the reason for use and potential side effects fully explained (Baldwin, 2007).

2.5.3 Psychological interventions

The history of specific psychological interventions designed to help people with borderline personality disorder is intertwined with changing conceptions of the nature of the disorder itself. The emergent psychoanalytic concept of 'borderline personality organisation', intermediate between neurosis and psychosis (Stern, 1938; Kernberg, 1967), was influential in the introduction of borderline personality disorder into DSM-III in 1980, but was not an approach taken by ICD-10. The borderline personality disorder concept was therefore first adopted in the US and had no wide currency in the UK before the mid-1980s. At this time, although a range of psychodynamic, experiential, behavioural and cognitive behavioural therapies were available within NHS mental health services, they were very patchy and in short supply. Cognitive therapy (CT) for depression was only in the early stages of being adopted. Many people who would now be described in terms of having borderline personality disorder presented with depression, anxiety and interpersonal difficulties and were offered these therapies. This spurred innovation as practitioners began to modify these techniques in order to help people with more complex psychological difficulties, and during the 1980s and 1990s systematic methods were developed specifically for this client group.

Specific therapies for borderline personality disorder, therefore, developed through modification of existing techniques. In both the US and UK, psychoanalytic methods were adapted to provide more structure, containment (such as explicit contracts between therapist and client) and responsiveness; for example, the classical technique of the 'blank screen' of therapist neutrality and abstinence was modified so that the therapist became more active. Derived (but distinct) from classical analytic technique, an approach based on developmental attachment theory led to a specific therapy emphasising mentalisation. A behavioural approach to self-harm and suicidality that incorporated skills training in emotion regulation and validation of client experience developed into dialectical behaviour therapy (DBT), a specific intervention for borderline personality disorder *per se*. Cognitive analytic therapy (CAT), which had from its outset explicitly addressed interpersonal difficulties, gained greater application to borderline problems through theoretical and practical attention to partially dissociated states of mind and their functional analysis. CT for depression was also adapted to personality disorders. For example, one method paid greater attention to the early maladaptive schemas underpinning cognitive biases. Adaptations have also been made in cognitive behavioural therapy (CBT) and interpersonal therapy (IPT). Some of these adapted therapies are offered as psychological therapy programmes (for example, mentalisation-based partial hospitalisation and DBT);

others are provided as more straightforward time-limited one-to-one or group treatments (for example, CBT or CAT).

Despite the developments of these specific psychological therapies (see Chapter 5), most 'talking treatments' offered to people with borderline personality disorder in the NHS are generic or eclectic and do not use a specific method. Clinical psychologists are trained to work flexibly around a range of assessment, treatment and rehabilitation needs, through psychological formulation, treatment planning, staff supervision and environmental change. The British Psychological Society requires chartered clinical and counselling psychologists to train in two evidence-based psychological therapies, with further post-qualification training required before they can register as practitioners. However, they may not use a specific approach during therapy sessions and, where a specific approach is used, it may not be available in the optimum format, that is, the one that was tested in clinical trials. A good example is DBT, which is a psychological therapy programme delivered by a team of therapists that includes one-to-one therapy sessions, psychoeducational groups and telephone support. Although NHS therapists may have trained in the method, it has proved organisationally difficult to ensure all elements of the DBT approach are available in practice.

Psychological and psychosocial interventions are delivered in a variety of ways and settings within the NHS by clinical psychologists and other staff trained in psychological therapies, such as psychiatrists, nurses, social workers and other mental health therapists. Individual and group therapies are available in psychology and psychotherapy departments, within day services and community mental health services. Day services have been established with specific expertise in programmes for this client group, some based on therapeutic community principles, but these are not universally available. In 2005, 11 pilot services were funded to demonstrate a range of service possibilities. All of these specified some element of psychological care, although few were based on provision of specific and formal psychological therapies (Crawford *et al.*, 2007).

In practice, the limiting factor in providing access to psychological therapies is the very small proportion of NHS staff trained to deliver these to a competent standard. A further challenge is how to embed psychological treatment into the overall care programme in health and social care, which may involve liaison among staff from many agencies who do not share a psychological understanding of the nature of the disorder. To address this, a psychological therapies framework can be applied to the care programme through multidisciplinary team-based training (Sampson *et al.*, 2006; Kerr *et al.*, 2007).

Together with greater understanding of the developmental origins and psychological mechanisms underpinning this disorder and epidemiological evidence on its natural history, the emergence of at least partially effective psychological treatments has challenged traditional views of borderline personality disorder as immutable. The therapeutic nihilism so characteristic of earlier decades is giving way to a belief that psychological therapies have an important role to play in the overall care, treatment and recovery of people with these disorders.

2.5.4   Arts therapies

Arts therapies developed mainly in the US and Europe. They have often been delivered as part of treatment programmes for people with personality disorders including those with borderline personality disorder. Arts therapies include art therapy, dance movement therapy, dramatherapy and music therapy which use arts media as its primary mode of communication; these four therapies are currently provided in the UK. Arts therapies are normally undertaken weekly, and a session lasts 1.5 to 2 hours. Patients are assessed for group (typically four to six members) or individual therapy. The primary concern is to effect change and growth through the use of the art form in a safe and facilitating environment in the presence of a therapist. Arts therapies can help those who find it hard to express thoughts and feelings verbally. Traditionally, art therapy is thought of as working with primitive emotional material that is 'preverbal' in nature, and thus made available to exploration and rational thought. The nature of the therapist's work can thus be similar to the interpretations of psychoanalysis, or less interpretative and more supportive, to enable patients to understand what they want to understand from the work. For people with more severe borderline personality disorder, it is generally accepted that 'plunging interpretations' without sufficient support are unlikely to be helpful (Meares & Hobson, 1977).

Arts therapies are more concerned with the process of creating something, and the emotional response to this and/or the group dynamics of this. This can be very active (involving the physical characteristics of the art work and movement), playful, symbolic, metaphorical or lead directly to emotions that need to be understood. Such understanding may be achieved through subsequent discussion, and the use of the art materials when helpful.

2.5.5   Therapeutic communities

A therapeutic community is a consciously designed social environment and programme within a residential or day unit in which the social and group process is harnessed with therapeutic intent. In the therapeutic community the community itself is the primary therapeutic instrument (Kennard & Haigh, 2009).

In England therapeutic communities first emerged in a form that we would recognise today during the Second World War, at Northfield Military Hospital in Birmingham and Mill Hill in London. The leaders of the Northfield 'experiments' were psychoanalysts who were later involved in treatment programmes at the Tavistock Clinic and the Cassel Hospital, and had considerable international influence on psychoanalysis and group therapy. The Mill Hill programme, for battle-shocked soldiers, later led to the founding of Henderson Hospital and a worldwide 'social psychiatry' movement, which brought considerably more psychological and less custodial treatment of patients of mental hospitals throughout the Western world.

Different forms of therapeutic community have evolved from these origins, one clear strand of which is for specific treatment of people with personality disorders.

The therapeutic communities for personality disorder range from full-time residential hospitals to units that operate for a few hours on one day each week. Although, as stated above, the community itself is the primary therapeutic agent, programmes include a range of different therapies, usually held in groups. These can include small analytic groups, median analytic groups, psychodrama, transactional analysis, arts therapies, CT, social problem solving, psychoeducation and gestalt. In addition to specific therapies, there are community meetings and activities.

Therapeutic communities generally use a complex admission procedure, rather than straightforward inclusion and exclusion criteria. This results in diagnostic heterogeneity, and none claims to treat borderline personality disorder exclusively; however recent work has demonstrated that the admission characteristics of members show high levels of personality morbidity, with most exhibiting sufficient features to diagnose more than three personality disorders, often in more than one cluster. The admission phase includes engagement, assessment, preparation and selection processes before the definitive therapy programme begins and is a model of stepped care, where the service users decide when and whether to proceed to the next stage of the programme. A voting procedure by the existing members of the community, at a specifically convened case conference or admissions panel, is normally used to admit new members. Programmes and their various stages are time limited, and none of the therapeutic communities specifically for personality disorder is open ended. Some have formal or informal, staff or service-user led post-therapy programmes.

Staff teams in therapeutic communities are always multidisciplinary, drawn mostly from the mental health core professions, including direct psychiatric input and specialist psychotherapists. They also frequently employ 'social therapists', who are untrained staff with suitable personal characteristics, and ex-service users. The role of staff is less obvious than in single therapies, and can often cover a wide range of activities as part of the sociotherapy. However, clear structures – such as job descriptions defining their different responsibilities, mutually agreed processes for dealing with a range of day-to-day problems and rigorous supervisory arrangements – always underpin the various staff roles.

There are several theoretical models on which the clinical practice is based, drawing on systemic, psychodynamic, group analytic, cognitive-behavioural and humanistic traditions. The original therapeutic community model at Henderson Hospital was extensively researched in the 1950s using anthropological methods and four predominant 'themes' were identified: democratisation, permissiveness, reality confrontation and communalism. More contemporary theory emphasises the following: the role of attachment; the 'culture of enquiry' within which all behaviours, thinking and emotions can be scrutinised; the network of supportive and challenging relationships between members; and the empowering potential of members being made responsible for themselves and each other. This has been synthesised into a simple developmental model of emotional development, where the task of the therapeutic community is to recreate a network of close relationships, much like a family, in which deeply ingrained behavioural patterns, negative cognitions and adverse emotions can be re-learned.

For personality disorders, the non-residential communities are mostly within the NHS mainstream mental health services, and the residential units are in both NHS and tier 3 organisations. Standards have been devised to ensure uniformity and quality of practice, and all NHS therapeutic communities for personality disorder participate in an annual audit cycle of self-review, peer review and action planning against these standards. The Department of Health in England has supported the recent development of 'NHS commissioning standards' upon which accreditation for therapeutic communities will be based.

2.5.6   Other therapies

This section includes various modalities that are not part of the general psychological treatments for borderline personality disorder. Group analytic psychotherapy, humanistic and integrative psychotherapy and systemic therapy can all be routinely employed in work with people with personality disorder, either as stand-alone therapies for less complex cases or as part of multidisciplinary packages of care – or long-term pathways – for those with more intractable or severe conditions.

Group analytic psychotherapy
This is also often known simply as 'group therapy'. It is characterised by non-directive groups (without pre-determined agendas), in which the relationships between the members, and the members and the therapist ('conductor'), comprise the main therapeutic tool. Such groups generally, and deliberately, build a strong *esprit de corps* and are both strongly supportive and deeply challenging. The membership of a group is fairly constant, with each member staying typically for 2 to 5 years. Suitably qualified group therapists (to United Kingdom Council for Psychotherapy [UKCP] standards) undergo at least 4 years' training, have regular clinical supervision and undertake continuing professional development (CPD) activities.

The group process can help prevent hazardous therapeutic relationships developing with a therapist, as can happen in individual therapy with people with severe personality disorders. They can actively address relationship difficulties that are manifest 'live' in the group, and they can avoid difficult dependency by helping participants to take responsibility for themselves by first sharing responsibility for each other and later learning how to ask for help for themselves, in an adaptive way.

Disadvantages include difficulty in initiating participation because of the fear of personal exposure; problems of finding a regular suitable meeting space; and issues of confidentiality.

Humanistic and integrative psychotherapies
These are therapies based on a variety of theoretical models that evolved in the mid-20th century as alternatives to the dominant model of psychoanalysis. There is a significant overlap with the term 'action therapies', which has increasing currency. They include: psychodrama, which is group-based and aims to understand particularly difficult past emotional episodes and link them to current

problems and difficulties; transactional analysis, which is based on parent, adult and child 'ego states' (a person's beliefs, mannerisms and emotional responses), and can be undertaken either individually or in groups; gestalt therapy, which aims to facilitate awareness and help achieve self-regulation and self-actualisation (therapeutic techniques include empty-chair work, role reversal and enactments); and person-centred therapy developed from Carl Rogers' humanistic approach.

Systemic therapy
This is most commonly used for work with families (or support networks), for example, where the index patient is a child. It aims to maximise family strengths and resilience to help people overcome problems experienced by individual family members or the family as a whole. It helps family members to understand how they function as a family and to develop more helpful ways of interacting with and supporting each other. It uses a format with long but widely-spaced sessions, for example 2 hours every 6 weeks. It requires a supervising team who watch the session live or who listen to it with audio equipment, and who discuss hypotheses of how the system is working and actions to bring about change. The individual and family or support network have access to the ideas and hypotheses discussed in the team, so that different experiences and points of view can be heard and acknowledged. The therapists help the family (or support network) to bring about the changes that they have identified as therapeutic goals. There are a number of models of systemic theory and interventions, such as Milan, social constructionist, narrative, solution focused, structural and strategic. The interventions are generally 'structural' or 'strategic', and include the use of such techniques as circular questioning (for example, 'what would your brother think about your mother's answer to that question?'), reframing and mapping the system with genograms (a pictorial representation of a patient's family relationships).

In cases of personality disorder where the dynamics within a whole family may be important in maintaining or exacerbating the presenting range of problems, and the family members are willing to participate, systemic therapy can be effective at starting new ways of communicating within a family that may be self-sustaining.

Nidotherapy
Nidotherapy, from the Latin, *nidus*, meaning nest (Tyrer *et al.*, 2003a), is distinct from psychotherapeutic approaches in that the emphasis is on making environmental changes to create a better fit between the person and their environment. In this sense it is not specifically a treatment, but it does have a therapeutic aim of improving quality of life, through acceptance of a level of handicap and its environmental accommodation.

2.6   MULTI-AGENCY PERSPECTIVE

2.6.1   The NHS and personality disorder

The perceived enduring and chronic nature of personality disorder poses a challenge to a healthcare system that is historically, and to a large extent still is, strongly influenced by the biological (illness) paradigm of mental health. Essentially, mental health services within the NHS have been configured in such a way as to 'treat' people during the acute phases of their illness. As personality disorders by their definition do not have 'acute' phases some have argued that a personality disorder should not be the responsibility of the NHS (see Kendell [2002] for further discussion).

Given the confusion that surrounds the nature of personality disorder, it is not surprising that this has impacted on NHS care for people with this diagnosis. Until recently, personality disorder services in the NHS had been diverse, spasmodic and inconsistent (Department of Health, 2003).

2.6.2   The National Service Framework (NSF) for Mental Health

In line with the NSF for Mental Health (Department of Health, 1999a) the National Institute for Mental Health in England (NIMHE) produced policy implementation guidance for the development of services for people with personality disorder (Department of Health, 2003). The main purpose of this document was:

- to assist people with personality disorder who experience significant distress or difficulty to access appropriate clinical care and management from specialist mental health services
- to ensure that offenders with a personality disorder receive appropriate care from forensic services and interventions designed both to provide treatment and to address their offending behaviour
- to establish the necessary education and training to equip mental health practitioners to provide effective assessment and management.' (Department of Health, 2003).

The Personality Disorder Capabilities Framework (NIMHE, 2003) soon followed. This document set out a framework to support the development of the skills that would enable practitioners to work more effectively with people with personality disorders. It also aimed to provide a framework to support local and regional partners to deliver appropriate education and training (NIMHE, 2003). This document did not focus solely on the needs of NHS organisations; it had a wider remit to include all agencies that had contact with people who met the diagnosis. These two documents, along with investments in pilot personality disorder services and training initiatives, have signalled a significant change in the perspective of the NHS on personality disorder and have led to its commitment to enhance and improve its service.

2.6.3   Social services

The role of social services, in providing care and support to people with mental health problems, covers a wide range of people, from those with mild mental health problems to people with severe and enduring mental disorders (Department of Health, 1998). Historically, care provided by social services is determined by the person's social need and is less influenced by diagnosis and the biological paradigm than the NHS. After the 1998 White Paper on modernising social services (Department of

Health, 1998), which aimed to set new standards of performance and to allow the NHS and social services to have closer partnerships in meeting the standards set down in the NSF for mental health, local implementation teams were set up across the country. With respect to personality disorder, their role is to review the progress that local mental health and social care services are making towards implementing the NSF's targets for personality disorder.

2.6.4   Criminal justice system

In law, personality disorder is generally seen as distinct from 'serious mental illness' because it is not considered to reduce the person's capacity to make decisions (Hart, 2001). Instead, it is thought of as an aggravating condition (Hart, 2001). Nevertheless, new legislation in the Mental Health Act amendment (HMSO, 2007) and the Mental Capacity Act (HMSO, 2005) will change both the rights and protections for people with personality disorders and their access to services. However, the legal position that people with personality disorder have held throughout the history of psychiatry has undoubtedly influenced the perspective of the criminal justice system regarding personality disorder and goes some way to explain why most people with personality disorder would generally find themselves in the criminal justice system as opposed to forensic mental health services. It is not uncommon within forensic mental health services for regional secure units to actively exclude patients with a primary diagnosis of personality disorder, because they do not consider this to be their core business (Department of Health, 2003). In many parts of the country there are no specific services, and, when services are offered, they tend to be idiosyncratic.

In March 1999, a report commissioned by the Department of Health about the future organisation of prison healthcare (Department of Health, 1999b) proposed that people in prison should have access to the same quality and range of services (including mental health) as the general public (Department of Health, 1999b). In the same year the NSF called for closer partnerships between prisons and the NHS at local, regional and national levels (Department of Health, 1999a). The emphasis was on a move towards the NHS taking more responsibility for providing mental healthcare in prisons and establishing formal partnerships.

In July 1998, the Secretary of State announced a review of the 1983 Mental Health Act (Department of Health, 1983), triggered by concerns that current legislation did not support a modern mental health service. These concerns were reiterated in the NSF for mental health since 'neither mental health nor criminal justice law currently provides a robust way of managing the small number of dangerous people with severe personality disorder' (Department of Health, 1999a).

2.7   YOUNG PEOPLE

Diagnosing borderline personality disorder in young people under 18 has often caused controversy. Although borderline personality disorder is thought to affect between 0.9 and 3% of the community population of under 18 year olds (Lewinsohn *et al.*, 1997; Bernstein *et al.*, 1993), there is some uncertainty about the rate (see Chapter 9). There are also certain caveats in DSM-IV and ICD-10 when making the diagnosis in young people (see Chapter 9). However young people with borderline personality disorder often present to services in seek of help (Chanen *et al.*, 2007a). Because interventions for young people with borderline personality disorder will usually be provided by specialist CAMHS, which has a different structure from adult mental health services, a full discussion of the issues relating to young people with borderline personality disorder can be found in Chapter 9.

2.8   THE EXPERIENCE OF SERVICE USERS, AND THEIR FAMILIES AND CARERS

There are particular issues for people with borderline personality disorder regarding the diagnosis, the label and associated stigma, which can have an impact on people accessing services and receiving the appropriate treatment. These issues are fully explored in Chapter 4, which comprises personal accounts from people with personality disorder and from a carer, and a review of the literature of service user and family/carer experience.

The families and carers of people may also feel unsupported in their role by healthcare professionals and excluded from the service user's treatment and care. The issues surrounding this are also further explored in Chapter 4. Although there are debates around the usefulness and applicability of the word 'carer', this guideline uses the term 'families/carers' to apply to all people who have regular close contact with the person and are involved in their care.

2.9   ECONOMIC IMPACT

Besides functional impairment and emotional distress, borderline personality disorder is also associated with significant financial costs to the healthcare system, social services and the wider society. The annual cost of personality disorders to the NHS was estimated at approximately £61.2 million in 1986 (Smith *et al.*, 1995). Of this, 91% accounted for inpatient care. Another study conducted in the UK, estimated the costs of people with personality disorders in contact with primary care services (Rendu *et al.*, 2002). The study reported that people with personality disorders incurred a cost of around £3,000 per person annually, consisting of healthcare costs and productivity losses; in contrast, the respective cost incurred by people without personality disorders in contact with primary care services was £1,600 (1998/99 prices). In both groups, productivity losses accounted for over 80% of total costs. Dolan and colleagues (1996) assessed the cost of people with personality disorders admitted to a UK hospital over 1 year prior to admission; this cost was reported to reach £14,000 per person (1992/93 prices), including inpatient and outpatient health-care costs, as well as prison-related costs (which amounted to approximately 10% of the total cost). Although the two UK studies (Rendu *et al.*, 2002; Dolan *et al.*, 1996) differed in methodology and costs considered, this difference in costs may be partly attributed to the different levels of severity of the disorders apparent in the two study populations (people engaged with general practice services versus people admitted to hospital).

The economic cost of personality disorders has been assessed in other European countries as well: in Germany, inpatient treatment of borderline personality disorder was estimated at €3.5 billion annually, covering about 25% of the total costs for psychiatric inpatient treatment in the country (Bohus, 2007). In the Netherlands, the average cost of a person with personality disorder referred for psychotherapeutic treatment was estimated at €11,000 (2005 prices) over 12 months prior to treatment (Soeteman *et al.*, 2008). Of this, 66.5% was associated with healthcare expenditure, while the rest reflected productivity losses. According to another study (Van Asselt *et al.*, 2007), the average cost per person with borderline personality disorder in the Netherlands was €17,000 in 2000. Of this, only 22% was health-related. The remaining cost was incurred by out-of-pocket expenses, informal care, criminal justice costs and productivity losses. Based on this average cost and a prevalence of borderline personality disorder of 1.1%, the study estimated that the total societal cost of borderline personality disorder in the Netherlands reached €2.2 billion in 2000. The authors noted that the direct medical costs represented only 0.63% of total Dutch healthcare expenditure in 2000, which meant that, given the 1.1% prevalence of the condition, people with borderline personality disorder seemed to use a less than proportionate share of the healthcare budget. However, the authors acknowledged that people in institutional care were not part of the study sample, and therefore medical costs associated with borderline personality disorder might have been underestimated.

Treatment-seeking people with personality disorders have been reported to place a high economic cost on society, compared with people with other mental disorders such as depression or generalised anxiety disorder (GAD) (Soeteman *et al.*, 2008). People with borderline personality disorder make extensive use of more intensive treatments, such as emergency department visits and psychiatric hospital services (Bender *et al.*, 2001 & 2006; Chiesa *et al.*, 2002), resulting in higher related healthcare costs compared with people with other personality disorders and major depression (Bender *et al.*, 2001 & 2006). In addition, they are more likely to use almost every type of psychosocial treatment (except self-help groups) and to have used most classes of medication compared with people with depression (Bender *et al.*, 2001). However, an American prospective study that followed people with borderline personality disorder over 6 years (Zanarini *et al.*, 2004a) reported that, although hospitalisation rates and rates of day or residential treatment were high at initiation of the study, these significantly declined overtime; similar patterns were observed for rates of intensive psychotherapy, although engagement in less intensive psychosocial therapeutic programmes remained stable over the 6 years of the study. Polypharmacy was a characteristic of people with borderline personality disorder that was not affected by time, with 40% of people taking three or more concurrent standing medications, 20% taking four or more and 10% taking five or more, at any follow-up period examined. The authors concluded that the majority of people diagnosed with borderline personality disorder carry on outpatient treatment in the long term, but only a declining minority continue to use restrictive and more costly forms of treatment.

The level of severity of symptoms of borderline personality disorder determines the level of usage of healthcare resources: in a study conducted in a primary care setting in the US, the severity of symptoms experienced by women with borderline personality disorder was shown to predict increased use of primary healthcare resources (Sansone *et al.*, 1996). This finding was consistent with the findings of another American study that examined male veterans with borderline personality disorder (Black *et al.*, 2006); the study reported that as the number of symptoms associated with borderline personality disorder increased, so did the levels of psychiatric comorbidity (such as depression, PTSD and GAD), the levels of suicidal and self-harming behaviour, as well as the rates of utilisation of healthcare resources (that is, inpatient stays, outpatient visits and emergency department visits). Moreover, the number of symptoms observed was positively related to rates of incarceration and other contacts with military forensic services (which are expected to incur extra costs). Psychiatric comorbidity is common in people with borderline personality disorder (Bender *et al.*, 2001; Black *et al.*, 2006) and, when present, results in a significant increase in total healthcare costs (Bender *et al.*, 2001; Rendu *et al.*, 2002).

The reported resource use and cost estimates have been made by studying people with borderline personality disorder in contact with health services. However, it is known that a significant proportion of people with personality disorders fail to seek treatment and, when they do, future disengagement with services is quite common. Moreover, contacts with social services, problems with housing, levels of unemployment and involvement with the criminal justice system incur further substantial costs that have not been thoroughly examined, if at all. Therefore, the financial and psychological implications of borderline personality disorder to society are likely to be wider than those suggested in the literature. Efficient use of available healthcare resources is required to maximise the benefits for people with borderline personality disorder, their family and carers, and society in general.

3. METHODS USED TO DEVELOP THIS GUIDELINE

3.1 OVERVIEW

The development of this guideline drew upon methods outlined by NICE (*The Guidelines Manual*[1] [NICE, 2006b]). A team of healthcare professionals, lay representatives and technical experts known as the Guideline Development Group (GDG), with support from the NCCMH staff, undertook the development of a person-centred, evidence-based guideline. There are six basic steps in the process of developing a guideline:

- define the scope, which sets the parameters of the guideline and provides a focus and steer for the development work
- define clinical questions considered important for practitioners and service users
- develop criteria for evidence searching and search for evidence
- design validated protocols for systematic review and apply to evidence recovered by the search
- synthesise and (meta-) analyse data retrieved, guided by the clinical questions, and produce evidence profiles
- answer clinical questions with evidence-based recommendations for clinical practice.

The clinical practice recommendations made by the GDG are therefore derived from the most up-to-date and robust evidence base for the clinical and cost effectiveness of the treatments and services used in the treatment and management of borderline personality disorder. In addition, to ensure a service user and family/carer focus, the concerns of service users and families/carers regarding health and social care have been highlighted and addressed by recommendations agreed by the whole GDG.

3.2 THE SCOPE

Guideline topics are selected by the Department of Health and the Welsh Assembly Government, which identify the main areas to be covered by the guideline in a specific remit (see *The Guideline Development Process – An Overview for Stakeholders, the Public and the NHS (Second Edition)* [NICE, 2006c][2]). The remit for this guideline was translated into a scope document by staff at the NCCMH.

---

[1] Available from www.nice.org.uk
[2] Available from: www.nice.org.uk

The purpose of the scope was to:
- provide an overview of what the guideline will include and exclude
- identify the key aspects of care that must be included
- set the boundaries of the development work and provide a clear framework to enable work to stay within the priorities agreed by NICE and the NCCMH and the remit from the Department of Health/Welsh Assembly Government
- inform the development of the clinical questions and search strategy
- inform professionals and the public about the expected content of the guideline
- keep the guideline to a reasonable size to ensure that its development can be carried out within an 18-month period.

The draft scope was subject to consultation with stakeholders over a 4-week period. During the consultation period, the scope was posted on the NICE website (www.nice.org.uk). Comments were invited from stakeholder organisations and the Guideline Review Panel (GRP). Further information about the GRP can also be found on the NICE website (www.nice.org.uk). The NCCMH and NICE reviewed the scope in light of comments received, and the revised scope was signed off by the GRP.

3.3   THE GUIDELINE DEVELOPMENT GROUP

The GDG was made up of professionals in psychiatry, clinical psychology, nursing, and general practice; academic experts in psychiatry and psychology; two former service users and a carer. The guideline development process was supported by staff from the NCCMH, who undertook the clinical and health economics literature searches, reviewed and presented the evidence to the GDG, managed the process, and contributed to drafting the guideline.

3.3.1   Guideline Development Group meetings

Seventeen GDG meetings were held between January 2007 and September 2008. During each day-long GDG meeting, in a plenary session, clinical questions and clinical and economic evidence were reviewed and assessed, and recommendations formulated. At each meeting, all GDG members declared any potential conflicts of interest, and service user and carer concerns were routinely discussed as part of a standing agenda.

3.3.2   Topic groups

The GDG divided its workload along clinically relevant lines to simplify the guideline development process, and GDG members formed smaller topic groups to undertake guideline work in that area of clinical practice. Topic group 1 covered questions relating to pharmacological interventions; topic group 2 covered psychological therapies (with a sub-group covering therapeutic communities); topic group 3 covered services; topic group 4 covered young people; and topic group 5 covered service user and family/carer issues. These groups were designed to manage the appraisal of the evidence more efficiently before presenting it to the GDG as a whole. Each topic group was chaired by a GDG member with expert knowledge of the topic area (one of the healthcare professionals or service users as appropriate). Topic groups refined the clinical questions, refined the clinical definitions of treatment interventions, reviewed and prepared the evidence with NCCMH staff before presenting it to the GDG as a whole, and also helped the GDG to identify further expertise in the topic. Topic group leaders reported the status of the group's work as part of the standing agenda. They also introduced and led the GDG discussion of the evidence review for that topic and assisted the GDG Chair in drafting the section of the guideline relevant to the work of each topic group.

3.3.3   Service users and families/carers

Individuals with direct experience of services gave an integral service user/carer focus to the GDG and the guideline. The GDG included two former service users and one carer. They contributed as full GDG members to writing the clinical questions, helping to ensure that the evidence addressed their views and preferences, highlighting sensitive issues and terminology relevant to the guideline, and bringing service user/carer research to the attention of the GDG. In drafting the guideline, they contributed to writing a chapter on service user and family/carer issues for the full guideline, and to formulating recommendations from the service user and family/carer perspective.

3.3.4   Special advisors

Special advisors, who had specific expertise in one or more aspects of treatment and management relevant to the guideline, assisted the GDG, commenting on specific aspects of the developing guideline, including attending topic group meetings and teleconferences if appropriate. Appendix 3 lists those who acted as special advisors.

3.3.5   Researchers contacted for unpublished studies

National and international experts in the area under review were identified through the literature search and through the experience of the GDG members. These experts were contacted to recommend unpublished or soon-to-be published studies in order to ensure up-to-date evidence was included in the development of the guideline. They informed the group about completed trials at the pre-publication stage, systematic reviews in the process of being published, studies relating to the cost effectiveness of treatment and trial data if the GDG could be provided with full access to the complete trial report. Appendix 5 lists researchers who were contacted.

3.3.6   Peer reviewers

Peer reviewers were identified by the GDG to review the guideline during the consultation phase, as well as stakeholders. In addition, the review of pharmacological treatments was sent to international experts for peer review during the guideline development process because this section of the guideline was completed ahead of time and the draft recommendations were potentially controversial because they contradicted current clinical opinion. Therefore peer reviewers who were leaders in the field were appointed; they were named as special advisers to ensure that confidentiality was maintained (see Appendix 3). Their comments and responses from the GDG are presented in Appendix 11.

3.4   CLINICAL QUESTIONS

Clinical questions were used to guide the identification and interrogation of the evidence base relevant to the topic of the guideline. Before the first GDG meeting, draft questions were prepared by NCCMH staff based on the scope. They were then discussed by the GDG at their first two meetings and a final list drawn up. Where appropriate, the questions were refined once the evidence had been searched and, where necessary, subquestions were generated. The final list of clinical questions can be found in Appendix 6.

For questions about interventions, the PICO (patient, intervention, comparison and outcome) framework was used. This structured approach divides each question into four components: the patients (the population under study), the interventions (what is being done), the comparisons (other main treatment options) and the outcomes (the measures of how effective the interventions have been) (see Text box 2).

**Text box 2: Features of a well-formulated question on effectiveness
intervention – the PICO guide**

Patients/population	Which patients or population of patients are we interested in? How can they be best described? Are there subgroups that need to be considered?
Intervention	Which intervention, treatment or approach should be used?
Comparison	What is/are the main alternative/s to compare with the intervention?
Outcome	What is really important for the patient? Which outcomes should be considered: intermediate or short-term measures; mortality; morbidity and treatment complications; rates of relapse; late morbidity and readmission; return to work, physical and social functioning and other measures such as quality of life; general health status; costs?

To help facilitate the literature review, a note was made of the best study design to answer each question. There are four main types of clinical question of relevance to NICE guidelines. These are listed in Text box 3. For each type of question, the best primary study design varies, where 'best' is interpreted as 'least likely to give misleading answers to the question'. However, in all cases, a well-conducted systematic review of the appropriate type of study is likely to yield a better answer than a single study. Deciding on the best design type to answer a specific clinical or public health question does not mean that studies of different design types addressing the same question were discarded.

Text box 3: Best study design to answer each type of question

Type of question	Best primary study design
Effectiveness or other impact of an intervention	Randomised controlled trial (RCT); other studies that may be considered in the absence of an RCT are the following: internally/externally controlled before and after trial, interrupted time-series
Accuracy of information (for example, risk factor, test, prediction rule)	Comparing the information against a valid gold standard in a randomised trial or inception cohort study
Rates (of disease, patient experience, rare side effects)	Cohort, registry, cross-sectional study
Costs	Naturalistic prospective cost study

3.5   SYSTEMATIC CLINICAL LITERATURE REVIEW

The aim of the clinical literature review was to systematically identify and synthesise relevant evidence from the literature in order to answer the specific clinical questions developed by the GDG. Thus, clinical practice recommendations are evidence-based, where possible. If evidence was not available, informal consensus methods were used (see Section 3.5.9) and the need for future research specified.

3.5.1   Methodology

A stepwise, hierarchical approach was taken to locating and presenting evidence to the GDG. The NCCMH developed this process based on methods set out in *The Guidelines Manual*[3] (NICE, 2006b) and after considering recommendations from a range of other sources. These included:

● Clinical Policy and Practice Program of the New South Wales Department of Health (Australia)

---

[3]Available from www.nice.org.uk

- Clinical Evidence online
- The Cochrane Collaboration
- New Zealand Guidelines Group
- NHS Centre for Reviews and Dissemination
- Oxford Centre for Evidence-Based Medicine
- Scottish Intercollegiate Guidelines Network (SIGN)
- United States Agency for Healthcare Research and Quality
- Oxford Systematic Review Development Programme
- Grading of Recommendations: Assessment, Development and Evaluation (GRADE) Working Group.

3.5.2   The review process

After the scope was finalised, a more extensive search for existing systematic reviews and published guidelines was undertaken to inform the review process. The review team, in conjunction with the GDG, assessed the available existing systematic reviews for relevance to the clinical questions. This helped to assess the quantity and likely quality of available primary research. The initial approach taken to locating primary-level studies depended on the type of clinical question and availability of evidence.

The GDG then decided which questions were best addressed by good practice based on expert opinion, which questions were likely to have a good evidence base and which questions were likely to have little or no directly relevant evidence. Recommendations based on good practice were developed by informal consensus of the GDG. For questions with a good evidence base, the review process depended on the type of key question. For questions that were unlikely to have a good evidence base, a brief descriptive review was initially undertaken by a member of the GDG.

Searches
The standard mental health related bibliographic databases were searched including EMBASE, MEDLINE, PsycINFO, and Central, together with the grey literature database HMIC. Search filters developed by the review team consisted of a combination of subject heading and free-text phrases. Specific filters were developed for the guideline topic and, where necessary, for individual clinical questions (see relevant chapters for details). The topic-specific filters were combined with appropriate research design filters developed for systematic reviews, RCTs and other appropriate research designs (Appendix 7).

The review team also scanned the reference lists of included studies and existing systematic reviews for additional references, together with evidence submitted by stakeholders. Unpublished evidence was also sought (see below). In addition, the tables of contents of appropriate journals were checked regularly for relevant studies. Searches for evidence were re-run every 6 months during the guideline development process with the final search undertaken between 6 and 8 weeks before submission of the consultation drafts. After this point, studies were included only if they were judged by the GDG to be exceptional (for example, the evidence was likely to change a recommendation).

The search process for questions concerning interventions
For questions related to interventions, the initial evidence base was formed from well-conducted RCTs that addressed at least one of the clinical questions (the review process is illustrated in Flowchart 1). Although there are a number of difficulties with the use of RCTs in the evaluation of interventions in mental health, the RCT remains the most important method for establishing treatment efficacy (this is discussed in more detail in the appropriate clinical evidence chapters). For other clinical questions, searches were for the appropriate study design (see above).

Since it was known from a review of existing systematic reviews in this area that the evidence base for borderline personality disorder was relatively small, a search for all RCTs for this topic area was undertaken together regardless of intervention.

After the initial search results were scanned liberally to exclude irrelevant papers, the review team used a purpose-built study information database to manage both the included and the excluded studies (eligibility criteria were developed after consultation with the GDG). For questions without good-quality evidence (after the initial search), a decision was made by the GDG about whether to (a) repeat the search using subject-specific databases (for example, CINAHL, AMED, SIGLE or PILOTS), (b) conduct a new search for lower levels of evidence, or (c) adopt a consensus process (see Section 3.5.9).

Study selection
All primary-level studies included after the first scan of citations were acquired in full and re-evaluated for eligibility at the time they were being entered into the study information database. Appendix 8 lists the standard inclusion and exclusion criteria. More specific eligibility criteria were developed for each clinical question and are described in the relevant clinical evidence chapters. Studies were critically appraised for methodological quality (see Appendix 9 and Appendix 16). The eligibility of each study was confirmed by at least one member of the appropriate topic group.

For some clinical questions, it was necessary to prioritise the evidence with respect to the UK context (that is, external validity). To make this process explicit, the topic groups took into account the following factors when assessing the evidence:
- participant factors (for example, comorbid diagnoses and setting)
- provider factors (for example, model fidelity, the conditions under which the intervention was performed and the availability of experienced staff to undertake the procedure)
- cultural factors (for example, differences in standard care and differences in the welfare system).

It was the responsibility of each topic group to decide which prioritisation factors were relevant to each clinical question in light of the UK context and then decide how they should modify their recommendations.

Unpublished evidence
The GDG used a number of criteria when deciding whether or not to accept unpublished data. First, the evidence must have been accompanied by a trial report containing sufficient detail to properly assess the quality of the data. Second, the

Flowchart 1: Guideline review process

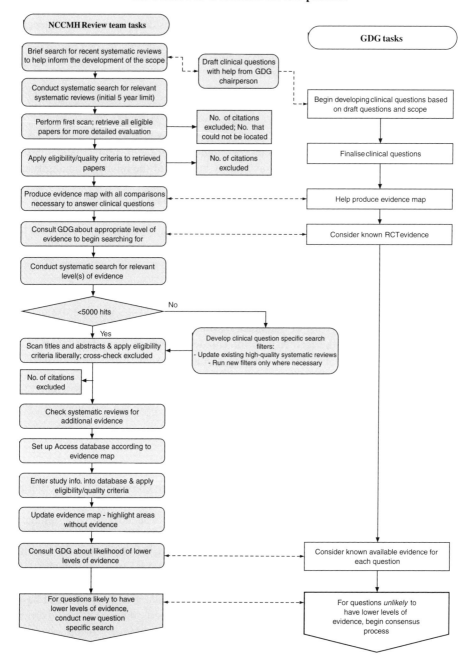

evidence must have been submitted with the understanding that data from the study and a summary of the study's characteristics would be published in the full guideline. Therefore, the GDG did not accept evidence submitted as commercial in confidence. However, the GDG recognised that unpublished evidence submitted by investigators might later be retracted by those investigators if the inclusion of such data would jeopardise publication of their research.

3.5.3   Outcomes

Outcome measurement on borderline personality disorder is problematic, partly because of the nature of the disorder and partly because of the relative immaturity of intervention research in this field. Since diagnosis of the disorder is based on the presence of five symptoms out of a possible total of nine with no requirement for the presence of particular symptoms (based on DSM-IV which is used by most treatment studies), trialists usually measure outcomes on all or some of these symptoms. In addition, more than one outcome measure has been developed for most areas of psychopathology caused by the disorder as well as psychosocial functioning affected by the disorder.

In order to deal with the plethora of outcomes reported by the trials forming the guideline's evidence base, the GDG appointed a special advisor with expertise in this area (see Appendix 3). A list of outcomes reported by the studies considered by the GDG is in Appendix 10, together with information on which were used and which were not. For a rating scale to be considered a validation study had to be published in a peer-reviewed journal. In order to increase the power of the meta-analyses, scales reporting the same outcome were examined in detail to assess whether they could be combined. However, self-report and clinical-rated scales were not combined.

3.5.4   Data extraction

Outcome data were extracted from all eligible studies, which met the quality criteria, using a standardised form (see Appendix 8). Study characteristics were also extracted into an Access database. Full study characteristics are in Appendix 16 with summary tables in the evidence chapters.

For a given outcome (continuous and dichotomous), where more than 50% of the number randomised to any group were not accounted for[4] by trial authors, the data were excluded from the review because of the risk of bias. However, where possible, dichotomous efficacy outcomes were calculated on an intention-to-treat (ITT) basis (that is, a 'once-randomised-always-analyse' basis). This assumes that those participants who ceased to engage in the study—from whatever group—had an

---

[4]'Accounted for' in this context means using an appropriate method for dealing with missing data (for example, last observation carried forward or a regression technique).

unfavourable outcome. This meant that the 50% rule was not applied to dichotomous outcomes where there was good evidence that those participants who ceased to engage in the study were likely to have an unfavourable outcome (in this case, early withdrawals were included in both the numerator and denominator). Adverse effects were entered into Review Manager 4.2.8 (Cochrane Collaboration, 2005) as reported by the study authors because it was usually not possible to determine whether early withdrawals had an unfavourable outcome. For the outcome 'leaving the study early for any reason', the denominator was the number randomised.

Where some of the studies failed to report standard deviations (for a continuous outcome), and where an estimate of the variance could not be computed from other reported data or obtained from the study author, the following approach was taken[5]:

1. When the number of studies with missing standard deviations was small and when the total number of studies was large, the pooled standard deviation from all the other available studies in the same meta-analysis was used. In this case, the appropriateness of the imputation was made by comparing the standardised mean differences (SMDs) of those trials that had reported standard deviations against the hypothetical SMDs of the same trials based on the imputed standard deviations. If they converged, the meta-analytical results were considered to be reliable.

2. When the number of studies with missing standard deviations was large or when the total number of studies was small, standard deviations were taken from a previous systematic review (where available), because the small sample size may allow unexpected deviation due to chance. In this case, the results were considered to be less reliable.

Consultation was used to overcome difficulties with coding. Data from studies included in existing systematic reviews were extracted independently by one reviewer and cross-checked with the existing dataset. Where possible, two independent reviewers extracted data from new studies. Where double data extraction was not possible, data extracted by one reviewer was checked by the second reviewer. Disagreements were resolved with discussion. Where consensus could not be reached, a third reviewer resolved the disagreement. Masked assessment (that is, blind to the journal from which the article comes, the authors, the institution and the magnitude of the effect) was not used since it is unclear that doing so reduces bias (Jadad *et al.*, 1996; Berlin, 1997).

3.5.5   Synthesising the evidence

Where possible, meta-analysis was used to synthesise the evidence using Review Manager 4.2.8 (Cochrane Collaboration, 2005). If necessary, reanalyses of the data or sub-analyses were used to answer clinical questions not addressed in the original studies or reviews.

---

[5]Based on the approach suggested by Furukawa and colleagues (2006).

Dichotomous outcomes were analysed as relative risks (RR) with the associated 95% confidence interval (CI) (for an example, see Figure 1). A relative risk (also called a risk ratio) is the ratio of the treatment event rate to the control event rate. An RR of 1 indicates no difference between treatment and control. In Figure 1, the overall RR of 0.73 indicates that the event rate (that is, non-remission rate) associated with intervention A is about three quarters of that with the control intervention or, in other words, the relative risk reduction is 27%.

The CI shows with 95% certainty the range within which the true treatment effect should lie and can be used to determine statistical significance. If the CI does not cross the 'line of no effect', the effect is statistically significant at the 5% significance level.

Figure 1: Example of a forest plot displaying dichotomous data

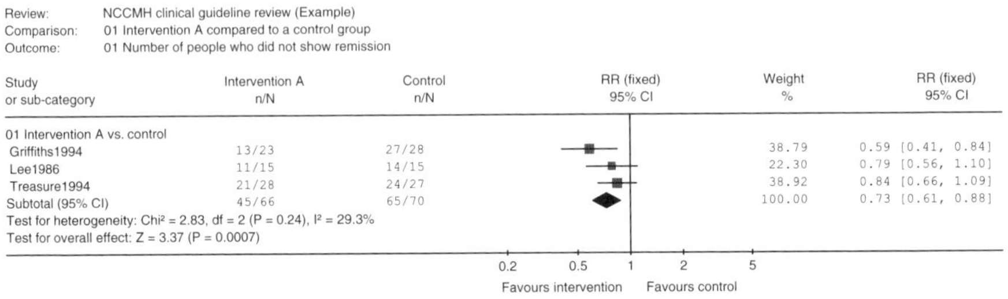

Continuous outcomes were analysed as weighted mean differences (WMD), or as a standardised mean difference (SMD) when different measures were used in different studies to estimate the same underlying effect (for an example, see Figure 2). If provided, ITT data, using a method such as 'last observation carried forward', were preferred over data from completers.

Figure 2: Example of a forest plot displaying continuous data

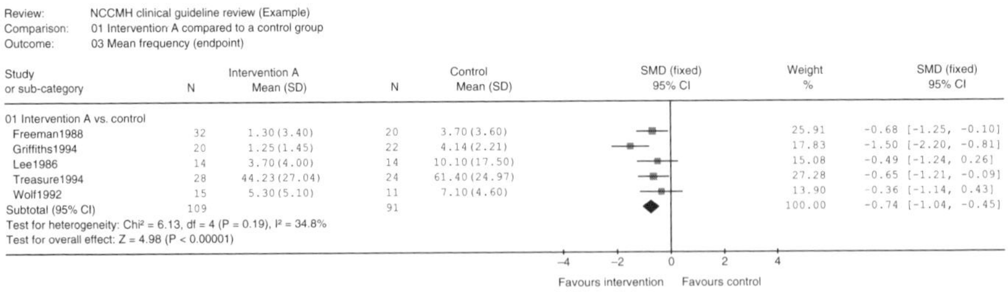

To check for consistency between studies, both the I^2 test of heterogeneity and a visual inspection of the forest plots were used. The I^2 statistic describes the proportion of total variation in study estimates that is due to heterogeneity (Higgins & Thompson, 2002). The I^2 statistic was interpreted in the following way:

● >50%: notable heterogeneity (an attempt was made to explain the variation, for example outliers were removed from the analysis or sub-analyses were conducted to examine the possibility of moderators. If studies with heterogeneous results were found to be comparable, a random-effects model was used to summarise the results [DerSimonian & Laird, 1986]. In the random-effects analysis, heterogeneity is accounted for both in the width of CIs and in the estimate of the treatment effect. With decreasing heterogeneity the random-effects approach moves asymptotically towards a fixed-effects model).

- 30 to 50%: moderate heterogeneity (both the chi-squared test of heterogeneity and a visual inspection of the forest plot were used to decide between a fixed and random-effects model)
- <30%: mild heterogeneity (a fixed-effects model was used to synthesise the results).

To explore the possibility that the results entered into each meta-analysis suffered from publication bias, data from included studies were entered, where there were sufficient data, into a funnel plot. Asymmetry of the plot was taken to indicate possible publication bias and investigated further.

An estimate of the proportion of eligible data that were missing (because some studies did not include all relevant outcomes) was calculated for each analysis.

The number needed to treat–benefit (NNTB) or the number needed to treat–harm (NNTH) was reported for each outcome where the baseline risk (that is, control group event rate) was similar across studies. In addition, NNTs calculated at follow-up were only reported where the length of follow-up was similar across studies. When the length of follow-up or baseline risk varies (especially with low risk), the NNT is a poor summary of the treatment effect (Deeks, 2002). The percentage with the event in question was reported for each treatment group.

Included/excluded studies tables, generated automatically from the study information database, were used to summarise general information about each study (see Appendix 16). Where meta-analysis was not appropriate and/or possible, the reported results from each primary-level study were also presented in the included studies table (and included, where appropriate, in a narrative review).

Skewed data

Continuous data reported by the trials may not be normally distributed. While this is not so much of a problem in larger trials, effect sizes calculated from data from smaller trials should be treated with caution. Given that many of the trials reviewed for this guideline used relatively small populations, skewedness was assessed based on the definition that the mean is greater than two times the standard deviation. Evidence was downgraded where skewed data existed (see section on evidence profile tables below). All effect sizes calculated with skewed data are marked with an asterisk and should therefore be interpreted cautiously.

3.5.6   Presenting the data to the GDG

Summary characteristics tables and, where appropriate, forest plots generated with Review Manager 4.2.8 (Cochrane Collaboration, 2005) were presented to the GDG in order to prepare an evidence profile for each review and to develop recommendations.

Evidence profile tables

An evidence profile table was used to summarise both the quality of the evidence and the results of the evidence synthesis (see Table 3 for an example of an evidence profile table). Each table included details about the quality assessment of each outcome: quality of the included studies based on the SIGN grade (see Appendix 9 for check-list), number of studies, and limitations, information about the consistency of the evidence (see below for how consistency was measured), directness of the evidence (that is, how closely the outcome measures, interventions and participants match those of interest) and any other considerations (for example, effect sizes with wide CIs would be described as imprecise data). Each evidence profile also included a summary of the findings: number of patients included in each group, an estimate of the magnitude of the effect, quality of the evidence, and the importance of the evidence. The quality of the evidence was based on the quality assessment components (study design, limitations to study quality, consistency, directness and any other considerations) and graded using the following definitions:

- **High** = Further research is very unlikely to change confidence in the estimate of the effect
- **Moderate** = Further research is likely to have an important impact on confidence in the estimate of the effect and may change the estimate
- **Low** = Further research is very likely to have an important impact on confidence in the estimate of the effect and is likely to change the estimate
- **Very low** = Any estimate of effect is very uncertain.

For further information about the process and the rationale of producing an evidence profile table, see GRADE Working Group (2004). Full evidence profiles are in Appendix 18 and summary profiles are included in the evidence chapters.

Forest plots

Each forest plot displayed the effect size and CI for each study as well as the overall summary statistic. The graphs were organised so that the display of data in the area to the left of the 'line of no effect' indicated a 'favourable' outcome for the treatment in question. Forest plots are in Appendix 17.

3.5.7 Determining clinical significance

In order to facilitate consistency in generating and drafting the clinical summaries, a decision tree was used to help determine, for each comparison, the likelihood of the effect being clinically significant (see Figure 3). The decision tree was designed to be used as one step in the interpretation of the evidence (primarily to separate clinically important from clinical negligible effects) and was not designed to replace clinical judgement. For each comparison, the GDG defined *a priori* a clinically significant threshold, taking into account both the comparison group and the outcome.

As shown in Figure 3, the review team first classified the point estimate of the effect as clinically significant or not. For example, if an RR of 0.75 was considered

Table 3: Example evidence profile for brief psychological interventions

Forest plot	Description	Study Ids	Quality	Consistency	Directness (all 100% BPD)	Other factors	N treatment group/N control	Effect size (SMD)	Absolute statistic (WMD)	Likelihood of clinically important effect	Overall quality
	Anxiety Measures										
Psych 03.01	01 HADS anxiety	Tyrer 2003 MACT	SIGN 1++	N/A		Sparse data (−1)	31/33	SMD = 0.01 (−0.48, 0.5)	WMD = 0.06 (−2.29, 2.41)	Unlikely	Moderate
	Depression measures										
Psych 03.02	01 MADRS (MACT vs TAU)	Tyrer 2003 MACT	SIGN 1++	N/A		Sparse, skewed and inconclusive data (−2)	31/33	SMD = 0.07 (−0.42, 0.56)	WMD = 0.74 (−4.42, 5.9)	Inconclusive	Very low
Psych 03.02	02 HADS depression (MACT vs TAU)	Tyrer 2003 MACT	SIGN 1++	N/A		Sparse, skewed and inconclusive data (−2)	31/33	SMD = 0.12 (−0.37, 0.61)	WMD = 0.69 (−2.12, 3.5)	Inconclusive	Very low

Continued

Table 3: (*Continued*)

Forest plot	Description	Study Ids	Quality	Consistency	Directness (all 100% BPD)	Other factors	N treatment group/N control	Effect size (SMD)	Absolute statistic (WMD)	Likelihood of clinically important effect	Overall quality
Self-harm and suicidal acts (reported together) (continuous)											
Psych 03.04	01 Self-harm and suicidal acts reported together	Weinberg 2006 MACT	SIGN 1+	N/A		Sparse and skewed data (−1)	15/13	SMD = −0.88 (−1.67, −0.1)	WMD = −3.03 (−5.68, −0.38)	Likely (favouring treatment)	Moderate
Psych 03.04	02 Self-harm and suicidal acts reported together (6-month follow-up)	Weinberg 2006 MACT	SIGN 1+	N/A		Sparse, skewed and inconclusive data (−2)	15/15	SMD = −0.51 (−1.24, 0.22)	WMD = −4.71 (−11.16, 1.74)	Inconclusive	Very low
Self-harm measures (dichotomous)											
Psych 03.05	01 No. with >=1 episode of parasuicide	Tyrer 2003 MACT	SIGN 1+	N/A		Sparse data (−1)	34/36	RR = 0.97 (0.88, 1.07)	94%	Unlikely	Moderate

Figure 3: Decision tree for helping to judge the likelihood of clinical significance

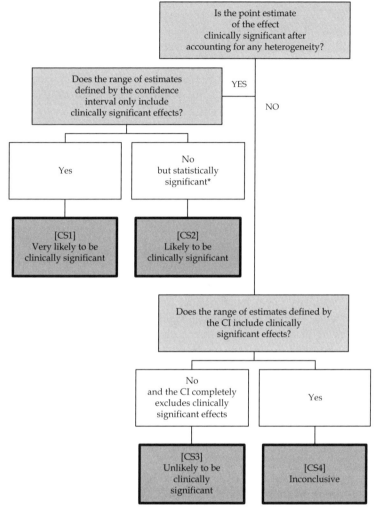

*Efficacy outcomes with large effect sizes and very wide confidence intervals should be interpreted with caution and should be described as inconclusive (CS4), especially if there is only one small study.

to be the threshold, then a point estimate of 0.73 (as can be seen in Figure 1), would meet the criteria for clinical significance. Where heterogeneity between studies was judged problematic, in the first instance an attempt was made to explain the cause of the heterogeneity (for example, outliers were removed from the analysis or sub-analyses were conducted to examine the possibility of moderators). Where homogeneity could not be achieved, a random-effects model was used.

Where the point estimate of the effect exceeded the threshold, a further consideration was made about the precision of the evidence by examining the range of estimates defined by the CI. Where the effect size was judged clinically significant for the full range of plausible estimates, the result was described as *very likely to be clinically significant* (that is, CS1). In situations where the CI included clinically unimportant values, but the point estimate was both clinically and statistically significant, the result was described as *likely to be clinically significant* (CS2). However, if the CI crossed the line of no effect (that is, the result was not statistically significant), the result was described as *inconclusive* (CS4).

Where the point estimate did not meet the criteria for clinical significance and the CI completely excluded clinically significant values, the result was described as *unlikely to be clinically significant* (CS3). Alternatively, if the CI included both clinically significant and clinically unimportant values, the result was described as *inconclusive* (CS4). In all cases described as inconclusive, the GDG used clinical judgement to interpret the results.

3.5.8   Forming the clinical summaries and recommendations

Once the evidence profile tables relating to a particular clinical question were completed, summary tables incorporating important information from the evidence profile and an assessment of the clinical significance of the evidence were produced (these tables are presented in the evidence chapters). Finally, the systematic reviewer along with the topic group lead produced a clinical summary. Once the evidence profile tables and clinical summaries were finalised and agreed by the GDG, the associated recommendations were produced, taking into account the trade-off between the benefits and risks as well as other important factors. These included economic considerations, values of the development group and society, and the GDG's awareness of practical issues (Eccles *et al.*, 1998).

3.5.9   Method used to answer a clinical question in the absence of appropriately designed, high-quality research

In the absence of level I evidence (or a level that is appropriate to the question), or where the GDG were of the opinion (on the basis of previous searches or their knowledge of the literature) that there were unlikely to be such evidence, either an informal or formal consensus process was adopted. This process focused on those questions that the GDG considered a priority.

Informal consensus
The starting point for the process of informal consensus was that a member of the topic group identified, with help from the systematic reviewer, a narrative review that most directly addressed the clinical question. Where this was not possible, a brief review of the recent literature was initiated.

This existing narrative review or new review was used as a basis for beginning an iterative process to identify lower levels of evidence relevant to the clinical question and to lead to written statements for the guideline. The process involved a number of steps:

1. A description of what is known about the issues concerning the clinical question was written by one of the topic group members.
2. Evidence from the existing review or new review was then presented in narrative form to the GDG and further comments were sought about the evidence and its perceived relevance to the clinical question.
3. Based on the feedback from the GDG, additional information was sought and added to the information collected. This may include studies that did not directly address the clinical question but were thought to contain relevant data.
4. If, during the course of preparing the report, a significant body of primary-level studies (of appropriate design to answer the question) were identified, a full systematic review was undertaken.
5. At this time, subject possibly to further reviews of the evidence, a series of statements that directly addressed the clinical question were developed.
6. Following this, on occasions and as deemed appropriate by the development group, the report was then sent to appointed experts outside the GDG for peer review and comment. The information from this process was then fed back to the GDG for further discussion of the statements.
7. Recommendations were then developed.
8. After this final stage of comment, the statements and recommendations were again reviewed and agreed upon by the GDG.

3.6   HEALTH ECONOMICS REVIEW STRATEGIES

The aim of the health economics was to contribute to the guideline's development by providing evidence on the cost effectiveness of interventions for people with borderline personality disorder covered in the guideline. For this reason, a systematic literature review of existing economic evidence in this area was conducted.

3.6.1   Search strategy

For the systematic review of economic evidence the standard mental-health-related bibliographic databases (EMBASE, MEDLINE, CINAHL and PsycINFO) were searched. For these databases, a health economics search filter adapted from the Centre for Reviews and Dissemination at the University of York was used in combination with the general strategy for borderline personality disorder. Additional searches were performed in specific health economics databases (NHS EED, OHE HEED), as well as in the HTA database. For the HTA and NHS EED databases, the general strategy for borderline personality disorder was used. OHE HEED was searched using a shorter, database-specific strategy. Initial searches were performed in January 2007. The searches were updated regularly, with the final search performed in May 2008. Details on the search strategies adopted for the systematic review of economic evidence are provided in Appendix 12.

In parallel to searches of electronic databases, reference lists of eligible studies and relevant reviews were searched by hand. Studies included in the clinical evidence review were also screened for economic evidence.

The systematic search of the literature resulted in 3,656 references in total. Publications that were clearly not relevant to the topic (that is, did not provide any information on the economics of borderline personality disorder) were excluded first. The abstracts of all potentially relevant publications (58 papers) were then assessed against a set of inclusion criteria by the health economist. Full texts of the studies potentially meeting the inclusion criteria (including those for which eligibility was not clear from the abstract) were obtained. At this stage, 30 studies had been selected. Studies that did not meet the inclusion criteria, were duplicates, were secondary publications of one study, or had been updated in more recent publications were subsequently excluded. Finally, 18 studies that provided information on the economics of borderline disorder were selected. Of these, ten were cost-of-illness studies or studies that reported data on healthcare resource use associated with borderline personality disorder in general, and eight were economic evaluations of specific interventions for people with borderline personality disorder covered in this guideline. All economic evaluations eligible for inclusion in the systematic review of economic literature were critically appraised according to the checklists used by the *British Medical Journal* to assist referees in appraising full and partial economic analyses (Drummond & Jefferson, 1996) (Appendix 13).

3.6.2 Inclusion/exclusion criteria

The following inclusion/exclusion criteria were applied to select studies identified by the economic searches for further analysis:

- No restriction was placed on language or publication status of the papers.
- Studies published from 1996 onwards were included. This date restriction was imposed in order to obtain data relevant to current healthcare settings and costs.
- Only studies from Organisation for Economic Co-operation and Development countries were included, as the aim of the review was to identify economic information transferable to the UK context.
- Selection criteria based on types of clinical conditions and patients were identical to the clinical literature review; the intention was to include studies that provided data exclusively on people with borderline personality disorder; however, when no studies answering a specific economic question met this criterion, the criterion was relaxed and economic studies considering a wider study population relevant to people with borderline personality disorder were included in the review, following consensus of the GDG.
- Studies were included provided that sufficient details regarding methods and results were available to enable the methodological quality of the study to be

assessed, and provided that the study's data and results were extractable; poster presentations or abstracts were excluded from the review.

● Full economic evaluations that compared two or more relevant options and considered both costs and consequences (that is, cost–consequence analyses, cost-effectiveness analyses, cost–utility analyses or cost–benefit analyses) as well as partial economic evaluations (that is, costing analyses) were included in the systematic review.

● Economic studies that omitted intervention costs from the analysis were excluded from the review because their results were considered potentially misleading.

3.6.3   Data extraction

Data were extracted by the health economist using a standard economic data extraction form (Appendix 14).

3.6.4   Presentation of economic evidence

The economic evidence identified by the health economics systematic review is summarised in the respective chapters of the guideline, following presentation of the clinical evidence. The characteristics and results of all economic studies included in the review are provided in the form of evidence tables in Appendix 15.

3.6.5   Economic modelling

Formal decision-analytic economic modelling was not undertaken, owing to lack of appropriate data. Overall, availability of clinical data was limited; clinical studies examined different study populations and reported a large number of outcomes, mainly expressed as scores in rating scales, which could not be pooled together and subsequently converted into a meaningful outcome for economic analysis, for example quality adjusted life years (QALYs). In addition, a well-defined treatment pathway that would form the basis for the structure of an economic model does not exist in the area of borderline personality disorder. A recent Health Technology Assessment (HTA) (Brazier *et al.*, 2006) identified the same problems in attempting to undertake formal economic modelling; instead, the authors used an alternative approach and carried out separate economic analyses for each of the RCTs reviewed in their report. These analyses by Brazier and colleagues (2006) are described in the respective sections of this guideline (in Chapter 5) and have been considered by the GDG when formulating recommendations. However, they are characterised by strong limitations, as acknowledged by the authors of the report (details on the methods adopted by Brazier and colleagues [2006] are provided in Chapter 5). The GDG estimated that adopting the same approach for the additional RCTs included in this guideline that were not covered by Brazier and colleagues (2006) would suffer from the same strong limitations and therefore would not add substantial information that would be useful in decision making. For this reason, no extra economic modelling was undertaken for this guideline and economic considerations were based exclusively on previously published economic evidence.

3.7   STAKEHOLDER CONTRIBUTIONS

Professionals, service users, and companies have contributed to and commented on the guideline at key stages in its development. Stakeholders for this guideline include:
- service user/carer stakeholders: the national service user and carer organisations that represent people whose care is described in this guideline
- professional stakeholders: the national organisations that represent healthcare professionals who are providing services to service users
- commercial stakeholders: the companies that manufacture medicines used in the treatment of borderline personality disorder
- Primary Care Trusts
- Department of Health and Welsh Assembly Government.

Stakeholders have been involved in the guideline's development at the following points:
- commenting on the initial scope of the guideline and attending a briefing meeting held by NICE
- contributing possible clinical questions and lists of evidence to the GDG
- commenting on the draft guideline (see below).

3.8   VALIDATION OF THIS GUIDELINE

Registered stakeholders commented on the draft guideline, which was posted on the NICE website during the 8-week consultation period. The GRP also reviewed the guideline and checked that stakeholders' comments had been addressed.

Following the consultation period, the GDG finalised the recommendations and the NCCMH produced the final documents. These were then submitted to NICE. NICE then formally approved the guideline and issued its guidance to the NHS in England, Wales and Northern Ireland.

4.   EXPERIENCE OF CARE

4.1   INTRODUCTION

This chapter provides an overview of the experience of people with borderline personality disorder and their families/carers. In the first section are first-hand personal accounts written by service users, former service users and a carer, which provide some experiences of having the diagnosis, accessing services and caring for someone with the disorder. It should be noted that these accounts are not representative of the experiences of people with borderline personality disorder, and therefore can only ever be illustrative. The accounts were obtained through contacts of the service users and carers on the GDG, and therefore illustrate a relatively narrow range of experience (the majority are from people whose primary mode of treatment was in a therapeutic community). It should also be borne in mind that writing about borderline personality disorder can be an extremely painful process for many people, which further restricts the number of available personal accounts.

This is followed by a review of the qualitative literature of service user experience and a narrative review of the available evidence and expert consensus regarding families/carers of people with borderline personality disorder. Finally there is a summary of the themes emerging from the personal accounts and the literature reviews, which provides a basis for the recommendations.

4.2   PERSONAL ACCOUNTS

4.2.1   Introduction

This section contains first-hand personal accounts from people with borderline personality disorder and a carer. The accounts offer different perspectives of the disorder: accounts A and B are written by former service users (both female); accounts C (male) and D (female) are written by current service users; and account E is from the mother of the author of account C. The writers of the accounts were contacted through the service user contacts on the GDG; they were asked to write about their experiences of diagnosis, accessing services and treatment, their relationship with healthcare professionals, and self-help and support during a crisis. Each author signed a consent form allowing the account to be reproduced in this guideline.

4.2.2   Personal account A

I'd been a troubled kid from about the age of 9. My Dad worked away a lot and I had a difficult relationship with my Mum; we clashed and there was limited physical affection between us as I got older. In general though, I would say that I had a spoilt, middle-class upbringing with no material hardships. Despite this I was still unable to cope with the out-of-control emotions inside of me. Looking back I am able to describe these emotions as anger, but at the time I didn't know what they were and they terrified me. I was hurt and lonely but didn't have the words to express how I felt or what I needed.

I remember the first time I started cutting myself. I was sitting in the school field at break time and rubbing a piece of glass up and down my arm. It hurt but the pain felt comforting and it focused my emotions on that point of my skin. When I bled it felt like all the bad feelings just flowed out of me.

From then on, it was as if I had found my escape mechanism. I never had to deal with out-of-control panic, fear, anger, rage or vulnerability again. I could just bleed. By my late teens I was an empty shell. I felt nothing any more, and no one could reach me or hurt me. I lived in a strange, safe, isolated world.

In my isolated world all communication shut down. At home I could count the number of words passing between my Mum and me each day on the fingers of one hand. At school I had friends and was academically successful but people were suspicious about the number of injuries I was developing.

One of my friends had read an article about self-harm and questioned me about it. Even though I was the one putting the razor blade against my arm, I was unable to accept that people would actually cut themselves on purpose and denied it. Teachers became involved but I think my horror at the suggestion of self-harm encouraged almost everyone to believe I was just clumsy.

From school I went on to medical school to train as a doctor. University is a challenging place for someone who struggles with emotions and relationships, and my cutting and other self-injurious behaviour increased quite dramatically in order for me to continue, but I did continue and was getting by. When I first started university I felt as though I had to re-learn how to talk to people – I had shut down so much that I didn't think I could communicate on a social level.

In my second year at university, I was attacked and raped on the way home from a student party. Life started to spiral out of control for me at this point. The bigger my inner turmoil the stronger the need was to bleed. I started making deeper and deeper cuts, sometimes I would go through arteries and need to be hospitalised. I could no longer be described as getting by.

After one such incident I was visited in hospital by a psychiatrist and taken by taxi to the local psychiatric clinic. This was a serious shock to the system – I felt I was descending into an unknown and terrifying world of 'loonies' and 'nutters', and someone thought I was one of them.

I was immediately prescribed chlorpromazine along with assorted antidepressants and the side effects left me feeling at home in the asylum very quickly. My legs were twitchy and my whole body felt lethargic. I wandered around dragging my feet with my head hung low, and soon relaxed into day room behaviour of cigarette smoking, rocking and leg twitching. The drugs had the effect of numbing both my mind and my body and I was able to get through my days without feeling desperately self-destructive. It was not a good way to be seen by friends though, and I don't think my partner and flatmates ever really got over seeing me like that.

I was diagnosed with post-traumatic stress disorder and depression. I started a course of psychotherapy at the same time, stayed at the clinic for a few weeks and then went back home. I continued with the therapy and my clinical studies but the two didn't combine very well. Psychotherapy can leave you very raw as you deal with any number of complex issues from the past. As I've said before, I didn't deal well with emotion; it was as if I hadn't been taught how to recognise it or deal with it.

I had a very good relationship with my psychotherapist; I trusted her and felt we were getting somewhere, but the trouble with psychotherapy is that you often feel a lot worse before you start to feel better. I had been seeing her for some months when she announced that she was going to have to hand me over to another therapist as she had to move away. I think this came at quite a tough point in the therapy and it coincided with an escalation in my self-harming.

I was spiralling out of control, becoming hugely self-destructive and suicidal and I was quickly readmitted to hospital. I spent a number of days on constant observation, with a nurse staying with me every second of the day, but I still managed to harm myself. It was getting to the point where members of staff were actually putting themselves at risk in order to prevent me from destroying myself.

At this point my psychotherapist called my parents and told them that she didn't believe I would still be alive to see my birthday at the end of the month. I didn't see my parents very often but they had visited me once at the clinic for a family session with my psychotherapist. I can't imagine how they handled this news. Even now that all this is behind us and we enjoy a good bond, I still feel desperately guilty for putting them through that entire trauma.

Shortly before my 22nd birthday I was called into a room with my psychotherapist and GP. They sectioned me and I was taken away to a regional secure unit 'for my own safety'. A secure unit is effectively a medical prison for the criminally mentally ill; it is no place for a distressed, depressed and self-destructive individual. I cannot really complain that my psychotherapist sent me there though; I think in part she was desperately trying to ensure my safety – she felt a certain amount of responsibility as she had to move on, and there really weren't any suitable alternatives at the time.

At the secure unit I found myself on a mixed ward with rapists and arsonists and for the second time I felt out of place. Despite the rigorous searches and removal of all my belongings, I still managed to secure razor blades. As a result, I was strip searched and I spent the next few days sleeping naked on a bomb-proof mattress on the floor of a padded cell, while under permanent observation.

It was here in the secure unit that the forensic psychiatrist gave me the label of 'borderline personality disorder'. Given the nature of my surroundings I felt that I was being punished – I was locked up with people who had committed crimes and my core being, my personality, was under attack.

This particular crisis period was time limited (my panic was related to my birthday), so when that day finally passed safely I began to take control of myself again. I could get though the day without focusing entirely on ways of disposing of myself and instead I began to look for ways to get out. Thankfully I didn't stay at the secure unit for very long. I had already started to appeal for my section to be quashed, but the staff also felt I was not in the best place – they felt somewhat compromised in retaining me as the only patient on a mental health section rather than one imposed via the courts. I was visited by the consultant at the local therapeutic community and invited for a community assessment.

I wasn't sure how to take this latest development. A therapeutic community had been mentioned to me before and I thought this would involve groups of people having crisis meetings to discuss how it made them 'feel' when someone took their milk from the fridge, for example. Again, I didn't think this was part of my life. I was a medical student – successful academically – but there was no getting around the fact I wasn't coping with living very well. It was unlikely that I'd ever be able to go back to my studies, so I had lost my career, my home and my friends. Life had pretty much reached rock bottom for me so it was time for me to accept any lifeline I was being thrown.

I went to the community meeting and it was clear that this group of about 25 residents were split on whether they wanted me to join them. Half felt I should be given a chance and the other half were adamant that I would be bad for the group. I was considered a big risk given my history of uncontrolled self-harm. Finally they came down on my side and let me join them but on the condition that I'd be out if I cut again.

The therapeutic community was the strangest, toughest, most homely place in which I have ever lived. I was there for about 15 months, learning how to feel and live again. It was as if I was given a second chance to do my growing up.

It's an incredibly challenging environment: if you mess up it affects other people and they don't hold back from telling you. That is really tough. You can be struggling and want to cut, but you have someone facing you in a group telling you how selfish you are and how that would make them feel. It's the group dynamic that gets you through in the end though. I learnt so much from the staff and residents in those 15 months and truly thank them for giving me back my life.

Part of the responsibility of living in a therapeutic community is to take on roles related to the running of the community. This varied between preparing meals, chairing meetings, writing notes on individual group sessions and feeding back after someone has spoken of their individual struggles. I often found myself assuming or being pushed into the role of spokesperson or advocate and the effect was to renew my feelings of self worth.

I arrived unsure of who I was and where I belonged but slowly, through the interaction with others, I was able to reassemble my understanding of me.

When I left the therapeutic community I was in a position to start putting my life back together. It took a while as I'd pretty much reached the bottom rung, but life is good for me now. I'm almost 15 years on and haven't purposefully injured myself in that time. I've had a number of jobs, got myself a career, a PhD and some good friends. It's taken me a long while to pick up from where I left off at 9 years old but I think I'm there now, happy, settled and coping again.

4.2.3   Personal account B

My psychiatrist gave me the diagnosis of borderline personality disorder when I was 24. I was an inpatient in a psychiatric hospital at the time. I had been expecting this for some time, having been aware of borderline personality disorder from my previ-ous work as a nursing assistant in child and adolescent mental health. However, I had been struggling a long time before I realised the diagnosis was applicable to me. Consequently, receiving the diagnosis wasn't a shock, and at that moment I found it reassuring that I wasn't going to tip into a deep psychosis from which I would never return. It also helped me start to piece together my understanding of how I had got to that point – why things had got so bad that the only place I could have any kind of existence was a psychiatric hospital.

Looking back, my whole life had seemed to be heading to that point. As a child I was hyperactive and was more interested in my environment and learning new things than being held by my parents. I think my parents interpreted this as a rejection and as being difficult. In addition, the family dynamics were difficult and incomprehensi-ble to me as a child and I blamed myself for them. However, I lived well and was lucky enough to be able to do most things that I wanted in terms of activities; my parents gave me everything that they could. Despite this, home felt too unsafe and volatile an environment to express my emotional and personal needs. Among my sisters I felt the odd one out. I felt that I didn't belong in my family. My way of coping with these feelings was to throw myself into school, where my joy of learning, music and sport allowed me to immerse myself to the extent that my success at school some-how became a substitute for parenting.

What I didn't realise at the time, however, was that I still had a huge yearning to be parented. I needed emotional connection, safety and understanding but didn't recognise those needs nor knew how to get them met. As I grew older, I struggled more and more socially because what I was missing meant that I did not acquire the empathic understanding needed to manage social relationships. This yearning for connection led me to seek refuge in any potential parenting figures that I came across. Unfortunately, one person who took me under his wing was interested in me for the wrong reasons – I was sexually abused and raped as a child over a period of 6 months to a year. This amplified my difficulties. I became even more socially isolated and emotionally inept as I tried to shut out these experiences that I couldn't begin to comprehend.

Not long after this I moved with my family to a different part of the country. At first, this was a welcome change and a relief from abuse. People had no prior knowl-edge or judgements about me and this was welcome. I could be different from before – I could start again. However, this relief only lasted for about 6 months. Now as a teenager, my difficulties and the emotions and memories I had temporarily locked away began to resurface. My behaviour at school deteriorated, my moods became unstable, I was withdrawn, I frequently sought out teachers for support but didn't know why, I'd leave lessons for no reason, I'd have arguments with teachers, I began to self-harm (hitting myself mainly), and became more preoccupied with the thought of suicide.

When I was 14, I was referred to child and adolescent mental health outpatient services where I began work with a clinical psychologist whom I saw weekly, some-times twice weekly, for approximately 4 to 5 years. I was diagnosed with post-traumatic stress disorder.

Having a psychologist meant that I finally had someone who could partly meet my need for a parent (in that they could give me an emotional connection and understanding I so desperately needed). I undertook some important work around understanding the abuse, but when she tried to initiate conversations about my family I couldn't say anything. All I knew then was that I didn't feel safe at home. She described my family life as being a 'ghost town'.

During this time my thoughts of self-harm and suicide became more prominent, but my drive towards destructiveness was most apparent in my relationships with men. Not knowing how to deal with men after the abuse, the conflict between needing to be close to someone and being frightened of intimacy became increasingly more difficult to handle as I was now at that age where male attention was inevitable. I would find myself in difficult situations where I would end up having sex with people I didn't want to as a result of fear and an inability to express my needs and say 'no'. After a while, I figured the only way to deal with this was to be the one in control. Instead of waiting to be seduced I became the seducer, placing myself in a number of risky situations.

Despite all this, I managed to get to university. Although I thrived in the freedom that university allowed and in being away from my family, I was still extremely fragile in my sense of self and in my emotions. There was still a lot I had to deal with and understand about my past, and this at times, especially combined with the pressure at university, meant that I found it extremely difficult to cope. I accessed the university counselling service on a number of occasions, but found that it didn't work at quite the depth I needed. In the holidays, I occasionally had the opportunity to have a number of sessions with my previous clinical psychologist. This support often enabled me to be 'topped up' just enough in order to survive another term. However, the final year of my degree saw things start to disintegrate; the added pressure combined with my limited resources meant that I had nothing left at times. My closest friendships broke down and I ended up taking two overdoses as I couldn't manage the situation with my friends, the exams, and the thought of leaving university – I wasn't ready to be an adult.

Just prior to these overdoses I had been referred to a psychologist at university and had been prescribed an antidepressant (paroxetine) by my GP. I struggled to work with this psychologist as he took more of a behaviourist approach, which I didn't find at all helpful. I also struggled with beginning a new therapeutic relationship after having had such a positive therapeutic experience with my previous psychologist. I eventually took myself off the antidepressant because I didn't feel that it was helping.

Somehow, I managed to complete my degree and returned to live with my parents. As a result of my overdoses at university, my GP wished to refer me to adult mental health services when I re-registered. This resulted in my referral to another clinical psychologist who I met approximately biweekly. Things had settled since returning from university, but my difficulties hadn't gone away – they were just more in the background. I still struggled a lot of the time, but I was able to keep this more private. I began working as a classroom assistant in a school with children with special needs, which I thoroughly enjoyed. I then started work in child and adolescent mental health. This proved to be a mixed blessing.

Therapeutically, the clinical psychologist and I had just started to unravel some of my family dynamics and make sense of my experiences growing up. I began to understand that my Mum and I had both struggled with insecure attachments throughout our lives and this helped me to understand some of the dysfunctional interactions I so often repeated in my other relationships. The combination of attachment and psychodynamic understanding worked well for me. It captured so much of the unexplained and helped me construct my life story, putting more solid foundations in place for a sense of self to develop. Understanding my Mum's difficulties and, in addition, my Dad's background (his Mum died when he was a teenager and he had had repeated episodes of depression and anxiety) also helped me understand the volatile interactions that often occurred in our family and my parents' capacity to be mildly physically and emotionally abusive at times.

However, doing this type of therapeutic work while working in child and adolescent mental health proved to be a destructive combination. I thoroughly enjoyed the work and felt that I was good at it. However, I was giving so much to the children I was working with and at the same time was more open to my emotions as a result of the therapeutic work I was undertaking. Everyday, I saw in the children how I was feeling inside being acted out in front of me. This triggered so much that when I went home in the evening I couldn't begin to recognise, name or understand the emotions I was feeling. Instead, all I experienced was a huge vacuum. I was being sucked into something I didn't feel I could survive. I literally felt that this feeling would kill me – it was so huge and consuming.

The only way I could handle these feelings and to feel any sense of control was through self-destruction, although more realistically I felt simultaneously out of control and in control at the same time. The drive to self-destruct was so strong that I felt I had no choice but to self-harm; but through the act I also found some way of regaining some temporary stability, relief from that vacuum, and some control. Previously, I had kept busy to keep this emotion at bay, but as time went on and the therapeutic work continued I couldn't do enough to stop feeling the emotions: overdosing, cutting, burning, blood-letting, balancing precariously on the top of car parks and bridges hoping I could throw myself off them – I tried almost everything. By day I was going to work and pretty much managing, but in the evenings and at weekends I was either being held at the police station detained on a section 136 or in A&E. No one in the police station or in casualty could understand that such a seemingly together person who had a good job could also be so destructive and wasting their resources. I was leading a completely parallel existence. Eventually, because I was so exhausted I started to struggle at work. I took sick leave, never to return.

As soon as I gave up work, which was the only thing holding my life together, I deteriorated rapidly. My self-destruction increased to two or three times a day, I didn't sleep or eat, and my finances were in chaos. My whole life became a constant game of Russian roulette. Although I struggled with suicidal thoughts, most of the time I didn't actively want to die. I just wanted to feel safe and access help, but equally, if I died by accident as a result of what I did, I didn't care either. Let fate decide.

Eventually, this led to a point where I was admitted to hospital and was diagnosed with borderline personality disorder. I was an inpatient for 8 months. At first it was a difficult admission as my determination not to be medicated left the staff struggling to meet my needs. I did, however, manage to build up relationships with some of the more experienced staff. They helped me feel safer and they had the skills to work psychotherapeutically with me. This I found more helpful than the interventions of less inexperienced staff who tried to control me and my emotions by becoming more authoritative. This tended to escalate situations.

The team was split between those who were more open minded about working with people with borderline personality disorder and those who felt I shouldn't be treated in hospital. This was difficult for me to deal with at times as it always came across as a personal rejection. Eventually, as my ability to build relationships and to learn to trust and ask for support increased, I gained more respect from the team as a whole. This improved consistency in their approach, helped me feel that staff responses were more predictable, and this in turn helped me to feel able to trust them and ask for help, rather than self-destruct.

Throughout this time, as well as receiving support from the nursing team and psychiatrist, the work with my clinical psychologist continued. I was able to make much more progress in an environment where I felt safe. We continued to work primarily in a psychodynamic/attachment orientated way, however, some inputs from cognitive analytic approaches were very helpful in understanding the cycles and patterns of behaviour in which I would get entangled and would lead to self-destruction.

Despite the progress I made during this lengthy admission, I didn't feel that I was yet at a stage where I could survive at home again. I had a mortgage, which made options such as supported housing feel too impossible, and I still didn't trust new people enough to have care at home. A therapeutic community was therefore suggested and after some consideration and a couple of meetings with the community's outreach team, I decided that it was probably the best way forward and a step that I now felt ready to make.

This transition was probably one of the hardest I have had to make: I was leaving the safety of the hospital and was going to have to interact with peers and to survive without parents in any form. However, the therapeutic community, although difficult, proved to be the right move. Its combination of different treatment approaches, group therapy and its emphasis on residents taking responsibility for running the place and for each other, meant that I became more honest with myself and others about how I was feeling, making it easier to identify my emotions and access the support I needed. It also allowed me to do what I hadn't got around to in hospital – linking my past story with my current patterns of behaviour. I saw for the first time how much my current thinking, interpretation and behaviour replicated my past survival methods in the family, and how these strategies I used as a child could no longer work as an adult. I recognised the need to learn new skills and although it sounds a simple process, the reality was that it was difficult and at times traumatic. I had to face up to the fact that, at times, I could be selfish, blame others for things that were my fault, and shut others out. I had to learn to accept all facets of myself and piece those functioning and malfunctioning parts of myself back together so that I could start to build a sense of self.

Another important thing I learned at the therapeutic community was that I needed to be my own parent and that I had the skills to do it. I had to look after myself in the way I wanted to be looked after. This would help me feel better about myself, increase my sense of self-agency, which in turn would further strengthen my sense of self. Perhaps most importantly, I learnt to interact socially. The therapeutic community gave me an environment in which I could learn what was acceptable and unacceptable in terms of dependency, and through the process of seeing my behaviour mirrored in the other residents, I realised the negative impact I could have on other people. After a year, when I came to leave I felt like I was functioning better than I had functioned in my entire life.

The difficulty for me was maintaining this once I had left the therapeutic community. Living a few hundred miles away I couldn't make use of the outreach services that easily and I was too far from the friends I made there to have regular contact with them. This meant that when I left I was socially isolated again, having not had much of a social network prior to my admission into hospital. I was also living on my own for the first time in 2 years, and dependent on the mental health services to fill the gap the therapeutic community left behind.

I continued to work with the clinical psychologist and psychiatrist I had prior to the therapeutic community, but in addition, I also had a community psychiatric nurse (CPN). I found it difficult to work individually again after group work and I also struggled with my relationship with the clinical psychologist. Having been dependent on her before, I wanted to manage the relationship in a different way using what I had learnt at the therapeutic community. However, we both found this a difficult change and consequently we struggled to find the same engagement and level of work we had achieved previously. In hindsight, this was probably one relationship I shouldn't have gone back to, but we both found it difficult to end the relationship and we got stuck in an unhelpful dynamic for a while.

The therapeutic work, at this point, came mainly from my psychiatrist, who prior to the therapeutic community was too 'advanced' for me to engage with for any more than just a general overview of my care. However, my improved ability to articulate my feelings meant that I could now engage with him therapeutically. In my community psychiatric nurse, I had a more general support that was whatever I needed it to be. This ranged from the practical and the therapeutic to the social (as much as it could be within the boundaries of the therapist-client relationship). This flexibility was hugely helpful, especially combined with the consistency and continuity in my care I had received before and after the therapeutic community.

Unfortunately, the lack of any social network and the loss of confidence caused by my disintegration and lengthy hospital admission meant that I struggled to build on the progress of the therapeutic community. Although I was managing more than I wasn't managing, I began to self-harm again, having previously resisted this urge at the therapeutic community. My CMHT helped me to keep this to a minimum by increasing visits at times of need when I asked for help and through short hospital admissions (2 to 3 days) where I could have some respite and feel safe. Also crucial in helping to keep self-harm to a minimum was the social services out-of-hours team. Although I had used this service before the therapeutic community, the calls would often escalate crises as I struggled to accept that at that time they couldn't meet my needs. However, now that I could articulate myself better and wished to use alternative methods to cope, I established good relationships with most of the team. The out-of-hours team were happy to engage in supportive conversations as long as they had time, and if they didn't they would explain that to me so that I wouldn't feel personally rejected and agree to ring me back when they had more time. This worked really well for me, as my most difficult times were at night and their consistent and predictable responses were helpful in settling me ready to sleep (with the aid of promethazine at times). This non-judgemental response allowed me to engage enough to articulate what I was feeling and to move away from the feelings (often onto mundane topics for a short while) until I felt calm enough to manage the rest of the night. Knowing that this service was there and that there was always an option to ring back made it such a huge part of my progress after leaving the therapeutic community.

All of this helped me to maintain a much higher level of functioning. However, my lack of confidence prevented me from making much progress in the other areas of my life. I was still a full-time patient and I struggled to believe that this would ever be different. Since the therapeutic community I had found the label of borderline personality disorder a hindrance. It made me feel like a second class citizen, like I could never be normal. I struggled not to believe the myth that it was untreatable and felt that no one would want to employ me.

Despite the progress I had made, I couldn't live with the thought that my life would always be limited. I sank into a depression, and this combined with the unfortunate timing of another rape, a destructive relationship as a way of coping with the rape, a pregnancy as a result of the destructive relationship and subsequent termination, and the retirement of my psychiatrist – all in the space of about 8 months – destabilised me so much that I ended up being hospitalised involuntarily under Section 2 of the Mental Health Act.

Although, at the time, this appeared to be a huge setback, this admission changed a lot for me. I was prescribed an antidepressant (mirtazapine) for a few months which I found really helped to lift my mood. However, towards the end of the admission when my mood had improved, I also realised that I had to make a choice – to live my life, reject the label's myths and decide for myself my limitations, or to believe the myths and accept that I would be a patient for the rest of my life. The latter was not an option to me, so after I came off the section I decided that I needed to face my fears and start to rebuild my life. I decided to enrol at university to undertake a degree in psychology. This proved to be a successful move, and one that gave me a good balance between commitment and space for me to manage myself and the transition I needed to take me from being a patient back to a being a functioning member of society. It also allowed me to gain confidence in an environment that didn't ask too much of me most of the time. It enabled me to get to a point where I had a social network, an identity other than 'patient' and feel able to leave behind my last connections with the service, my community psychiatric nurse, and the social services out-of-hours team.

I did it – I am no longer a patient. I completed my degree, and am managing to work full-time. I no longer consider myself to have a diagnosis of borderline personality disorder. I have none of the symptoms and when I look around at other people I don't seem to be any different from anyone else. The only time I feel different is when I recognise that my journey to this point in my life has been a lot more complicated than many people I come into contact with. However, when I look around I also see myself handling situations more competently than many other people. I have gained in strength and resilience as a result of my experience of handling such intense emotions, which means that I am not easily overwhelmed by life's challenges. I'm not perfect though. I still have bad days, but talking to friends, so do most people. I really am no different. I no longer have thoughts of self-harm. My moods are more recognisable as normal, and my sense of self is much stronger and doesn't fragment anymore. In addition, I am more open, and able to recognise, contain and talk about my emotions. I can also manage friendships and intimate relationships. The only thing that is remotely borderline personality disordered about me now is that I can still remember how it felt to be that way – but it is just a memory.

4.2.4   Personal account C

For me having borderline personality disorder is having constant and unremitting feelings of unbearable and overwhelming sadness, anger, depression, negativity, hatred, emptiness, frustration, helplessness, passivity, procrastination, loneliness and boredom. Feelings of anxiety are like silent screams in my head and it is as if masses of electricity are channelling through my body.

I feel unloved and unlovable and constantly doubt that anyone likes me or even knows I exist. Both my body and mind feel like they are toxic and polluted. I always felt dirty and scruffy no matter how many baths I take. My sense of physical self is constantly changing – I am not sure what I look like and my facial features keep changing shape and getting uglier and uglier. Mirrors are terrifying – I always think I'm fatter or skinnier than I am.

Sometimes it seems like people are sneering and laughing at me all the time and attractive women look at me like they are murdering me with their eyes. Other times it is as if I am invisible. At times I hate everyone and everything. Ideas about who I am and what I want to do fluctuate from week to week. My perspectives, thoughts and decisions are easily undermined by what other people think or say and I often put on different voices to fit in. I am never satisfied with my appearance, but then I am never satisfied *per se* – perfect is not even perfect enough.

My feelings lead me to self-medicate with alcohol and food and to overdose. I slash my arms, chest stomach and thighs with a razor blade and constantly think about killing myself or visualise my own death.

I have also had some hallucinations, such as the devil's face appearing on the wall and talking to me in Latin and the devil coming into my flat in the guise of black poodle and me putting my hand inside its body. I also have headaches, panic in my stomach, and feel sick and tired all the time. It is often hard to get to sleep and I have horrific nightmares.

Signs of my emerging personality disorder started in early childhood in the late 1960s/early 1970s. I was so disturbed that my adoptive parents had to put bars over my windows because I used to throw all my toys and bed linen out of the window every night and they were worried I would fall out.

I was told that I was adopted very early on and have no memory of ever thinking that my adoptive parents were my real parents. As far back as I can remember I used to pray that my real Mum would rescue me. When someone came to the front door I used to rush towards it shouting 'Is that my Mum? Has she come to get me?' My Nan remembers me asking women in the supermarket the same questions. I also pleaded with any women teachers from infant school upwards if they would adopt me.

I was a very disruptive, naughty child who wanted so desperately to be loved and accepted by my adoptive family. I had behavioural problems and used to rock backwards and forwards going into a trance-like state for hours everyday. I had terrible insomnia from early on and would repeatedly bang my head on the pillow and make a droning noise to distract myself from the unbearable agitation that I felt. This behaviour ignited a cycle of physical and emotional abuse at the hands of my adoptive parents who did not understand the mental distress I had to endure on a daily basis. My father, exasperated that he couldn't sleep because of my head banging, used to come into my bedroom and punch me until I stopped. I used to have dreams where the devil would tell me to go into my parents' bedroom and smash my Mum's and Dad's heads in with a hammer.

My father was a rigid disciplinarian and I quickly became the black sheep of the family – the source of all the family's woes and misery was my fault. I spoilt everything. I was to blame for everything. They went on family days out and I was excluded for being naughty, locked out of the family home, and left sitting in the back garden on my own for hours on end until they returned, happy that they had had a fun day out without me around to spoil it for them. I used to deliberately say all my Christmas presents were a load of shit to annoy them and ceremoniously smash them all up on Christmas day in utter defiance then eat as much chocolate I could until I threw up. I often spent Christmas day banished to my room.

I was a habitual liar at school telling my friends that I went on amazing holidays and had all these amazing toys (when the exact opposite was true). My father often withheld presents and instead gave them to my brother and sister to punish me. To punish me further he refused to fund school trips and would ration the sweets my Mum bought me in an attempt to control my behaviour.

I started to dress in increasingly attention-seeking clothes. I used to bite my nails down so far they would bleed and were very painful and as a punishment I was told my pocket money had been stopped for 5 years.

One time after I refused to rake the back garden my father beat me with the rake. I ran into the kitchen hoping my Mum would protect me but she grabbed me so that my Dad could beat me some more. I grabbed a carving knife and tried to stab her so she'd let me go. I was beaten severely for this and after that they contacted social services requesting I be put in a home for maladjusted children. I was 12 years old. Social services tried to work with the family to overcome our problems but my parents refused to attend the therapy sessions and I had to go on my own. When the decision was made not to send me away my father was so angry he just used to act as if I didn't exist. The rest of the family tried their hardest to get on with their lives but the silent aggression from both sides made me run away and spend hours on my own in the woods reading my comics. It was during this time that I started to feel suicidal and constantly tell my Mum and Dad that I wanted to die to which I was told that I had growing pains.

I hated my Mum and Dad and wished they where both dead and constantly spat on their food and urinated in their drinks if I could get away with it. I used to bully my younger brother because he was their flesh and blood and mercilessly beat and threatened both my brother and sister until they cried and begged me to stop. I started to set fire to things and torture insects. I prayed to the devil that people I hated at school would be killed in horrific accidents and I used to steal from my parents and smash my brother's and sister's toys to punish them. I remember watching the film 'The Omen' and thinking that I was the Antichrist.

I was very disruptive at school and repeatedly got the cane for verbal attacks, such as calling the headmaster a 'cunt' to his face in assembly. Even at junior school when I was 10, my father told me to tell my teacher she was a 'stupid bitch', which I did and got into a lot of trouble.

By 14 I had started sniffing glue to escape the misery I felt and also experimenting with cross-dressing. I was often sent home from school for wearing women's clothing. I started to alienate the few friends I had by doing this but I thought I was the messiah and they would all worship me one day.

My father hated my emerging transvestism and smashed my make-up box to pieces and forbade me from wearing any women's clothing around the house. The threat of being thrown out onto the street was made constantly. I went on hunger strike and stopped swallowing my food. I used to store all the rotting mouthfuls of half-digested food in shopping bags in my wardrobe.

I left school in 1983, failed to get into college and was on the dole for 3 years. During this time my eating disorder worsened and I developed severe acne. I drifted through the 1980s in a haze of solvent abuse and, due to my terror of women, found some relief in pretending to be homosexual.

The slow decline into hell that started in my childhood gathered pace during my twenties. I had one serious relationship with a girl but it was stormy and complex. I used to feel nausea after sex and constantly behaved like a homosexual and lied about my sexuality to her. In relationships I have an intense need for constant reassurance; and when I try to hold back I get unbearable feelings of panic and fear of imminent abandonment. I also find it very difficult to trust people.

I went through a particularly intense stage of religiosity in 1988 when I became a Jehovah's Witness but I very quickly started to feel disconnected from everyone in the congregation and habitually fantasised about murdering and torturing them.

When my relationship ended I stated to drink heavily and self-mutilate, which led to my first contact with mental health services in 1990 at the age of 23. I saw my GP first, who referred me to a consultant psychiatrist. After three lengthy assessments I was told I had symptoms of a classic disorder, but that it could not be treated with medication. I was formally discharged from services never knowing what the disorder was. Because of this I believed that the psychiatrist thought I was making it up.

My parents, who were divorced by this time, had the sense that because I had been discharged there mustn't be anything that wrong with me. My parents and friends also thought I was making it up. I was left thinking that my problems were not real even though I constantly felt suicidal and my behaviour by that time was very extreme. People thought I had mild depression or was just an attention seeker. I was put on an antidepressant by my GP. But my depression, drinking and self-harm worsened and I constantly spoke of suicide. After I did try to commit suicide in 1991, I was given ten or 12 1-hour sessions of CAT. This made no difference whatsoever and I continued to deteriorate. In 1993 after another suicide attempt I had 20 sessions of CBT but this also did nothing to help me.

In the early 1990s I was reunited with my real parents. This was not without problems. After I was told that my mother attempted to have me aborted I started to despise her and fantasise about murdering and torturing my real parents as well. I particularly hated my real sister.

I endeavoured to try and reconnect with them in 1997 after I was made homeless and had been living in a drug psychosis unit for 13 months because there was nowhere else to put me. I didn't have psychosis and often wondered why I was allowed to stay there. It was during that time that a junior staff member broke her professional boundaries and told me I had borderline personality disorder. I misunderstood what she had said and thought it meant I was on the borderline of having a personality disorder, and therefore was not that serious (even though I felt suicidal all the time).

After this I was housed in an old people's block on my own and rapidly spiralled out of control. I used to over-medicate with all the drugs I was taking: I would take a cocktail of SSRIs, sleeping tablets and alcohol that would make me go into a trance. I used to do this on a daily basis and just lie in bed all day in a haze rarely getting dressed or leaving the flat. I couldn't look after myself and lived off the same meal everyday: cornflakes, saveloy and chips.

My flat was undecorated and I slept on a mattress on the floor. I was obsessed with perfection and spent hours redoing the same small DIY jobs over and over again compelled by a vision of my dream home. In reality I was living in an uncarpeted, unfurnished flat with no furniture and which was covered in plaster dust from my endless attempts to make all the walls perfectly flat and smooth.

In the late 1990s I had a few therapy sessions for body dysmorphic disorder, but the therapist seemed very under-trained. She was a nice person and seemed to care, but she said that everyone has a personality disorder. She used to give me photocopies from books to read which were of no benefit whatsoever.

The thing that finally had an impact on my symptoms was attending a therapeutic community from 2005–2006. It enabled me to make some progress, to understand myself, understand boundaries, and to see the effect my behaviour had on others (a massive deterrent). I was able to start loving myself and to have respect for myself and others. It also allowed me to break my dependency on my real mother, to gain insight into my cognitive distortions, to learn how to make and keep friends, how to manage destructive impulses and to ask for help. I had not realised that the label 'personality disorder' was so stigmatising until I went to the therapeutic community and met other sufferers. However, even with a year in intensive therapy at the therapeutic community I still have only improved in some areas and will need ongoing support and help and further treatments.

After I left the therapeutic community, my consultant psychiatrist was advised that I should remain on an enhanced care programme approach, but he ignored this advice and withdrew my access to a CPN and the self-harm team. In my first out-patients appointment after leaving the therapeutic community he angrily raised his voice and told me 'there was no scientific evidence to show that you will ever improve'.

Borderline personality disorder has had a serious impact on my life. I can't concentrate for very long and I get confused by what people mean. My obsessions about perfection get in the way of doing almost anything practical and I can't complete tasks. Although I crave perfect order I live in total chaos, with rubbish, clothes, crockery and magazines strewn all over the place. I live in absolute squalor and never have any motivation to tidy up because attaining perfection is so stressful I don't even want to try. I am unable to make plans and keep to them and I find it almost impossible to make decisions. I get bored and agitated very easily and thoughts go round and round in circles in my head. To most people boredom is endurable, but when you've got borderline personality disorder boredom is a killer. You're too unmotivated and hate yourself so much that you don't want to do anything, go any-where or see anyone. Boredom will make you self-harm and start that fever pitch agony of wanting to commit suicide. I have hair trigger explosions of intense feelings. Sometimes I feel so excited about doing something it's as if I could conquer the world then a couple of hours later it just seems like a load of bollocks. I can't decide what I want to do with my life. I find it difficult to work unsupervised and I have started college courses but then I get angry with the other students and end up hating every-one, giving up and lying in bed all day for weeks on end.

It has also seriously impacted on my relationships and I find it very difficult to make friends. I feel angry that people don't understand me and in turn people are frightened by my rages. I am terrified of engaging in conversation people I've not met before because I am worried they will think I'm boring. I love people one minute and then hate them and want to hurt them the next. Likewise, I can fall in love with some-one almost instantaneously then be repulsed by them in a matter of hours. I can be abusive then feel terrible remorse and fear being abandoned. I have sexual feelings but can't have sex; this drives me insane as the hunger never goes.

My condition has changed since leaving the therapeutic community but not as much as I'd hoped. Some of the feelings are not as extreme as they were before I went there but because I refuse medication some are even worse. I'm learning how to deal with them better but I still relapse and battle with suicidal and violent feelings, and my obsessions around perfectionism are still really bad. I still self-harm but realise it is futile and I am alcohol dependent; if I'd got some help when I left the therapeutic community I would not have started self-harming or drinking again. I also have prob-lems cooking and looking after myself. However there are some days when I like who I am more than ever and I feel happier than I ever have done in my entire life. I am also in a relationship, which although is a bit unhealthy at times, is not as co-dependent as in the past, and I have made improvements to make it work.

In order to try and stay well I reassure myself and assume that things will be posi-tive. I relax more and meditate on what I want and not on what I don't want. I have a gratitude list of all the good things in my life that I read when I feel bad. To help with my self-esteem I try to take a pride in my appearance. I attend Alcoholics Anonymous, which is helpful although I find the interactions with other alcoholics can be problematic at times. I try to be more 'boundaried' with my emotions and read as much as I can about personal growth and recovery to give me hope. I keep myself busy and avoid people and situations that wind me up. I also try to have contact with other people recovering from borderline personality disorder at least once a month.

4.2.5   Personal account D

I don't know when I was first diagnosed with borderline personality disorder, but the first time I knew about it was when I read it on a report, about 5 years after I had been initially referred to psychiatric services. I was totally horrified and ashamed. I thought I was one of the 'untouchables', one of those patients I had heard described as untreatable and extremely manipulative by health professionals whom I regarded as highly competent. I fell into deep shock and crisis for some time after.

When I was a young child I was over-sensitive and needy, constantly acting out for attention. Unfortunately both my parents were ill-equipped for parenthood: my father was an alcoholic and my mother had her own mental health problems and never even wanted children. Early on I became the runt of the litter, constantly bullied and shamed, so I learnt to trust no one and keep to myself. This was an impossible task for someone with my personality.

At age 32 after having been severely bulimic for many years, and still not having managed to kill myself, I sought psychiatric help. This was initially an eating disorders unit. The staff there were very kind, but I always felt that they didn't know what to do with me. I felt like I was disintegrating.

I had two stays in the eating disorders unit with the second being followed by 5 months in a drug and alcohol rehabilitation unit, all of which helped regulate my behaviours. But without my usual coping strategies (alcohol, drugs, food and cutting) I had no way of surviving what felt like such a cruel and dangerous world. So despite doing everything I had been taught for a while, and despite all my determination to be well, I eventually succumbed to my old ways of coping. As all my treatment had been aimed at stopping them, I fell back into the bottomless pit of shame and disgust, only to then be forced back into hospital or a crisis unit for a short respite. My stays in both the hospital and the crisis unit were invaluable at those times of crisis, because they were time-limited and managed appropriately. As I had a strong need to be looked after and be rescued from myself, it was essential for me that it was like this.

But despite weekly psychotherapy, and regular appointments with several different health professionals, none of it was getting to the root of the problem and my admissions were becoming more frequent. So eventually I was admitted to a specialist day unit for borderline personality disorder. Here for the first time I was not looked at as a set of behaviours and stuck in an appropriate box. Instead I was seen as an individual with my own problems that staff wanted to learn about and help me with. Finally I felt listened to and understood as people could see me as a whole set of problems rather than looking at the individual bits of me. During my time at the unit

I learnt that I use what others see as unhealthy coping strategies; to some extent they work for me and they are what I have known for almost 30 years. There are times where I do fall back on them because life can feel just too painful and frightening without them. I use them as my armour to protect me from the outside world. So my goal changed from giving up all these behaviours to minimising them instead and not to shame and humiliate myself when I once again fell back on them.

My relationship with my psychiatrist is very good and I trust him implicitly as he has always tried to understand, and has always been totally reliable and consistent. I also know I can contact him between appointments if I am not able to cope and he will try to see me. This gives me a lot of strength and so reduces the need to contact him as a result.

I have also been one of the lucky few who was in the first instant referred to my local hospital, which has very good specialist services such as dual diagnosis, an eating disorders unit, a crisis unit and specialist psychotherapy services for borderline personality disorder. But I was plagued by long waiting lists and being passed from one health professional to another until I was given the right treatment.

I have always tried to find support groups to help myself as much as possible and help me through the gaps in between appointments. I have found these invaluable and very supportive, even though I felt there was a big gap between other people's problems and my own.

Borderline personality disorder affects my entire life, from the minute I get up to the minute I go to bed, although to a much lesser degree than it used to. But all day I have the misery of sitting in my flat by myself everyday because the fear of being with people is still greater than the fear of being alone; the sleepless nights and tired days, so that I can only work a few hours before feeling exhausted; the continual racing mind and appalling concentration, which makes conversations hard to follow; and feeling battered and hurt constantly by people due to my over-sensitivity. But on the worst days I'm learning that the safest and kindest thing I can do for myself is to climb back into bed for the day until the suicidal thoughts abate.

I'm learning to live life, which is often filled with pain, fear and mental torture, but I'm also learning that some days are better than others. I'm learning to accept my fragilities: that there are many everyday things that feel impossible to me, as well as many things that I do to myself in the secrecy of my flat that others would be totally appalled by. It all seems manageable so long as I don't compare myself and my mess of a life with others.

With no close friends or family and only razor blades, food and alcohol as my allies, I guess borderline personality disorder continues to be my only close friend.

4.2.6   Personal account E

I am the biological mother and carer of my son, who has borderline personality disorder. He was adopted and when we met in 1991, when he was 24, it was obvious he had some kind of mental health problem. In 1990 he was referred by his GP to a consultant psychiatrist at his local community mental health service. Suffering with obsessive behaviours, social phobias and eating problems, the final straw came when making an item of clothing and he had totally lost control. After several weeks of assessment he was told he had symptoms of an unnamed classic disorder that could not be treated with medication; the consultant told him there was nothing more he could do for him and discharged him from his care.

Once I got to know my son he eventually told me about his obsessions concerning his body and clothes, his aggressive thoughts, and his drinking and self-harming. He told me that when a relationship with a girlfriend had ended he made massive cuts with a razor on his chest and arms and put bleach in them. He covered up his initial self-harming episodes and he was left with hideous scars. He also told me about his physically abusive childhood and lack of emotional bonding with his adoptive parents.

I was beside myself with grief, appalled that nobody seemed to care enough to help or listen to my son's very distressing story. He went back to his GP who gave him antidepressants and arranged a course with a local counsellor. Looking back now this seems to me to be wilful neglect as he fell deeper into an abyss of misery.

This was all new to me but at that time I felt sure that with my support and further help there would be a light at the end of the tunnel. However, I watched him deteriorate even further over the next 5 years with no real support or constructive treatment from his CMHT. His adoptive mother couldn't cope with him and in 1994 when she decided to sell the family home she told him to leave. This threw him into total chaos and bouts of extreme anxiety and excessive anger, which he turned in on himself. At this time he seemed to draw away from me and for about a year had only spasmodic contact. He seemed to find some solace in the fact he was given a social worker who seemed to be trying to sort out his life for him while finding a place for him in a hostel.

The hostel was for people with schizophrenia and those with drug psychosis. He received no treatment and had only spasmodic visits with a consultant psychiatrist when in crisis. I felt totally helpless for the next 2 years as I watched an extremely intelligent and articulate young man with real creative talent living a distressing life, cleaning toilets to earn money, having no social life, taking antidepressants, drinking to excess, self-harming and attempting suicide by taking an overdose and slashing himself severely.

During this time my son learnt from a female member of staff at the hostel that he had borderline personality disorder. This was a lapse on her part and totally unprofessional, but at least we now knew. We mistakenly assumed it meant that he was only on the borderline of something, not having a full disorder, so we didn't really see it as that serious. Nobody told us any different and we were left floundering in the dark.

I could not bear to see my son suffering at the hands of his local CMHT any longer so in 1996 I asked him to stay with me temporarily and offered him some work in my office, which was a creative environment, just doing simple tasks that would keep him occupied. His care was transferred to our local CMHT under the care of a consultant psychiatrist. I remember thinking that at last, with a new mental health team, we had hope, we would be able to access better treatment and perhaps begin to understand what was really the problem. With my love, care and support and real treatment I thought I would see my son at last living a life he really deserved.

What followed then was the most traumatic 10 years of my life. The glimmer of hope we had at the outset was soon to be extinguished. The local trust was worse than my son's previous area. The people who had been entrusted with his care treated him with neglect and total disregard for his feelings yet again.

My son has been given so many diagnoses: in addition to borderline personality disorder he has been told he is body dysmorphic, schizotypal, schizoaffective and obsessive-compulsive. Sometimes when I asked the consultant for more information he denied he had even given that diagnosis – he changed it so many times he couldn't remember what he had said. The consultant never explained anything in great detail, all he seemed to do was prescribe medication and tell us both to be patient. He told us that the local trust was running with restricted budgets and staff and that there were no trained therapists because of maternity leave. He took months to follow things up and lost important letters. I complained there was no CPN but the consultant said there was no need for one. My son was never taken seriously and was told on numerous occasions when expressing his feelings of suicide that he didn't feel suicidal and should stop saying it. His anger grew and grew.

My son also met with no understanding from others, such as nurses who attempted to stitch his cuts with no anaesthetic. He was handled roughly, without any sympathy or care, and with an attitude of 'Oh well, you did this to yourself'. Usually when he was discharged we would go home with him caked in dried blood because nobody had bothered to clean him up. On more than one occasion I came home to see a noose hanging from the banisters and blood everywhere.

I also complained that my son's social worker was hardly ever available, especially in a crisis. She curtailed and cancelled appointments and gave him misinformation about housing. On one occasion when I was stressed and just couldn't take anymore I took my son to the CMHT and wanted to leave him there. All the staff did was leave us both in a room and kept telling me there was nothing they could do, our consultant wasn't available and to go home. In the end when I had calmed down I did go home, feeling totally defeated and completely alone.

Around 1998 it seemed that body dysmorphic disorder was the main diagnosis. A friend of my son heard of a specialist in her area and found out we could see him privately. After seeing my son the specialist agreed that his condition was extremely severe and needed lengthy inpatient treatment. He did not agree with the drugs regime he had been given – a cocktail of antipsychotics, mood stabilisers and anti-depressants. However, it was a private clinic, and while they had some funding arrangements for some NHS trusts, this did not include ours. We would have to fight for a place – and fight I did. We were told by our trust that it was procedure to apply to a hospital that the trust had connections with; if they denied him access to their programme then he would automatically get funding for the private clinic. This process took over 2 years, with much prompting and demands from me. After waiting a very long time for an appointment at the hospital and being told that they could not give him the 24-hour support he would need, they said that the private clinic would be the best place for him. I felt so relieved that at last he would get treatment from somebody who really understood him. But soon our hopes were dashed again. The hospital changed their criteria – there was inpatient treatment available after all.

My son was in total despair about this, which led to more self-harming and further suicide attempts.

During this period my son lived in total chaos even though I tried on a daily basis to help him cook and tidy his room and to learn coping strategies. One time I came home to find the house had been totally trashed, windows broken, furniture thrown outside, and armed police at the property asking if I wanted to press charges. The house was full of blood. He was sent home the following morning and there was no visit to assess if he was a danger to himself or me. With all this aggression it was obvious that the inability to be heard was growing and growing, but nobody was listening.

Because of the above episode my son was sent to see a forensic psychiatrist. She assessed him and wrote a report. We were not allowed to read this at the time, although when we subsequently made an official complaint we did see the notes. In this report the consultant said that my son was a danger to me and that it was in his best interest not to live with me. And yet they allowed us to live together for a good many years after this episode. He was becoming more and more dependant on me and would have anxiety attacks if I were ill or had to travel any distance in my car. He was afraid that I would not return or die.

On another occasion when I had gone to bed, he tried to kill himself with exhaust fumes from my car. Luckily the car was parked on a public road and someone banged on the window. He came staggering into my bedroom and dropped unconscious to the floor. As I waited for the ambulance, I held him in my arms and remember thinking that he was going to die. The ambulance staff were very supportive and caring but at the hospital it was seen as just another suicide attempt, and he received no sympathy.

I just had to keep going, keep working, and keep looking after my son. I was the only one who seemed to care. I wanted to scream from the rooftops, 'SOMEBODY HELP US PLEASE'. But I was also beginning to resent having my son living with me. I began to see my son as the disorder and forgot that it was an illness, but his behaviour around the house and in my office was becoming intolerable. I was totally overwhelmed by the enormity of it all – I was trying to run my own business, pay all the bills and single-handedly (I had separated from my husband) cope with my son's mood swings, self-harm and aggression. I begged his social worker to find somewhere for him to live apart from me and she told us she had found him a place at a shared housing scheme. He was shown a room and felt quite happy about it, but then we were told they could not accept him because he had borderline personality disorder. One would have thought that a social worker, working in this area with vulnerable people, would know this. So yet again his hopes were raised and then dashed.

By this point, as the social worker knew, my relationship with my son was very strained. We began to argue all the time, and I went from being an outgoing and fun person to someone who didn't sleep, was very tearful and extremely stressed. Like my son, I felt I was going down the same path of wanting to give up – I wanted to climb into bed and never wake up. I was assessed for carer support, but I didn't need money – I NEEDED TREATMENT FOR MY SON. If someone had taken us seriously I feel we would never have been allowed to get into this awful situation. In the end I saw a counsellor whom I found and paid out of my own money. In all these years I have had no support whatsoever. I was not told how to deal with personality disorder;

all I have gleaned is through books that I have found by searching on the web and purchasing myself.

Finally in 2004 after several failed attempts of gaining appropriate treatment – which included brief and ineffective sessions of CBT with poorly trained therapists whose expertise extended no further than a cup of tea and a chat and giving him photocopies from books to read – and continued episodes of self-harm and overdose, his consultant psychiatrist, who had expressed his own frustration that my son wasn't making progress despite the fact he had never been offered any significant inpatient treatment, informed us in a very offhand way that 'there may be somewhere that can help you, we have just sent someone here, just don't know what else to try, this is the last thing'.

This 'last thing' turned out to be a therapeutic community run on democratic lines for people with severe personality disorder. After several agonising months of waiting my son was accepted in the summer of 2005 for the year-long programme.

We have found out since that the CMHT had in fact been sending patients there for a number of years and that it did not cost them a penny. This infuriated us because my son was told he could not access treatment due to local PCT funding issues. I feel that the consultant wasted a good 10 years of my son's life through ineptitude and prejudice.

The therapeutic community helped my son to gain a sense of who he is and work through the pain of the abuse he suffered as a child. This was something he was never allowed to express in all the previous years because his consultant psychiatrist said it wasn't good to go over the past. It was a very challenging regime but it is a testimony of his will to succeed that he got through the year at the therapeutic community. I am very proud of him. My son's stay there changed his life for the better and immediately after his release he was extremely hopeful. For the first time since I had known him, I could hear his enthusiasm and optimism for life loud and clear. He was confident, had self-esteem and made plans for the future, registering at our local college for a course, working towards some qualifications in art therapy. I was so delighted and relieved that at last, at the age of 40, he could begin to lead a better life.

In that year I also went into therapy, which I continue to this day and have funded by myself, to try and unravel what had gone on in those past years, to come to terms with my son's adoption, his abuse by his adoptive parents and our relationship. I slowly began to get my life back, and to understand what my son's diagnosis actually means. I have read and researched so much and I have made new friends and been happier than I have been in years. Above all I have learnt to make boundaries, which I have tried hard to stick to since my son's discharge. This has led to my son having a lot of ill feeling towards me, which I find very distressing. However in therapy I am learning to deal with this. I can only hope in time he will come to see that the decisions I made about him living and working independently from me will serve him better in the long run.

So finally there seemed to be a light at the end of the tunnel, but we were proved wrong.

The therapeutic community offered outreach support, a weekly meeting held in London for 6 months, and they also put together a care package of support to help my son through the initial release period and help him sustain the massive gains he had made. They liaised with our local CMHT and consultant psychiatrist, and his CPN (whom my son had not met before) attended two CPA [care programme approach] meetings to make sure everything was in place prior to his discharge and ready for his aftercare. They advised his consultant that he should remain on an enhanced CPA to help him through the initial period post-discharge. But in their ignorance they denied him this, withdrew the CPN in the first week after he left the therapeutic community, and said that my son had made improvements and lowered his CPA level. He was not given a key worker or social worker. He was denied access to an emergency phone support network and told to make an appointment to see his GP if he felt suicidal. We tried to complain and saw our local MP in the hope that his intervention would effect a turn around. The staff at the therapeutic community requested a meeting with the CMHT to try to persuade them to reconsider their disastrous decision to ignore their recommendations. This was immediately refused and the week that my son was discharged the CMHT told him they no longer wanted him on their books. They said that because of his improvements they had nothing more to offer. The consultant even challenged the legitimacy of personality disorder as a real diagnosis telling my son he had to look after people with real mental illnesses and that there was no clinical evidence that he would ever fully recover. My son requested another consultant, but this person said the same kinds of things.

Since then my son has floundered. He has started to drink and self-harm again and last summer took a very serious overdose. He gave up college because his diagnosis leaked out and certain members of staff started to treat him differently. He fought extremely hard against all the odds to keep going without medication and with the support of the friends he made at the hospital.

Then we found out that at the time he was discharged from the therapeutic community the PCT had set up a personality disorder community support project about 10 minutes' walk from my son's flat. The CMHT had failed to mention this even though in a meeting with the therapeutic community they were asked if any such services were available in the area, as the therapeutic community was aware that at that time PCTs where being given funding to set them up in most areas. To date my son has not been offered a place there. At one time he paid to see a therapist for weekly sessions at a local counselling centre; when he told them of his diagnosis the therapist terminated the therapy.

I was trying to keep to my boundaries of supporting him to live independently but the fact that he was receiving no support from the local CMHT only made me feel compelled to help. This was driving him back to me, something he didn't want, but there was nobody else. All the professionals have advised us about us keeping healthy boundaries, which we have tried to do, but it's extremely difficult for my son who has no network of support. He has the friends he made in the therapeutic community, but sometimes this only adds to his anger and feelings of neglect because they live in areas that offer far more support. If he had received help and support from the appropriate channels I feel our relationship would now be stronger. However, it's falling apart because he feels I neglected him when he needed me.

Recently he has been offered 12 weeks of therapy by the head of the psychology department of our local trust. We believe this is a result of our official complaint that is still ongoing. He also applied for an art foundation course at the same college but was rejected. He was told that with his diagnosis he would not cope. He ended up doing a pre-foundation course, which is so elementary that he is unstimulated by it. His tutors could see he wasn't being stretched and his talents far exceeded the basic lessons.

It seems that whichever way he turns he is blocked by prejudice and outmoded beliefs. At this present time feelings of hopelessness permeate his waking hours and his extreme anger has returned. With two recent suicide attempts I have to face the fact that one day he may take his life. This would be such a tragedy for such a loving, caring man who is torn apart and struggling without help and understanding. He wants to stand on his own two feet and is not allowed to. He was so close to having a real life and through wilful neglect he is sliding back to how he was before.

Only through public awareness and the education of professionals in all areas will people suffering from this disorder get the real help and support they need. The biggest issues for both my son and me is being heard, understood, and having one's feelings validated. I also believe that it is valuable for professionals to hear the carer's views on the disorder. With help, education and support, carers could be an even greater asset than they already are and be properly recognised for the support that they give.

My son has a long way to go and sadly has slipped back for now, but he has made big strides forward since his stay in the therapeutic community and he has the confidence to fight for his right to appropriate care and support.

4.3   REVIEW OF THE QUALITATIVE LITERATURE

4.3.1   Introduction

A review of the qualitative literature was conducted to illuminate the experience of people with borderline personality disorder in terms of the broad themes of receiving the diagnosis, accessing services and having treatment. It was recognised by the GDG that the search of the qualitative literature would probably not capture the breadth of service user experience, which may include considerable periods when people with borderline personality disorder are not in treatment. It should be noted that the qualitative evidence was limited with regards to the treatments reviewed, with an emphasis on DBT, and very little on therapeutic communities to support the positive statements made in the personal accounts above. The literature on self-harm was not reviewed for this guideline (see the NICE guideline on self-harm [NCCMH, 2004]).

4.3.2   Evidence search

In order to draw on as wide an evidence base as possible the GDG asked the clinical question: what is the experience of people with borderline personality disorder of care in different settings?

The most appropriate research design to answer this is descriptive material collected from the first-hand experiences of service users, either from one-to-one or group interviews or focus groups, or from surveys. This kind of material can either be presented in a fairly 'raw' state or it can be subjected to analysis using a theoretically driven qualitative methodology, such as grounded theory or discourse analysis.

In order to source such material, a search for published studies was undertaken which was supplemented by a search of the grey literature. The electronic databases searched are given in Table 4. Details of the search strings used are in appendix 7.

Ten studies were found that contained material relevant to the clinical question (see Table 5).

4.3.3   Diagnosis and stigma

The experience of receiving the diagnosis of borderline personality disorder and issues surrounding the 'label' and the stigma associated with it were reported by six of the included studies.

Horn and colleagues (2007) summarised the results of semi-structured interviews conducted with five service users with a diagnosis of borderline personality disorder, focusing on their understanding of the diagnosis, how they thought it had affected them, their view of themselves and others' views of them. The following themes were identified.

Knowledge as power. For service users this was both positive and negative. Knowledge of the diagnosis and professional opinions was experienced as power, both for the service user and for others. For some the diagnosis provided a focus and sense of control, for example the 'label' could provide some clarity and organisation of the 'chaos' experienced by the service user. However, for others, who had been given little information or explanation about the diagnosis (and what information they

Table 4: Databases searched and inclusion/exclusion criteria
for studies of inpatient care

Electronic databases	HMIC, MEDLINE, EMBASE, PsycINFO, CINAHL
Date searched	HMIC: database inception to January 2007; others to August 2007
Update searches	March 2008; May 2008
Study design	Qualitative studies, surveys, observational studies
Patient population	People with a diagnosis of a personality disorder
Additional search terms	Health services; patient attitude, participation, experience or views
Outcomes	None specified

Table 5: Studies of service user views of services

Study	N	Diagnosis	Research design
Crawford *et al.*, 2007	Approx. 190*	Cluster B and C personality disorder	Individual interviews and focus group disorder
Cunningham *et al.*, 2004	14	Borderline personality disorder	Semi-structured interviews
Haigh, 2002	14	Personality disorder	Summary of views
Hodgetts *et al.*, 2007	5	Borderline personality disorder	Semi-structured interviews
Horn *et al.*, 2007	5	Borderline personality disorder	Summary of views gathered during semi-structured interviews
Hummelen *et al.*, 2007	8	Borderline personality disorder	Semi-structured interviews
Morant & King, 2003	15	Borderline personality disorder	Semi-structured interviews + questionnaires + routine clinical data
Nehls, 1999	30	Borderline personality disorder	Interviews
Ramon *et al.*, 2001	50	Personality disorder	Semi-structured interviews + questionnaires
Stalker *et al.*, 2005	10	Personality disorder	Interviews with analysis based on grounded theory

*Up to ten service users and three carers at each of 11 sites, plus six service users for a focus group; final numbers not given.

were given tended to be negative), the diagnosis represented knowledge withheld and the viewing of others as experts.

Uncertainty about what the diagnosis meant. While for some service users the diagnosis led to a sense of knowledge and control, for others it was not useful and too simplistic. It did not appear to match their understanding of their difficulties, and service users were left feeling unsure whether they were ill or just troublemakers.

Diagnosis as rejection. Some service users described diagnosis as a way for services to reject them and withdraw from them. This judgement was accepted and internalised by some service users, which led to service users in turn rejecting services if they were offered at a later stage.

Diagnosis is about not fitting. Some service users felt that that diagnosis was being used because they did not fit into any clear categories. They spoke of the diagnosis as a way for services to say that they could not do anything for them – a 'dustbin' label.

Hope and the possibility of change. Feelings of hope were related to the treatment a service user was offered. Inevitably if they were told that they were untreatable this led to a loss of hope and a negative outlook. The name of the disorder itself suggested a permanency, and service users questioned the use of the 'label' itself as a result, feeling that different terminology could engender more hope. Service users also found that they gained most support and hope from people they could trust and who treated them as a person and not as a diagnosis/label. For some these relationships led to a position where they felt able to question the diagnosis.

Summary. Horn and colleagues (2007) suggest that clinicians need to be aware of and sensitive to the impact of the diagnosis; clinicians should engage in discussion about the diagnosis and focus upon what may be useful to the individual user; clinical interactions should be characterised by trust and acceptance; service users should have clear communications about what 'borderline personality disorder' means; and service users should receive the message that people do move on from this diagnosis. Finally, clinicians should listen to users' own descriptions of their difficulties.

In a study by Crawford and colleagues (2007) diagnosis caused service users to have mixed views, largely due to the implications for accessing services. Many service users reported being denied services because of the diagnosis. Some felt that the terminology used was negative (having a 'disordered personality'), that stigma was attached to the diagnosis, and that they were stereotyped and judged by doctors. Some service users thought it was unfair to be labelled with such a derogatory term when they felt that the disorder had developed due to abuse at the hands of others – diagnosis made them feel like victims again. Others felt quite sceptical about the diagnosis having received a number of different diagnoses during their history of accessing services.

However, some service users welcomed the diagnosis, feeling that the symptoms fitted them quite well, and feeling some relief at having a label they could identify with. Service users were more positive about the diagnosis where the services they were accessing had a positive approach to the disorder and where they had gained a sense of shared identity with other service users (Crawford *et al.*, 2007).

In a study by Haigh (2002), which summarised the thoughts of fourteen service users on services for people with personality disorder in south England and the Midlands, people with personality disorder tended to feel labelled by society as well as by professionals after receiving the diagnosis. There was a feeling that many professionals did not really understand the diagnosis, instead equating it with untreatability. Other professionals did not disclose the diagnosis to the service user. Once the diagnosis was recorded, service users felt that the 'label' remained indefinitely and often felt excluded from services as a result. They described having the label as being the 'patients psychiatrists dislike' and felt that they were being blamed for the condition. For others, though, receiving the label was a useful experience, giving some legitimacy to their experience and helping them begin to understand themselves. Many felt that there was little clear information available about the diagnosis.

In a study by Ramon and colleagues (2001) of 50 people with personality disorder from Essex, the meaning of the term revealed a wide range of views from 'a life sentence – untreatable – no hope', to 'haven't got a clue'. The majority felt that they did not really know what the term meant (26%), where as 22% described it as 'a label you get when they don't know what else to do' and 18% referred to the meaning 'as being labelled as bad'. Eighteen percent referred to the diagnosis as being 'indicative of mood swings'. Service users' own descriptions of their problems tended to correspond with an additional diagnosis, most commonly of depression and severe anxiety (36%). Service users preferred not to use the term personality disorder and found that the diagnosis led to negative attitudes by staff across a range of agencies and a refusal of treatment. Only 20% perceived the diagnosis to have led to an improvement and better treatment. A proportion of service users also felt it would be helpful if the term 'borderline personality disorder' were changed.

In Nehls (1999), 30 people with borderline personality disorder were interviewed to establish what it means to live with the diagnosis. Service users reported feeling that professionals held preconceived ideas and unfavourable opinions of people with a diagnosis of borderline personality disorder. They felt that they were being labelled, rather than being diagnosed. They struggled with the ramifications of having a negative label rather than the diagnosis itself, such as it affected the delivery of mental health services and also other forms of healthcare. Most of the people felt that they were in a paradox, in that they felt that they fitted the criteria, yet experienced the diagnosis as having no beneficial purpose in guiding treatment.

Self-harm and suicide attempts were commonly reported among participants interviewed by Nehls (1999). They found the view of self-harm as manipulation to be unfair and illogical, revealing an underlying prejudice and leading to a negative response to such behaviour by clinicians. Such attitudes might mean that the reasons underlying the self-destructive behaviour are missed. Service users felt it was more productive and accurate to view self-harm as a means of controlling emotional pain and not as a deliberate attempt to control others.

In a study by Stalker and colleagues (2005), which elicited the views of ten people with a diagnosis of personality disorder and analysed the data using a grounded theory approach, half felt that the term 'personality disorder' was disparaging. However one male participant thought that it accurately described his problems: 'It doesn't particularly disturb me. I don't see any problem because that is exactly what I suffer from – a disorder of the personality' (Stalker *et al.*, 2005).

4.3.4   Services

Six of the included studies reported service user experience of accessing services, including specialist services, staffing issues, and of the community-based pilot services for people with personality disorder.

Access to services

In the study by Haigh (2002), there was strong agreement among service users that there were not enough services for people with personality disorder and there was a lot of negativity towards those services that were available, largely due to prejudicial staff attitudes. In addition, while service users acknowledged that the care programme approach had the potential to be beneficial, their experience was that it was often not followed or was unhelpful. Service users views often improved if they were offered a specialist personality disorder service. They felt that early intervention was crucial to preventing a major deterioration in personality disorder. Service users also felt that early intervention services held more positive attitudes towards treatability and intervention.

As people with personality disorders often present in crisis and enter the mental health service through the police and other emergency services, service users interviewed by Haigh (2002) believed that self-referral may prevent further negative and unhelpful experiences. It was also felt that immediate support, which is often needed, could be provided by a telephone service, but ideally 24-hour crisis intervention teams who had knowledge of and training in personality disorders should be available as this would reduce the need for inpatient care. As GPs were usually the initial contact for access to services, it was felt that they should receive more education about personality disorders.

People interviewed by Nehls (1999) experienced services as intentionally limited, in that some of them were on a programme that only allowed them to use hospital for 2 days a month, and that the opportunities for a dialogue with mental health professionals were also limited. When in crisis, a dialogue with someone who cares was desired by service users. The push by some services towards 'self-care' and 'helping yourself' was felt to divert attention away from what matters to people with borderline personality disorder (that is, a caring response).

Access to services may also be compromised for people from black and minority ethnic backgrounds (Geraghty & Warren, 2003; see also Chapter 8). Accessing services beyond primary care may be a protracted process. In general mental health services there has been reported a poor understanding of the needs of people from black and minority ethnic backgrounds, however a service user said that once they had a entered a specialist treatment service for personality disorder, it was largely able to meet their cultural needs (Jones & Stafford, 2007).

Staffing issues

Service users interviewed by Haigh (2002) felt that staff needed to be sensitive in their handling of therapeutic relationships, particularly regarding attachment, issues of gender, sexual orientation and abuse history. Staff also needed to be consistent in their assertion of boundaries and be willing to provide a reliable time commitment to a service and the people they were treating. Service users also valued input from staff who had experienced mental health difficulties, as it was felt they had more insight. All service users thought it was important to have respect from staff, to be perceived as an individual and with intelligence, to be accepting but also challenging and to view the therapeutic relationship as a collaboration. Problems arose for service users, however, when boundaries broke down and the staff began to share their own problems with service users, and when staff failed to show respect or were disinterested in the client. It was also felt that service users could provide a useful input to clinicians' training.

In the study by Ramon and colleagues (2001) based on semi-structured interviews and a questionnaire, advocates (98%) and GPs (60%) were perceived as most helpful, and CMHTs (45%) as least supportive. Service users felt that the ideal services should be those that advocated a more humane, caring response, an out-of-hours service and a safe house, an advocate service and helpline.

Specialist services
Specialist services (and long-term treatment) were viewed by the service users interviewed by Haigh (2002) as the most effective way of treating personality disorders. Service users preferred to make their own choice about services and treatments as this was felt to increase cooperation and engagement. It was stated that where there was a lack of choice and the service user opted not to engage with the treatment, this led to service users being labelled 'non-compliant'.

An acknowledgement by clinicians that short hospital admissions may be needed on occasion would be welcomed by service users (Haigh, 2002), although with less emphasis on drug treatments. An option for respite care, whether in hospital or safe/crisis houses would reduce the need for situations that result in Mental Health Act assessments. Coercive treatments were not helpful and tended to make situations worse. Service users said they would benefit from information on treatment options and being allowed to decide for themselves what would best meet their needs.

Morant and King (2003) evaluated an outpatient service attached to a therapeutic community during its first 2 years of operation. Fifteen service users (12 women, three men), the majority of whom had a diagnosis of borderline personality disorder (86%), who had received treatment for at least 1 month at the therapeutic community, were interviewed. Most service users found leaving the therapeutic community extremely difficult, particularly the adjustment from a 24-hour structure to independent living. Problems reported included depression and anxiety, feelings of isolation and loneliness, and lack of structure. Some service users returned to dysfunctional patterns of behaviour, struggled to manage relationships with family and friends, and had difficulties in managing the practical issues such as housing and contact with mental health services. Despite this post-therapeutic 'dip', most reported finding value in attending the outpatient service, but also found it to be insufficient. Those interviewed also struggled making the move back to a CMHT due to the passive and dependent role CMHTs encourage, in contrast with the responsibility people take for their own care in the therapeutic communities. Three people were admitted as inpatients during the period covered by the study. However, service users also reported a gradual structuring of daily life and establishing a network of resources. They additionally reported that the outpatient service helped them to make the transition to independent living.

Community-based pilot services for people with personality disorder
An evaluation of 11 community-based pilot sites with dedicated services for people with a personality disorder (Crawford *et al.*, 2007) included qualitative interviews and

focus groups with service users and carers. The study sought to interview seven to ten service users and up to three carers and former service users from each site; six current service users formed the focus group. A number of key themes emerged that covered the entire journey through the service from the entry or 'coming in' process and assessment, through experiences of different treatments, relationships with staff and other service users, boundaries and rules, out-of-hours services, to outcomes and 'endings'.

Experiences of entering the service depended on the service they were entering, but also on the user's prior experience of services. Many felt rejected or that they had been treated badly by other services, which they attributed to the personality disorder diagnosis and the complex needs and behaviours associated with it. Consequently, many of the services users felt desperate for help and relieved to be offered a service with specialist knowledge and skilled staff. Their hopes and expectations were high, but alongside this feeling was a fear of further rejection.

Service users valued receiving clear, written information about the service, particularly where it differed from mainstream services. It was also important for service users to have a welcoming response from the service; where this was not the case the service was experienced as negative and daunting.

Those interviewed tended to find assessment difficult, traumatic and upsetting, largely because of the focus on painful past experiences and the emotions these raised. Some service users felt that this process was over-long as they had to undertake tests and questionnaires over several weeks. The availability of staff to answer questions and offer support made the process easier, especially as support was often not felt to be available outside the service.

Service users welcomed services that were flexible and accessible, and staff who were responsive to the needs of service users. Service users also valued having a range of options to choose from and access at different times such as one-to-one sessions, out-of-hours phone support, crisis beds and an open clinic. It was also important that the therapy was not time limited.

Specialist services for personality disorder can lead to a strong sense of belonging for many service users due to sharing experiences with other service users and building relationships with staff. Service users also reported that these services tended to have a more positive focus, with staff having more optimistic beliefs about an individual's capacity for change and more discussions with service users about recovery.

Most of the services offered some form of psychotherapy. While most service users found psychotherapy complex and challenging, they also found it helpful and positive. Therapists' support in helping service users engage with and address their difficulties was valued and appreciated. Psychotherapy was viewed by service users as the element of the service that brought about the most significant changes and positive outcomes for people. It allowed them to understand themselves and improve their behaviour, and provided an opportunity to practice behaviours and/or communications in a safe environment. Aspects of psychotherapy, such as the DBT skills group, allowed people to find new ways of coping and thinking about their difficulties.

Rules and boundaries were a contentious issue in many of the pilot sites. People coped with these better when they were made explicit and transparent, and were able to be negotiated, rather than being implicit and/or forced upon them. Some of the rules were felt to be too rigid and impractical, for example, attending group therapy in order to access individual therapy, not having friendships with other service users, coming off medication before starting therapy, and various rules around self-harm, such as not being able to talk in a group until the person has stopped self-harming.

The need for out-of-hours support was a common theme raised by service users. Crises usually happened outside the hours of 9 am to 5 pm, and if people did have to access a service during a crisis outside this time, the staff often responded inappropriately. Service users felt that they needed a person-centred and responsive out-of-hours service.

Few services offered support to carers. Where they were offered, carers appreciated the educational and information-giving aspects and the support of other carers. However, carers would have liked more information about the diagnosis, suggestions for how to access help and more information about care and treatment. In addition, carers felt excluded from the service user's treatment.

It was felt that the most productive relationships were with staff who were non-judgmental, helpful, supportive, caring, genuine and 'real', positive, flexible, accessible, responsive, skilled and knowledgeable. Other valuable attributes were: treating service users as whole people rather than as a collection of symptoms; being unshockable; being honest about themselves to some degree while maintaining boundaries; treating the service user as an equal; believing in the service user's capacity for change; and consequently encouraging and supporting them to achieve their goals.

Having relationships with other service users was on the whole viewed as positive, although this depended on the service model offered. Service users found it productive to share their experiences with people, as it provided them with ideas for coping, a shared sense of identity, a social network, and helped to boost their confidence. However, these relationships were more difficult to negotiate if they spent long periods of time together and there was an imbalance between giving and receiving support.

Service users expressed much anxiety about leaving a service, which was mainly centred on being required to leave before feeling ready to do so. Service users felt that a more structured approach to 'endings' was needed, and that there should be some way of retaining a link with the service and/or service users. It was also felt that reassurance was needed that they had the opportunity to restart treatment in a service if a crisis developed. Most service users felt strongly that abrupt endings were unhelpful because there was little opportunity to prepare and to work through any issues that arose out of it.

The reports from service users suggest that nearly all of the pilot services had been beneficial to people. They improved services users' confidence, self-esteem and self-awareness. Service users also came to understand their behaviours and this frequently led to changes in behaviour (such as less self-harm and fewer A&E admissions and crises), particularly as they became better able to identify the warning signs and triggers. It was also reported that services improved service users' relationships and interactions with others, particularly as a result of improved communication skills.

In addition, service users felt more assertive and independent, felt that they had learnt new coping skills including managing their anger better, were able to accept care, and were increasingly thinking about returning to work or study, or able to remain in work. Service users also felt listened to and hopeful, and in more control of their lives. However, a few service users felt that the therapy they received had been damaging and/or humiliating and distressing.

However, it should be noted that in these pilot services the majority of service users were white women. Men and people of an ethnic minority were under-represented and their inclusion could have led to a less positive experience.

4.3.5 Treatments

Two studies reported on experiences of group psychotherapy for people with borderline personality disorder and there were two on DBT.

Group psychotherapy
Hummelen and colleagues (2007) interviewed eight people with borderline personality disorder who dropped out of long-term group psychotherapy following intensive day hospital treatment. The main reasons for dropping out were: finding the transition from day hospital treatment to outpatient group therapy too difficult and having bad experiences of the previous day hospital treatment; finding group therapy too distressing – service users reported having strong negative feelings evoked in therapy and feeling that these could not be adequately contained in an outpatient setting; outpatient group therapy being insufficient because too much time elapsed between sessions; being unable to make use of the group or being unsure of how the group was meant to work; experiencing a complicated relationship with the group and having a sense of not belonging; and various aspects of the patient-therapist relationship being negative (such as therapists not explaining adequately how the group worked, not dealing effectively with criticism and not acknowledging the patients' distress). Other service users found it too difficult combining work, study, or parenting responsibilities with therapy. Other reasons included a desire to escape from therapy and no interest in further long-term group therapy.

In Crawford and colleagues (2007) group psychotherapy was experienced by some service users as a good opportunity to share experiences with others and they valued the peer support. However, others, who would have preferred individual therapy, struggled where group therapy was the only option, particularly in understanding the way the group operated and its 'rules'.

Dialectical behaviour therapy (DBT)
Fourteen women with borderline personality disorder were interviewed to ascertain what is effective about DBT and why (Cunningham *et al.*, 2004). Participants reported that DBT allowed them to see the disorder as a controllable part of themselves rather than something that controlled them, providing them with tools to help them deal with the illness. They reported that the individual therapy played an important part,

particularly when the relationship with the therapist was viewed as non-judgemental and validating and the therapist pushed and challenged them. However, where the client felt that the therapist did not push enough or too much, the therapy seemed to become less effective. Another key component in the relationship is equality, with the client feeling that they were operating on the same level as the therapists and working towards the same goal. This equality seems to empower people to take more responsibility in their own therapy.

Skills training was seen as complimenting the individual therapy and being most effective when the skills trainers were able to help the service users apply the skills to their lives. The trainers needed to have a strong understanding of the skills themselves rather than just use the manual – the latter proved to be less effective for service users (Cunningham *et al.*, 2004).

Service users found some skills more helpful than others. 'Self-soothe', 'distract' and 'one mindfulness' were the skills reported as useful most commonly. The skills most used also corresponded to the skills most easily understood. The support that service users received in the skills group also proved to be valuable.

The 24-hour telephone skills coaching was valued by the service users as a means of supporting them through their crises (Cunningham *et al.*, 2004).

Service users reported that DBT had had a positive effect on their relationships in day-to-day interactions, and although problems with friends and family did not disappear, they were more manageable. Service users have also reported being less paranoid in public. Interpersonal skills were enhanced and this was believed to be as a result of the improvement in service users' abilities to control their emotions and a reduction in self-harm. Although most service users felt that there were still areas that they had difficulty dealing with, some participants felt that their level of suffering had decreased, although for others it remained constant. Clients also expressed higher levels of hope and a desire to live more independently (Cunningham *et al.*, 2004).

In a study by Hodgetts and colleagues (2007) of five people (three women and two men) with borderline personality disorder being treated in an NHS DBT service in the south west of England, the participants reported that DBT was presented to them as the only treatment for personality disorder. This may have raised anxieties in service users about what was expected of them. While some valued the sense of structure to the treatment, others would have preferred a more tailored and flexible approach. There were also mixed feelings about the combination of individual therapy and group skills training. For one person the challenges of DBT proved too much so she left the programme. Another factor in her leaving was that she believed she was refused support from a crisis service because she was in a DBT programme. All of the clients interviewed saw the therapeutic relationship as important, valuing the collaborative working and the sharing of experiences. The group work gave a sense of shared identity. The participants in the group all commented on how DBT had affected them; one said that he cut himself less; others were not sure if changes in their lives were due to DBT or other factors. One person was concerned that now that the option of self-harm had been removed, they had no other 'coping' mechanisms.

4.3.6   Personal coping strategies

One study by Stalker and colleagues (2005) reported on personal coping strategies. Participants in the survey recognised a number of strategies they employed to help them cope, the most common of which were: visiting a mental health resource centre; talking to a professional or a partner; keeping active; doing exercise; going to bed; medication; 'keeping yourself to yourself'; 'fighting the illness'; use of drugs and alcohol; overdosing; and cutting. The participants were fully aware that some of these activities were harmful, but felt they had no alternatives: 'When I am feeling really bad, [drinking is] the only thing that really blots out the memories' (Stalker *et al.*, 2005).

4.3.7   Public awareness and education

One study by Haigh (2002) reported on public awareness and education about personality disorder. It was felt by service users that more education about mental health difficulties should be provided in schools to reduce stigma, to educate about vulnerability and to teach students how to seek appropriate help if they experienced difficulties. Leaflets in GP surgeries and support groups for families/carers were also suggested. Service users also felt that it was important that people became aware that a diagnosis of personality disorder 'doesn't mean you're not a nice person'.

4.3.8   Summary of helpful and unhelpful features

Helpful features identified by service users (Haigh, 2002) included: early intervention before crisis point; specialist services; choice of treatment options; care tailored to the individual; therapeutic optimism and high expectations; developing service users' skills; fostering the use of creativity; respecting a service user's strengths and weaknesses; clear communication; staff that were accepting, reliable and consistent; supportive peer networks; shared understanding of boundaries; appropriate follow-up and care; and making use of service users as experts in developing services and staff training.

Unhelpful features noted by service users (Haigh, 2002) included: availability of services determined by postcode; services only operating in office hours; lack of continuity in staff; staff without appropriate training; treatment decided only by diagnosis and/or funding; inability to fulfil promises made; staff that were critical of service users' expressed needs; staff only responding to behaviour; negative staff attitudes; rigid adherence to a therapeutic model even when it is unhelpful; long-term admissions; use of physical restraint, obtrusive levels of observation, inappropriate use of medication, and withdrawal of contact used as sanction.

According to service users interviewed by Haigh (2002), services could be improved if: professionals acknowledged that personality disorder is treatable; they received a more positive experience on initial referral as this would make engagement with a service more likely; if the ending of a therapeutic relationship was addressed adequately; and if services were not removed as soon as people showed any signs of improvement, because this tended to increase anxiety and discourage maintenance of any improvement.

4.4   FAMILY AND CARER EXPERIENCE

4.4.1   Introduction

When a person is diagnosed with borderline personality disorder, the effect of the diagnosis on families and carers is often overlooked. However, a recent study has shown that psychological distress among the families and friends of people with borderline personality disorder has been likened to the distress experienced by carers of people with schizophrenia (Scheirs & Bok, 2007).

The use of the term 'family' in the literature generally refers to parents, siblings, spouses and children. This guideline uses the term 'family/carer' to apply to all people who have regular close contact with the person.

A systematic search for literature on family/carer needs, including interventions, was not undertaken on the advice of the GDG since little empirical research exists. This section therefore gives a narrative review of the available evidence and expert consensus views.

4.4.2   Do the families/carers of people with a borderline personality disorder have specific care needs?

It has been suggested (expert opinion) that families of people with a borderline personality disorder could experience what Hoffman and colleagues (2005) have described as 'surplus stigma', which is stigma over and above that experienced by families/carers of people with other mental illnesses. Unfortunately, there is scant empirical evidence available to support or refute this hypothesis.

Scheirs and Bok (2007) administered the Symptom Check List-90 (SCL-90) to 64 individuals biologically related (parents or siblings) or biologically unrelated (spouses or friends) to people with borderline personality disorder. The group had higher scores on all symptom dimensions of the SCL–90 than the general population. There was no significant difference between those who were biologically related to the person with borderline personality disorder and those who were not.

Hoffman and colleagues (2005) assessed burden, depression, guilt and mastery in families of people with borderline personality disorder. Forty four participants (representing 34 families) participated in a Family Connections programme (the outcome of this study is described in section 4.4.3) and found significant burden as measured by the Burden Assessment Scale and Perceived Burden Scale, significant depression as measured by the Revised Centre for Epidemiological Studies Depression Scale, significant grief as measured by a Grief Scale, and low levels of mastery as measured on the Mastery Scale. It is important to note that there was significant variation in scores. This study was replicated by Hoffman and colleagues (2007b) with 55 participants who found that mean scores on the measures of burden, guilt and depression were consistent with those in the previous study.

Families/carers of people with borderline personality may have needs that are at least equivalent to families/carers of people with other severe and enduring mental health problems.

4.4.3   What intervention/support is helpful to families/carers of people with borderline personality disorder?

No RCTs of interventions specifically aimed at families/carers of people with borderline personality disorder were identified from the search for RCTs described elsewhere in this guideline, and an additional systematic search was not undertaken on the advice of the GDG. There was therefore little empirical evidence to review.

Interventions for families of people with borderline personality disorder have been strongly influenced by the literature drawn from family intervention treatments for other disorders (for example, schizophrenia). This literature has indicated that carers find psychoeducation and information most helpful (Dixon *et al.*, 2001).

However, research by Hoffman and colleagues (2003) provides a note of caution to those who advocate interventions of this type. They assessed 32 family members for their knowledge of borderline personality disorder. Knowledge was then correlated with family burden, depression and expressed emotions. Contrary to expectations greater knowledge about borderline personality disorder was associated with higher levels of burden, depression, distress and hostility towards the person with the disorder.

Berkowitz and Gunderson (2002) have piloted a multi-family treatment programme strongly influenced by psychoeducative approaches used in schizophrenia. However no outcome data were reported.

Hoffman and colleagues (2005) conducted a study examining the impact of the Family Connections programme, which aims to reduce burden, grief, depression and enhance mastery in families of people with borderline personality disorder. The programme is a 12-week manualised education programme that is strongly influenced by DBT principles. The programme also had a strong educational component in which information is provided about borderline personality disorder and research. There is a great emphasis on learning new skills (coping and family skills) and the programme aimed to foster social support. This study had 44 participants (34 families) and the families were evaluated pre-intervention, post-intervention and at 6 months follow-up. Participants showed reductions in burden, grief and enhanced mastery. There was no significant difference in depression. The results were maintained at follow-up.

Hoffman and colleagues (2007b) was a replication of the 2005 study. Fifty five participants took part in this programme. They were assessed using the same measures as the 2005 study: pre- and post-intervention and at 3 months' follow-up (rather than

6 months in the previous study). As in the previous study, participants showed improvements in grief, burden and mastery. There was also a significant reduction in depression. While these findings are of interest and this intervention shows promise, clinical trials examining the effectiveness of this intervention have not yet been published.

There is a lack of high quality empirical evidence on interventions for families/ carers of people with borderline personality disorder, although emerging evidence suggests that structured family programmes may be helpful. Hoffman and colleagues' (2003) study provides a cautionary note about giving information. Their findings suggested that more information alone could be associated with more distress.

4.4.4   Do families/carers through their behaviours and styles of relating influence clinical and social outcomes or the well-being of people with borderline personality disorder?

This clinical question needs to be explored sensitively. Families/carers could have understandable concerns with respect to this question and may feel that they are being unfairly blamed for the person's problems.

Earlier chapters (see Chapter 2) have highlighted the high correlation between childhood adversity and borderline personality disorder. These findings are challenging to families caring for people with borderline personality and it is important not to assume that all family environments are 'toxic' and have 'caused' the disorder.

There are some studies suggesting that the current family environment could influence the course of borderline personality disorder. Gunderson and colleagues (2006) explored predictors of outcome in borderline personality disorder. In this study 160 patients were recruited and followed up for 2 years at 6, 12 and 24 months. Findings should be interpreted with caution because of the nature of the measures used. However, they concluded that alongside baseline psychopathology and history of childhood trauma, present relationships was also a predictor of outcome after 2 years. The longitudinal Interval Follow-Up Evaluation was used to assess impairment in relationships with parents, spouse, siblings and children.

A significant amount of research into the impact of the family environment has focused on parental hostility and involvement and the course of a disorder. These constructs are components of expressed emotion. Expressed emotion and its impact on recovery for people with schizophrenia has been more extensively researched (see Dixon and colleagues [2001] for review). Within the borderline personality disorder literature there was only one study on expressed emotion.

Hooley and Hoffman (1999) followed a group of 35 people with borderline personality disorder for 1 year post-discharge. They assessed expressed emotion using the Camberwell family interview. They found no association between hostility and criticism and re-admission rates in borderline personality disorder. Even more surprising, and contrary to research in psychosis, was that people with borderline personality disorder had fewer admissions in families that scored higher on expressed over-involvement.

In summary, there is not enough evidence to confidently answer this question. It appears that the relationship between the family environment and the prognosis of borderline personality disorder is complex and multi-dimensional (Lefley, 2005). There is some tentative evidence that families of people with borderline personality disorder could interact in ways that are unhelpful for the person with borderline personality disorder. However, Lefley (2005) cautions against overly blaming families and suggests that the literature does not fully consider temperamental vulnerabilities in people with borderline personality disorder.

4.4.5 Are there interventions/support for families/carers of people with borderline personality disorder that are helpful in altering social outcome and well-being of a person with borderline personality disorder?

There are no empirical studies to review in this section. The literature is restricted to expert opinion and consensus.

4.4.6 Overall clinical summary

There is little evidence to answer clinical questions relating to support for families/carers, although families/carers of people with borderline personality disorder appear to have significant needs. Consequently, it would not be prudent to make robust clinical recommendations. Further research is needed to build on the emerging evidence suggesting that structured psychoeducation programmes that also facilitate social support networks may be helpful for families. There is an absence of research into whether family interventions alter the social outcome and welfare of a person with borderline personality disorder.

4.5 SUMMARY OF THEMES

The personal accounts and the literature reveal that during its course, borderline personality disorder can be experienced as extremely debilitating. People with the disorder report having difficulty controlling their mood, problems with relationships, an unstable sense of self, and difficulty in recognising, understanding, tolerating and communicating emotions, which can lead to the use of coping mechanisms such as self-harm. When assessing people with borderline personality disorder it is important to recognise that physical expressions, such as self-harm, are usually indicative of internal emotions.

People with borderline personality disorder have reported that they fear rejection on entering a service, particularly if they have had prior negative experiences, and although they feel desperate for help, this can make engaging in an assessment more difficult. Assessments can be traumatic and upsetting, due in large part to the focus on painful past experiences. Explanation about the process, clear, written information about a service, and the opportunity to ask questions were all welcomed and valued.

People have reported that being diagnosed with borderline personality disorder can be both a positive and negative experience. For some it can provide a focus, a sense of control, a feeling of relief, and a degree of legitimacy to their experience. In general, people are more positive about the diagnosis when it has led to accessing services, and where those services have taken a positive approach to the disorder. However, for others, the diagnosis was equated with a loss of hope and there were reports of being denied services because of the diagnosis and associated misconceptions about its untreatability. Little information or explanation appears to be given with this diagnosis, and where it has been given it has tended to be negative. There was a feeling that different terminology, other than 'borderline personality disorder', could engender more hope. Both the personal accounts and the literature demonstrate that the diagnosis can provoke negative attitudes in healthcare professionals across a range of services and lead to a refusal of treatment.

Both the personal accounts and the qualitative literature highlight the need for healthcare professionals to be aware of the stigma surrounding borderline personality disorder and to be sensitive to the impact of the diagnosis on a person's life and their sense of hope for the future.

There is a general consensus from the literature that there are not enough services for people with personality disorder (and clinicians should be aware that access to services may be compromised for people from black and minority ethnic backgrounds). Service users felt that specialist services are most effective in treating personality disorders and that it is important to recognise that treatment may need to be long term. Early intervention was considered crucial in preventing a major deterioration in the disorder, and having the option to self-refer could prevent further unhelpful and negative experiences.

When working with people with borderline personality disorder, it was felt that healthcare professionals need to establish a collaborative partnership with the service user that is non-judgemental, supportive, caring, genuine and positive, and that they should believe in their capacity to change and encourage and support them to achieve their goals. Healthcare professionals also need to be sensitive in their handling of the therapeutic relationship, particularly regarding issues of attachment, sexual orientation and abuse history. They need to be consistent in their assertion of boundaries and willing to provide a time commitment to clients.

When in crisis, people felt that access to an out-of-hours crisis service was needed; a person-centred response from someone who cares and had knowledge of the disorder was felt to preferable. Working with service users to explore potential triggers for crises and strategies for managing these is useful as part of a care plan that also includes crisis advice.

Being able to have a choice about services and treatment was also important as this was felt to increase the service user's cooperation and engagement. Where this choice was lacking and the service user opted not to engage with a particular treatment this was often felt to lead to being labelled as non-compliant. Service users' own judgement about suitability or unsuitability of a service or treatment should be respected.

Service users felt that specialist personality disorder services were helpful in improving their self-esteem, self-awareness, and their understanding of their behaviour, which in turn led to a change in their behaviours (for example, a reduction in self-harm). These services also helped to improve their relationships, enabling them to feel more assertive and independent. They had established new coping skills and felt better able to accept care. However, where this service included a residential component, a 'post-therapeutic dip' was often reported as people adjusted to independent living.

Most of the services offered some form of psychotherapy, which although complex and challenging, was experienced as helpful and positive. Group psychotherapy was viewed as a good opportunity to share experiences with others and obtain peer support, although for some they would prefer individual therapy, as they found the group too distressing. This highlights the importance of how treatments can differ for individuals and the importance of client choice.

Service users have been positive about DBT because it has helped them to improve their relationships and their ability to control their emotions and reduce self-harm. However, while some valued the structure of the approach, others preferred the programme to be more tailored and flexible.

Leaving a treatment or service is often difficult for people with borderline personality disorder and can evoke strong emotions as they may feel rejected. It has been recognised that a more structured approach to 'endings' is needed. People also felt they would like reassurance that they could access the service again in a crisis. Information about support groups, activity groups and self-management techniques may also be useful.

Few services offer support to families/carers despite research that demonstrates that psychological distress in families and friends of people with borderline personality disorder is similar to that experienced by families/carers of people with schizophrenia, and they score highly on scales measuring burden and depression.

Where support is offered it tends to be centred on provision of education and information. Families/carers would like more information around the diagnosis, suggestions on how to access help and more information about care and treatment. However, there is a warning note that greater knowledge about borderline personality disorder could increase family/carer distress. Most families/carers reported feeling excluded from the service user's treatment.

There is evidence to suggest a correlation between childhood adversity and borderline personality disorder, and that a service user's current family environment could influence the course of the disorder. However, despite this evidence it is important not to assume that all family environments are 'toxic' and have 'caused' the disorder because families/carers could feel unfairly blamed for the service user's difficulties. Collaborating with families/carers (when the service user is in agreement) and supporting them could provide a valuable resource for the person with borderline personality disorder.

4.6   CLINICAL PRACTICE RECOMMENDATIONS

4.6.1   Access to services

4.6.1.1   People with borderline personality disorder should not be excluded from any health or social care service because of their diagnosis or because they have self-harmed.

4.6.2   Developing an optimistic and trusting relationship

4.6.2.1   When working with people with borderline personality disorder:
- explore treatment options in an atmosphere of hope and optimism, explaining that recovery is possible and attainable
- build a trusting relationship, work in an open, engaging and non-judgemental manner, and be consistent and reliable
- bear in mind when providing services that many people will have experienced rejection, abuse and trauma, and encountered stigma often associated with self-harm and borderline personality disorder.

4.6.3   Involving family/carers

4.6.3.1   Ask directly whether the person with borderline personality disorder wants their family or carers to be involved in their care, and, subject to the person's consent and rights to confidentiality:
- encourage family or carers to be involved
- ensure that the involvement of families or carers does not lead to withdrawal of, or lack of access to, services
- inform families or carers about local support groups for families or carers, if these exist.

4.6.4   Principles for healthcare professionals undertaking assessment

4.6.4.1   When assessing a person with borderline personality disorder:
- explain clearly the process of assessment
- use non-technical language whenever possible
- explain the diagnosis and the use and meaning of the term borderline personality disorder
- offer post-assessment support, particularly if sensitive issues, such as childhood trauma, have been discussed.

4.6.5   Managing endings and transitions

4.6.5.1   Anticipate that withdrawal and ending of treatments or services, and transition from one service to another, may evoke strong emotions and reactions in people with borderline personality disorder. Ensure that:

- such changes are discussed carefully beforehand with the person (and their family or carers if appropriate) and are structured and phased
- the care plan supports effective collaboration with other care providers during endings and transitions, and includes the opportunity to access services in times of crisis
- when referring a person for assessment in other services (including for psychological treatment), they are supported during the referral period and arrangements for support are agreed beforehand with them.

5. PSYCHOLOGICAL AND PSYCHOSOCIAL TREATMENTS IN THE MANAGEMENT OF BORDERLINE PERSONALITY DISORDER

5.1 INTRODUCTION

5.1.1 Classification of therapies

Psychosocial interventions designed to help people with borderline personality disorder cover a wide range of approaches, all of which are 'talking treatments' but which differ in intensity, complexity and method (for example, brief psychoeducational approaches, once-weekly psychological therapy sessions and structured programmes of treatment). This chapter reviews brief psychological interventions, individual psychological therapies, psychological therapy programmes, arts therapies, complementary therapies and therapeutic communities. In addition, data from RCTs, where they exist, are analysed by outcome across all therapies.

Besides arts therapies, complementary therapies and therapeutic communities, the GDG and review team delineated three broad classes of psychological therapies: first, brief psychological interventions, which were defined as low-intensity interventions given for less than 6 months; second, individual psychological therapies, usually offered weekly but sometimes twice-weekly, in an outpatient setting (individual psychological interventions can also be configured in different ways, including standard interventions and brief interventions, and these are reported separately); third, psychological therapy programmes that combine more than one treatment (for example, individual therapy plus group therapy) (Campbell *et al.*, 2000) and are delivered by more than one therapist. More detailed descriptions of the therapies are given in the relevant sections below.

5.1.2 Delivery of psychological interventions

The method of delivery of psychological interventions has an important impact on their effectiveness. Unlike pharmacological treatments, where prescribers are assured of the quality of the product by manufacturers, the quality of a psychological intervention depends on therapists having the skills and the organisational support to replicate the intervention found effective in research settings. The levels of training and supervision of therapists and their adherence and competence in therapy delivery are carefully monitored during research trials, but rarely in NHS practice. The translation of results from trials into routine clinical practice therefore depends on NHS Trusts being aware of these quality control issues and taking steps to ensure the interventions are appropriately delivered and outcomes monitored under clinical governance processes.

Typically, psychological interventions for people with borderline personality disorder are delivered by psychologists, psychiatrists, nurses and other mental health professionals with advanced training in the method being implemented and who receive regular specialist supervision. For example, therapists in DBT trials are usually doctoral or masters level professionals, have demonstrated competence in six or eight cases before being accepted and receive weekly supervision. Treatment fidelity is monitored through video or audiotape ratings. Mentalisation-based partial hospitalisation differs in that mental health staff do not hold formal qualifications, but they are trained in the method by a specialist consultant and receive twice-weekly supervision.

5.1.3   Issues in undertaking trials in patients with borderline personality disorder

There is no agreement on what constitutes the 'core' problem in borderline personality disorder. As the diagnosis merely requires five out of nine operational criteria to be present there are many different ways to qualify for the diagnosis, resulting in considerable heterogeneity among trial populations. This heterogeneity and variation in severity is compounded by frequent co-occurrence of other personality and axis 1 disorders, the detail of which is often not reported.

A related difficulty is in choice of outcome measures, as different treatments target specific problems and use measures designed to capture a specific outcome. For example, a common outcome measured is the incidence of deliberate self-harm, but only some people with borderline personality disorder harm themselves. The same applies to other outcomes, such as impulsivity and hostility. More universal symptom measures (such as depression) have broader applicability but are less specific to borderline personality disorder *per se*. Alternatively, pragmatic trials may measure variables related to service usage such as hospitalisation or health-related quality of life.

A challenge in conducting trials, and an important issue in developing clinically effective treatment models, is to engage and retain a representative sample of people with borderline personality disorder, since disengagement with services is common and high attrition rates from trials are usual.

5.1.4   Issues in reviewing the efficacy of psychological therapy for borderline personality disorder

The issues reviewed above have considerable implications for reviewing efficacy of treatments in borderline personality disorder, including psychological therapies. The heterogeneity of the population samples and the outcome measures makes it difficult to combine studies and to generalise across borderline personality disorder as a whole.

Some trials have been conducted on therapies for people with borderline personality disorder aiming to modify the specific features of the disorder, whereas others included these patients in treatments for depression or anxiety. Where it is possible to extract data on the borderline personality disorder sample separately they may provide useful information, but the outcomes will inevitably be more generic.

Allegiance effects are a potential problem in interpreting results from trials. Understandably, most initial research on specific therapies is conducted by 'product champions'—the originators of the treatment or enthusiastic followers—and almost invariably effect sizes are reported that may seldom again be demonstrated. This is probably a consequence of several factors: (a) small trials in one centre tend to create greater effect sizes than larger multicentre trials; (b) the originators may deliver the intervention more skilfully than the comparative intervention or than when replicated by others; (c) the initial collaborators also tend to be enthusiastic and more energetic in the face of difficulties so benefits are greater than when the treatment becomes standard therapy; and (d) there is scope for bias, whether conscious or not, which may exaggerate differences between the new treatment and existing ones, to emphasise the novelty of the new intervention. These factors need to be acknowledged when interpreting the results of studies. Although there is no reason to suggest that such research is itself of poorer quality, there is enough evidence that those with an allegiance to one form of therapy are more likely to find positive results for their method than independent investigators (Luborsky *et al.*, 1999) to recommend that independent studies be conducted.

5.1.5   Reviewing the evidence base

In order to make recommendations about specific psychological therapies for people with borderline personality disorder the GDG asked the clinical question:

For people with borderline personality disorder which treatments are associated with improvement in mental state and quality of life, reduction in self-harm, service use, and risk-related behaviour, and/or improved social and personal functioning while minimising harms?

The most appropriate research design to answer this is the RCT, therefore the evidence base reviewed comprised all available RCTs undertaken in people with a diagnosis of borderline personality disorder.

Summary study characteristics and descriptions of the studies are given in tables below but more information is available in Appendix 16. Similarly, summary evidence profiles are given in tables below with the full profiles in Appendix 18 and the forest plots in Appendix 17.

5.1.6   Evidence search

Searching for RCTs
Both published and unpublished RCTs were sought. A search was undertaken for all RCTs in people with borderline personality disorder regardless of the intervention.

Table 6: Databases searched and inclusion/exclusion criteria for RCTs of psychological and psychosocial treatments

Electronic databases	MEDLINE, EMBASE, PsycINFO
Date searched	Database inception to January 2007
Update searches	July 2007, January 2008, April 2008
Study design	RCT
Patient population	People with a diagnosis of borderline personality disorder according to DSM or similar criteria
Treatments	Any psychological or psychosocial therapy for people with borderline personality disorder as defined above
Outcomes	See below

Those for psychological and psychosocial therapies were separated from those for pharmacological interventions, which are considered elsewhere. The electronic databases searched are given in Table 6. Details of the search strings used are in Appendix 7.

Nineteen RCTs were found from searches of electronic databases and all were of brief psychological therapies, individual psychological therapies or psychological therapy programmes. One was excluded because it was found not to be randomised when the paper copy was retrieved (BOHUS2004[6]). A further two were analysed separately since they were undertaken in substance-dependent populations (LINEHAN1999; LINEHAN2002). There was one three-armed trial. Four further trials that included participants with borderline personality disorder among others, but did not report results separately, were also excluded at this stage (ABBASS2008; HUBAND2007; JOYCE2007; SPRINGER1996). Seven of the remaining trials were of DBT, but there were also trials of other cognitive behavioural therapies and psychodynamically-oriented therapies (see Table 7). In addition, four RCTs of combination therapy (that is, an individual psychological therapy or psychological therapy programme added to a pharmacological treatment) were found.

In addition, the GDG contacted known researchers working on relevant trials for which pre-publication data may be available or which were likely to be published while the guideline was being developed. This yielded seven studies: one on mentalisation-based therapy (MBT) (ANDREA unpublished[7]); one on systems training for emotional predictability and problem solving (STEPPS) (BLUM2008);

---

[6]Here and elsewhere reviewed studies are referred to by a study identifier made up of the first author's name in capital letters and date of the earliest publication relating to the study. All references relevant to a study identifier are in Appendix 16.
[7]Not an RCT.

Table 7: Included RCTs of psychological therapies

	Brief psychological therapies	Individual psychological therapies	Psychological therapy programmes
No. trials (Total participants)	2 RCTs (100)	6 RCTs (708)	8 RCTs (423)
Study IDs	(1) TYRER2003 (2) WEINBERG2006	(1) BLUM2008 (2) CHANEN2008 (3) CLARKIN2004[†] (4) DAVIDSON2006 (5) GIESEN- BLOO2006 (6) MUNROE-BLUM1995	(1) BATEMAN1999 (2) CLARKIN2004[†] (3) CARTER unpublished (4) KOONS2001 (5) LINEHAN1991 (6) LINEHAN2006 (7) TURNER2000 (8) VAN DEN BOSCH2002
Treatment	(1)–(2) MACT	(1) STEPPS (2) CAT (3) Transference-focused psychotherapy (4) CBT (5) Schema-focused therapy (6) Interpersonal group therapy	(1) Mentalisation/day hospital (3)–(8) DBT
Comparator	(1)–(2) Treatment as usual (TAU)	(1) TAU (2) Good clinical care (manualised intervention) (3) DBT or modified psychodynamic supportive psychotherapy (4) TAU (5) Transference-focused psychotherapy (6) Individual psychotherapy	(1) TAU (2) Transference-focused psychotherapy or modified psychodynamic supportive psychotherapy (3) Waitlist control (4)–(6) TAU (7) Client-centred therapy (8) TAU

[†] 3-armed trial, therefore appears in two columns.

two on DBT (CARTER unpublished[8]; FEIGENBAUM unpublished); one on CAT (CHANEN2008); and two on CT (COTTRAUX unpublished; GREGORY2008). Follow-up data from published trials (CLARKIN2004 and BATEMAN1999) were also identified. The trial by GREGORY2008 was excluded because the population had comorbid alcohol dependence and ANDREA unpublished because it was not an RCT. Two of the unpublished studies were not included to avoid compromising future publication (COTTRAUX unpublished[9], FEIGENBAUM unpublished). Three of these trials were therefore included (BLUM2008; CARTER unpublished; CHANEN2008).

No RCTs of arts therapies, complementary therapies or therapeutic communities were found and separate searches were undertaken to identify primary research trials of any design for each of these topics. Details of these are in the relevant sections below. In addition, a search for non-RCTs of psychological therapies was undertaken since there were relatively few RCTs of psychological therapies, particularly in some of the more recently developed therapies. This is described below rather than in the relevant sections to avoid duplication.

Searching for non-randomised controlled trials in psychological therapies
Both published and unpublished non-randomised trials were sought. The electronic databases searched are given in Table 8. Details of the search strings used are in Appendix 7.

In addition, the citations excluded during the search for RCTs (above) were re-sifted to ensure that all relevant studies had been included. Non-RCTs were synthesised in narrative reviews.

Twenty non-randomised studies of either individual psychological therapies or psychological therapy programmes were found; these are listed in Table 9. An unpublished study was also made available to the GDG.

Table 8: Databases searched and inclusion/exclusion criteria for non-RCTs of psychological treatments

Electronic databases	MEDLINE, EMBASE, PsycINFO
Date searched	Database inception to October 2007
Update search	April 2008
Study design	Any non-randomised trial
Patient population	People with a diagnosis of borderline personality disorder according to DSM or similar criteria
Treatments	Any psychological therapy for people with borderline personality disorder as defined above
Outcomes	See below

---

[8]Trial report was made available.
[9]The trial by COTTRAUX would have been excluded because the raters were not blinded.

Table 9: Non-randomised studies of psychological interventions

	Individual psychological therapies	Psychological therapy programmes
No. trials (Total participants)	13 non-randomised trials (638)	8 non-randomised studies (397)
Study IDs	(1) BELLINO2005 (2) BLUM2002 (3) BROWN2004 (4) CLARKIN2001 (5) GABBARD2000 (6) HENGEVELD1996 (7) LEICHSENRING2007 (8) LOFFLER-STASTKA2003 (9) LOPEZ2004 (10) MARKOWITZ2006 (11) NORDAHL2005 (12) RYLE2000 (13) WILBERG1998	(1) ALPER2001 (2) ANDREA unpublished (3) BARLEY1993 (4) CUNNINGHAM2004 (5) HARLEY2007 (6) LANIUS2003 (7) MCQUILLAN2005 (8) PRENDERGAST2007
Treatment	(1) IPT + medication (2) STEPPS (3) CT (4) Transference-focused psychotherapy (5) Psychodynamic psychotherapy (6) CBT (7) Psychoanalytically-derived therapy (8) Psychoanalytically-oriented psychotherapy (individual and group) (9) Transference-focused psychotherapy (10) IPT (11) Schema-focused therapy (12) CAT (13) Group psychotherapy	(1) DBT (2) MBT (3)–(8) DBT
Research design (comparator, if applicable)	(1) Non-randomised comparative study (2) Cohort study	(1) Case series (2) Prospective cohort study

Continued

Table 9: (*Continued*)

	Individual psychological therapies	**Psychological therapy programmes**
	(3) Uncontrolled cohort study (4)–(5) Non-comparative prospective study (6) Case series (7) Non-comparative naturalistic study (8) Unclear (9) Non-comparative prospective study (10) Abandoned RCT (11)–(12) Case series (13) Non-comparative prospective study	(3) Cohort study (4) Qualitative study of patients' views (5)–(8) Cohort study

5.1.7   Outcomes reported in RCTs

A large number of outcomes, particularly rating scales, were reported by the RCTs of psychological therapies. Those that reported sufficient data to be extractable and were not excluded are listed in Table 10. See Chapter 2 and Appendix 10 for more information on how the GDG addressed the issue of outcomes, including details of the outcomes reported by RCTs reviewed during the guideline development process.

Table 10: Outcomes extracted from psychological studies

Category	Scale
Aggression	Overt Aggression Scale (OAS) - aggression
Anger	Spielberger State-Trait Anger Expression Inventory (STAXI) Spielberger State-Trait Anger Scale (STAS)
Anxiety	Spielberger State-Trait Anxiety Inventory (STAI) – state anxiety and trait anxiety Hospital Anxiety and Depression Scale (HADS) – anxiety scale Hamilton Anxiety Rating Scale (HARS) Beck Anxiety Inventory (BAI)
Borderline personality disorder criteria	Mean number of borderline personality disorder criteria (DSM)

Continued

Table 10: (*Continued*)

Category	Scale
	Zanarini Rating Scale (ZAN) - borderline personality disorder
Depression	Hamilton Rating Scale for Depression (HRSD) Beck Depression Inventory (BDI) Montgomery Asberg Depression Rating Scale (MADRS) HADS – depression scale
Drug-related	Proportion of days abstinent from alcohol and drugs Proportion with clean urinalyses Mean % self-reported abstinent days (heroin)
General functioning	Global Severity Index (GSI) Global Assessment of Functioning (GAF) Global Assessment Scale (GAS) SCL-90 Clinical Outcomes in Routine Evaluation (- Outcome Measure)
Mental distress	GSI
Hopelessness	Beck Hopelessness Scale (BHS)
Impulsiveness	Barratt Impulsiveness Scale (BIS)
Irritability	OAS – irritability
Quality of life	World Health Organization Quality of Life Assessment (WHO QoL) European Quality of Life (Euro-QoL) Weight Health Score Value
Self-harm	See Table 11
Service use	Emergency department visits for psychiatric reasons Emergency department visits for suicidal ideation Hospital admissions for psychiatric reasons Hospital admissions for suicidal ideation Number on medication at endpoint Number with >=1 inpatient admission (unspecific reasons and after self-harm) Number with >=1 emergency department visit Length of psychiatric admission

Continued

Table 10: (*Continued*)

Category	Scale
	Length of admission following self-harm
	Further psychiatric outpatient treatment
	Number of years on $>=3$ prescribed drugs
Social functioning	Social Functioning Questionnaire (SFQ)
	Social Problem Solving Inventory
	Number of years with employment
Suicidality	See Table 11
Acceptability	Leaving the study early for any reason

5.1.8   Self-harm and suicide-related outcomes in the included RCTs

Self-harm and suicide-related outcomes are considered particularly important outcomes in the management of people with borderline personality disorder. They were widely reported by the RCTs of psychological therapies. However, there was considerable discrepancy among studies regarding how these were defined and reported. See Table 11 for more details.

5.1.9   Study populations

Study populations are predominantly female, particularly in trials of DBT; this is unrepresentative of men with borderline personality disorder, who are less likely to present to services, although evidence from community samples suggest that borderline personality disorder is equally prevalent in men (Singleton *et al.*, 2003). Age ranges in trials are also unrepresentative of older populations among whom modified forms of borderline personality disorder may be problematic and yet are largely unrecognised and untreated. Evidence is lacking for the effects of psychological therapies in people with borderline personality disorder from black and minority ethnic groups.

5.1.10   Potential sources of bias

Publication bias
There were too few RCTs to undertake funnel plots to ascertain publication bias so this could not be explored. However, unpublished studies were sought and included where possible.

Product champions
See Section 5.1.4 above.

Table 11: Self-harm and suicide-related outcomes in included RCTs

Study ID	Self-harm acts	Suicidal acts	Published scale	Suicidal ideation
BATEMAN1999	Definition: deliberate; resulted in visible tissue damage, nursing or medical intervention required	Definition: deliberate; life threatening; resulted in medical attention; medical assessment consistent with suicide attempt	Not reported	Not measured
BLUM2008	No definition given but suicidal acts reported separately	No definition given	Not used	Not measured
CLARKIN2004	Not reported	Not reported	Not reported	OAS suicidality
CARTER unpublished	Admission for deliberate self-harm (not defined)	Not reported	Not reported	Not reported
CHANEN2008	Frequency of non-suicidal self-injury (not defined or reported separately)	Frequency of suicide attempts (not defined or reported separately)	Not used (authors' schedule available on request)	Not measured
DAVIDSON2006	Definition: not a suicidal act; deliberate; results in potential/actual tissue damage; events occurring within 24 hours of each other considered a single act Data for number of acts given rather than number of acts per person so not extractable	Definition: deliberate; life threatening; required medical intervention (even if did not receive any) Data satisfactory as given as mean per person	Based on Acts of Deliberate Self-Harm Inventory (Davidson, 2008)	Not reported

Continued

Table 11: *(Continued)*

Study ID	Self-harm acts	Suicidal acts	Published scale	Suicidal ideation
GIESEN-BLOO2006	Reports parasuicidality subscale of the Borderline Personality Disorder Severity Index (BPDSI) (Arntz *et al.*, 2003) which the GDG chose not to extract (see Appendix 16)	Reports parasuicidality subscale of the BPDSI (see left)	BPDSI	Reports parasui-cidality subscale of the BPDSI (see left)
KOONS2001	Reports mean number of parasuicidal acts based on Parasuicide History Interview (PHI) (Linehan *et al.*, 1989)	Reports mean number of parasuicidal acts	PHI	Beck Suicidal Ideation Scale
LINEHAN1991	Number of parasuicidal acts (unclear how defined) – acts occurring as part of one episode were counted separately in number of acts count, but number of episodes also counted	An episode that the subject considered a serious attempt to die	PHI	Used scale (self-report Scale for Suicide Ideators)

LINEHAN2006	Reports 'highest medical risk' composite measure of suicide attempts and self-injury data aggregated per year; this has not been extracted as it is not analogous to data from other studies. Also reports non-suicidal injuries, which have been extracted	Also reports non-ambivalent suicide attempts (it is unclear how this is defined even in the paper that reports the development of the scale)	Suicide Attempt Self-Injury Interview (non-ambivalent suicide attempts)	Suicidal Behaviors Questionnaire (Linehan & Nielsen, 1981, unpublished)
MUNROE-BLUM1995	Not reported	Not reported	Not reported	Not reported
TURNER2000	No definition given for 'rating of parasuicide'; therefore data used is 'number of suicide/self-harm attempts', which is also not defined and is self-reported	See left	Based on an unpublished scale Target Behaviour Ratings (TBR)	Beck Suicidal Ideation Scale
TYRER2003	Parasuicidal events as defined by the PHI	Not reported separately	PHI	Not reported

Continued

113

Table 11: *(Continued)*

Study ID	Self-harm acts	Suicidal acts	Published scale	Suicidal ideation
VANDENBOSCH2002	Reported as parsuicidal/self-mutilating acts using score on Lifetime Parasuicide Count (LPC) Not useable as does not give count of episodes/ acts; it is more of a composite measure of overall 'parasuicidality' in period under review	Measured as parasuicidal acts score on BPDSI which the GDG chose not to extract (see Appendix 16)	BPDSI	Not reported
WEINBERG2006	Parasuicidal events as defined by the PHI	Not reported separately	PHI	Suicidal Behaviors Questionnaire

5.1.11   Sub-analyses

Since the dataset is fairly small and there are a large number of outcomes, with different rating scales being used for the same outcome, the following sub-analyses were planned *a priori* to explore potential moderators:

Potential moderator	Sub-categories
Length of treatment	<6 months versus >6 months
Manualised	Yes versus no
Number of sessions	–
Type of therapy	CBT-related versus psychodynamic-focused
Therapist experience	–
Author allegiance	–

However, since the RCTs had few outcomes in common, it was not possible to undertake these sub-analyses. Therapist experience and author allegiance are described.

5.2   ARTS THERAPIES

5.2.1   Introduction

Arts therapies developed mainly in the US and Europe during the 20th century. They have often been delivered as part of treatment programmes for people with personality disorders including those with borderline personality disorder. Four arts therapies are currently provided in Britain: art therapy, dance movement therapy, dramatherapy and music therapy. While the four different modalities use a variety of techniques and arts media, all focus on the creation of a trusting therapeutic and safe environment within which people can acknowledge and express strong emotions (Payne, 1993). These interventions are underpinned by the belief that creative processes encourage self-expression, promote self-awareness and increase insight, in the context of a reparative therapeutic relationship, thereby enhancing a person's psychological well-being. The creative medium in arts therapies allows the therapist to work with both verbal and non-verbal material and at different levels according to the level of disturbance in the client.

In art therapy, people are encouraged to use a range of art materials to make images and the focus is on the relationship between the image, the creator and the therapist (Waller & Gilroy, 1992; Gilroy, 2006). In dance movement therapy, therapists focus on the use of body movement and connections between mind, body and emotions are explored. Dramatherapy involves creativity, play, movement, voice, storytelling, and dramatisation so that the performance arts have a central position within the therapeutic relationship. Music therapists generally co-create improvised music with talking used to guide, interpret or enhance the musical experience and its therapeutic effect (Bruscia, 1998).

Art, music and drama therapists working in the UK are state registered professions, regulated by the Health Professions Council, which requires specialist training at a masters level.

5.2.2 Databases searched and inclusion/exclusion criteria

Studies of arts therapies were sought from the citations downloaded in the search for RCTs undertaken at the beginning of the guideline development process and described above. No studies were found, so an additional search was undertaken for primary research in arts therapies in any personality disorder. Information about the databases searched and the inclusion/exclusion criteria used are in Table 12.

No studies were found from the search, therefore a general narrative review was undertaken.

5.2.3 Narrative review of arts therapies

Arts therapies have been widely used as a part of treatment programmes for people with borderline and other forms of personality disorder in Britain (Bateman & Fonagy, 1999; Haigh, 2007; Crawford *et al.*, 2007). In this context arts therapies are usually delivered in groups; individual therapy is less commonly provided. While numerous case series have described the use of arts therapies for people with borderline personality disorder (for example, Olsson & Barth, 1983; Eren *et al.*, 2000; Schmidt, 2002; Gottschalk & Boekholt, 2004; Havsteen-Franklin, 2007) very little

Table 12: Databases searched and inclusion/exclusion criteria for clinical evidence

Electronic databases	MEDLINE, EMBASE, PsycINFO, CINAHL
Date searched	Database inception to 2 May 2008
Study design	Any primary research design
Patient population	Personality disorder
Interventions	Music therapy, psychodrama, art therapy, dance therapy, writing therapies, colour therapy
Outcomes	see Table 10

research has, so far, attempted to quantify the impact of arts therapies for people with this condition.

5.2.4   Clinical summary

There is very little research on the effectiveness of arts therapies for people with borderline personality disorder and therefore no recommendations could be made.

5.2.5   Health economic evidence

No economic evidence on arts therapies for people with borderline personality disorder was identified from the systematic search of the economic literature. Details on the methods used for the systematic review of economic literature are described in Chapter 3.

5.3   BRIEF PSYCHOLOGICAL INTERVENTIONS

5.3.1   Description of brief psychological therapy

For the purposes of this review therapy lasting less than 6 months is defined as 'brief'. (This is distinguished from 'time-limited' therapies lasting more than 6 months but less than 1 year).

Manual-assisted cognitive therapy (MACT; Evans *et al.*, 1999) was developed as a public health intervention for the large numbers of people who repeatedly attempt suicide (parasuicide) rather than for borderline personality disorder *per se*. However, a high proportion of people in this population meet criteria for borderline personality disorder, and this subpopulation is therefore similar to the one for whom DBT was developed. The intervention is a brief, cognitively-oriented and problem-focused therapy comprising up to five sessions within 3 months of an episode of self-harm, with the option of a further two booster sessions within 6 months. Bibliotherapy, in the form of a 70-page booklet (Schmidt & Davidson, 2002), is used to structure the treatment sessions and to act as an *aide-memoire* between sessions. The manual covers an evaluation of the self-harm attempt, crisis skills, problem solving, basic cognitive techniques to manage emotions and negative thinking, and relapse-prevention strategies.

5.3.2   RCT evidence

Two RCTs of brief psychological therapies were found, both of MACT (TYRER2003; WEINBERG2006), with a further trial being excluded because it was in a mixed personality disorder population and data for people with borderline personality disorder were not reported separately (HUBAND2007).

5.3.3   Manual-assisted cognitive therapy

Summary study characteristics of the two trials of MACT are in Table 13 and the summary evidence profile for RCTs of MACT is in Table 14.

There is some evidence that a low-intensity intervention (MACT) has some effect on reducing self-harm and suicidal acts (reported together as a continuous measure), but no effect when reported as parasuicide as a dichotomous measure. Both these outcomes were reported by a single study, therefore it is difficult to draw firm conclusions without further research. There was no evidence of other effects on the symptoms of borderline personality disorder.

Table 13: Summary study characteristics for studies of MACT

	MACT
No. trials (Total participants)	2 RCTs (100)
Study IDs	(1) TYRER2003 (2) WEINBERG2006
N/% female	(1) 70 (borderline personality disorder group only) (2) 30/100
Mean age (or range if not given)	(1) 31 (2) 18–40
Axis I/II disorders	Borderline personality disorder
Comparator	TAU
Additional intervention	None
Setting	(1) A&E following self-harm (2) Community and outpatients
Length of treatment	(1) 3 months (2) 8 weeks
Length of follow-up	(1) None (2) 6 months

Table 14: Summary evidence profile for RCTs of MACT

Symptom	Anxiety	Depression	Self-harm and suicidal acts reported together	No with >=1 episode of parasuicide	General functioning
Therapy (all versus TAU unless otherwise stated)	MACT	MACT	MACT	MACT	MACT
Clinician-rated effect size	SMD = 0.01 (−0.48, 0.5)	SMD = 0.07 (−0.42, 0.56)*	WMD = −3.03 (−5.68, −0.38)*	RR = 0.97 (0.88, 1.07) 94% versus 97%	SMD = −0.17 (−0.67, 0.32)
Quality of evidence	Moderate	Very low	Moderate	Moderate	Very low
Number of studies/participants	(K = 1; n = 64)	(K = 1; n = 64)	(K = 1; n = 28)	(K = 1; n = 70)	(K = 1; n = 64)
Forest plot	Psych 03.01	Psych 03.02	Psych 03.04	Psych 03.05	Psych 03.07
Clinician-rated effect size at follow-up 1	–	–	WMD = −4.71(−11.16, 1.74)* (6 months)	–	–
Quality of evidence	–	–	Very low	–	–
Number of studies/participants	–	–	(K = 1; n = 30)	–	–
Forest plot	–	–	Psych 03.04	–	–
Dichotomous data	–	–	RR = 0.97 (0.88, 1.07) (94% versus 97%)	–	–
Quality of evidence	–	–	Moderate	–	–
Number of studies/participants	–	–	(K = 1; n = 70)	–	–
Forest plot	–	–	Psych 03.05	–	–

*Based on skewed data.

5.3.4 Health economics evidence on brief psychological interventions

The systematic search of economic literature identified two studies that assessed the cost effectiveness of brief psychological interventions for borderline personality disorder (Byford *et al.*, 2003; Brazier *et al.*, 2006). The study by Byford and colleagues (2003) evaluated the cost effectiveness of MACT versus treatment as usual in people with recurrent deliberate self-harm; the study was carried out alongside a UK-based RCT, which was included in the guideline systematic review of clinical evidence (TYRER2003). In addition, Brazier and colleagues (2006) conducted a number of economic analyses exploring the cost effectiveness of various psychological interventions for people with borderline personality disorder. In this context, they undertook economic modelling to assess the cost effectiveness of MACT versus treatment as usual using data from TYRER2003, derived from the subgroup of people with borderline personality disorder participating in the trial. Details on the methods used for the systematic search of the economic literature are described in Chapter 3.

Overview of economic analyses conducted by Byford and colleagues, 2003
Byford and colleagues (2003) assessed the cost effectiveness of MACT versus treatment as usual in a sample of 397 people with recurrent deliberate self-harm participating in a UK-based RCT (TYRER2003). The analysis adopted a societal perspective, considering the costs of all sectors providing services (such as hospital and community healthcare services, community accommodation services, social and voluntary services and the criminal justice system), living expenses and productivity losses. Unit costs were taken from national sources, except hospital costs which were based on local prices. Outcomes were expressed as the proportion of people with a repeated episode of self-harm and as QALYs; the latter were generated based on patient-reported Euro-QoL 5-Dimension (EQ-5D) scores that were converted into utility scores using tariffs obtained from the general UK population. EQ-5D is a generic measure of health-related quality of life, covering five dimensions of health: mobility, self-care, usual activities, pain/discomfort and anxiety/depression (Euro-Qol Group, 1990). Parasuicide events were recorded using the PHI. The time horizon of the analysis was 12 months.

Results were presented in the form of incremental cost-effectiveness ratios (ICERs), which express the difference in total cost divided by the difference in the measure of effectiveness between interventions examined. The authors conducted univariate sensitivity analysis on a number of cost parameters, to investigate the robustness of the results under different values and assumptions. In addition, they used bootstrapping techniques to generate distributions of costs and clinical outcomes for the two interventions. Subsequently, they used these distributions in a probabilistic sensitivity analysis, which explored the probability of MACT being more cost effective than treatment as usual, after taking into account the underlying joint uncertainty characterising the cost and effectiveness parameters. Results of probabilistic analysis were presented in the form of cost-effectiveness acceptability curves, which demonstrate the probability of each treatment option being cost effective at different potential cost-effectiveness thresholds set by decision-makers.

MACT was found to be slightly less costly than treatment as usual (£13,450 versus £14,288, respectively, in 1999/2000 prices), but this difference was not significant. MACT was more effective than treatment as usual in terms of proportion of people with a repeated episode of self-harm (39% in the MACT group versus 46% in the treatment as usual group); again, this finding was not statistically significant. According to these results, MACT was less costly and more effective than treatment as usual; this means that MACT was *dominant* over treatment as usual and therefore more cost effective. Results were robust under different hypotheses tested in univariate sensitivity analysis. Probabilistic analysis demonstrated that the probability of MACT being cost effective exceeded 90% at any level of willingness-to-pay (WTP) for a 1% reduction in the proportion of people with repeated episodes of self-harm.

In terms of QALYs gained, MACT was shown to be less effective that treatment as usual, as it produced 0.118 fewer QALYs, although, again, the difference in QALYs between interventions did not reach statistical significance. The ICER of MACT versus treatment as usual was £66,000 per QALY, which meant that MACT saved £66,000 for every QALY lost by adopting MACT instead of treatment as usual (or, conversely, treatment as usual incurred an additional £66,000 per extra QALY it produced). NICE has a cost-effectiveness threshold of £20,000–£30,000 per QALY (NICE, 2007b). This means that, although less effective in terms of QALYs gained, MACT was more cost effective than treatment as usual according to NICE criteria; this result was not affected by alternative scenarios employed in univariate sensitivity analysis. Probabilistic analysis showed that the probability of MACT being cost effective was above 50% at a cost effectiveness threshold between 0 and 66,000/QALY, and fell below 50% at a higher cost-effectiveness threshold. Overall, the probability of MACT being cost effective ranged between 44 and 88% at the various levels of WTP per unit of outcome examined in the analysis; this probability reached its maximum value (88%) at a zero WTP per QALY gained. At a WTP equalling the NICE cost-effectiveness threshold, the probability of MACT being cost effective reached approximately 60 to 65%. It must be noted that productivity losses were excluded from the analysis that used QALYs as measure of benefit so as to avoid the risk of double counting (given that the impact of interventions on employment had already been considered when measuring quality of life by the EQ-5D).

According to the results of the analysis, MACT was more effective than treatment as usual in reducing repeated episodes of self-harm but less effective in terms of QALYs gained. The authors gave a number of possible explanations for this discrepancy: first, the difference in QALYs between interventions was insignificant and might have been observed by chance (the same applies for the other outcome of the analysis as well, that is, the proportion of people with repeated episodes of self-harm). This hypothesis was supported by the fact that there were no differences in any of the secondary outcome measures between the two groups. Another explanation was that EQ-5D is a generic measure of health-related quality of life and might have been insensitive in capturing changes in the quality of life of the study population. On the other hand, expressing the clinical benefit exclusively as the proportion of people experiencing a repeated episode of self-harm may have missed other aspects of the quality of life of these people. When outcome was measured as proportion of people with repeated episodes of self-harm, MACT dominated treatment as usual because it was also less costly. Its probability of being cost effective as a strategy to reduce episodes of self-harm was over 90%, regardless of the cost-effectiveness threshold. In terms of QALYs, MACT saved £66,000 per QALY lost compared with treatment as usual, and was the cost-effective option according to the NICE cost-effectiveness threshold of £20,000–£30,000 per QALY. Its probability of being cost effective at this threshold was roughly 60 to 65%. Based on these findings, the brevity of MACT and its applicability in a service context, the authors concluded that MACT should be offered to people with a history of recurrent self-harm. However, it should be emphasised that the results of this analysis may not be directly transferable to people with borderline personality disorder.

Overview of economic analyses conducted by Brazier and colleagues (2006)
A recent HTA (Brazier *et al.*, 2006) evaluated the effectiveness and cost effectiveness of psychological interventions for people with borderline personality disorder. Assessment of cost effectiveness was not based on a formal decision-analytic modelling approach, because of the following reasons, as stated by the authors of the report:

● borderline personality disorder has a complex nature and there is lack of evidence for a well-defined treatment pathway
● clinical evidence identified by systematic search of the literature was limited and diverse and did not allow for meta-analysis and subsequent use of pooled data in a single decision-analytic model.

Subsequently, the authors decided to undertake separate cost-effectiveness analyses for potentially every RCT included in their systematic review, using a combination of data reported in the published papers and unpublished trial datasets sent by the investigators, and a regression model relating length of inpatient stay and parasuicide events to respective healthcare costs; the regression model was developed using data from TYRER2003. Suitable data that could be used for this economic exercise were identified in six RCTs; of these, one involved MACT, four DBT and one MBT.

The economic analyses adopted a government perspective, including costs to the NHS, personal social services and the criminal justice system. Analyses from the perspective of the NHS and personal social services, as recommended by NICE (NICE, 2004d), and from a wider societal perspective were employed in one-way sensitivity analyses. Costs in the base-case analysis included intervention and staff supervision costs, hospital service costs (inpatient and outpatient care, day hospital, A&E services and medication), community health service costs (primary care, mental health teams, counselling and psychologists' and psychiatrists' time), community accommodation costs, social service costs (day centres, specialist education facilities, sheltered workshops and social workers), as well as criminal justice system costs. Voluntary sector service costs and productivity losses were examined in sensitivity analyses exploring cost effectiveness from a societal perspective. Intervention costs were estimated according to descriptions of the published papers of trials regarding the number of sessions (individual and group) provided and further assumptions. The types of therapists involved were determined based on a survey of DBT practitioners in the UK. Staff supervision costs relating to DBT and MBT were based on information provided in three DBT trials and further assumptions. Costs associated with extra training and telephone consultations were not included in the analyses because they were deemed to be negligible overall (training costs) or similar between the two arms of the analyses (telephone consultation costs).

The majority of other resource use data, such as those related to hospital and community health services, social and voluntary services, community accommodation and the criminal justice system, as well as data on productivity losses, were available for three trials, either in the published papers or from data supplied by the trial investigators to Brazier and colleagues (2006). Of the remaining three studies, two reported only data on length of inpatient stay, and one had no available data on resource use. To overcome this scarcity in data, the authors developed a regression cost model, linking length of inpatient stay and parasuicide events (independent variables) with costs (dependent variable), based on UK patient-level trial data, derived after combining both arms in the RCT described in TYRER2003. Regression analysis demonstrated that inpatient stay and parasuicide effects accounted for approximately two-thirds of the variation in costs. Unit costs were taken from national sources (Curtis & Netten, 2003). Costs were uplifted to 2003/2004 prices.

Outcomes were expressed in all six analyses as the number of parasuicide events avoided, since this measure of outcome was reported in all RCTs included in the economic analyses. However, it must be noted that parasuicide activity had been defined in slightly different ways in the RCTs and therefore might not be comparable across studies. In addition, where available data permitted, outcomes were expressed in the form of QALYs. This was possible in four analyses: one of the trials had used a preference-based measure that could be directly converted into QALYs; three other trials had reported data on BDI scores, a measure that had been previously mapped onto the EQ-5D, allowing the authors to generate QALYs for these trials too. The time horizon of all analyses was 12 months.

Results were reported as incremental cost per parasuicide event avoided and cost per QALY. Probabilistic sensitivity analysis was employed to explore the impact of the uncertainty characterising the model input parameters on cost-effectiveness results: all variables in the analyses were simultaneously varied randomly over a range of plausible values in 10,000 simulations, thus generating a distribution of cost-effectiveness results. The outcome of probabilistic sensitivity analyses was presented in the form of cost-effectiveness acceptability curves, which demonstrated the probability of the evaluated intervention being cost effective at various levels of decision-makers' WTP (that is, at various cost-effectiveness thresholds) after taking into account the underlying joint uncertainty in model input parameters. In addition, one-way sensitivity analyses explored the impact of the chosen perspective on the results (using a NICE or societal perspective, rather than government, which was the base-case perspective as described above), as well as the supervision costs of DBT relative to its comparators.

Overview of the economic analysis conducted by Brazier and colleagues (2006) based on TYRER2003

Using the methods described in the previous section, Brazier and colleagues (2006) undertook a model-based economic analysis using a sub-set of data from TYRER2003 specific to people with borderline personality disorder, which they obtained from the trial investigators. Resource use data for the sub-group of people with borderline personality disorder were fully available; only staff supervision costs needed to be estimated for the economic model, and these were assumed to be the same in both arms of the trial. Parasuicide events were measured using the PHI. EQ-5D scores reported by study participants were used to estimate QALYs in the model-based economic analysis.

The results revealed that MACT was somewhat costlier than treatment as usual (£9,580 versus £7,563, respectively). It was also less effective with regard to the number of parasuicide events per person (4.9 events per person in the MACT group versus only 1.7 events per person in the treatment as usual group). Therefore, MACT was less cost effective than treatment as usual when outcome was measured as number of parasuicide events because it was dominated by treatment as usual (it was more costly and less effective). In contrast, MACT resulted in a higher number of QALYs compared with treatment as usual (0.19 versus 0.14, respectively). Even in this case, however, the ICER of MACT versus treatment as usual was £84,032/QALY, exceeding by far the NICE cost-effectiveness threshold of £20,000–£30,000 per QALY gained (NICE, 2008). The probability of MACT being more cost effective than treatment as usual was roughly 40% at any WTP per parasuicide event avoided and 45% at a cost-effectiveness threshold of £20,000 per QALY. These findings demonstrate the high uncertainty characterising the study results. Results were insensitive to changes in the adopted perspective (NICE or societal).

The above analysis, referring specifically to people with borderline personality disorder, suggests that MACT is unlikely to be cost effective as a treatment option for this population, although the results were characterised by considerable uncertainty. A potential limitation of the analysis was the use of EQ-5D for the generation of QALYs; as previously discussed, this is a generic instrument, which may have failed to capture changes in health-related quality of life of people with borderline personality disorder. On the other hand, the number of parasuicide events avoided is a limited measure of outcome that may have potentially failed to capture other benefits resulting from provision of MACT to people with borderline personality disorder.

Details on the characteristics and results of Byford and colleagues (2003) and the analysis by Brazier and colleagues (2006) on TYRER2003 are presented in the form of evidence tables in Appendix 15.

5.4   COMPLEMENTARY THERAPIES

5.4.1   Introduction

Complementary therapies, such as aromatherapy, acupuncture and homeopathy are not widely used in the treatment of people with borderline personality disorder. This is surprising to some extent as the urgent need for intervention to reduce distress leads many service users to ask for drug treatments, many of which have significant side effects, particularly if used for any length of time. Omega-3 fatty acids have been used to some extent and have been the subject of RCTS (see Chapter 6).

5.4.2   Evidence search

In order to make recommendations for people with borderline personality disorder the GDG asked the clinical question:

For people with borderline personality disorder which treatments are associated with improvement in mental state and quality of life, reduction in self-harm, service use, and risk-related behaviour, and/or improved social and personal functioning while minimising harm?

In addition to pharmacological and psychological treatments, the GDG also considered complementary therapies. All relevant RCTs undertaken in people with a diagnosis of borderline personality disorder were sought from the citations downloaded in the search as described above. No studies were found (except for those on omega-3 fatty acids, which are included in Chapter 6); therefore, the GDG contacted a special advisor who advised on terms for a search string for a further search for studies of any research design. This search was broadened to search for studies on any personality disorder. Information about the databases searched and the inclusion/exclusion criteria used are in Table 15. The GDG looked for evidence on therapies either available through the NHS or otherwise easily accessible.

5.4.3   Studies considered

No studies were found from the search undertaken. The GDG's special advisor knew of no studies on the use of complementary therapies in people with a personality disorder, other than those on the use of omega-3 fatty acids already identified.

Table 15: Databases searched and inclusion/exclusion criteria for clinical evidence

Electronic databases	MEDLINE, EMBASE, PsycINFO, Cochrane Library, AMED
Date searched	Database inception to 2 May 2008
Study design	Any primary research design
Patient population	Personality disorder
Interventions	Aromatherapy, acupuncture, homeopathy, alternative medicine*, complementary therapy*, relaxation techniques
Outcomes	See Table 10

*Terms used by some databases to cover a range of therapies.

5.4.4   Clinical evidence summary

There is no evidence on the use of complementary therapies as a treatment in people with a personality disorder, therefore no recommendations could be made.

5.4.5   Health economic evidence

No economic evidence on complementary therapies as a treatment in people with borderline personality disorder was identified from the systematic search of the economic literature. Details on the methods used for the systematic review of economic literature are described in Chapter 3.

5.5   INDIVIDUAL PSYCHOLOGICAL THERAPIES

5.5.1   Description of individual psychological therapies

Cognitive behavioural therapy (CBT) is a structured psychological treatment that focuses on helping a person make connections between their thoughts, feelings and behaviour. CBT was originally developed as a treatment for depression, and has since been modified for the treatment of people with personality disorders including borderline personality disorder. While CBT for axis I disorders is generally focused on the 'here and now', CBT for people with personality disorders takes account of previous experiences in the development of core beliefs, which are also referred to as 'schemas'.

Cognitive therapy (CT) focused on changing fundamental beliefs has applied the work of Aaron Beck, in particular, to the needs of people with both borderline and antisocial personality disorders. Building on experience of using CBT with a variety of mental health problems, it provides guiding principles on formulation, identifying and changing core beliefs and addressing behavioural problems. It is adapted for people with borderline personality disorder and pays attention to the structure of the therapy and the problems that can disrupt the therapeutic relationship, such as non-engagement in treatment, shifting problems and goals, losing focus on the aims of therapy, losing structure and lack of compliance with assignments (Davidson, 2000).

CBT for people with borderline personality disorder is generally delivered in sessions lasting between 30 and 90 minutes. The number of sessions that are offered tends to be greater for people with personality disorder compared with depression and other axis 1 disorders and is delivered on a weekly basis over a period of 9 to 36 months. Patients are asked to undertake homework in between sessions. Some service models also provide access to therapists by telephone outside individual sessions.

Systems training for emotional predictability and problem solving (STEPPS) is a CBT-based skills development package presented in 2-hour sessions over a period of 20 weeks. It includes a 2-hour session for family members and significant others, including members of the treatment team, to introduce them to the concepts and skills enabling them to provide support and reinforcement of skills for participants. It comprises three phases in which patients: (1) are encouraged to 'replace misconceptions about borderline personality disorder with an awareness of the thoughts, feelings and behaviours that define it' (Blum *et al.*, 2008); (2) receive skills training aimed at helping them achieve improved emotional regulation; and (3) receive behaviour skills training. It is designed to be used to complement other treatments.

Problem-solving therapy (Huband *et al.*, 2007) is a brief psychological treatment for depression based on cognitive-behavioral principles (D'Zurilla & Goldfried, 1971; Nezu & Perri, 1989). It has also been used extensively as a form of crisis intervention following deliberate self-harm or attempted suicide (Hawton & Kirk, 1989). Like CBT, problem-solving therapy is structured, collaborative and focuses on generating solutions to current problems. Problem solving is seen as having five stages: adopting a problem-solving orientation; defining the problem and selecting goals; generating alternative solutions; choosing the best solution; and implementing the best solution and evaluating its effects. Methods used include cognitive modelling, prompting, self-instructions and reinforcement. Problem-solving therapy has been adapted to help people with personality disorders in a format of 16 group sessions preceded by three individual psychoeducational sessions (Huband *et al.*, 2007).

Schema-focused cognitive therapy (Young, 1990; Young & Klosko, 1994) emphasises the role of dysfunctional cognitive schemas learned early in life (early maladaptive schemas) and the processes that inflexibly maintain them and prevent new learning: schema maintenance, schema avoidance and schema compensation. People are encouraged to explore the role that these core beliefs played in helping them adapt to previous adverse circumstances, and to question whether they are appropriate for helping them adapt to their current situation. Treatment aims to facilitate affective engagement and re-learning, which may sometimes involve elements of reparenting.

Cognitive analytic therapy (CAT; Ryle, 1997; Ryle & Kerr, 2002) is an integrative and relational approach that combines CBT methods with attention to the therapeutic relationship as the vehicle of change, through understanding how problematic, harsh and punitive relationship patterns (reciprocal roles) have been learned and continue to be re-enacted, both with others and in the person's relationship with him or herself. A particular feature is jointly constructed psychological 'tools' of narrative and diagrammatic reformulations. These describe recurrent historic patterns of relating with others (possibly including mental health workers) and of self-management. They are designed to help people reflect upon and understand their experience of 'switching' between different states of mind in response to unmanageable feelings or unmet needs. The CAT model sees borderline personality disorder as representing a form of more severe and pervasive damage to the self resulting largely from long-term experiences of complex developmental trauma and deprivation in possibly vulnerable individuals. This is understood to result in a tendency to dissociate into different 'self states' with a resultant highly distressing impairment of self-reflective capacity and sense of identity, impaired executive function and disturbed interpersonal relations. Therapy aims to offer a reparative relational experience and to provide the motivation, skills and opportunities for learning new patterns of relating to oneself and others. CAT is used both as a therapy method and as a consultancy and training framework to help mental health workers avoid harmful relationship patterns (Thompson *et al.*, 2008).

Interpersonal therapy (IPT) is a structured, time-limited supportive therapy which was first developed to treat outpatients with major depression. In IPT for depression the therapist pays systematic attention to one of four main areas, namely interpersonal sensitivity, role transitions, interpersonal disputes, or losses, linking them to changes in mood. A number of studies using randomised controlled designs have shown it to be effective in depression and other disorders. It has been further developed to treat patients with borderline personality disorder.

Psychodynamic interpersonal therapy (PIT) as a manualised therapy for borderline personality disorder is based on the conversational model of Hobson (1985), developed and adapted for people with borderline personality disorder (Stevenson *et al.*, 2005). The goal of therapy is maturational aiming to help the patient discover, elaborate, and represent a personal reality. Therapists establish an enabling therapeutic atmosphere striving to increase the 'connectedness' between patient and therapist and to develop a shared language for feelings. By amplifying elements of the personal and inner world of the patient as they appear in the conversation, therapists identify moments when traumatic memories break into consciousness in order to work towards their integration into the system of self. Such disjunctions are indicated by negative affect, linear thinking, orientation towards events and the outer world, changes in the self-state (for example, grandiosity) and the emergence of transference phenomena.

Psychodynamic/psychoanalytic psychotherapy emphasise the role of unconscious conflict between wishes that provoke anxiety and defences that oppose those wishes. These conflicts are understood within the context of internal representations of self and others. Problems in relationships are seen to be repeated within the therapy relationship in the form of transference and counter-transference, which is interpreted by the therapist. Traditionally, psychoanalytic therapists have maintained neutrality, a 'blank screen' on which the patient's inner conflicts and wishes can be projected. However, these methods have been modified in working with people with borderline personality disorder so that the therapist provides more structure and is more active. One example of such a method is transference-focused psychotherapy (Clarkin *et al.*, 2006), a structured and manualised form of psychodynamic therapy that aims to activate dysfunctional patterns of interpersonal relationships within the therapy relationship (transference) so that these can be understood through interpretation. The emphasis is on reducing identity diffusion and facilitating reflective functioning. There is an additional focus on ameliorating difficulties in everyday social and work functioning. Transference-focused psychotherapy is delivered as an individual therapy twice per week, although some people may also be given an ancillary treatment for a specific problem (for example, a 12-step group for a person with substance misuse).

5.5.2   RCT evidence

There were six RCTs of individual psychological therapies in the treatment of people with borderline personality disorder. The studies were all of different therapies, including CBT (DAVIDSON2006), CAT (CHANEN2008), schema-focused cognitive therapy (GIESEN-BLOO2006), STEPPS (BLUM2008), transference-focused psychotherapy (CLARKIN2004) and individual dynamic psychotherapy (MUNRO-BLUM1995). CLARKIN2004 is a three-armed trial including DBT and is also considered in the section on psychological therapy programmes (see Section 5.7). A further trial (ABBASS2008) was excluded because so few participants had a diagnosis of borderline personality disorder (n = 12). However, since there are no other studies of short-term dynamic psychotherapy, it is briefly discussed below but was not included in any analyses. See Table 16 for summary study characteristics of the included studies.

Table 16: Summary study characteristics of included RCTs of individual psychological therapies

	Individual psychological therapies
No. trials (Total participants)	6 RCTs (708)
Study IDs	(1) BLUM2008 (2) CHANEN2008 (3) CLARKIN2004* (4) DAVIDSON2006 (5) GIESEN-BLOO2006 (6) MUNROE-BLUM1995
N/% female	(1) 165/81 (2) 78/76 (3) 90/93 (4) 106/82 (5) 88/91 (6) 110/81
Mean age (or range if not given)	(1) 32 (2) 16 (3) 31 (4) 32 (5) 31 (6) 18–62
Axis I/II disorders	(1) 100% borderline personality disorder (2) 100% traits of borderline personality disorder/ (2 to 9 DSM-IV criteria) (43% borderline personality disorder)/63% mood disorders/40% anxiety disorder/4% eating disorder/33% substance misuse/26% disruptive behaviour disorder (3) 100% borderline personality disorder/77% mood disorders/48% anxiety disorders/

Continued

Table 16: (*Continued*)

	Individual psychological therapies
	33% eating disorders/38% drug or alcohol dependence (4)–(6) 100% borderline personality disorder
Treatment	(1) STEPPS (2) CAT (3) Transference-focused psychotherapy (4) CBT (5) Schema-focused therapy (6) Individual dynamic psychotherapy
Comparator(s)	(1) TAU (2) Good clinical care (manualised intervention) (3) DBT/supportive psychotherapy (4) TAU (5) Transference-focused psychotherapy (6) Interpersonal group therapy
Setting	(1)–(2) Outpatients (3)–(4) Mixed sample (5) Outpatients (6) Mixed sample
Length of treatment protocol	(1) 20 weeks (2) 12 months (3)–(4) 1 year (5) 3 years (6) 1 year
Length of follow-up (from end of treatment)	(1)–(2) 1 year (3) None (4) 24 months (5) 24 and 36 months (6) None

*3-armed trial; no extractable data.

Summary of evidence for individual psychological therapies

A large number of outcomes were reported by the studies of individual psychological interventions (see Table 17).

Individual psychological interventions had very little effect on symptoms compared with treatment as usual, other than for general functioning which showed some improvement (reported by the study of STEPPS, BLUM2008). Data from CLARKIN2004 were supplied by the study authors since no extractable data were

Table 17: Summary evidence profile for RCTs of individual psychological interventions: general outcomes

Symptom	Anxiety	Depression	Impulsiveness	Mental distress	Borderline personality disorder symptoms	Social functioning	General functioning	Quality of life	Leaving treatment early because of side effects
Therapy (all versus TAU unless otherwise stated)	CBT	CBT STEPPS	STEPPS	CBT STEPPS	STEPPS CAT (follow-up only)	CBT STEPPS	STEPPS CAT (follow-up only)	Schema-focused therapy versus psychodynamic	CAT CBT STEPPS
Clinician-rated effect size	SMD = −0.03 (−0.43, 0.36)	(Self-report) SMD = −0.18 (−0.44, 0.07)*	SMD = −0.29 (−0.64, 0.07)	SMD = −0.18 (−0.45, 0.08)*	SMD = −0.45 (−0.81, −0.1)*	SMD = 0 (−0.39, 0.39)	SMD = −0.55 (−0.91, −0.19)	SMD = 0.29 (−0.11, 0.68)*	RR = 1.28 (0.82, 1.99) (39% versus 28%)
Quality of evidence	Moderate	Very low	Very low	Very low	Very low	Moderate	Moderate	Very low	Very low
Number of studies/participants	(K = 1; n = 99)	(K = 2; n = 236)	(K = 1; n = 124)	(K = 2; n = 223)	(K = 1; n = 124)	(K = 1; n = 99)	(K = 1; n = 123)	(K = 1; n = 99)	(K = 3; n = 357)
Forest plot	Psych 02.01	Psych 02.02	Psych 02.03	Psych 02.04	Psych 02.09	Psych 02.10	Psych 02.11	Psych 02.12	Psych 02.13
Clinician-rated effect size at follow-up 1	SMD = −0.18 (−0.57, 0.21) (24 months)	SMD = −0.15 (−0.54, 0.24)* (24 months)	–	SMD = −0.12 (−0.51, 0.27)* (24 months)	WMD = −0.27 (−2.39, 1.85) (24 months)	SMD = 0.14 (−0.26, 0.53)	SMD = −0.22 (−0.66, 0.23)	SMD = −0.23 (−0.62, 0.16)* (24 months)	–
Quality of evidence	Very low	Moderate		Moderate	Very low	Moderate	Very low	Very low	
Number of studies/participants	(K = 1; n = 101)	(K = 1; n = 101)	–	(K = 1; n = 101)	(K = 1; n = 78)	(K = 1; n = 101)	(K = 1; n = 78)	(K = 1; n = 101)	–
Forest plot	Psych 02.01	Psych 02.02	–	Psych 02.04	Psych 02.09	Psych 02.10	Psych 02.11	Psych 02.12	–

*Based on skewed data.

available in the published reports. The data was supplied provided the following caveat from the study authors was included:

> 'these data are <u>not</u> raw end-point data and should not be considered or treated as such. These data represent estimated (ordinary least squares regression) end-points based on the origin and slope for each subject assuming 12 months of treatment. The Clarkin et al. (2007) report used an individual growth curve analytic approach and the primary dependent variable of interest in that study was the rate of change. The estimated end-point data reported below are <u>not</u> the rate of change data. Post-hoc group mean comparisons of these estimated end-point means would not be statistically appropriate, nor would it be expected to duplicate the pattern of results obtained from the analyses of the rate of change variable in the IGC analyses reported in Clarkin et al. (2007)'. (Private information, 2008)

The authors declined further requests to use the data to calculate between-group effect sizes. The study was therefore excluded from our analysis since it was not possible to make a comparison between groups in the way in which other studies were analysed.

The study by Abbass and colleagues (2008), which was not included in the analyses because so few participants had a diagnosis of borderline personality disorder (n = 12), showed that an intensive short-term dynamic psychotherapy was effective in reducing symptoms and interpersonal problems compared with a waitlist group in people with a range of personality disorders (n = 27). Treatment was given in weekly 1-hour sessions. Participants received an average of 27.7 (+− 20) sessions (range 2 to 64) which makes it hard to specify the optimum number of sessions.

Individual psychological interventions also showed little effect on reducing self-harm or suicide attempts (see Table 18) compared with treatment as usual, although there was some effect when the two outcomes were reported together (reported by the study of CAT, CHANEN2008). There was some effect on the number of suicide attempts when this was reported as a continuous rather than dichotomous measure (reported by the study of STEPPS, BLUM2008).

Service outcomes (see Table 19) such as hospital attendance and admission in individual psychological interventions were reported only by DAVIDSON2006 (CBT). There was little effect on service use outcomes.

5.5.3 Non-RCT evidence

Fourteen non-RCTs were found of individual psychological interventions. Study characteristics can be found in Table 20.

STEPPS

BLUM2002
In this study Blum and colleagues (2002) monitored changes in symptoms in a cohort of 52 people who made use of the STEPPS programme and conducted a

Table 18: Summary evidence profile for RCTs of individual psychological interventions: self-harm and suicide-related outcomes

Outcome	Self-harm	Suicide attempts	Self-harm and suicide attempts
Therapy	STEPPS (follow-up only)	CBT STEPPS (follow-up only)	CAT
Dichotomous data	–	RR = 0.78 (0.47, 1.27) (34% versus 44%)	RR = 0.81 (0.5, 1.31) (41% versus 51%)
Quality of evidence	–	Very low	Very low
Number of studies/ participants	–	(K = 1; n = 101)	(K = 1; n = 78)
Forest plot	–	Psych 02.06	Psych 02.06
Follow-up 1	RR = 1.03 (0.71, 1.48) (52% versus 51%) (1 year follow-up)	RR = 1.08 (0.53, 2.21) (23% versus 21%) (1 year follow-up)	RR = 1.8 (0.88, 3.72) (39% versus 22%)
Quality of evidence	Very low	Very low	Moderate
Number of studies/ participants	(K = 1; n = 108)	(K = 1; n = 108)	(K = 1; n = 78)
Forest plot	Psych 02.06	Psych 02.06	Psych 02.06
Follow-up 2	–	RR = 0.8 (0.54, 1.2) (43% versus 54%) (24 months' follow-up)	RR = 0.98 (0.51, 1.87) (32% versus 32%)
Quality of evidence	–	Very low	Very low
Number of studies/ participants	–	(K = 1; n = 101)	(K = 1; n = 78)
Forest plot	–	Psych 02.06	Psych 02.06

Continued

Table 18: *(Continued)*

Outcome	Self-harm	Suicide attempts	Self-harm and suicide attempts
Continuous data	–	WMD = −0.41 (−0.72, −0.1)	–
Quality of evidence	–	Moderate	–
Number of studies/ participants	–	(K = 1; n = 101)	–
Forest plot	–	Psych 02.05	–
Follow-up 1	–	WMD = −0.86 (−1.82, 0.1) (24 months)	–
Quality of evidence	–	Moderate	–
Number of studies/ participants	–	(K = 1; n = 101)	–
Forest plot	–	Psych 02.05	–

cross-sectional survey of views of service users. It is unclear whether the 52 people who were included in the study represent a complete sample of all those referred to the programme during the study period. Forty-nine (94%) of the study sample were female.

Scores on the BDI and the Positive and Negative Affect Scale (PANAS) were monitored every week over a 19-week period. All 52 participants attended at least one session and 28 (54%) attended ten sessions or more. Repeat means analysis demonstrated statistically significant decreases in negative affects on the PANAS, and reductions on total score on the BDI (equivalent to an effect size of 0.78). At the end of the programme, 18 (35%) of the 52 participants completed a 14-item cross-sectional survey that measured the extent to which people would endorse a series of statements. The mean score on a question about the usefulness of the survey was 2.4. The mean score on whether, after attending the programme, 'people say I have fewer problems' was 5.6. Negative effects of the programme were not reported.

BROWN2004

In this uncontrolled cohort study participants with borderline personality disorder who reported suicidal ideation or engaged in self-injurious behaviour received weekly

Table 19: Summary evidence profile for RCTs of individual psychological interventions: service use outcomes

Outcome	No. of A&E contacts	Admission for psychiatric reasons
Therapy	CBT	CBT
Effect size	WMD = −0.24 (−1.98, 1.5)*	WMD = −0.44 (−1.67, 0.79)*
Quality of evidence	Very low	Very low
Number of studies/ participants	(K = 1; n = 101)	(K = 1; n = 101)
Forest plot	Psych 02.07	Psych 02.07
Follow-up at 24 months	WMD = −0.15 (−4.26, 3.96)*	WMD = −0.67 (−1.98, 0.64)*
Quality of evidence	Very low	Very low
Number of studies/ participants	(K = 1; n = 101)	(K = 1; n = 101)
Forest plot	Psych 02.07	Psych 02.07

* Skewed data.

CBT over a 12-month period and were followed up over an 18-month period. Individual sessions lasting 1 hour were supplemented by access to emergency telephone contact with an on-call therapist between sessions.

Two-thirds of the study sample were recruited from mental health practitioners in the public and private sector, with the remainder being recruited by advertisements in local press or from referrals made by a family member or friend. Of the 44 people who met study criteria, seven (16%) failed to complete the baseline assessment and five (11%) declined to participate in the study; the remaining 32 (73%) formed the study sample. Of these, 28 (88%) were female and 11 (34%) were in full-time employment. In addition to borderline personality disorder, study participants usually met diagnostic criteria for other mental disorders. Twenty-five (78%) had a major depressive disorder, 13 (41%) had an eating disorder and 23 (72%) met criteria for at least one other personality disorder. Participants attended between 3 and 63 sessions, with a mean of 34. Information on the extent of use of telephone contact with therapists is not provided.

Follow-up assessment comprised number of borderline criteria, suicidal ideation and behaviour, hopelessness and depression (using the HRSD and the BDI-II) measured at 6, 12 and 18 months. Twenty-nine (91%) people completed the 12-month follow-up interview 24 (83%) completed the interview at 18 months. Fourteen (48%) of the 29 who completed the 12-month follow-up interview, and 4 (28%) of the 24 who completed the 18-month follow-up interview, were judged to still have a

Table 20: Non-randomised studies of individual psychological interventions

	CBT	STEPPS	CAT	Schema-focused cognitive therapy	IPT	Psychodynamic psychotherapy
No. trials (Total participants)	2 non-randomised trials (41)	1 non-randomised trial (52)	1 non-randomised trial (27)	1 non-randomised trial (6)	2 non-randomised trials (64)	5 non-randomised trials (242)
Study IDs	(1) BROWN 2004 (2) HENGEVELD 1996.	(1) BLUM2002	(1) RYLE2000	(1) NORDAHL2005	(1) BELLINO2005 (2) MARKOWITZ 2006	(1) CLARKIN2001 (2) LEICHSEN-RING2007 (3) LOPEZ2004 (4) STEVENSON2005 (5) WILBERG1998
N/% female	(1) 32/88 (2) 9/100	(1) 52/94	(1) 27/59	(1) 6/100	(1) 56/57 (2) 8	(1) 23/100 (2) 132/86 (3) 14/100 (4) 30/66 (5) 43/77
Mean age (or range if not given)	(1) 29 (2) 31	(1) 33	(1) 34	(1) 26	(1) 27 (2) not reported	(1) 33 (2) 30 (3) 25 (4) 30 (5) 31
% participants with borderline personality disorder	(1) 100 (2) 44	(1) 100	(1) 100	(1) 100	(1) 35, 100% major depressive disorder (2) 100	(1)–(5) 100

Research design	(1) Cohort study (2) Case series	(1) Cohort study	(1) Case series	(1) Case series	(1) Non-randomised comparative study (2) Abandoned RCT	(1) Non-comparative prospective study (2) Non-comparative naturalistic study (3) Non-comparative prospective study (4) Case-control (hypothetical controls) (5) Non-comparative prospective study
Setting	(1) Outpatient, US (2) Outpatient, Netherlands	(1) Outpatient, US	(1) Outpatient, UK	(1) Outpatient, Norway	(1) Outpatient, Italy (2) US	(1) Outpatient, US (2) Germany (3) Outpatient, Mexico (4) Australia (5) Inpatient followed by outpatient, Norway
Length of follow-up	(1) 18 months (2) 10 months	(1) No follow-up	(1) 18 months	(1) 1 year	(1) No follow-up (2) No follow-up	(1) No follow-up (2) Not available (3) No follow-up (4) 5 years (5) No follow-up

diagnosis of borderline personality disorder. The proportion of participants who reported at least one episode of deliberate self-injury in the year before treatment was 88% compared with 34% 12 months after the start of treatment. ITT analysis, with last value carried forward for those who failed to complete follow-up interviews, was used to examine changes in depression scores. Statistically significant reductions in BDI scores of 20 points and HRSD scores of 11 points were seen between baseline and 18-month follow-up. Negative effects of treatment were not reported.

HENGEVELD1996
Hengeveld and colleagues report a case series of nine female outpatients who had attempted suicide on at least two occasions and were offered up to ten sessions of group CBT. Seven of the nine met criteria for personality disorder and of these four had borderline personality disorder. Ten months after the last session, recurrence of self-harm was examined using telephone contacts with participants and examination of hospital records. Four of the seven participants reported further suicide attempts – all four had borderline personality disorder.

Cognitive analytic therapy (CAT)

RYLE2000
This is a descriptive study of a case series of 27 inner-city participants from London who received 24 sessions of CAT and four follow-up sessions over approximately 1 year. The study aimed to examine the scope for outpatient NHS therapy for people with borderline personality disorder and to examine predictors of response. The sample excluded four participants who dropped out of treatment. Participants were re-assessed 6 months and 18 months after completing therapy (at approximately 18 months' and 30 months' post-assessment), but nine participants were lost to follow-up at the later stage. Most of the participants (78%) were treated by trainees under supervision. The referral, recruitment, diagnosis, demographic, clinical features, psychometric scores and the response to treatment of a series of participants meeting DSM–IV criteria for borderline personality disorder are described. Diagnosis was made by the PAS and confirmed by the authors independently rating DSM-IV criteria from case note evidence. Patient characteristics recorded included demographic factors, history of childhood abuse, self-cutting, self-poisoning, alcohol and substance misuse, binge-eating, hospitalisation following over-dosing, loss of control, violence, forensic history and major adverse life events. Psychometric pre-post measures were the BDI, the Inventory of Interpersonal Problems (IIP), the SCL-90 and the Social Questionnaire. Changes in self-harm were not reported. Six months after completing therapy, 14 (52%) of the sample no longer met criteria for borderline personality disorder on the PAS and 13 (48%) were judged not to require further treatment. Six-month outcomes on the symptom and interpersonal problem measures were significant at the 1% level, and on the social questionnaire at the 5% level. One year outcomes (n = 18) were significant at the 5% level for the symptom measures but not the interpersonal or social measures. Only three patient characteristics were associated with non-response (in terms of a continuing borderline personality disorder diagnosis): a poor occupational history, self-cutting either in the past year or at any time and a

past history of alcohol misuse. No suicides or other adverse events are reported. The acceptability of CAT to participants was not investigated.

This phase I study is uninformative about the efficacy of CAT because it has no control group, suffers from allegiance effects, has a key outcome measure that was reactive, had assessors who were not independent and because the treatment was delivered by unqualified therapists. It suggests shorter-term outpatient weekly psychotherapy is feasible and that CAT is a promising intervention for further research.

Schema-focused cognitive therapy

NORDAHL2005
Nordahl and Nysæter (2005) report findings based on a 36-month follow-up study of six women with borderline personality disorder. In the first instance participants were offered 1-hour weekly sessions of schema-focused cognitive therapy. The frequency of sessions was tailed off during the last 6 months of therapy and people were offered sessions for between 12 and 36 months. Therapy was supported by continuing input from the patient's referring physician and a nurse from a CMHT.

All participants were assessed using SCID I and SCID II before and after the end of the treatment period. A variety of measures were used to assess mental distress including the GSI, and the GAF was used to assess global functioning. Post-treatment three of the six women were reported to no longer meet SCID-II criteria for borderline personality disorder. Mean GAF score increased from 52 (pre-treatment) to 68 (post-treatment). Based on self-report scores, five of the six women reported marked reductions in symptoms of anxiety and depression. Negative effects of treatment were not reported.

Interpersonal psychotherapy (IPT)

BELLINO2005
This study compared the efficacy of combined medication and interpersonal psychotherapy in participants with depression and either borderline personality disorder or a different axis II disorder. Forty-eight participants completed 6 months of treatment. Participants in both groups improved. But participants with depression and borderline personality disorder showed poorer results on global symptomatology (Clinical Global Impressions [CGI]), interpersonal functioning (IIP) and satisfaction in life than depressed patients with other axis II disorders.

MARKOWITZ2006
Markowitz and colleagues also developed IPT for borderline personality disorder (IPT-borderline personality disorder) and reported on the model and preliminary outcomes from an RCT that was abandoned because of the high drop-out rate from the control group. Participants were offered 18 sessions of IPT on a 16-week acute course and an additional 16 weekly continuation sessions depending on the response to the acute phase. The treatment appeared to be acceptable as only two of the eight participants dropped out of treatment, either because of substance misuse or substance dependence. Five participants who completed both phases of treatment showed improvement in depression

symptoms and general mental distress as measured by the SCL-90 and other measures including diagnostic criteria. The paper does not provide endpoint data or details of statistical tests, so it is unclear how the authors arrived at their conclusions.

Psychodynamic interventions

CLARKIN2001
This pilot study of transference-focused psychotherapy compared number and severity of suicide and self-harm attempts, medical and psychiatric service utilisation and the GAF scores of 23 female participants with borderline personality disorder before and after treatment with 1-year of transference-focused psychotherapy. Four participants dropped out and two were discharged early following failure to follow the treatment contract. Compared with the year before treatment, the number of participants who made suicide attempts was significantly lower but there was no significant reduction in self-injurious behaviours although medical risk was significantly reduced. Medical and psychiatric service utilisation was also significantly reduced. GAF scores were not reported.

LEICHSENRING2007
This is a naturalistic study in which 132 participants were treated in a single clinic with a psychoanalytically-derived therapy. Standardised measures were used for diagnosis and outcomes included symptom measures and interpersonal functioning such as the SCL-90 and the IIP respectively. Life satisfaction was also assessed. Psychoanalytic-interactional therapy was found to significantly improve all areas of patient functioning.

LOPEZ2004
Fourteen female patients with borderline personality disorder were treated with 48 sessions of transference-focused psychotherapy provided by therapists with limited levels of training but who received regular supervision from experts. Four patients dropped out before reaching 24 sessions. Assessments were made at entry, at the mid-point and at the end of treatment. All sessions were video-recorded and all therapists were assessed as adhering to the manual. Participants showed improvements on all measures including diagnostic criteria with remarkable changes in global assessment of function. Improvements were apparent after 24 sessions.

STEVENSON2005
This paper reports a 5-year follow-up of a cohort of 30 people with borderline personality disorder who received twice-weekly psychodynamic interpersonal therapy for 1 year. An earlier paper (Stevenson & Meares, 1992) had reported on outcomes 1 year after cessation of treatment. This had found, in contrast to 30 people who had been on a waiting list for therapy during the same period, significant change on a 27-item measure based on DSM-III. The 5-year follow-up provided data over 6 years for these 30 participants on violent episodes, drug use, medical visits, self-harm, hospital admissions, inpatient episodes, time off work, Cornell Index and the DSM-II-R scale. Contact had been maintained with these patients over this period. The original comparison group was not accessible, so a hypothetical natural history comparison was made by examining the

association of four outcome measures with age in a sample of 150 patients with border-line personality disorder. The treatment group had maintained the DSM-II-R improvements noted at 1-year follow-up and showed good outcomes on the other measures, even when compared with the hypothetical controls. The study limitations include the lack of independent assessment and uncertainty over the validity of the control comparison.

WILBERG1998

This paper is one of a number of reports from the same group of researchers who routinely monitor progress of patients with personality disorder who are being treated in day hospitals that are part of the Norwegian Network of Psychotherapeutic Day Hospitals. Patients are offered 18-weeks of group-orientated day hospital treatment followed by outpatient group psychotherapy. This study, a naturalistic follow-up of people with borderline personality disorder, compared participants treated with a combination of day hospital treatment and subsequent outpatient group psychother-apy with participants treated in the same day hospital but without subsequent outpatient group psychotherapy. The numbers were small but overall those who continued in outpatient group psychotherapy fared significantly better than those who did not at 34 months' post-discharge from the day hospital.

5.5.4   Clinical summary for individual psychological interventions

There is very little evidence for the efficacy of individual psychological interventions in the treatment of people with borderline personality disorder because almost all studies are uncontrolled. The RCT evidence showed some weak evidence that CAT (in young people) and STEPPS may help to improve general functioning, and reduce self-harm and suicide. The effect size for self-harm and suicide outcome was not quite statistically significant for CAT, which was compared with a manualised treatment and 'good clin-ical practice'. Other outcomes from the studies of CAT and STEPPS, and outcomes from RCTs of other therapies (CBT, schema-focused psychotherapy and individual dynamic psychotherapy), did not show any benefit of treatment. Data from the study of transference-focused psychotherapy were not extractable so effect sizes could not be calculated and the study was excluded from the analysis. It should also be noted that the studies had few outcomes in common making the dataset as a whole hard to evaluate.

The non-RCT evidence suggests that individual psychological interventions are acceptable to people with borderline personality disorder. They showed generally positive outcomes (based on authors' conclusions from statistical significance testing rather than calculating effect sizes from extracted data), which need to be tested against control conditions in randomised trials before firm conclusions about the effi-cacy of these treatments can be drawn.

5.5.5   Health economics evidence on individual psychological interventions

The systematic search of economic literature identified three studies that assessed the cost effectiveness of individual psychological interventions for borderline personality disorder. One study examined the cost effectiveness of CBT (Palmer *et al.*, 2006), another compared the cost effectiveness of schema-focused cognitive therapy and transference-focused psychotherapy (Van Asselt *et al.*, 2008), while the third study assessed costs incurred by people with borderline personality disorder before starting and after completing psychodynamic interpersonal therapy (Hall *et al.*, 2001). Details on the methods used for the systematic search of the economic literature are described in Chapter 3.

Overview of the cost-utility analysis conducted by Palmer and colleagues, 2006
Palmer and colleagues (2006) was a cost-utility analysis undertaken alongside a multicentre RCT conducted in the UK (DAVIDSON2006), included in the guideline systematic review of clinical evidence. The study compared CBT in addition to treatment as usual versus treatment as usual alone, in a sample of 106 people with borderline personality disorder. Costs considered in the analysis included intervention costs, hospital costs (inpatient, outpatient, day case, day hospital and A&E attendances), primary and community care costs, including community day services and accommodation, criminal justice system costs and patient expenses. QALYs were generated based on EQ-5D scores reported by the study participants, using preferences elicited from the UK general population. The time horizon of the analysis was 2 years.

Overall CBT was found to be less costly than treatment as usual (£12,785 versus £18,356, respectively, in 2003/04 prices); intervention costs in the CBT group were more than offset by a reduction in hospitalisation costs. At the same time, CBT resulted in a lower number of QALYs compared with treatment as usual (1.06 versus 1.20, respectively). Both differences in cost and outcome were not statistically significant between interventions. Consequently, CBT in addition to treatment as usual was less costly and less effective than treatment as usual alone; the ICER of CBT versus treatment as usual was £6,376/QALY, reflecting the amount of money saved per QALY sacrificed by adding CBT in addition to treatment as usual. This value is below the NICE cost-effectiveness threshold of £20,000–£30,000 per QALY gained (NICE, 2007b). At this threshold, according to the results of the study, treatment as usual alone is more cost effective than CBT in addition to treatment as usual (as it costs only £6,000 more than CBT per extra QALY gained). Probabilistic sensitivity analysis demonstrated that the probability of CBT being cost effective was 53% at a cost-effectiveness threshold of £2,000/QALY; this probability fell with increasing values of the cost-effectiveness threshold.

The results of this analysis indicate that CBT is unlikely to be a cost-effective option for people with borderline personality disorder. One potential limitation of the analysis is the use of EQ-5D for generation of QALYs; as already discussed, this is a generic instrument that may have failed to capture changes in health-related quality of life of people with borderline personality disorder. This hypothesis is supported by the fact that CBT in addition to treatment as usual was shown to be significantly more effective than treatment as usual alone in a number of secondary clinical outcomes assessed in the study, such as positive symptom distress, state anxiety, dysfunctional beliefs and quantity of suicidal acts (Davidson *et al.*, 2006a). On the other hand, the difference in QALYs between the two interventions was not statistically significant, and therefore may not exist in reality.

Overview of the economic analysis conducted by Van Asselt and colleagues, 2008

Van Asselt and colleagues (2008) performed an economic analysis alongside a multi-centre RCT conducted in the Netherlands (GIESEN-BLOO2006) to assess the cost effectiveness of schema-focused cognitive therapy versus transference-focused psychotherapy in people with borderline personality disorder. This study was included in the guideline's systematic review of the clinical literature. The study population consisted of 86 people with borderline personality disorder and the analysis adopted a societal perspective. Costs included healthcare costs (such as intervention costs, other psychological treatment, hospital, primary and community care, medication and alternative therapies), social service costs, costs of informal care and out-of-pocket expenses, as well as productivity losses. Outcomes were expressed as the proportion of people recovered according to the BPDSI-IV and as number of QALYs gained; the latter were generated based on EQ-5D scores reported by the study participants, using preferences elicited from the UK general population. The time horizon of the analysis was 4 years.

Overall, schema-focused cognitive therapy was less costly than transference-focused psychotherapy over the 4 years of the analysis (total cost per person of €37,826 versus €46,795, respectively, in 2000 prices), but this difference in total costs was not statistically significant. Schema-focused cognitive therapy resulted in a higher proportion of people recovered compared with transference-focused psychotherapy: 52% of people under schema-focused cognitive therapy recovered according to the BPDSI versus 29% of people treated with transference-focused psychotherapy. Logistic regression analysis with treatment group and BPDSI baseline score as covariates revealed a significant effect in favour of schema-focused cognitive therapy. In contrast, schema-focused cognitive therapy produced a lower number of QALYs compared with transference-focused psychotherapy (2.15 versus 2.27, respectively), although this difference was not statistically significant.

In terms of proportion of people recovered, schema-focused cognitive therapy dominated transference-focused psychotherapy because it was more effective and less costly. Probabilistic analysis using bootstrap methods indicated that, regardless of the level of WTP (that is, the cost-effectiveness threshold), the probability of schema-focused cognitive therapy being cost effective was over 90%. On the other hand, expressing outcome in the form of QALYs resulted in schema-focused cognitive therapy being less effective and less costly than transference-focused psychotherapy, with an ICER of €90,457 per QALY. This means that schema-focused cognitive therapy saved €90,457 per QALY lost relative to transference-focused psychotherapy. Therefore, if the decision-maker had a WTP above €90,457 per QALY, then transference-focused psychotherapy would be the preferred therapy; for lower levels of WTP schema-focused cognitive therapy would be the cost-effective option. Probabilistic analysis showed that the probability of schema-focused cognitive therapy being cost effective was 84% at a WTP of €20,000 per QALY, with the probability decreasing with increasing levels of WTP.

Secondary sensitivity analyses showed that overall results in terms of the proportion of people recovered were robust to completers' analyses, imputation of missing values, and regression analyses undertaken to correct difference in costs at baseline. On the other hand, the ICER of schema-focused cognitive therapy versus transference-focused psychotherapy was sensitive to the above parameters: using, for example, the baseline values for imputation of missing data, schema-focused cognitive therapy became the dominant strategy (it was more effective and less costly than transference-focused psychotherapy). The probability of schema-focused cognitive therapy being cost effective in secondary analyses ranged from 55 to 95% at a cost- effectiveness threshold of €40,000 per QALY.

In this case, the potential inappropriateness of EQ-5D as a measure of health-related quality of life in people with borderline personality disorder must be emphasised.

Overview of the economic analysis conducted by Hall and colleagues, 2001
Hall and colleagues (2001) examined the healthcare costs incurred by 30 people with borderline personality disorder 12 months before starting and after completing psychodynamic interpersonal therapy. The study was conducted in Australia. Costs consisted of emergency hospital and ambulatory care, inpatient care, diagnostic tests and medication. Intervention costs were also measured. It was assumed that psychodynamic interpersonal therapy was provided by trainee therapists.

The average total cost per person over 12 months before starting psychodynamic interpersonal therapy was AUS$25,526 (1998 prices). The intervention cost was AUS$4,335. Finally, the average total cost per person incurred over 12 months following completing psychodynamic interpersonal therapy was AUS$2,974. Therefore provision of psychodynamic interpersonal therapy to people with borderline personality disorder resulted in a net cost saving of AUS$18,217 per person treated. When separate analyses were undertaken for high users of health services (defined as people who incurred over $10,000 in hospital costs annually) and low users, then the cost saving for high users reached $46,000 per person; however, for low users intervention became cost neutral overall. When the intervention cost was raised to $13,070 per person to reflect therapy provided by specialist psychiatrists, the intervention was cost saving only in the group of high users of healthcare resources.

The study had a pre-post design and no comparator, the study design was subject to bias, and the sample was small. Some resource use data were based on study participants' recall for the previous 12-month period; although these data were tested against medical records, it is possible that this method of data collection introduced bias to the analysis. Because resource use and unit costs refer to the Australian healthcare setting, the results of the study are not directly applicable to the UK context.

Details on the characteristics and results of economic studies on individual psychological interventions for borderline personality disorder are presented in evidence tables in Appendix 15.

5.6 COMBINATION THERAPY

5.6.1 Studies reviewed

The aim of combining pharmacological treatment with a psychological therapy or a psychological therapy programme is to control symptoms while providing a strategy for improved long-term outcomes and to improve retention in pharmacological treatment. Four RCTs were found from searches of electronic databases, none of which were excluded (see Table 21). Three studies compared the antidepressant fluoxetine in combination with a psychological therapy (IPT, CT or DBT) and one compared the antipsychotic olanzapine in combination with DBT.

5.6.2 Fluoxetine plus IPT versus fluoxetine

BELLINO2006B
This a 24-week trial comparing fluoxetine with a combination of fluoxetine plus IPT in 39 outpatients (62% women). All patients had comorbid major depressive disorder and baseline HRSD scores indicate moderate depression at the start of the study. The fluoxetine group received clinical management, although there is no description of what this involved. The number leaving the study early and the number completing the trial do not correspond.[10] The authors concluded that combination therapy was more effective.

The study authors reported outcomes for anxiety, depression and quality of life. For quality of life, the subscales of the Satisfaction Profile (SAT-P) were reported separately because a significant result was found on only two of the subscales (psychological and social functioning). Combination treatment was more effective in reducing depression symptoms (clinician-rated only) and psychological and social functioning aspects of the quality-of-life measure used (self-rated). See Table 22 and Table 23 for the summary evidence profiles. Despite this limited dataset it is likely that quality of life improves for service users as specific symptoms (such as depression, aggression and anxiety) improve.

5.6.3 Fluoxetine plus IPT versus fluoxetine plus CT

BELLINO2007
This is a 24-week trial comparing a combination of fluoxetine plus IPT with a combination of fluoxetine plus CT in 35 outpatients (73% women). All patients had comorbid major depressive disorder and baseline HRSD scores indicate moderate to severe depression at the start of the study.

The study authors reported outcomes for anxiety, depression and quality of life. There was evidence that fluoxetine plus CT improved social functioning compared with fluoxetine plus IPT. All other outcomes were inconclusive, probably because of the low numbers of participants in the study.

See Table 24 and Table 25 for the summary evidence profiles.

---

[10]Clarification was sought from the study authors, but not received.

Table 21: Summary study characteristics of RCTs of combination therapy

	Fluoxetine + IPT versus fluoxetine	Fluoxetine + IPT versus fluoxetine versus CT	Fluoxetine + DBT versus placebo + DBT	Olanzapine + DBT versus placebo + DBT
No. trials (Total participants)	1 RCT (39)	1 RCT (35)	1 RCT (90)	1 RCT (60)
Study IDs	BELLINO2006B	BELLINO2007	SIMPSON2004	SOLER2005
N/% female	39/62	35/73	90/76	60/87
Mean age (or range if not given)	26	30	25	27
Axis I/II disorders	100% major depressive disorder	100% major depressive disorder	60% major depressive disorder; 44% PTSD	Not given, but some depression and anxiety present at baseline*
Setting	Outpatients	Outpatients	Partial hospitalisation	Outpatients
Length of treatment	6 months	6 months	12 weeks	12 weeks
Length of follow-up	None	None	None	None
Notes				Allowed to continue existing medication (benzodiazepines, antidepressants, mood stabilisers) – up to 80% did so

*Based on mean HRSD and HARS scores at baseline.

Table 22: Summary evidence profile for efficacy evidence for fluoxetine + IPT versus fluoxetine

Outcome	Anxiety (clinician-rated)	Depression (clinician-rated)	Depression (self-rated)	QOL: Physical	Psychological	Sleep, food, free time	Social functioning	Work
Effect size	SMD = 0.2 (−0.49, 0.9)	SMD = −0.9 (−1.63, −0.16)	SMD = 0.45 (−0.23, 1.13)	SMD = 0.22 (−0.47, 0.92)	SMD = −0.87 (−1.59, −0.14)	SMD = 0.44 (−0.26, 1.14)	SMD = −1.4 (−2.18, −0.61)	SMD = −0.06 (−0.76, 0.63)*
Evidence quality	Very low	Moderate	Very low	Very low	Moderate	Very low	Moderate	Very low
Number of studies/ participants	(K = 1; n = 32)	(K = 1; n = 32)	(K = 1; n = 34)	(K = 1; n = 32)	(K = 1; n = 32)	(K = 1; n = 32)	(K = 1; n = 32)	(K = 1; n = 32)
Forest plot	Combo 01.01	Combo 04.02	Combo 04.01	Combo 06.01	Combo 06.01	Combo 06.01	Combo 06.01	Combo 06.01

* Based on skewed data.

147

Table 23:   Summary evidence profile for acceptability/tolerability evidence for fluoxetine + IPT

Outcome	Leaving treatment early for any reason	Leaving treatment early because of side effects	Number reporting side effects
Effect size	RD = 0.04 (−0.2, 0.28) 20% versus 16%	RD = 0 (−0.09, 0.09) 0% versus 0%	RD = 0 (−0.09, 0.09) 0% versus 0%
Evidence quality	Very low	Very low	Very low
Number of studies/ participants	(K = 1; n = 39)	(K = 1; n = 39)	(K = 1; n = 39)
Forest plot	Pharm 09.01	Pharm 10.01	Pharm 10.01

5.6.4   Fluoxetine plus DBT versus placebo plus DBT

SIMPSON2004

This is a 12-week placebo-controlled trial of fluoxetine in 25 women with a comorbid axis I disorder (major depressive disorder [60%] and/or PTSD [44%]). All patients were in a day hospital (partial hospitalisation) and received DBT. It is unclear how data from participants not completing the trial were dealt with.

The trial reported outcomes for aggression, anger, anxiety, depression, global functioning, self-injury and suicidality. There was no evidence for efficacy of either arm of the trial on any outcome measure.

See Table 26 and Table 27 for the evidence summary profiles.

5.6.5   Olanzapine plus DBT

SOLER2005

This is a 12-week trial comparing a combination of olanzapine plus DBT with a combination of placebo plus DBT. There were 60 participants (87% women) all with borderline personality disorder. The DBT offered was delivered in weekly 150-minute group sessions and was adapted from the 'standard version' (not referenced) in which 'two of the four types of intervention were applied: skills training and tele-phone calls'. The precise setting of the trial is unclear. Those with an unstable axis I disorder were excluded from the trial at baseline. There were pre-treatment differ-ences between the groups on anxiety scores, so baseline anxiety scores were used as a covariate in an ANCOVA analysis (analysis of covariance) which found a signifi-cant decrease in anxiety in those taking olanzapine. For these participants there was

Table 24: Summary evidence profile for efficacy evidence for fluoxetine + IPT versus fluoxetine + CT

Outcome	Anxiety (clinician-rated)	Depression (clinician-rated)	Depression (self-rated)	QOL: Physical	Psychological	Sleep, food, free time	Social functioning	Work
Effect size	SMD = 0.27 (−0.5, 1.05)	SMD = 0.07 (−0.7, 0.84)	SMD = 0.27 (−0.5, 1.05)	SMD = −0.45 (−1.23, 0.34)	SMD = −0.5 (−1.28, 0.29)	SMD = −0.02 (−0.79, 0.75)	SMD = 1.06 (0.22, 1.89)	SMD = 0.75 (−0.05, 1.55)
Evidence quality	Very low	Very low	Very low	Very low	Very low	Very low	Moderate	Very low
Number of studies/participants	(K = 1; n = 26)	(K = 1; n = 26)	(K = 1; n = 26)	(K = 1; n = 26)	(K = 1; n = 26)	(K = 1; n = 26)	(K = 1; n = 26)	(K = 1; n = 26)
Forest plot	Combo 03.01	Combo 04.02	Combo 04.01	Combo 06.01	Combo 06.01	Combo 06.01	Combo 06.01	Combo 06.01

Table 25: Summary evidence profile for acceptability/tolerability evidence for fluoxetine + IPT versus fluoxetine + CT

Outcome	Leaving treatment early for any reason
Effect size	RD = −0.13 (−0.39, 0.14) 13% versus 25%
Evidence quality	Very low
Number of studies/participants	(K = 1; n = 32)
Forest plot	Pharm 09.01

also a decrease in the frequency of impulsivity/aggressive behaviours compared with those taking placebo. However, they also experienced more weight gain and increased cholesterol levels. It is unclear how many were included in the ITT sample.[11] Baseline levels of depression and anxiety were high.

The trial reported outcomes for anxiety and depression, self-harm/suicide attempts and service use (number of visits to emergency psychiatric services). See Table 28 and Table 29 for the evidence summary profiles. There was no evidence for efficacy of either arm of the trial on any outcome measure.

5.6.6   Clinical summary

There are few studies comparing the effects of adding a drug to a psychological therapy on symptoms of borderline personality disorder. Consequently the evidence for an effect is weak. There was no evidence of an effect on symptoms of adding fluoxetine or olanzapine to DBT. However, adding IPT to fluoxetine showed some efficacy (compared with fluoxetine alone) in reducing depression symptoms (clinician-rated measure only), and psychological and social functioning aspects of the quality-of-life measure used (self-rated measures). However, the number of participants in this latter trial is very low (n = 25) and therefore further research is needed to replicate this finding. In the trial comparing IPT with CT, the effect of treatment on outcomes was inconclusive, other than for social functioning where CT improved scores more than IPT. However, this trial is also very small.

The evidence does not support any recommendations specifically about the combined use of psychotropic medication and a psychological therapy in the treatment of borderline personality disorder.

5.6.7   Health economic evidence

No evidence on the cost effectiveness of combining pharmacological treatment with psychological therapies for people with borderline personality disorder was

---

[11]Clarification was sought from the study authors, but not received.

Table 26: Summary evidence profile for fluoxetine + DBT versus placebo + DBT

Outcome	Anger (clinician-rated)	Aggression (clinician-rated)	Anxiety (clinician-rated)	Depression (self-rated)	Global functioning	Self-injury subscale of OAS	Suicidality subscale of OAS
Effect size	SMD = −0.55 (−1.45, 0.35)*	SMD = −0.59 (−1.5, 0.31)*	SMD = 0.15 (−0.73, 1.03)	SMD = 0.76 (−0.16, 1.68)*	SMD = 0.06 (−0.82, 0.94)	SMD = 0.03 (−0.85, 0.92)*	SMD = 0.44 (−0.46, 1.33)*
Evidence quality	Very low	Very low	Very low	Very low	Very low	Very low	Very low
Number of studies/ participants	(K = 1; n = 20)	(K = 1; n = 20)	(K = 1; n = 20)	(K = 1; n = 20)	(K = 1; n = 20)	(K = 1; n = 20)	(K = 1; n = 20)
Forest plot	Combo 02.01	Combo 01.01	Combo 03.01	Combo 04.01	Combo 04.02	Combo 07.01	Combo 07.01

*Based on skewed data.

151

Psychological and psychosocial treatments

Table 27: Summary evidence profile for acceptability/tolerability evidence for fluoxetine + DBT

Outcome	Leaving treatment early for any reason	Leaving treatment early because of side effects	Number reporting side effects
Effect size	RD = 0.1 (−0.22, 0.41) 25% versus 15%	RD = 0 (−0.14, 0.14) 0% versus 0%	RD = 0 (−0.14, 0.14) 0% versus 0%
Evidence quality	Very low	Very low	Very low
Number of studies/ participants	(K = 1; n = 25)	(K = 1; n = 25)	(K = 1; n = 25)
Forest plot	Combo 09.01	Combo 10.01	Combo 11.01

Table 28: Summary evidence profile for olanzapine + DBT versus placebo + DBT

Outcome	Anxiety	Depression (clinician-rated)	Self-harm/ suicide attempts	Service use
Effect size	SMD = −0.23 (−0.74, 0.28)	SMD = −0.35 (−0.86, 0.16)	SMD = 0.15 (−0.36, 0.65)	SMD = 0.04 (−0.08, 0.16)
Evidence quality	Very low	Very low	Very low	Moderate
Number of studies/ participants	(K = 1; n = 60)	(K = 1; n = 60)	(K = 1; n = 60)	(K = 1; n = 60)
Forest plot	Combo 03.01	Combo 04.02	Combo 07.01	Combo 08.01

Table 29: Summary evidence profile for acceptability/tolerability evidence for olanzapine + DBT versus placebo + DBT

Outcome	Number reporting side effects	Weight gain
Effect size	RD = 0 (−0.06, 0.06) 0% versus 0%	WMD = 2.79 (1.36, 4.22)
Evidence quality	Very low	Moderate
Number of studies/participants	(K = 1; n = 60)	(K = 1; n = 60)
Forest plot	Combo 11.02	Combo 12.01

identified from the systematic search of the economic literature. Details on the methods used for the systematic review of economic literature are described in Chapter 3.

5.7   PSYCHOLOGICAL THERAPY PROGRAMMES

5.7.1   Description of psychological therapy programmes

Dialectical behaviour therapy (DBT; Linehan, 1993) is a multi-modal treatment programme which was first developed for women who self-harm, and has since been applied to other populations. Four stages of treatment are described: (1) pre-treatment and achieving behavioural control, (2) emotionally processing the past, (3) resolving ordinary problems in living and (4) capacity to experience sustained joy. Service users are unlikely to obtain treatment in the last two stages in most public healthcare settings. Research in DBT has focused on the first two stages with the aim of achieving behavioural control to help the individual develop and sustain motivation for treatment while reducing suicidal behaviours, non-suicidal self-injury and other impulsive behaviours (for example, substance misuse and binge eating). Treatment of other psychiatric diagnoses and other seriously destabilising behaviours are also targeted for treatment.

Weekly individual therapy and a weekly psychoeducational and skills training group are offered concurrently for a contracted period (usually 1 year). The key principles of stage 1 treatment involve moving flexibly between acceptance-based procedures (for example, validation and mindfulness) and behavioural change strategies (which include behavioural and solution analysis). If appropriate, and when service users are more stable and have made effective connections with care providers, they may proceed to second stage treatment (emotional experiencing and reprocessing of past trauma).

Solutions from four sets of cognitive behavioural procedures are used: skills training, contingency management, exposure and cognitive modification. Dialectical strategies, that encompass aspects of both acceptance and change (for example, use of metaphor and paradox) are an integral feature of the treatment. The DBT 'package' also includes weekly supervision and consultation meetings for the therapists, who work as a team, and telephone consultation, where therapists are available to patients outside office hours for 'coaching'.

Mentalisation-based therapy (MBT) and partial hospitalisation (Bateman & Fonagy, 1999) is based on an understanding of borderline personality disorder as a disorder of the self resulting from developmental disturbance of attachment, leading to a failure in mentalisation (the capacity to understand one's own and others' mental states). The intervention is aimed at increasing the self-reflective capacity of the patient. In psychoanalytically-oriented partial hospitalisation, treatment is in the context of a day hospital and consists of many elements, including weekly individual therapy, thrice-weekly group analytic therapy, weekly expressive therapy with psychodrama, and a weekly community meeting, for a maximum of 18 months. The method has more recently been developed for use in outpatient settings.

153

5.7.2   RCT evidence

The majority of the RCTs of psychological therapy programmes were of DBT, with one trial of MBT/partial hospitalisation.

Dialectical behaviour therapy (DBT)
Nine RCTs of DBT met inclusion criteria with two being excluded (see Appendix 16). Trials all followed the manualised treatment designed by Linehan (1993), although several modified it. In two trials this was for substance-dependent populations (LINEHAN1999, 2002) and these trials were not included in the main review of RCTs because these populations are outside the scope of the guideline. However, since substance misuse and dependence are important issues in the treatment of people with borderline personality disorder, the studies are discussed in the narrative.

There was a range of patient populations represented in the included trials: outpatients (CLARKIN2004, LINEHAN1991, VANDENBOSCH2002); primary care (KOONS2001); and referrals to a community mental health outpatient clinic following emergency department treatment for a suicide attempt (TURNER2000). CLARKIN2004 was a three-armed trial of DBT, transference-focused psychotherapy and modified psychodynamic supportive psychotherapy, but included no extractable data. Data from CLARKIN2004 were supplied by study authors since no extractable data were available in the published reports. The data supplied were estimated mean endpoint data calculated from ordinary least squares regression based on the origin and slope of each participant assuming 12 months' treatment. The primary outcome of the study was the rate of change on each outcome for each therapy separately. The authors refused permission to use thier data to calculate effect sizes to make comparisons with other studies. Therefore this study could not be considered further (see section 5.5.2). In addition the study had no treatment-as-usual arm and data were given for only 61 of the total 90 participants randomised. Further details of the included studies (including the two in substance-dependent populations) are in Table 30.

Mentalisation-based therapy (MBT) and day hospital treatment
One trial reported a treatment combining MBT with day hospital treatment (BATEMAN1999). See Table 31 for study characteristics.

Evidence profile for psychological therapy programmes
A wide range of outcomes were reported, which also included some follow-up data. The summary evidence profiles are in the tables below.

Compared with treatment as usual, psychological therapy programmes showed some effect on anxiety, depression and symptoms of borderline personality disorder, although the evidence quality was moderate. These interventions also retained people in treatment compared with treatment as usual. People with borderline personality disorder also reported better employment outcomes (number of years in employment) following a psychological therapy programme (specifically MBT with partial hospitalisation) at 5-year follow-up.

Table 30: Summary study characteristics of RCTs of DBT

Study ID	N	Population	Standard DBT or adapted?	Length of treatment protocol	Manu-alised?	Number of sessions	Therapist experienced?	Comparator	Comparator details	Other interventions
CARTER unpublished	76	Borderline personality disorder	Modified but modification unclear	1 year but outcomes taken at 6 months	Yes	Weekly (individual and group)	Not reported	Waitlist	N/A	
CLARKIN2004[†]	90	Borderline personality disorder	Standard	1 year	Yes	Weekly (individual and group)	Yes	(1) Transference-focused psychotherapy (2) Supportive psychotherapy	(1) Structured 2× weekly sessions (2) 1 or 2× weekly sessions	Medication as needed
KOONS2001	28	Borderline personality disorder (women veterans)	Standard	6 months	Yes	Weekly (individual and group)	Yes	TAU	Weekly individual therapy at discretion of therapist plus supportive/ psychoeduca-tional groups	–
LINEHAN1991	63	Borderline personality disorder and parasuicidal	Standard	1 year	Yes	Weekly (individual and group)	Yes	TAU	Referral to other therapy	Medication tapered off

Continued

155

Table 30: *(Continued)*

Study ID	N	Population	Standard DBT or adapted?	Length of treatment protocol	Manu-alised?	Number of sessions	Therapist experienced?	Comparator	Comparator details	Other interventions
LINEHAN2006	101	Borderline personality disorder and self-harm	Standard	1 year	Yes	Weekly (individual and group)	–	Community treatment by experts	1 session per week; similar to TAU, so treatment uncontrolled, but therapist characteristics controlled for	–
TURNER2000	24	Borderline personality disorder	Modified to include psychodynamic techniques and skills training in individual sessions	1 year	Yes	Weekly or twice weekly (between 49 and 84 sessions)	–	Client-centred therapy	2× weekly; emphasises patient's sense of aloneness and provides supportive atmosphere for individuation - 1) increased support during crises, 2) problem assessment, 3) supportive treatment, and 4) termination	Drugs as needed
VAN DEN BOSCH2002	64	Borderline personality disorder (women with/without substance misuse)	Standard	1 year	Yes	Weekly (individual and group)	–	TAU	Ongoing outpatient treatment from original referral source	–

†3-armed trial.

Table 31: Summary study characteristics of RCTs of MBT/day hospital treatment

	Partial-hospitalisation/MBT
No. trials (Total participants)	1 RCT (44)
Study IDs	BATEMAN1999
N/% female	44/50
Mean age (or range if not given)	32
Axis I/II disorders	100% borderline personality disorder
Comparator	Standard care
Setting	Day hospital
Length of treatment	18 months
Length of follow-up	5 years

Psychological therapy programmes also showed some benefit on the rate of self-harm and suicidal ideation, with benefits persisting at follow-up (measured at 5 years for MBT with partial hospitalisation only). See Table 33. One study of DBT (in opiate-dependent participants), LINEHAN2002, did not provide extractable data in the paper, although reported no effect of treatment on parasuicide rates of treatment (measured using PHI).

Psychological therapy programmes also had some benefit on service-use outcomes such as hospital admissions and emergency department visits. MBT with partial hospitalisation also reduced the amount of psychiatric outpatient treatment required and the number of years on three or more drugs at 5-year follow-up (see Table 34).

There was some benefit for psychological therapy programmes on social functioning outcomes on employment performance, but not on other outcomes (see Table 35).

Psychological therapy programmes in people with borderline personality disorder and substance dependence

In addition to the RCT evidence of psychological therapy programmes in people with a diagnosis of borderline personality disorder, two RCTs reported DBT in people with comorbid substance dependence (LINEHAN1999, 2002). These reported a range of drug-related outcomes. DBT helped to improve the proportion of days abstinent from drugs and alcohol (at endpoint and 16-month follow-up), but did not increase the proportion of people with clean urinalyses or self-reported days abstinent from heroin.

Table 32: Summary evidence profile for psychological therapy programmes versus treatment as usual: general outcomes

Symptom	Anger	Anxiety	Depression	Mental distress	Borderline personality disorder symptoms	Employment related (no. years employment)	General functioning	Leaving treatment early because of side effects
Therapy	DBT	DBT (MBT at follow-up)	DBT (MBT for self-rated)	MBT	DBT (MBT at follow-up)	MBT	MBT	DBT MBT
Clinician-rated effect size	SMD = −0.59 (−1.52, 0.35)	SMD = −1.22 (−1.92, −0.52)†	SMD = −0.57 (−0.92, −0.22)*	SMD = −0.39 (−1.03, 0.26)	SMD = −0.6 (−2.34, 1.14)*	–	–	RR = 0.61 (0.43, 0.86) (23% versus 39%)
Quality of evidence	Very low	Moderate	Moderate	Very low	Moderate	–	–	Moderate
Number of studies/participants	(K = 1; n = 19)	(K = 1; n = 38)	(K = 3; n = 133)	(K = 1; n = 38)	(K = 1; n = 20)	–	–	(K = 5; n = 294)
Forest plot	Psych 01.01	Psych 01.02	Psych 01.04	Psych 01.9	Psych 01.12	–	–	Psych 01.16
Clinician-rated effect size at follow-up 1	SMD = −0.91 (−1.99, 0.18) (12 months)	SMD = −3.49 (−4.63, −2.36) (18 months)	–	SMD = −2.09 (−2.93, −1.25) (18 months)	–	–	–	–
Quality of evidence	Moderate	Moderate	–	Very low	–	–	–	–
Number of studies/participants	(K = 1; n = 15)	(K = 1; n = 33)	–	(K = 1; n = 36)	–	–	–	–
Forest plot	Psych 01.01	Psych 01.02	–	Psych 01.9	–	–	–	–
Clinician-rated effect size at follow-up 2	SMD = −0.59 (−1.52, 0.35) (24 months)	–	–	–	SMD = −9.6 (−12.83, −6.38)* (5 years)	WMD = −2 (−3.29, −0.71)* (5 years)	SMD = −0.74 (−1.38, −0.1) (5 years)	–

Quality of evidence	Very low	—	—	—	Moderate	Moderate	Moderate	—
Number of studies/participants	(K = 1; n = 19)	—	—	—	(K = 1; n = 41)	(K = 1; n = 41)	(K = 1; n = 41)	—
Forest plot	Psych 01.01	—	—	—	Psych 01.12	Psych 01.14	Psych 01.15	—
Self-rated effect size	—	SMD = −0.7 (−1.53, 0.13)*	SMD = −1.49 (−1.99, −0.99)*	—	—	—	—	—
Quality of evidence	—	Moderate	Moderate	—	—	—	—	—
Number of studies/participants	—	(K = 1; n = 24)	(K = 3; n = 82)	—	—	—	—	—
Forest plot	—	Psych 01.03	Psych 01.05	—	—	—	—	—
Self-rated effect size at follow-up	—	—	SMD = −1.15 (−1.85, −0.45) (18 months)	—	—	—	—	—
Quality of evidence	—	—	Moderate	—	—	—	—	—
Number of studies/participants	—	—	(K = 1; n = 38)	—	—	—	—	—
Forest plot	—	—	Psych 01.06	—	—	—	—	—

*Based on skewed data.

[†]2 different measures of anxiety were reported which the GDG did not consider could be combined (HARS and STAI - state anxiety). Since the effect sizes from both measures were very similar, only one is reported here (STAI - state anxiety).

Table 33: Summary evidence profile for psychological therapy programmes versus treatment as usual: self-harm and suicide-related outcomes

Outcome	Self-harm	Self-harm and suicidal acts reported together	Self-harm with suicidal intent	Beck suicidal ideation scale	Suicide attempts	No. of A&E visits (presumed because of self-harm)
Therapy	DBT	DBT	DBT	DBT	MBT	MBT
Continuous data effect sizes	WMD = −0.17 (−2.15, 1.82)*	WMD (random effects) = −2.50 (−6.63, 1.62)*	WMD = −0.2 (−0.55, 0.15)*	SMD = −1.04 (−1.68, −0.4)*	–	–
Quality of evidence	Moderate	Very low	Very low	Moderate	–	–
Number of studies/participants	(K = 3; n = 185)	(K = 2; n = 44)	(K = 1; n = 44)	(K = 2; n = 44)	–	–
Forest plot	Psych 01.07	Psych 01.07	Psych 01.07	Psych 01.07	–	–
Continuous data effect sizes at follow-up 1	–	–	–	–	SMD = −0.63 (−1.26, 0)* (5 years)	SMD = −1.4 (−2.09, −0.7)* (5 years)
Quality of evidence	–	–	–	–	Moderate	Moderate
Number of studies/participants	–	–	–	–	(K = 1; n = 41)	(K = 1; n = 41)
Forest plot	–	–	–	–	Psych 01.07	Psych 01.07

	DBT, MBT			DBT, MBT (MBT only at follow-up)	
Therapy		–	–		–
Dichotomous data effect sizes	RR = 0.54 (0.34, 0.86) (33% versus 58%)	–	–	RR (random effects) = 0.37 (0.16, 0.87) (15% versus 37%)	–
Quality of evidence	Moderate	–	–	Moderate	–
Number of studies/ participants	(K = 2; n = 96)	–	–	(K = 4; n = 260)	–
Forest plot	Psych 01.8	–	–	Psych 01.8	–
Dichotomous data at follow-up 1		–	–	RR = 0.31 (0.14, 0.7) (23% versus 74%) (5 years)	–
Quality of evidence	–	–	–	Moderate	–
Number of studies/ participants	–	–	–	(K = 1; n = 41)	–
Forest plot	–	–	–	Psych 01.8	–

*Based on skewed data.

Table 34: Summary evidence profile for psychological therapy programmes versus treatment as usual: service-use outcomes

Outcomes are based on the number of participants having at least one visit or admission unless stated

Outcome	Emergency department visits for psychiatric reasons	Emergency department visits for suicide ideation (endpoint)	Hospital admission for psychiatric reasons	Hospital admission for suicidal ideation	Hospital admission for self-harm	No. on medication at endpoint	No. years further psychiatric outpatient treatment	No. years on three or more drugs (5-year follow-up)
Therapy	DBT	DBT	DBT	DBT	DBT	MBT	MBT	MBT
Continuous data effect sizes	–	–	WMD (random effects) = −5.42 (−14.01, 3.17)*†	–	WMD = −0.72 (−1.97, 0.53)*†	–	–	–
Quality of evidence	–	–	Very low	–	Moderate	–	–	–
Number of studies/participants	–	–	(K = 3; n = 136)	–	(K = 1; n = 73)	–	–	–
Forest plot	–	–	Psych 01.11	–	Psych 01.11	–	–	–
Continuous data at follow-up 1	–	–	WMD = −0.45 (−0.57, −0.33) (24 months)*	–	–	–	–	–
Quality of evidence	–	–	Moderate	–	–	–	–	–
Number of studies/participants	–	–	(K = 1; n = 37)	–	–	–	–	–
Forest plot	–	–	Psych 01.11	–	–	–	–	–
Continuous data at follow-up 2	WMD = −5.63 (−8.23, −3.03) (5 years)	–	WMD = −5.93 (−8.47, −3.39)*† (5 years)	–	–	–	WMD = −1.6 (−2.64, −0.56)* (5 years)	WMD = −1.7 (−2.56, −0.84)* (5 years)
Quality of evidence	Moderate	–	Moderate	–	–	–	Moderate	Moderate

Number of studies/participants	(K = 1; n = 41)	—	(K = 1; n = 41)	—	—	—	(K = 1; n = 73)	(K = 1; n = 73)
Forest plot	Psych 01.11	—	Psych 01.11	—	—	—	Psych 01.11	Psych 01.11
Dichotomous data effect sizes	RR = 0.61 (0.42, 0.89)	RR = 0.48 (0.22, 1.04)	RR = 0.54 (0.32, 0.91)†	RR = 0.28 (0.11, 0.71)	RR = 0.82 (0.36, 1.89)	RR = 0.47 (0.25, 0.88)	—	—
Quality of evidence	Moderate	Moderate	Moderate	Moderate	Very low	Moderate	—	—
Number of studies/participants	(K = 1; n = 89)	(K = 1; n = 89)	(K = 2; n = 162)	(K = 1; n = 89)	(K = 1; n = 73)	(K = 1; n = 38)	—	—
Forest plot	Psych 01.10	Psych 01.10	Psych 01.10	Psych 01.10	Psych 01.10	Psych 01.10	—	—
Dichotomous data at follow-up 1	RR = 0.65 (0.35, 1.23) (24 months)	RR = 0.63 (0.21, 1.91) (24 months)	RR = 1.05 (0.47, 2.32) (24 months)	RR = 0.89 (0.33, 2.41) (24 months)				
Quality of evidence	Very low	Very low	Very low	Very low	—	—	—	—
Number of studies/participants	(K = 1; n = 81)	(K = 1; n = 81)	(K = 1; n = 81)	(K = 1; n = 81)	—	—	—	—
Forest plot	Psych 01.10	Psych 01.10	Psych 01.10	Psych 01.10	—	—	—	—

*Based on skewed data.

†Based on number of days' admission.

Table 35: Summary evidence profile for psychological therapy programmes versus treatment as usual: social functioning outcomes

Outcome	Social Adjustment Scale (SAS) – work performance (18 months)	SAS – anxious rumination (18 months)	SAS – employment performance (18 months)
Therapy	DBT	DBT	DBT
Continuous data effect sizes	SMD = −0.33 (−0.9, 0.24)	SMD = −0.71 (−1.56, 0.14)	SMD = −0.8 (−1.4, −0.2)
Quality of evidence	Moderate	Very low	Moderate
Number of studies/ participants	(K = 1; n = 14)	(K = 1; n = 13)	(K = 1; n = 10)
Forest plot	Psych 01.13	Psych 01.13	Psych 01.13
Continuous data at follow-up 1	SMD = −0.44 (−1.18, 0.3)	SMD = −0.44 (−1.42, 0.54)	SMD = −1.04 (−1.73, −0.35)
Quality of evidence	Very low	Very low	Moderate
Number of studies/ participants	(K = 1; n = 14)	(K = 1; n = 13)	(K = 1; n = 8)
Forest plot	Psych 01.13	Psych 01.13	Psych 01.13

5.7.3   Non-RCT evidence of psychological therapy programmes

Seven non-RCTs were found of psychological therapy programmes, all of DBT. In addition, the outline findings of an unpublished study were also made available to the GDG (ANDREA unpub). Study characteristics are in Table 36.

Non-RCT evidence of DBT

ALPER2001

This paper presents outcome data on a case series of 15 'court committed' women with a clinical diagnosis of borderline personality disorder who underwent treatment with nurse-led DBT in an inpatient forensic setting. There was a reduction in the frequency of self-harm over the 4-week period. In addition, the authors conducted qualitative interviews with four nurses to describe their experience of administering

Table 36: Non-randomised studies of psychological therapy programmes

	Psychological therapy programmes
No. trials (Total participants)	8 non-randomised studies (397)
Study IDs	(1) ALPER2001 (2) ANDREA unpublished (3) BARLEY1993 (4) CUNNINGHAM2004 (5) HARLEY2007 (6) LANIUS2003 (7) MCQUILLAN2005 (8) PRENDERGAST2007
N/% female	(1) 15/100 (2) 33 (3) 130/79 (4) 14/100 (5) 49/92 (6) 18/100 (7) 127/81 (8) 11/100
Mean age (or range if not given)	(1) 22–42 (2) Not available (3) 16–57 (4) 39 (5) 40 (6) 35 (7) 31 (8) 36
% participants with borderline personality disorder	(1)–(5) 100 (6) 100 borderline personality disorder and PTSD (7) 92 (8) 100
Research design	(1) Case series (2) Prospective cohort study (3) Cohort study (4) Qualitative study of patients' views (5)–(8) Cohort study
Setting	(1) Inpatients, US (2) Partial hospitalisation, Netherlands (3) Inpatients, UK

Continued

Table 36: *(Continued)*

	Psychological therapy programmes
	(4)–(5) Outpatients, US (6) Mostly outpatients, Canada (7) Outpatients, Switzerland (8) Community, Australia
Length of follow-up (from end of treatment)	(1) No follow-up (2) 18 months (3)–(8) No follow-up

DBT; their responses were uniformly positive. Despite the considerable methodological limitations, the authors main conclusion was that 'this study provided evidence that DBT is an effective treatment approach for people diagnosed with borderline personality disorder'.

ANDREA unpublished

This was a non-comparative study of MBT in 33 people with borderline personality disorder. Treatment lasted 18 months and a further 18 months of follow-up data were collected. The study found that suicide attempts and acts of self-harm were reduced, as was service use. It also reported improvement in quality of life, depression symptoms, general distress, and social and interpersonal functioning.

BARLEY1993

This paper describes the modification and application of outpatient DBT in an American inpatient setting. According to the authors, this was the first time that the use of DBT in an inpatient setting had been described. Most of the paper is a descriptive account of the treatment programme and underlying theory, however, some longitudinal data is also presented. 'Parasuicide rates' in a sample of 130 patients admitted to the DBT personality disorder inpatient unit are compared with those in an unspecified number of patients admitted to a general adult psychiatry unit that maintained a 'consistent non-DBT' treatment programme over a parallel 43-month period. The median age of patients treated on the DBT unit was 30 years (range 16–57) and 79% were female; their personality status is not described, other than that they were 'largely severely parasuicidal borderline patients'. No descriptive information is given about the patients who were admitted to the general adult psychiatry unit. The authors compared the frequency of self-inflicted injuries and overdoses in three time intervals over the 43-month follow-up period: pre-introduction of DBT (19 months); introduction of DBT (10 months); and a period of active treatment (14 months). The authors present the results of a one-way ANOVA (analysis of variance) to show that there was a statistically significant change ($p = 0.007$) in the frequency of parasuicide events across the three time periods in those treated on the DBT unit. There was no statistically significant change in the general adult group ($p = 0.09$). On the basis of these data, the authors conclude that 'DBT has been associated with a significant reduction in the rate of parasuicide'. In terms of adding to the evidence on the effectiveness of DBT for borderline personality disorder, no definitive conclusions can be made because the study is of poor quality. No information is given about the general adult control group, the data collection methods used or adherence to treatment or drop-outs and the reduction in self-harm may simply have been explained by these methodological limitations. The paper does, however demonstrate that it is feasible to apply DBT in an inpatient setting. The acceptability of inpatient DBT to the patients was not examined.

CUNNINGHAM2004

This qualitative study, conducted within an assertive community treatment team in Michigan County, aimed to gain further understanding about what makes DBT effective. Sixteen percent of the team's caseload consisted of people with borderline personality disorder and 14 women with the disorder were interviewed. Their involvement in the DBT programme ranged from 6 months to 3 years (median 15 months) and their ages ranged from 23 to 61 years (median 39). All had previously engaged in parasuicidal behaviour and 11 out of 14 had been previously hospitalised. The frequency of hospitalisation and parasuicidal behaviour within the group had diminished over time. All qualitative interviews were conducted by trained students from the local university who had no official connection with the treating team. All interviews were semi-structured, tape recorded and transcribed. The components of DBT (individual therapy, skills training and skills coaching) were each explored in the interviews. Data analysis was aimed at identifying common themes running through the interviews.

All the clients believed that DBT had a positive impact on their lives and all reported that behavioural changes had occurred and that they were leading more manageable lives. They all talked about a decrease in levels of self-harm and reported that they were better at interacting with others. They also believed that they had a better ability to modulate their emotions and pursue non-mood dependent goals. Although some felt that their level of suffering had diminished, most reported that they continued to suffer. Nevertheless, clients consistently expressed higher levels of hope and fundamentally they reported that DBT had helped them to build a 'life worth living'.

HARLEY2007

This paper describes a non-randomised, naturalistic study of 49 American patients with DSM-IV borderline personality disorder, treated within a modified outpatient DBT programme. The authors compared pre-post treatment outcomes for those allocated to a DBT skills group and DBT individual therapy with those allocated to the skills group and non-DBT individual therapy. Sixty-seven patients completed intake procedures, of whom 49 (73%) were eligible to participate in the study. In addition to meeting SCID-II criteria for borderline personality disorder, inclusion criteria for treatment in the skills group included the identification of appropriate behavioural goals and commitment to DBT goals via a written contract (the number of referred patients who were excluded is not described). Patients entering the DBT programme were contracted to participate for one full cycle of the skills group and to attend concurrent weekly individual therapy. All patients completed the Personality Assessment Inventory (PAI; a 344-item self-report measure of borderline personality disorder psychopathology) and the Schwartz Outcome Scale (SOS; a 10-item self-report measure of outcomes including life satisfaction). Fifty-one percent (n = 25) dropped out of group treatment and pre-post comparisons are only provided on those who completed treatment. Sixteen out of 23 (70%) group participants whose individual therapists were located outside the hospital system failed to complete a full cycle of group treatment. This compared with nine out of 26 (35%) group participants whose individual therapists were 'in-system'. After completion of one skills group cycle, statistically significant reductions in symptom severity were observed on each of the PAI subscales and SOS, with the exception of the PAI anxiety subscale. When the analyses were re-run using only those patients receiving non-DBT individual therapy (n = 14), the results remained the same.

This study demonstrated that a modified DBT programme for patients with borderline personality disorder could be successfully implemented in a 'real-world, resource limited setting'. Patients completing one cycle of skills treatment showed significant improvement in the severity of their psychopathology, although no conclusions can be drawn about treatment efficacy as patients were highly selected for treatment and there was no control group. It is possible that 'in-system therapists' enhance retention in a treatment programme by improving coordination of care between individual and group therapists.

LANIUS2003

This letter presents some brief descriptive data from a case series of 18 Canadian women who fulfilled DSM-IV criteria (on clinical grounds) for borderline personality disorder and PTSD and who were treated with DBT in a predominantly outpatient setting. The sample included women with comorbidity including bipolar disorder, major depression and eating disorders. The authors examined the patients' use of resources and employment status pretreatment and 1 year after a course of DBT. One-year outcome data showed that there was a 65% decrease in duration of inpatient stay, a 45% decrease in the number of emergency room visits, a 153% increase in outpatient visits and a 700% (n = 1 pre-treatment; n = 8 at 1 year) increase in employment. The main limitations of these data include the absence of any control group and the very small sample size. Little can be concluded from the letter, short of the fact that DBT might be a promising treatment.

MCQUILLAN2005

This study examined pre-post symptom scores in a group of 87 Swiss patients who were 'in crisis' and admitted to an intensive 3-week outpatient DBT programme. Over the 2-year study period, 127 patients were referred to the programme, of whom, 87 (69%) were admitted and 40 were referred elsewhere. All patients were screened for personality disorder using the IPDE screening questionnaire. Patients also completed the BDI, the BHS and the Social Adaptation Self-Evaluation Scale (SASS). Those not recruited for DBT had a greater number of antisocial personality traits. Of the 87 who were admitted, 82% completed the programme and 18% dropped out. Statistically significant improvements were observed in BDI and BHS scores, although there was no significant change in SASS scores.

There are confusing disparities between the numbers presented in the abstract of the study and those presented in the results (six patients are unaccounted for in the results). In addition, the study failed to achieve its main aim (to examine effectiveness of this form of DBT) because of its naturalistic design and the absence of a control group. However, a high proportion of the referred sample was recruited for treatment, which increases the generalisability of the findings. Moreover, the majority of people completed the course of treatment and there were significant improvements in hopelessness and depressive symptoms. These findings suggest that outpatient DBT is deliverable and may be helpful for people with borderline personality disorder who are in crisis. The effectiveness of such treatment is, however, unclear.

PRENDERGAST2007

This paper describes the 6-month treatment outcomes of a case series of 11 Australian women who met DSM-IV criteria (on clinical grounds) for borderline personality disorder. Their mean age was 37 years and the majority had a comorbid axis 1 diagnosis. They were all treated in the community. Originally, 16 women entered into two DBT programmes, although five dropped out of treatment (these people had more hospital admissions in the previous 6 months than the DBT group). Data is presented on 20 outcomes and although there were improvements at the 5% level at 6 months on nine outcomes, there was no significant change on frequency of self-harm, which was the authors' main outcome variable of interest. Notwithstanding, the authors state that 'DBT is an effective treatment for parasuicidal behaviour'. The main value of the study is that the (non-Linehan affiliated) authors appear to have demonstrated that DBT can be applied in an Australian context. The data are limited in terms of the absence of any control group and the very small sample size.

Summary of non-RCT evidence of DBT

All of the above papers provide some evidence to suggest that it is feasible to apply DBT (with minor modifications described) in a variety of settings (inpatient, outpatient and community). However, none of these papers provides evidence as to whether DBT is an effective treatment for borderline personality disorder. This is because methodological quality was poor – many of the papers reached conclusions that were not justified on the basis of the data presented or the quality of the methods used. The qualitative study (Cunningham *et al.*, 2004) provides some intriguing insights into what might constitute the effective ingredients of DBT.

Non-RCT evidence of other psychological therapy programmes

GABBARD2000

This study monitored 216 patients diagnosed with personality disorder who were admitted to two specialist inpatient units; this represented a sub-sample of those initially entered into the study. Interventions within the milieu therapy included psychodynamic psychotherapy two to three times per week, group therapy, patient and staff groups and daily meetings with a psychiatrist. There were marked differences in patient drop out between the two sites (10.7 versus 75.5%) possibly related to the introduction of

169

managed care. Patient length of stay varied widely with a median of 58 days. Substantial changes, especially on the GAS were reported at the end of treatment and at 1-year follow-up. Outcomes for borderline personality disorder were not reported separately.

LOFFLER-STASTKA2003

Twenty patients with borderline personality disorder, half of whom were male, were treated with psychoanalytically-oriented psychotherapy in an inpatient setting for 6 weeks as a preparation for outpatient psychotherapy. Treatment consisted of an initial diagnostic and clarification phase followed by psychotherapy including individual and group psychoanalytic therapy, group ergotherapy focusing on perceptiveness, music therapy, and skills training. Measures were used to assess anxiety levels (STAI), aggression, interpersonal problems and locus of control. Significant predictors of engagement in further outpatient psychotherapy were being female, having subjective recognition of interpersonal problems and experiencing a generalised negative concept of one's own capacities. High reactive readiness for aggression and thorough conviction of self-efficacy predicted non-engagement in further psychotherapy. A correlation between aggression, belief in capability of one's self and severity of interpersonal problems was found only in those not treated with psychotherapy.

5.7.4   Clinical summary for psychological therapy programmes

The RCT evidence for psychological therapy programmes showed some benefit in reducing symptoms such as anxiety and depression. They also have some benefit on rates of self-harm. Most of the evidence is of moderate quality, and the majority is of DBT, with a single study of MBT with partial hospitalisation. The non-RCT evidence provides support for the feasibility of using DBT in various settings.

5.7.5   Health economics evidence on psychological therapy programmes

The systematic search of economic literature identified two studies assessing the cost effectiveness of psychological therapy programmes for borderline personality disorder (Brazier *et al.*, 2006; Bateman & Fonagy, 2003). Brazier and colleagues (2006) conducted a number of economic analyses to explore the cost effectiveness of various psychological interventions for people with borderline personality disorder. Among their analyses, four explored the cost effectiveness of DBT and one of MBT. Details on the overall economic methods adopted by Brazier and colleagues (2006) are provided in Section 5.3.4. Details on the methods used for the systematic search of the economic literature are described in Chapter 3.

Dialectical behaviour therapy (DBT)
Brazier and colleagues (2006) conducted four economic analyses to explore the cost effectiveness of DBT using data from four respective RCTs. All four RCTs have been included in the systematic review of clinical evidence conducted for this guideline

(TURNER2000; LINEHAN1991; VAN DEN BOSCH2002, KOONS2001; see Table 28 for more details on the study characteristics).

Economic analysis by Brazier and colleagues (2006) based on TURNER2000
TURNER2000 evaluated the clinical effectiveness of DBT versus client-centred therapy in 24 people with borderline personality disorder in the US. The study reported suicidal/self-harming behaviour and BDI scores of participants. The latter were converted into QALYs by Brazier and colleagues (2006), using the mapping function between BDI and EQ-5D. No data were available on resource use apart from some data relating to the provision of the interventions and data on inpatient length of stay; therefore, the regression cost model was applied in order to estimate total costs of the two arms.

According to the results of the economic analysis by Brazier and colleagues (2006), DBT was less costly overall than client-centred therapy (£15,743 versus £20,985, respectively). Extra intervention costs were offset by savings in health, social and criminal justice service costs. At the same time, DBT resulted in significantly fewer parasuicidal events compared with client-centred therapy (2.92 versus 12.33 per person, respectively) and a better health-related quality of life, as expressed in QALYs gained over a year (0.17 versus 0.05). Given the above findings, DBT was the dominant strategy (less costly and more effective than its comparator). Probabilistic sensitivity analysis showed that the probability of DBT being dominant over client-centred therapy (that is, less costly and more effective) was 80% when the measure of outcome was the reduction in parasuicidal events, and 85% when the outcome was the number of QALYs gained. The probability of DBT being cost effective was 85% at a WTP of λ = £5,000 per parasuicidal event avoided, and 90% at a cost effectiveness threshold of λ = £20,000 per QALY. Results were insensitive to changes in the analysis perspective (NICE or societal) and supervision costs.

Economic analysis by Brazier and colleagues (2006) based on LINEHAN1991
LINEHAN1991 compared the clinical effectiveness of DBT compared with treatment as usual in 63 chronically parasuicidal women with borderline personality disorder in the US. The study reported parasuicidal events measured using the PHI. Although some data on BDI were available, these were insufficient and therefore not possible to convert into QALYs. Resource use data and costs were available in another publication; as the study was conducted in the US, Brazier and colleagues (2006) re-estimated costs based on reported resource use and further assumptions, to reflect clinical practice in the UK.

DBT was less costly overall than its comparator (DBT £15,691; treatment as usual £16,898). Additional intervention costs were outweighed by reductions in overall service costs. DBT led to a significantly lower number of parasuicidal events than treatment as usual (6.82 per person versus 33.54, respectively); consequently it was again the dominant strategy. The probability of DBT being dominant over treatment as usual was 53%, whereas the probability of it being cost effective was approximately 60% at a WTP of λ = £5,000 per parasuicidal event avoided. Results were insensitive to changes in the analysis perspective (NICE or societal) and supervision costs.

Economic analysis by Brazier and colleagues (2006) based on VAN DEN BOSCH2002
VAN DEN BOSCH2002 also examined the clinical effectiveness of DBT versus treatment as usual in women with borderline personality disorder with or without comorbid substance misuse. The study was undertaken in the Netherlands in a sample of 47 women. Parasuicidality was measured by the LPC. The number of parasuicide events was estimated by Brazier and colleagues (2006) from LPC trial data provided by the trial investigators. The BDI was not used in this study and therefore estimation of QALYs was not possible. The only data available regarding resource use were those related to interventions assessed and inpatient length of stay. The regression cost model developed by Brazier and colleagues (2006) was applied in this case in order to estimate total costs for the economic model.

DBT was found to be slightly more expensive than treatment as usual (£17,430 versus £16,706, respectively) and resulted in fewer parasuicidal events (16 versus 34.1, respectively). The ICER of DBT versus treatment as usual was £40 per additional parasuicidal event avoided. The probability of DBT being more cost effective than treatment as usual was 65% at any level of WTP per parasuicidal event avoided (that is, at any cost-effectiveness threshold). Results were not affected by adopting the NICE perspective. When the societal perspective was adopted, DBT became the dominant strategy. Results were moderately sensitive to changes in staff supervision costs of the treatment-as-usual arm.

Economic analysis by Brazier and colleagues (2006) based on KOONS2001
KOONS2001 assessed the clinical effectiveness of DBT compared with treatment as usual in 28 women veterans with borderline personality disorder in the US. The number of parasuicide attempts was measured using the PHI. BDI scores were also reported and translated into QALYs by Brazier and colleagues (2006) using the methodology already described in Section 5.3.4. However, as BDI scores were reported at baseline and at 3 and 6 months, it was assumed that the mean BDI scores remained constant between 6 and 12 months in order to estimate QALYs over the time horizon of the economic analysis (that is, 12 months). Apart from resource use information on provision of interventions, no other data were available for this trial (including regarding inpatient stay). In this case, the regression cost model was applied using the number of parasuicidal events as the only factor affecting costs. Brazier and colleagues (2006) acknowledged that this model was even cruder than the other regression model that used parasuicidal events and inpatient stay as predictors of total costs, and therefore the results of this analysis should be interpreted with extreme caution.

DBT was found to be considerably costlier than treatment as usual in this case (£23,439 versus £14,815, respectively). The authors suggested that the difference in cost might be the consequence of using a regression model where the number of parasuicidal events was the only factor affecting costs, while potential difference in inpatient stays was not taken into account. Nevertheless, they stated that the trial report indicated little difference between the arms in terms of hospital admissions. The benefits of DBT compared with treatment as usual were marginally higher: DBT was associated with four parasuicide events and 0.07 QALYs, while treatment as usual was associated with slightly more parasuicide events (4.2) and 0.04 QALYs gained.

The ICER of DBT versus treatment as usual was very high, at £43,124 per parasuicide event avoided, or £273,801 per QALY. The latter is far beyond the cost-effectiveness threshold determined by NICE, which lies between £20,000 and £30,000 per QALY gained (NICE, 2007b). The probability of DBT being cost effective in this analysis was lower than 40% at a cost-effectiveness threshold of £5,000 per parasuicidal event avoided, and around 5% at a cost-effectiveness threshold of £20,000 per QALY. One-way sensitivity analysis demonstrated that results were insensitive to changes in the perspective and only moderately sensitive to changes in supervision costs for treatment as usual.

Overall conclusions and limitations of Brazier and colleagues' (2006) economic analyses of DBT

The above four economic analyses did not lead to the same results: in two (based on TURNER2000 and LINEHAN1991) DBT dominated its comparator (it was more effective and resulted in lower total costs). In one analysis (based on VAN DEN BOSCH2002) it was more effective at a slightly higher cost. These three economic analyses indicated that DBT could be a potentially cost-effective intervention. On the other hand, results based on KOONS2001 suggested that DBT was significantly costlier and only slightly more effective than treatment as usual, with a cost per QALY exceeding the NICE cost-effectiveness threshold. However, lack of any data on inpatient resource use in KOONS2001 led to the need for the development of a regression cost model where the number of parasuicidal events was the sole factor affecting total costs estimated; this may have introduced bias and reduced validity of the findings of the analysis, the results of which, as emphasised by its authors, should be interpreted with extreme caution. Overall, results of the four economic analyses of DBT undertaken by Brazier and colleagues (2006) were characterised by considerable uncertainty, as demonstrated in probabilistic sensitivity analysis.

The analyses by Brazier and colleagues (2006) are characterised by a number of limitations: the study-specific approach limited the robustness, the generalisability and the comparability between the results because the clinical studies referred to slightly different study populations, with varying baseline disease conditions, who received care in different settings. The comparator was not entirely comparable across studies, despite being characterised as treatment as usual in three out of four trials. Although the number of parasuicidal events was a common measure of outcome in all four analyses, the definition of parasuicide was not consistent and therefore the instruments used to capture this measure varied across studies. Moreover, the number of parasuicidal events avoided is a limited measure of outcome that cannot capture the overall health-related quality of life of people with borderline personality disorder. It was possible to model outcomes in the form of QALYs in only two of the four analyses of DBT trials. QALYs were generated by translating available data on BDI scores into EQ-5D profiles. However, as it has been already emphasised, EQ-5D is a generic instrument and appears to be insensitive to changes in health-related quality of life of people with borderline personality disorder.

The clinical studies on which the economic analyses by Brazier and colleagues (2006) were based were very small and characterised by high drop-out rates. Three of the trials (LINEHAN1991, VAN DEN BOSCH2002 and KOONS2001) were conducted outside the UK, in settings where clinical practice and related resource use may be substantially different from the UK context. For this reason, and owing to lack of comprehensive data on resource use, a significant number of assumptions were required in order to estimate cost parameters and populate the economic models according to the UK setting. The use of the regression cost model, which was necessary in order to estimate total costs in three of the four analyses of DBT, further increased the uncertainty characterising the results of the economic analyses.

Given the inconsistency across the results, the high levels of uncertainty and the strong limitations characterising the economic analyses, the authors were unable to draw any firm conclusions from their study. However, they suggested that DBT could be a potentially cost-effective intervention in people with borderline personality disorder.

Mentalisation/day hospital treatment

Two studies assessing the cost effectiveness of mentalisation/day hospital treatment (MBT with partial hospitalisation) were identified in the systematic economic literature review. One study (Bateman & Fonagy, 2003) was carried out alongside an RCT (BATEMAN1999) included in the guideline systematic review of clinical evidence. In addition, Brazier and colleagues (2006) conducted an economic modelling exercise using the same trial.

Bateman & Fonagy (2003)

This study assessed the total costs of MBT with partial hospitalisation compared with treatment as usual, in a sample of 41 people with severe parasuicidal borderline personality disorder, participating in a UK-based RCT (BATEMAN1999). The analysis adopted the perspective of the NHS. The authors collected resource use data on inpatient and outpatient care, partial hospitalisation, medication and emergency room visits. Total costs were estimated for 18 and 36 months following initiation of treatment. Analysis of clinical data had demonstrated that MBT with partial hospitalisation was more effective than treatment as usual, as measured by a number of outcomes such as number of suicide attempts and acts of self-harm, as well as self-reported measures of depression, anxiety, general symptom distress, interpersonal function and social adjustment. Positive outcomes at 18 months remained at 36 months' follow-up. Economic analysis showed that, over the first 18 months, the total annual cost per person was similar in the two arms (MBT $27,303 and treatment as usual $30,976). However, there was a significant reduction in cost associated with provision of MBT in the next 18 months (total annual cost per person based on data from 18–36 months: MBT $3,183 and treatment as usual $15,490). The authors concluded that MBT with partial hospitalisation could lead to great cost savings, especially in the long term. Nevertheless, they acknowledged a number of limitations, such as the small study sample, some problems with randomisation (such as cross-overs and early drop-outs) and the inability to adequately cost community support over the course of treatment.

Economic analysis by Brazier and colleagues (2006) based on BATEMAN1999

Brazier and colleagues (2006) considered data from BATEMAN1999 in one of their economic analyses. The number of suicide and self-harm events was estimated by data supplied by the trial investigators. BDI scores were translated into QALYs using the mapping function between BDI and EQ-5D. Resource use data were already available and only supervision costs were estimated specifically for the economic analysis. Using a time horizon of 1 year, MBT with partial hospitalisation was found to be slightly more costly that treatment as usual overall (£18,174 versus £17,743, respectively). It was also found to result in significant reduction in parasuicidal events (6.1 events per person for MBT versus 17.5 for treatment as usual), and a higher number of QALYs (0.05 more than treatment as usual). The ICER of MBT versus treatment as usual was found to be £38 per parasuicidal event avoided, or £7,242 per QALY gained. This value is below the cost-effectiveness threshold set by NICE, which means that, according to this result, MBT is a cost-effective option for people with borderline personality disorder. Probabilistic analysis demonstrated that the probability of MBT being cost effective was 80% at a cost-effectiveness threshold of £5,000 per parasuicidal event avoided but only 55% at a cost-effectiveness threshold of £20,000 per QALY. Results were sensitive to changes in supervision costs for treatment as usual.

The above findings indicate that MBT might be potentially a cost-effective option in the management of borderline personality disorder. However, economic evidence is very limited, based on data from one small RCT only, and characterised by great uncertainty as the results of probabilistic analysis indicate.

Details of the characteristics and results of the studies assessing the cost effectiveness of psychological therapy programmes are provided in Appendix 15.

5.8 THERAPEUTIC COMMUNITIES

5.8.1 Introduction

A therapeutic community is a planned environment that exploits the therapeutic value of social and group processes (see Chapter 2, Section 2.5.5 for a history of therapeutic communities). It promotes equitable and democratic group living in a varied, permissive but safe environment. Interpersonal and emotional issues are openly discussed and members can form close relationships. Mutual feedback helps members confront their problems and develop an awareness of interpersonal actions (Haigh & Worrall, 2002). Their various structures have been systematised through a standards-based quality network, called 'Community of Communities' (Haigh & Tucker, 2004).

The nature of personality disorders, and in particular borderline personality disorder, often makes traditional hospital treatment problematic. For example, in traditional hospital settings patients are expected to conform to strict treatment regimes, rules and regulations (Kernberg & Haran, 1984), which may be inappropriate for the maladaptive patterns of functioning such as internally or externally directed aggression, lack of trust, unstable personal relationships, low self-esteem and withdrawal from human contact often exhibited by patients with personality disorder. Treatment in therapeutic communities and psychotherapy hospitals may help to address this (Chiesa, 1989). The ultimate aim of therapeutic community treatment is to rehabilitate individuals with levels of social adjustment necessary to function in the wider community.

Different forms of therapeutic community have evolved over the years but the model described here is the democratic type first introduced by Maxwell Jones 50 years ago. Therapeutic communities for personality disorder range from full-time residential hospitals to units that operate largely by the internet with occasional physical meetings. Between these extremes, there are communities that are weekly residential, full-time day units (5 days per week), and between 1 and 4 days per week. Most operate a rolling programme of 1 to 2 years' duration, and they are generally seen in four clusters of 'dose intensity':

● residential (supplying the research evidence discussed below)
● 3 or more days per week (Haigh, 2007)
● less than 3 days per week (Pearce & Haigh, 2008)
● substantially by internet communication.

There are several types of therapeutic community, several of which are located within the NHS (the Henderson Hospital, Cassel Hospital and Francis Dixon Lodge) and are often at the tertiary level of provision. Apart from in prison-based therapeutic communities, treatment is voluntary.

Although the community itself is seen as the primary therapeutic agent, programmes include a range of specific therapies, usually held entirely in groups. These can include small analytic groups, median analytic groups, psychodrama, transactional analysis, arts therapies, CT, social problem solving, psychoeducation and gestalt. In addition to specific therapies, there are community meetings (which normally have a set agenda), activities such as meal preparation and household maintenance, playful activities such as games, and opportunities for members or staff to call crisis meetings. In many therapeutic communities for personality disorder medication is prohibited. Behavioural interventions are often included as part of community meetings, for example by agreeing contracts and consequences for certain behaviours. There is a variable proportion of the programme available for informal time together and extramural activities. Non-residential programmes may also make provision for members to maintain contact with each other out of hours, including using telephone calls, texts, or the internet, as well as face-to-face meetings. It is well recognised that people with borderline personality disorder react adversely to separations from established relationships, and so leaving therapeutic communities is often difficult for patients, and requires careful management with suitable after care.

Therapeutic communities commonly employ psychodynamic principles, with professional staff using both formal therapy sessions and informal contact to help members develop healthy relationships, for example, by using all aspects of day-to-day interactions to enable them to understand their past experiences to understand behaviour in the present and learn to change problematic behaviour.

They generally work with time-limited placements. Within these treatment settings, the acting-out behaviour of the patient is valued as an important insight into the nature of the disorder and is actively utilised to assist in treatment as a route to understanding and interpreting the personal, historical meaning of these behaviours (Chiesa *et al.*, 2004a).

Therapeutic communities are run on democratic lines, which includes collective decision making and often involves voting procedures. The relationship between staff and community members is structured to minimise formal roles so that there is a 'flattened hierarchy' where all members and staff have equal voting rights and influence all decisions relevant to the community. This means that community members participate in the organisation and management of the community, and staff and residents work collaboratively with decisions being made through democratic voting systems in the community meetings. Everything that happens in all parts of the programme is discussed or otherwise used as part of the therapy.

5.8.2   Studies considered[12]

The review team conducted a systematic of primary research studies assessing the efficacy of residential therapeutic community treatment for people with a diagnosis of personality disorder. To be included, studies had to provide quantifiable outcome data and focus on therapeutic communities (rather than inpatient wards based on therapeutic community principles or residential programmes that do not conform to the principles described above) either in the UK, or in countries with similar healthcare systems. Evidence for therapeutic communities where residents stay long term were considered alongside evidence for other highly structured therapy programmes such as partial hospitalisation and intensive psychotherapy.

Nineteen papers, published in peer-reviewed journals between 1989 and 2007, met the eligibility criteria, providing data on 2,780 participants. Nine studies were excluded. See Appendix 16 for details of excluded studies with reasons for exclusion.

Studies of therapeutic communities in the UK (Henderson Hospital, Cassel Hospital and Francis Dixon Lodge), Australia and Finland were found.

5.8.3   UK-based residential therapeutic communities

Although the Henderson Hospital closed in April 2008, and the Cassel Hospital has developed a substantially different programme, they have both been important in undertaking relevant research. Many other therapeutic communities for borderline

---

[12]Here and elsewhere in the guideline, each study considered for review is referred to by a study ID in capital letters (which denotes the primary author and date of study publication, except where a study is in press or only submitted for publication, in which case a date is not used).

personality disorder have used and developed their treatment approaches, including those that use modified non-residential and less intensive programmes.

Henderson Hospital

The first therapeutic community established in the UK was the Henderson Hospital, which was founded in 1947 to treat psychological casualties from the Second World War with the aim of rehabilitation. In its role in treating people with emotional, inter-personal and behavioural difficulties, the Henderson offered a year of inpatient treat-ment for adults up to the age of 60. Residents may also have had a past history of drug and/or alcohol misuse, eating disorders, mood disorders and other psychiatric prob-lems. Specific exclusion criteria for admission to the hospital were psychological dependence on medication, active dependence on illicit drugs or alcohol, a learning disability and current, active, continuous psychosis.

Four prospective cohort studies were found that examined treatment effectiveness at the Henderson (see Table 37 and Table 38).

Copas and colleagues (1984) describe a 3- to 5-year follow-up of a sample of patients referred to the Henderson between September 1969 and February 1971; 194 were admitted and 51 not admitted. The cohort was originally reported on in an earlier paper (O'Brien *et al.*, 1976). The diagnoses of the participants are unclear, therefore it is difficult to judge whether the findings of this study are relevant to people with borderline personality disorder. The study was not considered further for this reason.

Table 37: Primary research studies of the Henderson Hospital

Study	N	Study design	Participants	Control group	Diagnosis
DOLAN1992	95	Cohort study	All referrals (admitted only)	No control	Range of personality disorder – majority borderline
DOLAN1997	137	Cohort study	All referrals	Non-admitted patients	Range of personality disorder – majority borderline
WARREN2004 and 2006	135	Cohort study	All referrals	Non-admitted patients	All personality disorder; 84% borderline personality disorder and eating disturbances (unclear if met diagnosis for an eating disorder)

Table 38: Primary research studies of the Henderson Hospital: outcomes

Study	Outcomes	Findings	Notes
DOLAN1992	GSI	SMD = 0.88, 95% CI 0.51, 1.25	Effect size calculated from pre-post data
DOLAN1997	BPDSI	SMD = −0.81, 95% CI −1.16, −0.47	–
WARREN2004	EAT-26 scores	SMD = 0.18, 95% CI −0.16, 0.52	–
	MIS hitting others – action	SMD = −0.53, 95% CI −0.88, −0.19	–
	Firesetting – impulse	SMD = −0.33, 95% CI −0.67, 0.01	–
	Overdosing – impulse	SMD = −0.25, 95% CI −0.59, 0.1	–

Dolan and colleagues (1992) investigated change in neurotic symptomatology in a sample of 95 patients admitted to the Henderson between 1985 and 1988 (age range 17 to 44, mean 25 years). Although the characteristics of the study sample are not given, a description of residents found that 87% met DSM-III-R criteria for borderline personality disorder (Dolan, 1991). Patients were required to complete baseline SCL-90 measures before treatment and again at 6 months' post-discharge; 65% of the sample completed outcome measures. Results demonstrated a significant reduction in GSI scores, indicating improvement in levels of distress caused by associated symptoms for borderline personality disorder. There was a tendency for greater levels of improvement among those remaining in treatment for more than 9 months, but this result was not statistically significant.

Dolan and colleagues (1997) examined changes in core personality disorder features 1 year post-treatment. They compared a group of patients admitted to the Henderson between September 1990 and November 1994 (n = 70) with a group who were not admitted (n = 69); approximately 80% met criteria for DSM-III-R borderline personality disorder, although on average participants met criteria for seven personality disorder categories. Significant differences in BPDSI scores were found for those admitted to the therapeutic community compared with those not admitted. For example, 42% of the admitted group achieved clinically significant change at 1-year follow-up compared with only 22% of those not admitted. Furthermore, there was a significant correlation between the length of time residents stayed in the therapeutic community and change in BPDSI scores. It should be noted, however, that between group differences may be because of selection

179

methods or different follow-up periods; those admitted to the Henderson were followed up 1 year post-treatment whereas those not admitted were followed-up 1 year after referral.

Warren and colleagues (2004) followed 135 patients referred to the Henderson between September 1990 and December 1994, 74 of whom were admitted. They measured impulsivity on a range of items (including self-harm, binge eating and fighting) 1 year after discharge (and 1 year after assessment for the non-admitted group) using a self-report measure (the Multi-Impulsivity Scale [MIS]). They reported statistically significant differences between the admitted and non-admitted groups, showing a reduction in the action of hitting others, and the impulses to set fires and to take overdoses. However, the review team for this guideline calculated effect sizes and found a statistically significant effect size for only the action of hitting others favouring the admitted group (SMD $= -0.53$, 95% CI -0.88, -0.19). Since there were more women and more patients with a diagnosis of schizotypal personality disorder in the admitted group than the non-admitted group, these factors were explored as potential confounders but not found to affect the results. Eating disturbances were also reported (Warren *et al.*, 2006) and there was a reduction in dieting but not in other aspects of eating disturbance (for example, bulimia) in those admitted compared with those not admitted.

Cassel Hospital
The Cassel Hospital is also a tertiary referral facility offering a type of therapeutic community treatment for individuals with personality disorder from different regions of the UK. The Cassel differs from the Henderson in that its programme also involves formal individual psychoanalytically-oriented therapy on a twice-weekly basis, sociotherapy within the therapeutic community and a few features of the 'flattened hierarchy', such as voting on decisions such as membership of the community. Additionally, limited use of psychotropic medication is permitted. For these reasons, it may not be considered a typical therapeutic community. However, the Cassel programme does include sociotherapy within the hospital environment, and like the Henderson, patients are actively encouraged to share responsibility for their own treatment and to participate in the running of the social functioning of the hospital. In both hospitals, an important aspect of treatment is to explore, through confrontations in the 'here and now', patients' behaviour and any potential conflicts and difficulties. This provides opportunities for individuals to develop considerable insight into their own problems and to resolve recurrent difficulties. The Cassel excludes patients with current severe addiction to alcohol or drugs, although includes those with substance use disorders.

Traditionally the Cassel offered a one-stage long-term programme in which individuals were admitted for 11 to 16 months, but post-discharge patients were expected to seek further treatment and additional support independently. However in 1993, a two-stage programme was devised in response to the need to reduce inpatient stay and to support patients in the transition period of leaving the intensive programme. Thus, the initial stage of inpatient treatment was reduced to 6 months, followed by a second component of treatment comprising 12 to 18 months of outpatient group psychotherapy plus 6 months of concurrent community outreach nursing. Patients referred from outside Greater London were admitted to the one-stage programme and those from inside Greater London to the two-stage programme.

Three prospective cohort studies were found comparing the two different treatment programmes offered by the Cassel (see Table 39).

Chiesa and Fonagy (2000) conducted a 5-year prospective cohort study comparing the two different treatment programmes offered by the Cassel. Forty-five participants formed the one-stage group and 44 were in the two-stage group. Recruitment took place between January 1993 and July 1997. Inclusion criteria for the study were being aged between 18 and 55 years, having a good command of English, having an IQ above 90 and having a diagnosis of an axis II disorder according to DSM-III-R criteria. Exclusion criteria included a previous diagnosis of schizophrenia or delusional (paranoid) disorder, previous continuation stay in hospital for more than 2 years, evidence of organic brain damage and involvement in criminal proceedings for violent crime. Seventy per cent of the sample had borderline personality disorder. For people with this disorder in the two-stage group, statistically significantly higher rates of improvement were found, as indicated by higher GAS scores (SMD = 0.64; 95% CI 0.21, 1.06 favouring the two-step group) and SAS scores at 12 months (SMD = 0.55; 95% CI 0.13, 0.97 favouring the two-step group). This may reflect long-term benefits of a short-term inpatient stay followed by post-discharge support.

In a further study, Chiesa and colleagues (2004a) examined the treatment effectiveness of the two treatment programmes, plus a general community sample, over 24 months. Treatment in the general community sample reflected that offered in non-specialist treatment services in the UK: participants in this group received standard

Table 39: Primary research studies of the Cassel Hospital

	N	Study design	Control group	Diagnosis
Chiesa & Fonagy (2000)*	90	Prospective cohort study	One-stage versus two-stage (see below)	Axis II disorders (70% borderline personality disorder)
Chiesa et al. (2004a)*	73	Prospective cohort study	One-stage versus two-stage (see below)	Axis II disorders (70% borderline personality disorder)
Chiesa & Fonagy (2007)	73	Prospective cohort study	One-stage versus two-stage (see below)	Axis II disorders (70% borderline personality disorder)

*A 6-year follow-up study has also been published (Chiesa et al., 2006).

psychiatric care including psychotropic medication (that is, treatment as usual). Results indicated that those in the two-stage group experienced better outcomes than the one-stage group or the treatment as usual group. For example, at 24-month follow-up a statistically significantly greater proportion of patients in the two-stage group scored below the cut-off point for borderline personality disorder symptom severity. Furthermore, a greater proportion of this group achieved clinically significant increases in GAS scores compared with the other two groups. A 50% reduction in the number of self-mutilating acts was observed for those in the two-stage group, compared with only 8% in the treatment as usual group and no change in the one-stage group respectively. Most importantly, however, patients rehabilitated into the community were four times less likely to be readmitted to psychiatric services in the year after discharge compared with the other two groups.

A 6-year follow-up study showed that the two-stage group maintained and clinically improved on several measures, whereas these effects were not apparent for the treatment as usual or one-stage group (Chiesa *et al.*, 2006). In particular, levels of symptom severity were most decreased in the two-stage programme, with 62% of patients below the clinical cut-off point at 6-year follow-up compared with only 26% in the one-stage group and 13% in the treatment as usual group. Patients treated in the two-stage group were less likely to utilise NHS resources at 6-year follow-up, as indicated by the marked reduction in the number of committed acts of parasuicide and self-mutilation, plus a decrease in the number of suicide attempts and lower rates of readmission to psychiatric units compared with the one-stage and treatment as usual groups.

A further study of 73 patients admitted to the Cassel specifically examined predictive factors of positive outcome (Chiesa & Fonagy, 2007). This found that at 2-year follow-up younger age, high general functioning at admission, longer length of treatment, absence of self-harm and avoidant personality disorders significantly predicted outcomes among participants with diagnoses of cluster B personality disorders.

Francis Dixon Lodge

Francis Dixon Lodge is based in Leicestershire and at the time of the studies described below had 15 beds, which were lost when it was converted into a day unit in 2007. It took 20% of its intake as extra-contractual referrals, mainly from its own geographical region, but some were from as far away as South Wales. At the time of the research described, residents stayed at the lodge unit from Monday to Friday but returned to their private lodgings at the weekend. Francis Dixon Lodge offers similar treatment to the Henderson in that therapy takes place exclusively in group settings. Treatment comprises twice-daily community meetings, twice-weekly small group psychotherapy sessions, a once-weekly art therapy group and a once-weekly care-planning group. Residents also participate in additional recreational activities, housekeeping tasks and are involved in the assessment of referrals.

Francis Dixon Lodge also offers a 'next steps' service for patients who are about to be discharged to help them prepare for their departure; this support is maintained for 6 months post-discharge. It also offers ex-residents ongoing crisis support in the form of a weekly drop-in group.

Table 40: Primary research studies of Francis Dixon Lodge

	N	Study design	Participants	Control group	Diagnosis
DAVIES1999	52	Cohort study	All referrals	None (although some data given comparing local patients with others)	Emotionally unstable personality disorder (87%)

One cohort study was found that examined treatment effectiveness of Francis Dixon Lodge (see Table 40).

Davies and colleagues (1999) examined 52 patients admitted to Francis Dixon Lodge, of whom 40 were referrals from Leicestershire and the remaining 12 were extra-contractual referrals. Comparison of the two samples showed that the latter had greater service usage costs, as reflected by greater inpatient stays in general psychiatry wards, in the 3 years preceding treatment at Francis Dixon Lodge, than the referrals from Leicestershire. No other data were reported.

A follow-up study over a period of 3 years of the same sample (Davies & Campling, 2003) demonstrated a significant reduction in the number of inpatient admissions 1 year post-treatment; moreover, these effects were maintained at 3-year follow-up. Evidence also suggests that those who terminated treatment early (under 42 days) had the poorest outcomes in terms of suicide and accidental death. The number of days of hospitalisation in the 3 years before admission was compared with the number post-admission, showing fewer days of hospitalisation post-admission (WMD = 46.30; 95% CIs 7.75, 84.85). However, the CIs are wide (between 8 and 85 days) making it hard to draw firm conclusions from these data.

5.8.4 UK-based non-residential therapeutic communities

No outcome studies examining the efficacy of therapeutic community treatment in the modified programmes, as mentioned above, have yet been published. This includes day units that function as partial hospitalisation programmes, 'mini' therapeutic communities of less than two days per week, and 'virtual' therapeutic communities that function predominantly via the internet.

5.8.5 Non-UK-based therapeutic communities

Outside the UK, the term therapeutic community most commonly refers to residential treatment units for addictions, which frequently operate similar programmes to the UK-based therapeutic communities described above. Dual diagnosis and comorbidity are increasingly recognised and shared features of history, theory and practice have been described (Haigh & Lees, 2008).

Several studies examining the efficacy of therapeutic community treatment for people with borderline personality disorder have been conducted in Australia and Finland. Two prospective cohort studies conducted in Australia claimed support for therapeutic community treatment. Hafner and Holme (1996) investigated a therapeutic community ward run on democratic principles in a psychiatric hospital. The therapeutic community ran from Monday to Friday, and was closed at the weekend, when residents were expected to maintain their own accommodation outside the hospital. No psychotropic medication or alcohol was permitted. The maximum stay was 6 months and residents had to form links with the wider community through activities such as leisure or educational courses, sports or voluntary work. Forty-eight residents completed measures at three time points: at baseline, within 2 weeks of discharge and at 3 months post-discharge. Twenty-nine residents completed the final questionnaire. Results demonstrated a significant reduction in GSI scores, indicating improvement in levels of distress caused by associated symptoms for borderline personality disorder for those completing post-discharge questionnaires. The three treatment components reported by patients to be most helpful were therapy groups (72%), living closely with others (56%) and community meetings (54%). The four components found to be most unhelpful were mandatory weekend leave (14%), assessment procedures (12%), rules (10%) and client outings (10%).

A more recent Australian study (Hulbert & Thomas, 2007) investigated the effects of a new public sector treatment called spectrum group treatment. This comprises adapted DBT skills training, experiential sessions to facilitate modelling and coaching of appropriate behaviour, together with peer support. Residents were followed up at three time points: pre-treatment, post-treatment and 1 year post-discharge. Results showed a statistically significant reduction in the number of borderline personality disorder diagnoses made at discharge and 1 year post-discharge. Furthermore, patients reported significantly lower levels of depression, anxiety, hopelessness and dissociation at the end of treatment, and these effects were maintained at 1-year follow-up. There was also a reduction in the number of self-harm acts, but this was not a statistically significant improvement.

A prospective cohort study conducted in Norway by Vaglum and colleagues (1990) investigated the efficacy of a therapeutic community day ward for three different groups of patient: those with severe personality disorder (including borderline personality disorder, schizotypal personality disorder, and mixed borderline and schizotypal personality disorder), 'other non-severe' personality disorder and no personality disorder. Treatment on the day ward included daily community meetings, group therapy and individual psychotherapy for 1 to 2 hours weekly. Psychotropic medication was also permitted. Results indicated that there were no significant differences in length of stay between groups, but a positive correlation was found between length of stay and GSI outcome. Patients with severe personality disorder were more likely to have negative views about the therapeutic community environment than those without personality disorder. Those with no personality disorder were more likely to benefit from treatment; for example, patients in this group were more likely to be considered a non-psychiatric case at endpoint than the other two groups.

Using the same sample as Vaglum and colleagues (1990), Karterud and colleagues (1992) further investigated whether the day hospital is an adequate treatment for individuals with personality disorder. Measures taken included: suicidal attempt rates, numbers leaving treatment early, number of psychotic breakdowns, level of medication, symptom levels and psychological functioning. Approximately 60% of patients were on psychotropic medication at the beginning of the trial, but this reduced to 42% by the end and medication doses were also lower. Treatment was successful in engaging patients, with a mean stay of 171 days. However there was a higher rate of dropout among the borderline personality disorder group compared with the less severe and no personality disorder groups. Karterud and colleagues (1992) concluded that day ward treatment is sufficient for the treatment of individuals with borderline personality disorder as it produces modest improvements in symptom reduction and psychological functioning.

Two Finish cohort studies conducted within a psychiatric hospital aimed to investigate whether modified therapeutic community principles are applicable to the institutional care of acute and sub-acute psychotic and borderline personality disorder patients (Isohanni & Nieminen, 1989 & 1990b). Formal treatment ran from Monday to Friday and at the weekend patients were discharged (but where this was not possible, they were allowed to rest and engage with recreational activities). Treatment included community group meetings in which decisions regarding the running of the community were made. Every weekday morning, 'problem' meetings occurred whereby patients and staff negotiated treatment plans and how to manage any critical situations. Patients also had time throughout the day to engage in individual psychotherapy, treatment planning and extracurricular activities.

Both studies (Isohanni & Nieminen, 1989 & 1990b) investigated which patient and programme factors were predictive of treatment outcome in relation to psychiatric status. Outcomes were examined 1 to 2 weeks after departure from the therapeutic community. For the majority of patients, therapeutic community treatment was beneficial (as defined by Isohanni and Nieminen as achieving goals and undergoing noticeable change), but for a small proportion (5%) there was an unexpected negative change (that is, clinical status remained the same as at the beginning of study or worsened during hospital treatment). Factors associated with negative outcomes were short treatment time (under 18 days), and also, for those taking a passive role in the group, the therapeutic community environment and individual therapy in particular. Also, a small correlation was observed between negative outcome and involuntary admission (Isohanni & Nieminen, 1989). Furthermore, age – in particular, being under 21 years – was also associated with negative outcome (Isohanni & Nieminen, 1990b).

5.8.6   Clinical summary

Although the cohort studies provide some interesting data, there are a number of factors that limit their usefulness in evaluating residential therapeutic community treatment. There would be methodological difficulties with setting up such trials, including ethical problems associated with withholding residential treatment for those most in need and the related problem of creating adequate control groups. There are no RCTs of treatment in therapeutic communities.

Caution must therefore be exercised in drawing conclusions from the cohort studies for five reasons. First, the studies lack meaningful comparison groups; in several studies all those referred for treatment are included in the study, with those admitted compared with those not admitted. Admission is based on criteria set by the individual therapeutic community. This is likely to mean that those not admitted are dissimilar in some ways to those admitted, thus weakening the use of this group as a control. Second, simple comparisons of pre- versus post-treatment changes in outcome for the residential treatment group are problematic because there is a possibility that changes may be because of spontaneous recovery or some systematic bias in the selection of those who entered residential treatment. For example, admittance to the Henderson Hospital depended partly on availability of funding from the local health authority, and so it is possible that districts with less available funding either have alternative non-residential treatment programmes for those with personality disorders or have fewer resources for other reasons. This may reduce the generalisability of the available data further. Third, many of the studies examined follow-up patients over a relatively short period of time (for example, 1 year). Fourth, the necessarily multi-component nature of many the therapeutic community programmes makes it difficult to identify the active components. For example, it is unclear whether admitting an individual into a hospital, the nature of the hospital environment, the therapeutic relationships with staff or other patients, the use of psychotropic medication, or a combination of these factors, contribute to the effectiveness of the treatment. Lastly, the number of residentially-based communities is being reduced (for example, the Henderson Hospital has closed) and while several new non-residential community treatment programmes have been established, there is as yet no evidence on their effectiveness.

Consideration of these limitations means that conclusions about the efficacy of therapeutic community treatment remain tentative.

5.8.7   Health economic evidence

The systematic search of the literature identified two economic studies on therapeutic communities that met the criteria for inclusion in the review of economic evidence. Both studies were conducted in the UK. One study had a before-after design and examined costs associated with treatment of people with personality disorders at the Henderson Hospital (Dolan *et al.*, 1996); the other was a cohort study examining two programmes for people with personality disorders at the Cassel

Hospital (Beecham *et al.*, 2006). Details on the methods used for the systematic review of the economic literature are described in Chapter 3.

Economic evidence from Henderson Hospital – Dolan et al., 1996
Dolan and colleagues (1996) assessed the costs of psychiatric and prison services incurred by 24 people with personality disorders admitted to the Henderson Hospital. Costs were estimated for the year before admission and for the year following discharge. Total treatment costs at Henderson were also reported.

The average total cost per person in the year before admission was £13,966 (1992/93 prices). Of this, 79% was for inpatient psychiatric care, 11% for outpatient psychiatric care and 10% for prison costs. The average total cost per person fell at £1,308 in the year following discharge, reflecting more than a ten-fold reduction in total cost. Of the post-discharge cost, 62% was attributed to inpatient psychiatric care and the rest (38%) to outpatient psychiatric care; no prison costs were incurred in the post-discharge period of the study. The difference in total cost between the year before admission and the year following discharge was £12,658 per person treated. The average treatment cost per person admitted to the Henderson Hospital was £25,641.

Based on the study results, the authors suggested that if the reduction in psychiatric care usage was maintained in the years following treatment, then the cost of treatment at Henderson Hospital would be recovered in just over 2 years following discharge. However, they admitted that usage levels of psychiatric care in this population over time were unknown and further research was required to confirm the potential benefits of treatment at the Henderson in terms of expected future cost-offsets. In addition, the study had a before-after design which is subject to bias; no comparator to specialist treatment at the Henderson was used. Furthermore, costs reflected local prices from regional health authorities. Collection of resource use data was based on retrospective review of case notes (for the before-treatment costs) and self-reports from study participants and their GPs (for the after-treatment costs); the authors admitted that data might be inaccurate. For all these reasons, results of this analysis should be interpreted with extreme caution.

Economic evidence from Cassel Hospital – Beecham et al., 2006
Beecham and colleagues (2006) estimated the cost effectiveness of two treatment programmes provided in the Cassel Hospital for people with personality disorders: the 'one-stage programme', in which individuals receive inpatient treatment over 11 to 16 months, and the two-stage programme, which comprises inpatient therapy for 6 months followed by 12 to 18 months of outpatient follow-up psychosocial treatment. The two programmes were compared with standard general psychiatric care for people with personality disorders. The economic analysis was conducted alongside a prospective cohort study (Chiesa & Fonagy, 2000), details of which are provided in Section 5.8.3. The analysis included cost and effectiveness data derived from 107 of the study participants.

The study adopted a wide public sector perspective, including health, social and criminal justice system services. Costs consisted of primary care costs (for example

GP, social worker and employment service costs), mental healthcare costs (such as costs of psychiatrists, psychologists and CPNs), hospital costs, accommodation service costs and costs associated with legal services (police and lawyer costs). Outcomes were expressed as average changes in the GAS, the GSI and the Positive Symptom Total (PST). Costs and outcomes were measured at baseline, at end of treatment and at 12 months following termination of treatment.

Analysis of clinical data showed that clinical outcomes had improved over time in all three groups, with the one-stage group and the two-stage group showing the greatest improvement, and the general psychiatric care group showing the least improvement. Both the one-stage and two-stage groups improved significantly more than the general psychiatric care group in all three outcomes. Compared with the one-stage group, the two-stage group had significantly better outcomes on the PST and marginally better outcomes on the GSI; it also had better outcomes on the GAS, but the result was statistically insignificant.

Regarding costs, the one-stage and two-stage programmes had similar total costs from initiation of the study to end of the follow-up period (cost per person £58,241 and £59,041 respectively, in 1998/1999 prices), while general psychiatric care was significantly less costly overall (cost per person £29,002). Follow-up costs (that is, costs from completion of treatment to endpoint of analysis) for all groups were similar, but the one-stage and two-stage groups incurred much higher costs than general psychiatric care during the period of treatment. Both the one-stage and two-stage programmes were therefore more effective and more costly than general psychiatric care; the one-stage programme had similar costs to the two-stage programme but was less effective. The ICER of the two-stage programme versus general psychiatric care was £3,405 per additional point gained on the GAS, £30,304 per additional point gained on the GSI and £1,131 per additional point gained on the PST.

The results of the study indicate that both programmes provided at the Cassel are potentially more effective and more costly than general psychiatric care. The two-stage programme seemed to be more effective than the one-stage programme at a similar cost. However, the study is characterised by a number of limitations, such as the small study samples and the differential attrition between groups over the follow-up period, which may have introduced bias, as acknowledged by the authors of the study.

The findings of the economic literature review indicate the need for further research on the cost effectiveness of therapeutic community programmes for people with personality disorders.

Evidence tables for the economic studies on therapeutic communities included in the systematic economic literature review are provided in Appendix 15.

5.9   DATA BY OUTCOME

5.9.1   Introduction

In this section, the outcomes analysed from RCTs are reported by outcome rather than by therapy. It does not include data from combination trials.

Table 41: Summary evidence table for anger outcomes

Therapy (all versus TAU unless otherwise stated)	DBT
Clinician-rated effect size	SMD = −0.98 (−1.81, −0.16)
Quality of evidence	Moderate
Number of studies/participants	(K = 1; n = 26)
Forest plot	Psych 01.01
Clinician-rated effect size at follow-up 1	SMD = −0.91 (−1.99, 0.18)
Quality of evidence	Moderate
Number of studies/participants	(K = 1; n = 15)
Forest plot	Psych 01.01
Clinician-rated effect size at follow-up 2	SMD = −0.59 (−1.52, 0.35)
Quality of evidence	Very low
Number of studies/participants	(K = 1; n = 19)
Forest plot	Psych 01.01

5.9.2   Effect of treatment on anger

Measures of anger were reported in one study (LINEHAN1991) (see Table 41). This showed some effect of treatment (DBT) on anger which was sustained at 1-year follow-up but not at 2 years. However, the sample size was very small (n = 26) (smaller at follow-up) so the effect on symptoms is far from certain.

5.9.3   Effect of treatment on anxiety

Measures of anxiety were reported in four studies (BATEMAN1999; DAVIDSON2006; KOONS2001; TYRER2004), using a range of measures that were not possible to combine in meta-analysis (see Table 42). This showed a range of treatment effects. DBT had positive effect on anxiety symptoms, but CBT did not. At follow-up MBT showed large effects while CBT did not. However, the sample sizes were mostly fairly small so the effect on symptoms is far from certain.

Table 42: Summary evidence table for anxiety outcomes

	HARS	STAI	HADS	BAI
Clinician-rated effect size	SMD = −1.22 (−2.2, −0.25)	SMD (random effects) = −0.59 (−1.75, 0.57)	SMD = 0.01 (−0.48, 0.5)	SMD = −4.66 (−9.81, 0.49)*
Quality of evidence	Moderate	Very low	Moderate	Very low
Number of studies/ participants	(K = 1; n = 20)	(K = 2; n = 137)	(K = 1; n = 64)	(K = 1; n = 24)
Forest plot	Psych 06.01	Psych 06.01	Psych 06.01	Psych 06.02
Clinician-rated effect size at follow-up 1 (18 months)	–	SMD = −3.49 (−4.63, −2.36)	–	–
Quality of evidence	–	Moderate	–	–
Number of studies/ participants	–	(K = 1; n = 33)	–	–
Forest plot	–	Psych 06.01	–	–
Clinician-rated effect size at follow-up 2 (24 months)	–	SMD = −0.18 (−0.57, 0.21)		–
Number of studies/ participants		K = 1; n = 101		
Quality of evidence	–	Very low	–	–
Forest plot	–	Psych 06.01	–	–

*Based on skewed data.

5.9.4   Effect of treatment on depression

Measures of depression were reported in six studies (see Table 43). There was an effect on symptoms for both clinician-rated and self-rated measures, which persisted at follow-up (both 18 and 24 months) although only a single study provided follow-up data (for MBT with partial hospitalisation).

5.9.5   Effect of treatment on impulsiveness

Measures of impulsiveness were reported in one study (BLUM 2008) (STEPPS). There was insufficient data to draw any conclusions about the effect of treatment on impulsiveness (see Table 44).

Table 43: Summary evidence table for depression outcomes

Clinician-rated effect size	SMD (random effects) = −0.45 (−0.92, 0.02)*
Quality of evidence	Moderate
Number of studies/participants	(K = 4; n = 197)
Forest plot	Psych 07.01
Self-rated effect size	SMD (random effects) = −0.84 (−1.47, −0.21)*
Quality of evidence	Moderate
Number of studies/participants	(K = 5; n = 318)
Forest plot	Psych 07.02
Self-rated effect size at follow-up 1 (12 months)	SMD = −1.15 (−1.85, −0.45)
Quality of evidence	Moderate
Number of studies/participants	(K = 1; n = 38)
Forest plot	Psych 07.02
Self-rated effect size at follow-up 2 (24 months)	SMD = −0.15 (−0.54, 0.24)*
Quality of evidence	Very low
Number of studies/participants	(K = 1; n = 101)
Forest plot	Psych 07.02

*Based on skewed data.

191

Table 44: Summary evidence table for impulsiveness outcomes

Clinician-rated effect size	SMD $= -0.29$ $(-0.64, 0.07)$
Quality of evidence	Very low
Number of studies/participants	(K $= 1$; n $= 124$)
Forest plot	Psych 08.01

5.9.6   Effect of treatment on mental distress

Measures of mental distress were reported in three studies (BATEMAN1999; BLUM2008; DAVIDSON2006). There was only a small effect of treatment on mental distress, although follow-up data reported by one study of MBT with partial hospitalisation showed a large effect at 18-month follow-up, while another study of CBT showed very little difference at 2-year follow-up (see Table 45).

Table 45: Summary evidence table for mental distress outcomes

Clinician-rated effect size	SMD $= -0.21$ $(-0.46, 0.03)*$
Quality of evidence	High
Number of studies/participants	(K $= 3$; n $= 261$)
Forest plot	Psych 09.01

*Based on skewed data.

5.9.7   Effect of treatment on self-harm and suicide-related measures

Measures of self-harm were reported in twelve studies (BATEMAN1999; BLUM2008; CARTER unpublished; CHANEN2008; DAVIDSON2006; LINEHAN1991; LINEHAN2006; VANDEN BOSCH2002; KOONS2001; TURNER2000; TYRER2004; WEINBERG2006) (see Table 46 for the summary evidence profile). A range of measures was used (see above), both continuous variables and dichotomous, which meant that it was hard to combine more than a few studies in meta-analyses. There was some effect of treatment on reducing self-harm and suicide attempts when these measures were reported dichotomously, otherwise there appeared to be little effect. This may be because the data is weakened by the large range of outcome measures reported as well as the effect of different kinds of treatments. Some studies reported self-harm and suicide attempts as a combined measure and these showed a small effect on rates

Table 46: Summary evidence table for self-harm and suicide-related outcomes

Outcome	Self-harm	Suicide attempts	Self-harm and suicide attempts	Hospital admission for self-harm
Effect size continuous	WMD = −0.17 (−2.15, 1.82)*	WMD = −0.32 (−0.55, −0.09)	WMD = −1.83 (−3.07, −0.59)*	–
Quality of evidence	High	High	Moderate	–
Number of studies/ participants	(K = 3; n = 185)	(K = 2; n = 145)	(K = 3; n = 72)	–
Forest plot	Psych 10.01	Psych 10.01	Psych 10.01	–
Effect size at follow-up 1	WMD = −4.71 (−11.16, 1.74)* (6 months)	WMD = −0.47 (−0.9, −0.04)* (5 years)	WMD = −0.86 (−1.82, 0.1)* (24 months)	–
Quality of evidence	Very low	Moderate	Moderate	–
Number of studies/ participants	(K = 1; n = 30)	(K = 1; n = 41)	(K = 1; n = 101)	–
Forest plot	Psych 10.01	Psych 10.01	Psych 10.01	–
Effect size dichotomous	RR = 0.54 (0.34, 0.86) (33% versus 58%)	RR (random effects) = 0.52 (0.31, 0.89) (21% versus 39%)	RR = 0.97 (0.88, 1.07) (94% versus 97%)	RR = 0.82 (0.36, 1.89) (21% versus 26%)
Quality of evidence	Moderate	Moderate	Moderate	Very low

Continued

Table 46: *(Continued)*

Outcome	Self-harm	Suicide attempts	Self-harm and suicide attempts	Hospital admission for self-harm
Number of studies/ participants	(K = 1; n = 108)	(K = 5; n = 361)	(K = 1; n = 70)	(K = 1; n = 73)
Forest plot	Psych 10.02	Psych 10.02	Psych 10.02	Psych 10.02
Follow-up 1	RR = 1.03 (0.71, 1.48) (1 year) 52% versus 51%	RR = 1.08 (0.53, 2.21) (23% versus 21%) 1 year	RR = 0.98 (0.51, 1.87) (32% versus 32%) 24 months	–
Quality of evidence	Very low	Very low	Very low	–
Number of studies/ participants	(K = 1; n = 108)	(K = 1; n = 108)	(K = 1; n = 78)	–
Forest plot	Psych 02.06	Psych 10.02	Psych 10.02	–
Follow-up 2	–	RR = 0.8 (0.54, 1.2) (43% versus 54%) 24 months	–	–

Quality of evidence	–	Very low	–	–
Number of studies/participants	–	(K = 1; n = 101)	–	–
Forest plot	–	Psych 10.02	–	–
Follow-up 3	–	RR = 0.31 (0.14, 0.7) (23% versus 26%) 5 years		
Quality of evidence	–	Moderate	–	–
Number of studies/participants	–	(K = 1; n = 41)	–	–
Forest plot	–	Psych 10.02	–	–

*Based on skewed data.

(nearly two episodes fewer in the treatment group compared with treatment as usual) (for DBT and MACT).

5.9.8   Effect of treatment on service-use measures

Measures were reported in seven studies (BATEMAN1999; BLUM2008; CARTER unpublished; DAVIDSON2006; LINEHAN1991; LINEHAN2006; TURNER 2000) (see Table 47 and Table 48). A range of measures was used, both continuous variables and dichotomous, which meant that it was hard to combine more than a few studies in meta-analyses. There was little effect of treatment on reducing service use, other than a few outcomes based on single studies. These included number of years of further psychiatric outpatient treatment, number of years taking three or more drugs, the number of partipants on medication at endpoint, and emergency department visits both for any reason and for psychiatric reasons at 5-year follow-up. All of these were reported by the study of MBT and partial hospitalisation (BATEMAN 1999). DBT also showed some effect on hospital admission for suicidal ideation and emergency department visits for psychiatric reasons.

5.9.9   Effect of treatment on borderline personality disorder symptomatology

Measures of borderline personality disorder symptomatology were reported in four studies (BATEMAN1999; BLUM2008; CHANEN unpublished; KOONS2001), although none reported measures that could be combined in meta-analyses. One study of STEPPS (BLUM2008) showed some effect of treatment on symptoms as measured by the ZAN-borderline personality disorder, and another of MBT with partial hospitalisation showed a large effect at 5-year follow-up (see Table 49).

5.9.10   Effect of treatment on social functioning

Measures of social functioning were reported in two studies (DAVIDSON2006; LINEHAN1999), although neither reported measures that could be combined in meta-analyses. One study of DBT showed some effect of treatment on both work and employment performance although this did not persist at follow-up (see Table 50).

5.9.11   Effect of treatment on general functioning

Measures of general functioning were reported in three studies (BATEMAN1999; BLUM2008; TYRER2004). One study of STEPPS (BLUM2008) showed some effect of treatment on outcome (see Table 51).

196

Table 47: Summary evidence table for service-use outcomes (hospital admission and emergency department visits)

Outcome	No days hospitalised	Hospital admission for psychiatric reasons	Hospital admission for suicidal ideation	Hospital admission for self-harm	Emergency department visits (any reason)	Emergency department visits for psychiatric reasons	Emergency department visits for suicide ideation (endpoint)
Continuous data effect sizes	WMD (random effects) = −5.42 (−14.01, 3.17)*	WMD = −0.36 (−1.19, 0.46)*	–	WMD = −4.38 (−17.31, 8.55)	WMD = −0.24 (−1.98, 1.5)*	–	–
Quality of evidence	Very low	Moderate		Very low	Very low		
Number of studies/participants	(K = 3; n = 136)	(K = 2; n = 174)		(K = 1; n = 73)	(K = 1; n = 101)		
Forest plot	Psych 11.01	Psych 11.01		Psych 11.01	Psych 11.02		
Continuous data at follow-up 1	WMD = −0.29 (−0.65, 0.07) (18 months)	WMD = −0.67 (−1.98, 0.64)* (24 months)	–	–	WMD = −0.15 (−4.26, 3.96)* (24 months)	WMD = −5.63 (−8.23, −3.03)* 5 years (presumed self-harm related)	–
Quality of evidence	Moderate	Moderate			Very low	Moderate	–
Number of studies/participants	(K = 1; n = 15)	(K = 1; n = 101)			(K = 1; n = 101)	(K = 1; n = 41)	–
Forest plot	Psych 11.01	Psych 11.01			Psych 11.02	Psych 11.01	–

Continued

Table 47: (*Continued*)

Outcome	No days hospitalised	Hospital admission for psychiatric reasons	Hospital admission for suicidal ideation	Hospital admission for self-harm	Emergency department visits (any reason)	Emergency department visits for psychiatric reasons	Emergency department visits for suicide ideation (endpoint)
Continuous data at follow-up 2	WMD = −0.45 (−0.57, −0.33)* (24 months)	–	–	–	WMD = −5.63 (−8.23, −3.03)* (5 years)	–	–
Quality of evidence	Moderate	–	–	–	Moderate	–	–
Number of studies/participants	(K = 1; n = 37)	–	–	–	(K = 1; n = 41)	–	–
Forest plot	Psych 11.01	–	–	–	Psych 11.02	–	–
Continuous data at follow-up 3	WMD = −5.93 (−8.47, −3.39)* (5 years)	–	–	–	–	–	–
Quality of evidence	Moderate	–	–	–	–	–	–
Number of studies/participants	(K = 1; n = 41)	–	–	–	–	–	–
Forest plot	Psych 11.01	–	–	–	–	–	–

		RR (random effects) = 0.57 (0.26, 1.24) (19% versus 35%)	RR = 0.28 (0.11, 0.71) (10% versus 36%)	RR = 0.82 (0.36, 1.89) (21% versus 26%)	–	RR = 0.61 (0.42, 0.89) (44% versus 72%)	RR = 0.48 (0.22, 1.04) (16% versus 33%)
Dichotomous data effect sizes	–						
Quality of evidence	–	Very low	Moderate	Very low	–	Moderate	Moderate
Number of studies/participants	–	(K = 2; n = 162)	(K = 1; n = 89)	(K = 1; n = 73)	–	(K = 1; n = 89)	(K = 1; n = 89)
Forest plot	–	Psych 11.03	Psych 11.03	Psych 11.03	–	Psych 11.03	Psych 11.03
Dichotomous data at follow-up 1	–	RR = 1.05 (0.47, 2.32) (24% versus 23%) (24 months)	RR = 0.89 (0.33, 2.41) (15% versus 18%) (24 months)	–	–	RR = 0.65 (0.35, 1.23) (26% versus 40%) (24 months)	RR = 0.63 (0.21, 1.91) (11% versus 17%) (24 months)
Quality of evidence	–	Very low	Very low	–	–	Very low	–
Number of studies/participants	–	(K = 1; n = 81)	(K = 1; n = 81)	–	–	(K = 1; n = 81)	–
Forest plot	–	Psych 11.03	Psych 11.03	–	–	Psych 11.03	–

*Based on skewed data.

Table 48: Summary evidence table for service-use outcomes (outpatient services and medication use)

Outcome	No. years of further psychiatric outpatient treatment (5-year follow-up)	No. years on three or more drugs (5-year follow-up)	No. on medication at endpoint
Continuous data at follow-up	WMD = −1.6 (−2.64, −0.56)* (5 years)	WMD = −1.7 (−2.56, −0.84)* (5 years)	–
Quality of evidence	Moderate	Moderate	–
Number of studies/ participants	(K = 1; n = 41)	(K = 1; n = 41)	–
Forest plot	Psych 11.01	Psych 11.01	–
Dichotomous data effect sizes	–	–	RR = 0.47 (0.25, 0.88) (37% versus 79%)
Quality of evidence	–	–	Moderate
Number of studies/ participants	–	–	(K = 1; n = 38)
Forest plot	–	–	Psych 11.01

*Based on skewed data.

5.9.12 Effect of treatment on employment-related outcomes

Measures of employment-related outcomes were reported in one study (BATEMAN 1999). This showed that at 5-year follow-up those who had received treatment (MBT with partial hospitalisation) had been in employment for an average of 2 years more than those who received usual treatment (see Table 52).

Table 49: Summary evidence table for borderline personality disorder symptomatology

	No. of borderline personality disorder criteria (DSM)	ZAN-borderline personality disorder	SCID-II borderline personality disorder
Clinician-rated effect size	WMD = −0.6 (−2.34, 1.14)*	SMD = −0.45 (−0.81, −0.1)*	WMD = −0.37 (−1.95, 1.21)
Quality of evidence	Very low	Moderate	Very low
Number of studies/ participants	(K = 1; n = 20)	(K = 1; n = 124)	(K = 1; n = 78)
Forest plot	Psych 12.01	Psych 12.01	Psych 12.01
Clinician-rated effect size at follow-up 1	–	SMD = −1.79 (−2.53, −1.06)* (5 years)	WMD = −0.59 (−2.34, 1.16) (12 months)
Quality of evidence	–	Moderate	Very low
Number of studies/ participants	–	(K = 1; n = 41)	(K = 1; n = 78)
Forest plot	–	Psych 12.01	Psych 12.01
Clinician-rated effect size at follow-up 2	–	–	WMD = −0.27 (−2.39, 1.85) (24 months)
Quality of evidence	–	–	Very low
Number of studies/ participants	–	–	(K = 1; n = 78)
Forest plot	–	–	Psych 12.01

*Based on skewed data.

201

Table 50: Summary evidence table for social functioning

Outcome	SAS – work performance	SAS – anxious rumination	SAS – employment performance	SFQ
Continuous data effect sizes	SMD = −0.33 (−0.9, 0.24)	SMD = −0.71 (−1.56, 0.14)	SMD = −0.8 (−1.4, −0.2)	SMD = 0 (−0.39, 0.39)
Quality of evidence	Moderate	Very low	Moderate	Moderate
Number of studies/participants	(K = 1; n = 14)	(K = 1; n = 13)	(K = 1; n = 10)	(K = 1; n = 99)
Forest plot	Psych 13.01	Psych 13.01	Psych 13.01	Psych 13.01
Continuous data at follow-up (24 months)	SMD = −0.44 (−1.18, 0.3)	SMD = −0.44 (−1.42, 0.54)	SMD = −1.04 (−1.73, −0.35)	SMD = 0.14 (−0.26, 0.53)
Quality of evidence	Very low	Very low	Moderate	Moderate
Number of studies/participants	(K = 1; n = 14)	(K = 1; n = 13)	(K = 1; n = 8)	(K = 1; n = 101)
Forest plot	Psych 13.01	Psych 13.01	Psych 13.01	Psych 13.01

Table 51: Summary evidence table for general functioning

Outcome	GAF	GAS
Continuous data effect sizes	SMD = −0.17 (−0.67, 0.32)	SMD = −0.55 (−0.91, −0.19)
Quality of evidence	Very low	Moderate
Number of studies/participants	(K = 1; n = 64)	(K = 1; n = 123)
Forest plot	Psych 14.01	Psych 14.01
Continuous data at follow-up (24 months)	SMD = −0.74 (−1.38, −0.1) (5 years)	–
Quality of evidence	Moderate	–
Number of studies/participants	(K = 1; n = 41)	–
Forest plot	Psych 01.15	–

Table 52: Summary evidence table for employment-related outcomes

Outcome	No. years employment
Continuous data effect sizes	WMD = −2 (−3.29, −0.71)* (5-year follow-up)
Quality of evidence	Moderate
Number of studies/participants	(K = 1; n = 41)
Forest plot	Psych 14.01

*Based on skewed data

5.9.13   Effect of treatment on quality of life outcomes

Measures of quality of life were reported in two studies (DAVIDSON2006; GIESEN-BLOO2006). There was no effect on outcome of either treatment compared with treatment as usual, or when two treatments were compared head-to-head (schema-focused CT versus transference-focused psychotherapy) (see Table 53).

Table 53: Summary evidence table for quality of life

Outcome	EuroQOL	WHO QOL total score (schema-focused CT versus transference- focused psychotherapy)
Continuous data effect sizes	SMD = 0.29 (−0.11, 0.68)*	SMD = 0 (−0.42, 0.42)
Quality of evidence	Very low	Moderate
Number of studies/ participants	(K = 1; n = 99)	(K = 1; n = 86)
Forest plot	Psych 16.01	Psych 16.01
Continuous data effect sizes at follow-up	SMD = −0.23 (−0.62, 0.16)* (24 months)	SMD = −2.01 (−2.53, −1.49) (32 months)
Quality of evidence	Very low	Moderate
Number of studies/ participants	(K = 1; n = 101)	(K = 1; n = 86)
Forest plot	Psych 16.01	Psych 16.01

*Based on skewed data.

5.9.14   The acceptability of treatment

The acceptability of treatment was measured using the number of participants leaving treatment early for any reason, which was extractable from eight studies (BATEMAN1999; BLUM2008; CHANEN unpublished; DAVIDSON2006; KOONS2001; LINEHAN1991; LINEHAN2001; LINEHAN2006; TURNER2000; VANDENBOSCH2002). The data were inconclusive, but there appeared to be no difference between treatment and treatment as usual (see Table 54).

5.10   OVERALL CLINICAL SUMMARY

The overall evidence base for psychological therapies in the treatment of borderline personality disorder is relatively poor: there are few studies; low numbers of patients and therefore low power; multiple outcomes with few in common between studies;

Table 54: Summary evidence table for the acceptability of treatment

Outcome	Leaving treatment early for any reason
Continuous data effect sizes	RR (random effects) = 0.86 (0.57, 1.3) (32% versus 33%)
Quality of evidence	Very low
Number of studies/participants	(K = 8; n = 651)
Forest plot	Psych 17.01

and a heterogeneous diagnostic system that makes it hard to target a specific treatment on patients with specific sets of symptoms because the trials may be too 'all inclusive'. This means that the state of knowledge about the current treatments available is in a development phase rather than one of consolidation. Conclusions are, therefore, provisional and more and better-designed studies need to be undertaken before stronger recommendations can be made.

There is some evidence that psychological therapy programmes, specifically DBT and MBT with partial hospitalisation, are effective in reducing suicide attempts and self-harm, anger, aggression and depression. MBT with partial hospitalisation also reduces anxiety and overall borderline personality disorder symptomatology and improves employment and general functioning. DBT is effective in reducing self-harm in women and therefore should be considered if reducing self-harm is a priority. Otherwise, if a psychological therapy is being considered, it should be delivered in the formats that the evidence suggests are most likely to be effective. That is, rather than outpatient therapy being offered in isolation, it should be provided within a structured programme where the person with borderline personality disorder has other inputs and access to support between sessions, all provided within a coherent theoretical framework. In addition, therapists should be properly trained and provided with adequate supervision.

There is as yet no convincing evidence that the individual psychological therapies are efficacious, although the non-RCT evidence gives some encouragement to the search for less intensive interventions. More well-designed RCTs that test whether individual psychological therapies are effective are needed. Very brief interventions (less than 3 months) do not appear to be effective in the treatment of borderline personality disorder.

Research results are typically reported in terms of comparison of group means before and after treatment. While this gives an indication of the overall treatment effect, it can mask deterioration in a minority of patients. The possibility that some individuals have adverse effects during or following psychological interventions remains. Research trials should report deterioration rates in active treatment and control groups, and clinical services should monitor individual patients' response to treatment.

Referral for psychological treatment should take into account service user preference and where practicable offer a choice of approach.

5.11   OVERALL SUMMARY OF ECONOMIC EVIDENCE

Existing evidence on the cost effectiveness of psychological therapies in the treatment of people with borderline personality disorder is limited and weak. The systematic search of economic literature identified a few studies that assessed the cost effectiveness of a number of interventions covered in this chapter. The results of most studies were characterised by a high degree of uncertainty and could not lead to firm conclusions regarding cost effectiveness. Moreover, in some cases results across studies were inconsistent; further research is needed.

MACT was found to be a potentially cost-effective option for people with recurrent episodes of deliberate self-harm in a RCT conducted in the UK. However, economic modelling undertaken specifically on people with borderline personality disorder suggested that MACT was unlikely to be cost effective in this population.

CBT did not appear to be cost effective when added to treatment as usual in people with borderline personality disorder participating in a UK-based clinical trial. Although it reduced overall healthcare costs, it also reduced considerably the health-related quality of life of people receiving the intervention. Schema-focused cognitive therapy was potentially more cost effective than transference-focused psychotherapy for people with borderline personality disorder in an RCT conducted in the Netherlands. Schema-focused cognitive therapy was slightly less effective than transference-focused psychotherapy but at a substantially lower cost. A cost analysis suggested that provision of psychodynamic interpersonal therapy to people with borderline personality disorder in the US was associated with a reduction in healthcare costs incurred before and after the intervention; however, the study design (before-after design with lack of comparator), the small study sample and the lack of measurement of effectiveness made any inference on the cost-effectiveness of psychodynamic interpersonal therapy impossible.

Four economic modelling studies undertaken using common methods and based on data from a respective number of DBT trials gave somewhat conflicting results: in two of the studies DBT was more effective and less costly than its comparator (which was treatment as usual and client-centred therapy, respectively), in one study DBT was more effective and slightly more costly than treatment as usual (but with an ICER well below the NICE cost-effectiveness threshold) and one study suggested that DBT was slightly more effective than treatment as usual at a significantly higher cost (with an ICER also far above the NICE cost-effectiveness threshold). All studies were characterised by high uncertainty and a number of important limitations, which were more prominent in the fourth analysis. Although no firm conclusions could be drawn regarding the cost effectiveness of DBT, the results of the above analyses indicated that DBT could be a potentially cost-effective option for people with borderline personality disorder. Further modelling carried out to explore the cost effectiveness of MBT with partial hospitalisation suggested that it might also be potentially cost effective in the management of borderline personality disorder. However, economic evidence was very limited, based on data from one small RCT only, and characterised by great uncertainty.

Finally, in a cohort analysis conducted in the UK, therapeutic communities were shown to provide potentially more benefits than general psychiatric care at an increased cost. The cost effectiveness of therapeutic communities is difficult to ascertain from these results because there is no outcome measure that is meaningful across different disease areas (such as QALYs).

It must be noted that the majority of the studies assessing the cost effectiveness of psychological interventions in people with borderline personality disorder used QALYs as the measure of outcome. QALYs were generated based on EQ-5D scores. It has been argued that the EQ-5D is a generic instrument and that it has appeared to be insensitive to changes in health-related quality of life of people with borderline personality disorder. A more condition-specific instrument is required in order to fully capture the impact of psychological interventions on various aspects of health-related quality of life of people with borderline personality disorder.

Future research is needed to explore the cost effectiveness of psychological interventions for people with borderline personality disorder. The full costs of providing such interventions in the context of the NHS are currently unknown; research on these costs will provide some further indications of the potential cost effectiveness of such therapies. Moreover, economic evaluations using a wide economic perspective need to be conducted alongside RCTs evaluating these treatments, so that their clinical and cost effectiveness can be assessed in parallel.

5.12   CLINICAL PRACTICE RECOMMENDATIONS

5.12.1   Role of psychological treatment

5.12.1.1   When providing psychological treatment for people with borderline personality disorder, especially those with multiple comorbidities and/or severe impairment, the following service characteristics should be in place:

- an explicit and integrated theoretical approach used by both the treatment team and the therapist, which is shared with the service user

207

- structured care in accordance with this guideline
- provision for therapist supervision.

Although the frequency of psychotherapy sessions should be adapted to the person's needs and context of living, twice-weekly sessions may be considered.

5.12.1.2 Do not use brief psychological interventions (of less than 3 months' duration) specifically for borderline personality disorder or for the individual symptoms of the disorder, outside a service that has the characteristics outlined in 5.12.1.1.

5.12.1.3 For women with borderline personality disorder for whom reducing recurrent self-harm is a priority, consider a comprehensive dialectical behaviour therapy programme.

5.13   RESEARCH RECOMMENDATIONS

5.13.1   Psychological therapy programmes for people with borderline personality disorder

What is the relative efficacy of psychological therapy programmes (for example, mentalisation-based therapy, dialectical behaviour therapy or similar approach) delivered within well structured, high-quality community-based services (for example, a day hospital setting, or a community mental health team [CMHT]) compared with high-quality community care delivered by general mental health services without the psychological intervention for people with borderline personality disorder?

This question should be answered using a randomised controlled design which reports medium-term outcomes (including cost-effectiveness outcomes) of at least 18 months' duration. They should pay particular attention to the training and supervision of those providing interventions in order to ensure that systems for delivering them are both robust and generalisable.

Why is this important
Research suggests that psychological therapy programmes, such as dialectical behaviour therapy and mentalisation-based therapy as delivered in the studies reviewed for this guideline, may benefit people with borderline personality disorder. However, trials are relatively small, and research is generally at an early stage of development with studies tending to examine interventions delivered in centres of excellence. In addition, few trials have included large numbers of men. Pragmatic trials comparing psychological therapy programmes with high-quality outpatient follow-up by community mental health services would help to establish the effectiveness, costs and cost effectiveness of these interventions delivered in

generalisable settings. The effect of these interventions among men and young people should also be examined.

5.13.2   Outpatient psychosocial interventions

What is the efficacy of outpatient psychosocial interventions (such as cognitive analytic therapy, cognitive behavioural therapy, schema-focused therapy and transference-focused therapy) for people with less severe (fewer comorbidities, higher level of social functioning, more able to depend on self-management methods) borderline personality disorder? This question should be answered using randomised controlled trials which report medium-term outcomes (for example, quality of life, psychosocial functioning, employment outcomes and borderline personality disorder symptomatology) of at least 18 months. They should pay particular attention to training and supervision of those delivering interventions.

Why is this important
The evidence base for the effectiveness of psychosocial interventions for people with personality disorder is at an early stage of development. Data collected from cohort studies and case series suggest that a variety of such interventions may help people with borderline personality disorder. Trials of these interventions would help to develop a better understanding of their efficacy. They should examine the process of treatment delivery in an experimental study, and explore logistical and other factors that could have an impact on the likelihood of larger scale experimental evaluations of these interventions succeeding.

5.13.3   Development of an agreed set of outcomes measures

What are the best outcome measures to assess interventions for people with borderline personality disorder? This question should be addressed in a three-stage process using formal consensus methods involving people from a range of backgrounds, including service users, families or carers, clinicians and academics. The outcomes chosen should be valid and reliable for this patient group, and should include measures of quality of life, function and symptoms for both service users and carers.

The three-stage process should include: (1) identifying aspects of quality of life, functioning and symptoms that are important for service users and families or carers; (2) matching these to existing outcome measures and highlighting where measures are lacking; (3) generating a shortlist of relevant outcome measures to avoid multiple outcome measures being used in future. Where measures are lacking, further work should be done to develop appropriate outcomes.

Psychological and psychosocial treatments

Why is this important

Existing research examining the effects of psychological and pharmacological interventions for people with borderline personality disorder has used a wide range of outcomes measures. This makes it difficult to synthesise data from different studies and to compare interventions. Also, outcomes do not always adequately reflect patient experience. Agreeing outcome measures for future studies of interventions for people with borderline personality disorder will make it easier to develop evidence-based treatment guidelines in the future.

6. PHARMACOLOGICAL AND OTHER PHYSICAL TREATMENTS IN THE MANAGEMENT OF BORDERLINE PERSONALITY DISORDER

6.1   INTRODUCTION

Although the treatment of borderline personality disorder with drugs is normally considered to be adjuvant rather than primary treatment, it is surprisingly common. For example, of 112 people identified using a screening instrument as having borderline personality disorder in a national morbidity survey (personal communication from Dr Min Yang, 2007), 31 (28%) were taking antidepressants, 18 (15.5%) sedative and anxiolytic drugs, and four (4%) antipsychotics. Of these, four (13% of the total) were taking one drug only, 34 (30%) were taking two or more drugs, and four were taking five drugs simultaneously. Although this is a small study, these data suggest polypharmacy is common among this client group.

Possibly because of this widespread use of psychotropic drugs, there have been attempts to justify such interventions on a rational pharmacological basis. Previous guidelines, such as those of the American Psychiatric Association, have divided the symptoms of personality disorders into 'affective dysregulation symptoms', 'impulsive-behavioural dyscontrol symptoms' and 'cognitive-perceptual symptoms' (APA, 2001). The justification for this separation is based on a psychobiological theory of personality pathology (Siever & Davis, 1991) that has been used pragmatically in assisting drug treatment but which has no satisfactory evidence base. Its purpose appears to be to justify pharmacotherapy in the form of selective serotonin reuptake inhibitors (SSRIs) or related antidepressants such as venlafaxine for affect dysregulation, SSRIs for impulsive behaviour and antipsychotic drugs in low dosage for cognitive perceptual symptoms. However, this subdivision of symptoms in borderline personality disorder has never been tested in hypothesis-driven studies and most of the recommendations for individual treatments are based on *post hoc* reconstructions rather than primary evidence.

No psychotropic drug has specific marketing authorisation in the UK for the treatment of borderline personality disorder, although some are licensed for the management of individual symptoms or symptom clusters. This means that recommendations for specific pharmacological interventions would be for off-licence indications. The UK drug licensing process involves submission of at least two placebo-controlled RCTs in human subjects proving efficacy and safety. Furthermore, the UK drug regulatory body (the MHRA) also undertakes post-licensing monitoring of drug safety, collecting and assessing information about adverse reactions and reassessing a drug's safety if necessary. Therefore, in order to make a strong recommendation for a partic-ular drug, robust evidence of its efficacy and safety had to be available to the GDG.

6.1.1   Current practice

Polypharmacy
Published follow-up studies describing the care received by people with borderline personality disorder report between 29 and 67% of people studied are taking psychotropic drugs (median 33%) (Zanarini *et al.*, 2004a). Indeed, many people are taking several classes of psychotropic drugs simultaneously. For example, in a controlled cohort study of mental health service utilisation in the US with 6-year follow-up, over 50% of the 264 patients with borderline personality disorder studied were taking two or more drugs concurrently, over 36% were taking three or more drugs, over 19% were taking four or more and over 11% were taking five or more at 6 years (Zanarini *et al.*, 2004a).

6.1.2   Issues in undertaking trials in people with borderline personality disorder

Participants
The generalisability of clinical trials to clinical populations depends partly on the clinical characteristics of the participants recruited. For example, participants with mild illnesses may be recruited because they are more likely to complete a trial's protocol than participants with more severe illness. In trials involving people with borderline personality disorder there are additional issues. For example, because they can present with a range of symptoms, studies may selectively recruit those with specific symptoms that are not always representative of the disorder.

Also, many trials of borderline personality disorder recruit participants through media advertisements, which may reduce their ability to be representative of those seen in clinical practice. Zanarini and colleagues in the NIMH whitepaper on guide-lines for borderline personality disorder research (Herpertz *et al.*, 2007) have suggested that such participants ('symptomatic volunteers') may be representative of patients with less severe symptoms found in some areas of clinical practice. However, this may reflect the different healthcare system in the US and may not be applicable to the UK. While patients recruited from clinical settings are likely to have serious psychosocial impairment, high service use without much benefit and are symptomati-cally severe, those recruited via media advertisements may have less psychosocial impairment, but still have a history of service use and serious borderline psychopathology. The former are described as chronically symptomatic or treatment-resistant and the latter as acutely symptomatic. Therefore, the findings of trials that recruit symptomatic volunteers are likely to be relevant to those with acute symptoms while those recruiting existing patients may be chronically symptomatic or treatment-resistant. Of course, dichotomising participants like this is artificial since the severity of symptoms occurs on a spectrum. However, it may help to assess the effectiveness

of treatments in different settings. For example, symptomatic volunteers may be analogous to patients presenting in primary care settings, with treatment resistant patients
being more like those in outpatient or hospital settings.

Diagnosis

Another factor affecting the generalisability of trials is the inclusion of patients with
or without comorbid psychiatric disorders. While most trials specifically exclude
people with serious mental illnesses, particularly schizophrenia and bipolar disorder,
as well as substance misuse, all of which can make diagnosing borderline personality
disorder difficult, some trials also exclude people with any comorbid axis I disorder.
In addition, some trials do not specify whether they have excluded people with an axis
I comorbidity. This may reduce generalisability, particularly for some settings such as
forensic or inpatient populations with challenging behaviour, where many people
with borderline personality disorder have a cormobid axis I disorder.

Placebo effect

There is some suggestion that placebo effects are higher in some psychiatric populations than other conditions, and appear to be higher in people with milder illness
(Kirsch *et al.*, 2008). It is unclear whether this is also true in people with borderline
personality disorder.

The placebo effect generally acts more rapidly than with a true drug response,
with the effect later being lost. However, large datasets are needed to examine this
fully, particularly in patients with borderline personality disorder where symptoms
can wax and wane relatively rapidly compared with those of other disorders.

Therapeutic alliance

Most studies do not disentangle the effects of the therapeutic relationship from those
of the drug being studied. Research studies tend to be organised to ensure excellent
clinical management and reliable collection of data, which together may enhance the
therapeutic alliance, which in turn links to positive outcomes in the treatment of
patients with borderline personality disorder. Although studies may be controlled
there is often little information about the non-specific components of clinical
management in the experimental and the control group.

6.1.3   Reviewing the evidence base

In order to make recommendations about specific drug treatments for people with
borderline personality disorder the GDG asked the clinical question:

For people with borderline personality disorder, which treatments are associated
with improvement in mental state and quality of life, reduction in self-harm, service
use, and risk-related behaviour, and/or improved social and personal functioning
while minimising harm (see Appendix 6)?

The most appropriate research design to answer this is the RCT, and therefore the
evidence base reviewed comprised all available RCTs undertaken in people with a

diagnosis of borderline personality disorder. This chapter considers evidence for pharmacological treatments compared with placebo or with another active drug (either alone or in combination). Studies of pharmacological treatments in combination with psychological treatments are considered in the chapter on psychological treatments.

It should be noted that most of the reviewed trials were set up to examine the efficacy of a particular drug in people with a diagnosis of borderline personality disorder rather than to look at specific symptoms. However, while some outcomes used in studies are directly related to the borderline personality disorder diagnosis, others are not and while this does not preclude such outcomes being measured and having some value, they should be recognised as secondary. Therefore, the evidence is presented in this chapter both by drug class and by symptom (as defined by the outcomes). In addition, analyses were undertaken combining all active treatments (compared with placebo) for each symptom.

The summary study characteristics and descriptions of the studies are given in tables below but more information is available in Appendix 16. Similarly, summary evidence profiles are given in tables below with the full profiles in Appendix 18 and the forest plots in Appendix 17. Reviewed studies are referred to by first author surname in capitals plus year of publication. Full references for these studies are in Appendix 16.

6.1.4 Evidence search and overview of studies found

Both published and unpublished studies were sought. The electronic databases searched are given in Table 55. Details of the search strings used are in Appendix 7.

Table 55: Databases searched and inclusion/exclusion criteria for clinical effectiveness of pharmacological treatments

Electronic databases	MEDLINE, EMBASE, PsycINFO
Date searched	Database inception to January 2007
Update searches	July 2007; January 2008; May 2008
Study design	RCT
Population	People with a diagnosis of borderline personality disorder according to DSM or similar criteria
Treatments	Any pharmacological treatment for the treatment of the symptoms of borderline personality disorder
Outcomes	See Table 59

Twenty-eight evaluable RCTs were found in all, of which six were excluded (see Appendix 16). One study was unpublished (see below) and three were three-armed trials. Three trials were identified from the internet-based list of trials undertaken by pharmaceutical companies (ClinicalTrials.Gov) that did not appear to have been published; one was of divalproex by Abbott Laboratories and two were of olanzapine by Eli Lilly. Both companies were contacted for data and Eli Lilly supplied full trial reports (one of which was later published [SCHULZ2008]). A further two trials in press were known to the GDG, one of olanzapine (already identified in the search of ClinicalTrials.Gov) and one comparing haloperidol with risperidone, which was not available.

Data were available to compare anticonvulsants, antidepressants, antipsychotics, naloxone and omega-3 fatty acids with placebo, plus some comparisons of one active agent with another (see Table 56). There is one trial of polypharmacy (two or more drugs at once) and none of treatment sequencing (replacing one treatment with another depending on response). There were no trials of benzodiazepines or of ECT.

Most of the included studies required participants to be drug free before starting the trial, although a few allowed them to continue with existing medication and these are noted in the summary study characteristics tables below. The majority of trials were relatively short (between 4 and 12 weeks), but a few were longer (up to 24 weeks). There were very few follow-up data, with only one trial providing long-term follow-up data (at 18 months). No trial specifically recruited participants during a crisis.

6.1.5 Outcomes

A large number of outcomes, particularly symptom rating scales, were reported by the pharmacological studies. Those that reported sufficient data to be extractable and were not excluded (see Appendix 10) are in Table 57.

See Chapter 2 and Appendix 10 for more information on how the GDG addressed the issue of outcomes.

6.1.6 Potential sources of bias

Since both publication bias and bias because of study funding can affect the conclusions of a review, attempts were made to explore both sources of bias.

Publication bias
There were too few studies to undertake funnel plots to ascertain publication bias so this could not be explored. However, unpublished studies were sought and included where possible. Since no drug has specific marketing approval for borderline personality disorder there may be unpublished studies in which a drug marketed for another disorder has been tested in people with borderline personality disorder. It is not known whether licensing has ever been sought for any drug specifically for people with borderline personality disorder.

Table 56: RCTs of pharmacological treatments

	Anticonvulsants	Antidepressants	Antipsychotics	Other
No. trials (Total participants)	8 RCTs (422)	5 RCTs (306)	10 RCTs (1111)	2 RCTs (79)
Placebo controlled	DELAFUENTE1994 FRANKENBURG2002 HOLLANDER2001 HOLLANDER2003 LOEW2006 NICKEL2004 NICKEL2005 TRITT2003	RINNE2002 SIMPSON2004 SOLOFF1989[†] SOLOFF1993[†]	BOGENSCHUTZ2004 ELILILLY#6253 NICKEL2006 PASCUAL2008 SCHULZ2008 SOLER2005 SOLOFF1989[†] SOLOFF1993[†] ZANARINI2001	HALLAHAN2007 (omega-3 fatty acids) ZANARINI2003 (omega-3 fatty acids)
Versus other active drugs	–	–	SOLOFF1989[†] ZANARINI2004[†]	
Combination trials	–	ZANARINI 2004[†]	ZANARINI2004[†]	

[†]3-armed trial.

Table 57: Outcomes extracted from pharmacological studies

Category	Scale
Aggression	Aggression Questionnaire (AQ) (s) OAS-M - Aggression subscale OAS-M total
Anger	STAXI total (s) STAXI - State Anger (s)
Anxiety	HARS SCL-90 Anxiety (s) STAI (s)
Borderline personality disorder symptomatology	ZAN-BPD
Depression	BDI (s) HRSD MADRS SCL-90 Depression (s)
General functioning	GAF GAS SAT-P - Physical functioning (s) SAT-P - Psychological functioning (s) SAT-P - Sleep, food, free time (s) SAT-P - Work (s) SCL-90 Total (s)
Hostility	Buss-Durkee Hostility Inventory (BDHI) Total SCL-90 - Hostility (s)
Impulsiveness	BIS (s) Self Report Test of Impulse Control (STIC) Total
Mental distress	GSI (part of SCL-90) (s)
Self-harm	OAS-M - Self-injury
Social functioning	SAT-P - Social functioning (s) SCL-90 - Insecurity in social contacts (s) SCL-90 - Interpersonal sensitivity (s)
Suicidality	OAS-M - Suicidality
Acceptability	Number leaving treatment early for any reason
Tolerability	Number leaving treatment early because of side effects Number reporting side effects Number with specific side effects (see individual reviews)

(s) self-completed scale.

Funding bias

Since study funding has been shown to have an effect on study outcome in drug trials, with studies which are industry sponsored or involved a drug company employee more likely to find a positive result than independently funded studies (for example, Tungaraza & Poole, 2007), this was explored as a source of bias. Studies' funding source was therefore noted with the study characteristics and a sub-analysis performed of the placebo-controlled trials to ascertain whether this could be a cause of bias, and therefore whether study funding should be taken into account when grading the evidence. Since so many outcomes were reported by the included studies, this analysis was undertaken by combining all the efficacy outcomes for studies reporting more than one[13], keeping clinician-rated and self-rated outcomes separate. Funding sources were classified as follows:

> None = no funding received to undertake the study (must be explicitly stated in the study)
> Pharma = funding from a pharmaceutical company
> Part-pharma = funding by a combination of funding from a pharmaceutical company and other sources
> Research = funding from research bodies, such as NIMH
> Unclear = funding unclear or not stated.

The sub-analysis showed little difference between the funding sources, other than for studies receiving no funding, which showed much larger effect sizes favouring treatment than studies funded from other sources (see Table 58). This was a surprising finding. Also, the number of studies in each category was low. Therefore, the GDG decided that study funding could not be used as a factor in grading the quality of evidence.

In addition, as a result of this analysis, it was noted that four of the RCTs included for analysis showed large effect sizes favouring treatment compared with those from other pharmacology trials, and that the authors of these trials declared that they had had no funding. The GDG contacted the authors to seek clarification about the funding for these trials. The responses were unclear. The GDG then contacted one of the journals that had published one of the trials to seek clarification about their understanding about sources and levels of funding. The GDG were unable to gain clarity in this regard and took the decision not to consider these trials when drawing up their conclusions. These trials were LOEW2006, NICKEL2004, NICKEL2005 and NICKEL2006.

6.2   ANTICONVULSANTS AND LITHIUM

6.2.1   Introduction

Mood lability is a core symptom of borderline personality disorder, which is often comorbid with bipolar disorder (see Chapter 2). Nevertheless, the degree of overlap

---

[13]Effect sizes calculated with Comprehensive Meta-Analysis and entered into RevMan using the generic inverse variance method to generate forest plots.

Table 58: Summary evidence profile for sub-analyses by study funding

Clinician-rated measures (Forest plot: Pharm 23.01)	SMD (95% CIs)	Overall evidence quality	Number of studies/ number of participants
01 None	−0.99 (−1.56, −0.42)	Moderate	(K = 1; n = 52)
02 Pharma	−0.12 (−0.26, 0.03)	Moderate	(K = 3; n = 696)
03 Research body	−0.4 (−0.73, −0.07)	Moderate	(K = 3; n = 144)
04 Unclear	−0.51 (−1.38, 0.35)	Very low	(K = 1; n = 20)
Total	−0.21 (−0.34, −0.08)	Moderate	(K = 8; n = 912)
Self-rated measures (Forest plot: Pharm 23.02)			
01 None	−1.99 (−2.68, −1.29)*	Moderate	(K = 4; n = 179)
02 Pharma	−0.23 (−0.41, −0.05)	Moderate	(K = 4; n = 652)
03 Research body	−0.25 (−0.61, 0.12)	Very low	(K = 2; n = 117)
04 Unclear	−1.6 (−3.8, 0.6)*	Very low	(K = 2; n = 47)
05 Part-pharma	−0.8 (−2.03, 0.44)	Very low	(K = 1; n = 9)
Total	−0.97 (−1.40, −0.55)*	Moderate	(K = 13; n = 1004)

*Random effects.

is small once the effects of mood lability are accounted for (Paris *et al.*, 2007); in addition some of the association may represent mis-diagnosis. Antimanic drugs including anticonvulsants and lithium are associated with varying degrees of efficacy in bipolar disorder (NCCMH, 2006) and are therefore often used in the treatment of mood-related symptoms in people with borderline personality disorder (Frankenburg & Zanarini, 2002).

Impulsive aggression is also a key feature of borderline personality disorder. Anticonvulsant drugs, mainly carbamazepine and valproate, have a long history of being used to treat aggression and irritability in a wide range of psychiatric and neurological conditions. This use was originally based on the theory that episodic behavioural dyscontrol is a symptom of abnormal CNS neuronal conduction in the same way as an epileptic seizure is (for example, Lewin & Sumners, 1992).

Anticonvulsant drugs act in a number of ways that may be relevant to the treatment of symptoms of borderline personality disorder. These include stabilisation of neuronal conduction via voltage-dependent blockade of Na channels, agonist activity at GABA (an inhibitory neurotransmitter) receptors and antagonist activity at glutamate (an excitatory neurotransmitter) receptors. Glutamate antagonists may have anti-manic and anti-panic effects, and GABA agonists are known to be anxiolytic.

Different anticonvulsant drugs have different mechanisms of action, although the choice of drug tends to be based much more on empirical than pharmacodynamic evidence.

Lithium has mood stabilising effects and is licensed for the treatment and prophylaxis of bipolar disorder. It is also licensed for the treatment of aggressive and self-mutilating behaviour. Impulsive aggression has been linked with reduced CNS serotonergic activity, and this may be influenced by lithium.

Ten studies of anticonvulsants were found. These included two cross-over trials that are difficult to include in meta-analyses unless pre-cross-over data are also provided. Since this was not the case in either trial, both were excluded (one was of lithium and one of alprazolam, carbamazepine, trifluoperazine and tranylcypromine). See Table 59 for a summary of the study characteristics of included studies.

6.2.2   Carbamazepine

Carbamazepine is an anticonvulsant drug that is also licensed for the treatment of trigeminal neuralgia and for prophylaxis in bipolar affective disorder where symptoms have not responded adequately to lithium. It is commonly believed that carbamazepine has specific anti-aggressive properties but the supporting evidence is weak.

The theoretical basis for the use of carbamazepine both to regulate mood and to decrease aggression centres around its mechanism of action: carbamazepine blocks Na channels, decreases glutamate release and reduces the turnover of dopamine and nor-adrenaline (Summary of Product Characteristics: www.medicines.org.uk).

Carbamazepine is a potent inducer of hepatic cytochrome enzymes and therefore interacts with many other commonly prescribed drugs. For example, it induces the metabolism of oral contraceptives, thus increasing the risk of unwanted pregnancy. It is also a human teratogen (for example, Morrow *et al.*, 2006).

Studies reviewed

DELAFUENTE1994
This study compared carbamazepine with placebo in a very small sample of inpatients (n = 20) who met criteria for borderline personality disorder (DSM-IIIR) but not for any axis I 'disturbances' and not for major depressive disorder. However, at baseline the levels of depression were high (HRSD-24 28 [10.92] to 30.7 [4.11]). Participants also received supportive atheoretical psychotherapy throughout, but no details are given as to what this involved. The study found no effect on outcomes for carbamazepine compared with placebo apart from severe psychopathology (favouring placebo). Levels of depression were reduced, but participants would still be classified as depressed based on the APA severity categories for the HRSD (APA, 2000). However, only two patients (both taking carbamazepine) left treatment early. Table 60 shows the summary evidence profile.

Table 59: Study characteristics of included placebo-controlled trials of anticonvulsants

	Carbamazepine	Valproate	Lamotrigine	Topiramate
No. trials (Total participants)	1 RCT (20)	3 RCTs (292)	1 RCT (27)	3 RCTs (129)
Study IDs	DELAFUENTE1994	(1) FRANKENBURG2002 (2) HOLLANDER2001 (3) HOLLANDER2003	TRITT2003	(1) LOEW2006 (2) NICKEL2004 (3) NICKEL2005
N/% female	20/70	(1) 30/100 (2) 16/unclear but around 50 (3) 246/31	27/100	(1) 56/100 (2) 31/100 (3) 44/0
Mean age	32	(1) 27 (2) 39 (3) 40	29	(1) 25 (2) 26 (3) 29
Axis I/II disorders	Specifically excluded	(1) Bipolar II (2) Specifically excluded (3) Cluster B, intermittent explosive disorder or PTSD	Excluded most major axis I disorders	(1) 73% depressive disorders; 52% anxiety; 13% obsessive-compulsive disorder (OCD); 63% somatoform disorders (2)–(3) SMI excluded
Treatment	Carbamazepine mean serum levels achieved 6.44μg to 7.07 μg	(1)–(3) Divalproex	Lamotrigine	(1) Topiramate 200 mg (2) 250 mg (3) 250 mg

Continued

221

Table 59: *(Continued)*

	Carbamazepine	Valproate	Lamotrigine	Topiramate
Additional intervention	Atheoretical psychotherapy	(1)–(2) None (3) 17% used an antidepressant; small number used zolpidem for sleep problems	None	None
Setting	Inpatients, Belgium	(1) Symptomatic volunteers (2) Mixed sample (3) Outpatients, all US	Symptomatic volunteers; Finland	Symptomatic volunteers; Germany
Length of treatment	Mean 4.5 weeks	(1) 6 months (2) 10 weeks (3) 12 weeks	8 weeks	(1) 12 weeks (2) 8 weeks (3) 8 weeks
Length of follow-up	None	None	None	None
Notes		(2) Very high dropout rate data not useable (3) Allowed to continue antidepressants if taken them for ≥ 2 months at baseline and stable		

Table 60: Summary evidence profile for carbamazepine versus placebo

Symptom	Depression	Hostility	Severe psycho-pathology	Leaving treatment early	Leaving treatment early because of side effects	N reporting side effects
Clinician-rated effect size	SMD = −0.52 (−1.41, 0.38)*	–	SMD = 1.27 (0.29, 2.25)	RD = 0.2 (−0.08, 0.48) 20% versus 0%	RD = 0 (−0.17, 0.17) 0% versus 0%	RD = 0 (−0.17, 0.17) 0% versus 0%
Quality of evidence	Very low		Moderate	Very low	Very low	Very low
Number of studies/participants	(K = 1; n = 20)		(K = 1; n = 20)	(K = 1; n = 20)	(K = 1; n = 20)	(K = 1; n = 20)
Forest plot	Pharm 06.06		Pharm 13.01	Pharm 15.06	Pharm 16.05	Pharm 17.05
Self-rated effect size	SMD = −0.67 (−1.57, 0.24)	SMD = −0.34 (−1.23, 0.54)*	–	–	–	–
Quality of evidence	Very low	Very low	–	–	–	–
Number of studies/participants	(K = 1; n = 20)	(K = 1; n = 20)	–	–	–	–
Forest plot	Pharm 07.07	Pharm 09.02	–	–	–	–

*Based on skewed data.

Comment

Only one RCT of carbamazepine in people with borderline personality disorder met inclusion criteria. This study is small and does not show any significant advantage for carbamazepine over placebo with respect to overall psychopathology, depression or hostility. There is no evidence for its use as a mood stabiliser in people with borderline personality disorder, and no good quality evidence on its acceptability and tolerability. Carbamazepine has a propensity to interact with other drugs, and is not recommended for routine use in the treatment of bipolar disorder (NICE, 2006a). There is therefore insufficient evidence on which to recommend carbamazepine for the treatment of borderline personality disorder.

6.2.3 Valproate

Valproate is available as sodium valproate and valproic acid (both of which are licensed only for the treatment of epilepsy) and semisodium valproate (licensed for the treatment of mania). The active ingredient of all preparations is the same and is usually referred to as valproate. Valproate is widely prescribed in the treatment of mania and prophylaxis of bipolar affective disorder. The mechanism of action of valproate is not understood. It is thought to potentiate GABA pathways (Summary of Product Characteristics, www.medicines.org.uk). Valproate is a major human teratogen (for example, Wyszynski *et al.*, 2005) and is not recommended for women of child-bearing potential (NICE, 2007a).

Studies reviewed

FRANKENBURG2002

This study compared divalproex with placebo in 30 women with borderline personality disorder and comorbid bipolar II disorder. The women were moderately ill with borderline personality disorder but were euthymic at baseline. There was a high attrition rate (65% versus 60%).

HOLLANDER2001

This was a small study comparing divalproex with placebo in 16 people (about half were women, but this was unclear because the demographics given for the larger group initially recruited were not all randomised [n = 21]). All the placebo group and half the divalproex group left treatment early.

HOLLANDER2003

This was a large trial comparing divalproex with placebo in 246 people (96 had cluster B personality disorder; the rest had intermittent explosive disorder or PTSD). A relatively large number of participants left treatment early: 47% in the divalproex group and 45% in the placebo group (cluster B group only).

There are three studies of divalproex in the treatment of the symptoms of border-line personality disorder, although one includes other cluster B personality disorders, intermittent explosive disorder or PTSD. Two of the trials were very small, but that which included other cluster B personality disorder diagnoses, was relatively large (n = 246). The attrition rate in all studies was very high.

There appears to be some effect on depression, although the overall findings are not convincing given the mix of personality disorder diagnoses in the larger study. The summary evidence profile is in Table 61.

Comment
Valproate (as divalproex) does not appear to have a reliable effect on symptoms experienced by people with borderline personality disorder. In addition, there is no good quality evidence on its acceptability and tolerability. There is therefore insufficient evidence on which to base a recommendation for the use of valproate in the management of borderline personality disorder.

6.2.4   Lamotrigine

Lamotrigine is an anticonvulsant drug that also has some efficacy in the acute treatment and prophylaxis of depression in the context of bipolar disorder (Calabrese *et al.*, 1999; Schaffer *et al.*, 2006). It is also used to augment clozapine in treatment-resistant schizophrenia (Tiihonen *et al.*, 2003). Lamotrigine is licensed only for the treatment of epilepsy.

Lamotrigine blocks Na channels and reduced glutaminergic neurotransmission (Summary of Product Characteristics; www.medicines.org.uk).

Although generally well tolerated, lamotrigine is associated with skin reactions, some of which are life-threatening, such as Stevens-Johnson syndrome. The risk is greatest during dosage titration and is increased in people also taking valproate (Summary of Product Characteristics; www.medicines.org.uk).

Studies reviewed

TRITT2003
This study compared lamotrigine (up to 200 mg) with placebo for anger symptoms in 27 women with a borderline personality disorder diagnosis aged between 20 and 40. The 8-week study was undertaken in Finland with moderately ill patients recruited through GP advertisements (symptomatic volunteers). Patients were recruited if they perceived that the excessive burdens caused by the situations in their lives produced feelings of constantly increasing anger.

The study found that lamotrigine was statistically significantly more effective on all five subscales of the STAXI anger expression scale, but other symptoms, such as affective instability commonly found in association with anger (Weinstein & Jamison, 2007), were not recorded. No significant side effects were reported.

The summary evidence profile is in Table 62.

Table 61: Summary evidence profile for valproate

Symptom	Aggression	Depression	Hostility	Leaving treatment early	Leaving treatment early because of side effects	N reporting side effects	Weight
Clinician-rated effect size	SMD = −0.15 (−0.56, 0.27)*	–	–	RD = 0.03 (−0.09, 0.14) 47% versus 42%	RD = 0.09 (0.02, 0.17) 14% versus 5%	RD = 0.1 (0.02, 0.17) 74% versus 74%	WMD = 1.04 (−0.54, 2.62)
Quality of evidence	Very low	–	–	Very low	Very low	Very low	Very low
Number of studies/participants	(K = 1; n = 91)	–	–	(K = 3; n = 292)	(K = 3; n = 292)	(K = 3; n = 292)	(K = 1; n = 30)
Forest plot	Pharm 03.01	–	–	Pharm 15.06	Pharm 16.05	Pharm 17.05	Pharm 18.03
Self-rated effect size	SMD = −0.54 (−1.89, 0.82)*	SMD = −0.61 (−1.29, 0.07)*	SMD = −0.15 (−0.91, 0.61)	–	–	–	–
Quality of evidence	Very low	Low	Very low	–	–	–	–
Number of studies/participants	(K = 1; n = 9)	(K = 2; n = 39)	(K = 1; n = 30)	–	–	–	–
Forest plot	Pharm 03.02	Pharm 07.07	Pharm 09.02	–	–	–	–

*Based on skewed data.

Table 62: Summary evidence profile for lamotrigine

Symptom	Anger (state anger)	Leaving treatment early	Leaving treatment early because of side effects	N reporting side effects	Weight change
Clinician-rated effect size	SMD = −2.75 (−3.87, −1.62)	RD = −0.17 (−0.46, 0.12) 6% versus 22%	RD = 0 (−0.15, 0.15) 0% versus 0%	RD = 0 (−0.1, 0.1) 0% versus 0%	WMD = −0.13 (−9.82, 7.22)
Quality of evidence	Moderate	Very low	Very low	Moderate	Very low
Number of studies/ participants	(K = 1; n = 27)	(K = 1; n = 27)	(K = 1; n = 27)	(K = 1; n = 36)	(K = 1; n = 27)
Forest plot	Pharm 04.01	Pharm 15.06	Pharm 16.05	Pharm 17.05	Pharm 18.03

Comment

One small study showed that lamotrigine is effective in reducing anger symptoms in people with borderline personality disorder. There is no evidence for its use as a mood stabiliser in this population. There is no good quality evidence on the acceptability of lamotrigine, although there is no evidence of an increase in reported side effects. However, lamotrigine is associated with risks such as skin rashes, although these can be minimised by titrating the dose gradually. There is insufficient evidence on which to base a recommendation for the use of lamotrigine in the management of borderline personality disorder.

6.2.5   Topiramate

Topiramate is an anticonvulsant drug that is licensed for the treatment of epilepsy and for the prophylaxis of migraine. It has also been used in the treatment of mania (Vieta *et al.*, 2003) and rapid cycling bipolar disorder (Chen *et al.*, 2005) but is not licensed for these indications. Topiramate blocks Na channels, increases the activity of GABA and weakly antagonises the kainate/AMPA subtypes of the glutamate receptor.

It is of note that in RCTs of epilepsy, 5 to 10% of patients randomised to topiramate experienced concentration and/or memory difficulties, depression, nervousness, mood problems and anxiety (Summary of Product Characteristics; www.medicines. org.uk). There are also post-marketing reports of treatment-emergent suicidal ideation and acts (Summary of Product Characteristics; www.medicines.org.uk). It is unknown if people with borderline personality disorder are particularly vulnerable to these side effects. Topiramate is associated reliably with weight loss, a side effect that has been utilised in the management of antipsychotic-induced weight gain (for example, Dursan & Devarajan, 2000).

Studies reviewed

NICKEL2005

This is an 8-week RCT undertaken in Germany comparing topiramate (mean dose 250 mg) with placebo in 44 men who were moderately ill with borderline personality disorder but who did not have depression or substance use disorder. Participants were recruited from outpatients and media advertisements. Those taking topiramate experienced some weight loss during the study (5 kg difference in weight loss compared with those in the placebo group, which was not significant in the overall analyses). The study may have limited generalisability since it was relatively short-term, included only men (although the authors undertook a similar trial in women; see below), participants were excluded if they were taking concurrent psychotropic medication, and there was no follow-up.

NICKEL2004

This is an 8-week RCT undertaken in Germany comparing topiramate (mean dose 250 mg) with placebo in 29 women aged between 20 and 35 who were moderately ill with borderline personality disorder but did not have depression or substance use disorder. Results were similar to the later trial in men (see above), although average difference in weight loss between the two groups was lower (2.3 kg).

LOEW2006

This is a 10-week RCT undertaken in Germany comparing topiramate (mean dose 200 mg) with placebo in 56 women aged between 18 and 35 with borderline personality disorder. The protocol is similar to that for other studies (NICKEL2004, 2005), although different outcomes measures were used. A number of women had axis I comorbidities including depressive disorders (>70%), anxiety disorders (>50%), OCD (>10%) and somatoform disorders (>60%).

It is also of note that the same group found almost identical results with the same instruments in the treatment of women with recurrent depressive disorder who also showed anger symptoms (Nickel *et al.*, 2005a).

There are three small short-term RCTs of topiramate in borderline personality disorder populations recruited by advertisement that are all from the same group of authors based in Germany. They find some benefit for topiramate (mean doses 200 mg to 250 mg) on some aspects of borderline personality disorder symptomatology, including anger, anxiety, depression and hostility. There was an average difference in weight between topiramate and placebo of nearly 5 kg (with those taking topiramate losing weight) but this was not statistically significant. Table 63 shows the summary evidence profile.

Comment

There is some evidence that topiramate is effective in reducing symptoms of anger, anxiety, depression and hostility in people with borderline personality disorder.

Table 63: Summary evidence profile for topiramate

Symptom	Anger (state anger)	Anxiety	Depression	Hostility	Leaving treatment early	Leaving treatment early because of side effects	N reporting side effects	Weight
Clinician-rated effect size	SMD (random effects) = −2.67 (−4.41, −0.94)	SMD = −1.4 (−1.99, −0.81)	–	–	RD = −0.04 (−0.13, 0.05) 4% versus 8%	RD = 0 (−0.05, 0.05) 0% versus 0%	RD = 0 (−0.06, 0.06) 0% versus 0%	WMD = −4.93 (−20.34, 10.48)
Quality of evidence	Moderate	Moderate	–	–	Very low	Very low	Very low	Very low
Number of studies/participants	(K = 2; n = 71)	(K = 1; n = 56)	–	–	(K = 3; n = 131)	(K = 3; n = 131)	(K = 2; n = 86)	(K = 3; n = 127)
Forest plot	Pharm 04.01	Pharm 05.03	–	–	Pharm 15.06	Pharm 16.05	Pharm 17.05	Pharm 18.03
Self-rated effect size	–	–	SMD = −0.51 (−1.04, 0.02)	SMD = −3.1 (−3.89, −2.3)	–	–	–	–
Quality of evidence	–	–	Moderate	Moderate	–	–	–	–
Number of studies/participants	–	–	(K = 1; n = 56)	(K = 1; n = 56)	–	–	–	–
Forest plot	–	–	Pharm 07.07	Pharm 09.02	–	–	–	–

229

There is no evidence for its use as a mood stabiliser in this population and no good-quality evidence on its acceptability and tolerability.

6.3 ANTIPSYCHOTICS

6.3.1 Introduction

Antipsychotic drugs can be broadly described as fitting into two groups; first-generation (typical antipsychotics) and second-generation (atypical antipsychotics). All are licensed for the treatment of schizophrenia. Some second-generation antipsychotics are also licensed for the treatment of mania and prophylaxis of bipolar disorder. First-generation antipsychotics have broader licensed indications than second-generation antipsychotics; as well as psychosis, these include psychomotor agitation, violent or dangerously impulsive behaviour and the short-term management of severe anxiety.

Antipsychotics are associated with a wide range of side effects. First-generation antipsychotics tend to cause more extrapyramidal symptoms and second-generation antipsychotics more weight gain. It should be noted that licensed indications and the nature and severity of individual side effects are drug specific. Further information can be found in the BNF or Summary of Product Characteristics (www.medicines.org.uk).

Many of the licensed indications for antipsychotics are similar to some of the core features of borderline personality disorder. In particular, cognitive and perceptual distortions (such as paranoid ideation, illusions and dissociation), mood symptoms, irritability and aggression may respond to antipsychotics, although in borderline personality disorder they tend to be transient symptoms strongly linked to crisis and mood instability.

Antipsychotic drugs exert their therapeutic effect through dopamine pathways. Most are D_2 antagonists. Some also affect serotonin pathways.

Antipsychotic treatment is sometimes combined with psychological therapy in an attempt to reduce attrition rates (these data are reviewed in the Chapter 5).

6.3.2 Studies reviewed

Eight placebo-controlled trials and one head-to-head trial met inclusion criteria with one being excluded from each category (see Appendix 16). In addition, there was one trial comparing antipsychotic treatment with combined antipsychotic and antidepressant treatment.

6.3.3 Placebo-controlled trials

Summary study characteristics of the included placebo-controlled trials are shown in Table 64.

Table 64: Summary study characteristics of placebo-controlled antipsychotic trials

	Olanzapine	Haloperidol	Aripiprazole	Ziprasidone
No. trials (Total participants)	4 RCTs (833)	2 RCTs (198)	1 RCT (52)	1 RCT (60)
Study IDs	(1) BOGENSCHUTZ2004 (2) ELILILLY#6253 (3) SCHULZ2008[†] (4) ZANARINI2001[†]	(1) SOLOFF1989 (2) SOLOFF1993	NICKEL2006	PASCUAL2008
N/% female	(1) 40/63 (2) 451/74 (3) 314/71 (4) 28/100	(1) 90/76 (2) 108/76	52/83	60/82
Mean age	(1)–(2) 33 (3) 32 (4) 27	(1) 25 (2) 27	22	29
Axis I/II disorders	100% borderline personality disorder	(1) 39% borderline personality disorder/4% schizotypal personality disorder/57% mixed (2) 61% mixed	100% borderline personality disorder	100% borderline personality disorder
Additional intervention	(3) 7.2% (n = 11) of the olanzapine group and	(1) Usual group milieu or individual therapies in	–	Continued previously

Continued

Table 64: (*Continued*)

	Olanzapine	Haloperidol	Aripiprazole	Ziprasidone
	1.9% (n = 3) of the placebo group used psychotherapy	inpatient unit, biperiden hydrochloride for extrapyramidal symptoms (2) Supportive psycho-therapy weekly		prescribed benzodiazepines, antidepressants and mood stabilisers
Setting	(1) Outpatient/community (2)–(3) Outpatients (4) Symptomatic volunteers	Inpatients	Symptomatic volunteers	Outpatients
Length of treatment	(1) (2) (3) 12 weeks (4) 24 weeks	5 weeks	8 weeks	12 weeks
Length of follow-up	None	None	18 months	None
Notes	(2) Three-armed trial (4) Very high attrition rate	–	–	–

†Efficacy data not extractable.

There were few data that could be combined in meta-analysis in order to evaluate antipsychotics as a class, apart from on depression outcomes where there was considerable heterogeneity. A sensitivity analysis was undertaken removing one study (SOLOFF1993) (see Table 65).

Since there were few data that could be combined the individual drugs are considered separately.

6.3.4   Olanzapine versus placebo

Studies reviewed

BOGENSCHUTZ2004
This 12-week study of 40 patients (66% women) compared olanzapine with placebo. The authors used a scale that they had developed as the main outcome (CGI-BPD) based on the nine DSM-IV criteria and the CGI. Data were not extractable because means were given in graphs. Also, the scale does not appear to have been validated. However, the authors concluded that olanzapine was more effective than placebo, although weight gain was significantly greater.

ELILILLY#6253
This 12-week three-armed study of 451 patients (71% women) compared olanzapine (at 2.5 mg and 5 mg to 10 mg) with placebo. The study continued with an open-label phase from which data were not extracted. At the time it was considered by the GDG, the study was unpublished and data were supplied specifically for the development of the guideline. Other than on weight change where those on the higher dose gained more weight than those on the lower dose, there was little or no difference between the outcomes of the two doses (see forest plots 23.1 and 23.2 in Appendix 17). Therefore, data were combined for dichotomous variables; for continuous variables, data from the higher dose group were used since the lower dose is not usually considered a therapeutic dose.

SCHULZ2008
This 12-week study of 314 patients (71% women) compared olanzapine with placebo. The study continued with an open-label phase from which data were not extracted. At the time it was considered by the GDG, the study was unpublished and data were supplied specifically for the development of the guideline. The study reported an average weight gain of 2.86 kg in those taking olanzapine and a mean weight loss of 0.37 kg for those on placebo. The difference was reported as statistically significant (p < 0.001).

ZANARINI2001
This is a 24-week placebo-controlled trial of olanzapine in 28 women with borderline personality disorder. The study suffered a very high attrition rate (58% versus 89%). However, the authors reported that most of the participants who left treatment early

Table 65: Summary evidence profile for antipsychotics versus placebo

Symptom	Aggression	Depression	Mental distress	Self-harm	Suicidality	Borderline personality disorder symptomatology	Leaving treatment early	Leaving treatment early because of side effects	N reporting side effects
Clinician-rated effect size	SMD = 0.04 (−0.12, 0.2)	SMD (random effects) = −0.68 (−1.21, −0.15)	SMD (random effects) = −0.12 (−0.42, 0.18)	RD = 0.01 (−0.02, 0.04) 5% versus 3%	SMD = −0.26 (−0.43, −0.1)*	SMD = −0.15 (−0.31, 0.01)*	RD (random effects) = 0.01 (−0.08, 0.09) 39% versus 38%	RD (random effects) = 0 (−0.04, 0.04) 7% versus 9%	RD (random effects) = 0.02 (−0.03, 0.07) 49% versus 36%
Quality of evidence	Moderate	Low	Very low	High	Moderate	Moderate	Very low	Very low	Very low
Number of studies/participants	(K = 2; n = 585)	(K = 3; n = 168)	(K = 3; n = 615)	(K = 2; n = 608)	(K = 2; n = 586)	(K = 2; n = 596)	(K = 6; n = 945)	(K = 7; n = 1011)	(K = 5; n = 666)
Forest plot	Pharm 0.3.01	Pharm 06.04	Pharm 01.11	Pharm 12.01	Pharm 12.02	Pharm 14.01	Pharm 15.03	Pharm 16.03	Pharm 17.03
Self-rated effect size	–	SMD = −0.41 (−0.77, −0.04)	–	–	–	–	–	–	–
Quality of evidence	–	Moderate	–	–	–	–	–	–	–
Number of studies/participants	–	(K = 2; n = 116)	–	–	–	–	–	–	–
Forest plot	–	Pharm 07.04	–	–	–	–	–	–	–

*Based on skewed data.

234

did so in the last month of the trial. Endpoint data were not extracted and monthly data sought from the study authors.

There were no extractable efficacy data. There was moderate quality evidence that those taking olanzapine gained an average of 2 kg in weight, which seems low compared with clinical experience (see Table 66 and Table 67).

Comment

There is little evidence that olanzapine is efficacious in the treatment of people with borderline personality disorder. People taking olanzapine also tend to experience weight gain compared with those taking placebo.

6.3.5   Haloperidol versus placebo

Studies reviewed

SOLOFF1989

This is a three-arm 5-week placebo-controlled trial comparing amitriptyline (mean 149.1 mg) and haloperidol (mean 4.8 mg) in 90 patients (80%) with borderline and/or schizotypal personality disorder. Participants began the study as inpatients. Several publications were produced from the study, which makes some of the data unclear (for example, the number leaving the study early). The final report does not give details about those leaving early apart from those dropping out in the first 2 weeks, while an interim report on the first 64 patients details drop-outs.

The study reports many outcomes that appear to be measuring similar aspects of functioning. Therefore for depression, the HRSD-24 and BDI were extracted, but not the relevant SCL-90 subscales. For anxiety/hostility, the SCL-90 hostility subscale was extracted but not the relevant Inpatient Multidimensional Psychiatric Scale (IMPS) subscales or the Buss-Durkee Hostility Inventory (BDHI). For cognitive/schizotypal functioning, the IMPS total score was extracted, but not the relevant subscales on either the IMPS or SCL-90. For impulsive/behavioural functioning, the BIS was extracted but not the Ward Scale of Impulsive Action Patterns (WSIAP) (this was developed for the study) or a self-report test of impulse control.

Haloperidol was more effective than placebo for global functioning, depression, hostility, schizotypal symptoms and impulsive behaviour. Amitriptyline was more effective for depression. The authors found no significant interactions based on borderline subtype (borderline personality disorder or schizotypal-borderline) on any outcome measure.

SOLOFF1993

This is a three-arm 5-week placebo-controlled trial (with a 16-week continuation period) comparing haloperidol (mean dose 3.93 mg) and phenelzine in 108 patients with borderline personality disorder (61% with mixed borderline and schizotypal personality disorder). Participants began the study as inpatients. The numbers leaving treatment early are unclear and the study is too old to contact the study authors. The

Table 66: Summary evidence profile for olanzapine versus placebo (efficacy and self-harm/suicidality data)

Symptom	Aggression	Anger	Depression	Mental distress	Self-harm	Suicidality	Borderline personality disorder symptomatology
Clinician-rated effect size	SMD = 0.04 (−0.12, 0.2)	SMD = −0.18 (−0.4, 0.04)	–	SMD (random effects) = −0.21 (−0.53, 0.1)	RD = 0.00 (−0.03, 0.03) 5% versus 3%	SMD = −0.26 (−0.43, −0.1)*	SMD = −0.15 (−0.31, 0.01)*
Quality of evidence	Moderate	Moderate		Very low	High	Moderate	Moderate
Number of studies/ participants	(K = 2; n = 585)	(K = 1; n = 314)		(K = 2; n = 557)	(K = 2; n = 608)	(K = 2; n = 586)	(K = 2; n = 596)
Forest plot	Pharm 03.01	Pharm 04.02		Pharm 11.01	Pharm 12.01	Pharm 12.02	Pharm 14.01
Self-rated effect size	–	–	SMD = 0.45 (−0.23, 1.13)	–	–	–	–
Quality of evidence	–	–	Very low	–	–	–	–
Number of studies/ participants	–	–	(K = 1; n = 34)	–	–	–	–
Forest plot	–	–	Pharm 07.05	–	–	–	–

*Based on skewed data.

236

**Table 67: Summary evidence profile for olanzapine versus placebo
(tolerability and acceptability data)**

	Leaving treatment early	Leaving treatment early because of side effects	N reporting side effects	Weight
Clinician-rated effect size	RD (random effects) = −0.01 (−0.16, 0.14) 39% versus 40%	RD (random effects) = 0.01 (−0.09, 0.1) 8% versus 11%	RD (random effects) = 0.1 (−0.05, 0.25) 64% versus 54%	WMD = 2.96 (2.37, 3.55)
Quality of evidence	Very low	Very low	Very low	Moderate
Number of studies/ participants	(K = 4; n = 833)	(K = 4; n = 833)	(K = 2; n = 488)	(K = 4; n = 668)
Forest plot	Pharm 15.03	Pharm 16.03	Pharm 17.03	Pharm 18.02

study authors reported superior efficacy for phenelzine over haloperidol and placebo. They were unable to replicate their earlier results for haloperidol.

Haloperidol showed an effect on only self-rated depression and hostility symptoms (see Table 68).

Comment
There is some evidence of the effectiveness of haloperidol in reducing symptoms of depression, hostility and impulsivity in people with borderline personality disorder when given in lower doses than for psychotic disorders. However, this is based on a small number of participants. Haloperidol is known to be associated with extrapyramidal symptoms and can prolong the cardiac QTc interval. Prescribers should monitor for extrapyramidal symptoms and follow the advice in the Summary of Product Characteristics regarding cardiac monitoring.

6.3.6   Aripiprazole versus placebo

Studies reviewed

NICKEL2006
This is an 8-week placebo-controlled trial of aripiprazole in 52 patients aged 16 and over (83% women) with an 18-month naturalistic follow-up. During the follow-up period those initially taking aripiprazole continued treatment, and those in the placebo group started treatment, either with aripiprazole or another medication. The follow-up data are therefore difficult to interpret. In addition, the study authors declared in the published paper that no funding had been received for the study. See

Table 68: Summary evidence profile for haloperidol versus placebo

Symptom	Depression	Global functioning	Hostility	Impulsivity	Mental distress	N reporting side effects
Clinician-rated effect size	SMD = −0.05 (−0.42, 0.32)*	SMD = −0.31 (−0.83, 0.21)	SMD = −0.18 (−0.69, 0.34)	SMD = 0.07 (−0.3, 0.43)	–	RD = 0 (−0.04, 0.04) 0% versus 0%
Quality of evidence	Low	Very low	Very low	Very low	–	Very low
Number of studies/ participants	(K = 2; n = 114)	(K = 1; n = 58)	(K = 1; n = 58)	(K = 2; n = 114)	–	(K = 2; n = 126)
Forest plot	Pharm 06.03	Pharm 08.01	Pharm 09.01	Pharm 10.01	–	Pharm 17.03
Self-rated effect size	SMD = −0.09 (−0.46, 0.28)*	–	SMD = −0.46 (−0.84, −0.09)*	SMD = 0.18 (−0.34, 0.7)	SMD = 0.23 (−0.28, 0.75)*	–
Quality of evidence	Very low	–	Low	Moderate	Very low	–
Number of studies/ participants	(K = 2; n = 114)	–	(K = 2; n = 114)	(K = 1; n = 58)	(K = 1; n = 58)	–
Forest plot	Pharm 07.03	–	Pharm 09.02	Pharm 10.02	Pharm 11.01	–

*Based on skewed data.

Section 6.1.6 for the reasons why the GDG did not include this and other studies by this research group when drawing up their overall conclusions about the dataset. See Table 69 for the summary evidence profile.

Comment
There is some evidence from one trial (n = 52) of the effectiveness of aripiprazole in the treatment of anger, anxiety, depression and hostility symptoms in symptomatic volunteers with a diagnosis of borderline personality disorder. However, these studies were undertaken by Nickel and colleagues. There is insufficient evidence on which to base a recommendation for the use of aripiprazole in the management of borderline personality disorder.

6.3.7   Ziprasidone versus placebo

Studies reviewed

PASCUAL2008
This 12-week study of 60 patients (82% women) compared ziprasidone with placebo. Analysis of variance indicated no statistically significant differences between ziprasidone and placebo on the CGI-BPD. Nor were significant differences observed between groups in depressive, anxiety, psychotic or impulsive symptoms. The mean daily dose of ziprasidone was 84.1 mg/day (SD = 54.8; range, 40–200). The drug was seen to be safe and no serious adverse effects were observed. See Table 70 for the summary evidence profile.

Comment
The trial did not show a difference between ziprasidone and placebo on any of the reported outcome measures. There is insufficient evidence on which to base a recommendation for the use of ziprasidone in the management of borderline personality disorder.

6.3.8   Head-to-head trials

For study characteristics of trials of antipsychotics versus another active drug see Table 71.

Table 69: Summary evidence profile for aripiprazole versus placebo

Symptom	Anger	Anxiety	Depression	Hostility	Mental distress	Leaving treatment early	Leaving treatment early because of side effects	N reporting side effects
Clinician-rated effect size	SMD = −1.78 (−2.43, −1.13)	SMD = −0.73 (−1.29, −0.17)	SMD = −1.25 (−1.85, −0.65)	–	–	RD = 0 (−0.07, 0.07) 0% versus 0%	RD = 0 (−0.07, 0.07) 0% versus 0%	RD = 0 (−0.07, 0.07) 0% versus 0%
Quality of evidence	Moderate	Moderate	Moderate	–	–	Very low	Very low	Very low
Number of studies/ Participants	(K = 1; n = 52)	(K = 1; n = 52)	(K = 1; n = 52)	–	–	(K = 1; n = 52)	(K = 1; n = 52)	(K = 1; n = 52)
Forest plot	Pharm 04.01	Pharm 05.01	Pharm 06.03	–	–	Pharm 15.04	Pharm 16.03	Pharm 17.03
Self-rated effect size	–	–	SMD = −1.96 (−2.63, −1.29)	SMD = −1.14 (−1.73, −0.55)	SMD = −1.27 (−1.87, −0.67)	–	–	–
Quality of evidence	–	–	Moderate	Moderate	Moderate	–	–	–
Number of studies/ Participants	–	–	(K = 1; n = 52)	(K = 1; n = 52)	(K = 1; n = 52)	–	–	–
Forest plot	–	–	Pharm 07.03	Pharm 09.02	Pharm 11.01	–	–	–

Table 70: Summary evidence profile for ziprasidone versus placebo

Symptom	Anxiety	Depression	Impulsiveness	Leaving treatment early
Clinician-rated effect size	SMD = -0.11 ($-0.62, 0.39$)	SMD = -0.31 ($-0.82, 0.2$)	SMD = -0.06 ($-0.57, 0.44$)	RD = 0.1 ($-0.15, 0.35$) 57% versus 47%
Quality of evidence	Very low	Very low	Very low	Very low
Number of studies/ participants	(K = 1; n = 60)	(K = 1; n = 60)	(K = 1; n = 60)	(K = 1; n = 60)
Forest plot	Pharm 05.01	Pharm 06.04	Pharm 10.01	Pharm 15.03
Self-rated effect size	–	WMD = -4.4 ($-11.16, 2.36$)	–	–
Quality of evidence	–	Very low	–	–
Number of studies/ participants	–	(K = 1; n = 60)	–	–
Forest plot	–	Pharm 07.03	–	–

Table 71: Study characteristics of trials of antipsychotics versus another active drug

	Loxapine versus chlorpromazine	Olanzapine versus fluoxetine	Amitriptyline versus haloperidol
No. trials (Total participants)	1 RCT (80)	1 RCT (452)	1 RCT (90)
Study IDs	LEONE1982	ZANARINI2004	SOLOFF1989
N/% female	80/55	45/100	90/76
Mean age	31	23	25
Axis I/II	None	None	39% borderline personality disorder/4% schizotypal personality disorder/57% mixed disorders
Additional intervention	Fluorazepam and chloral hydrate as sedatives	None	Usual group milieu or individual therapies in inpatient unit, biperiden hydrochloride for extrapyramidal symptoms
Setting	Outpatients	Outpatients	Inpatients
Length of treatment	6 weeks	8 weeks	5 weeks
Length of follow-up	None	None	None
Notes	Efficacy outcomes not extractable	–	–

Studies reviewed of loxapine versus chlorpromazine

LEONE1982

This is a 6-week trial comparing loxapine with chlorpromazine in 80 outpatients (55% women). Efficacy data were not extractable, but the authors report a statistically significant advantage for loxapine on depression symptoms. No other aspect of functioning was significantly improved for either treatment. See Table 72 for the summary evidence profile.

Table 72: Summary evidence profile for loxapine versus chlorpromazine

Outcome	Efficacy data	Leaving treatment early	Leaving treatment early because of side effects	N reporting side effects
Risk difference	Not extractable	RD = −0.03 (−0.18, 0.13) 13% versus 15%	RD = −0.05 (−0.14, 0.04) 3% versus 8%	RD = −0.08 (−0.28, 0.13) 28% versus 35%
Overall evidence quality	–	Very low	Very low	Very low
Number of studies/ number of participants	–	(K = 1; n = 80)	(K = 1; n = 80)	(K = 1; n = 80)
Forest plot	–	Pharm 15.05	Pharm 16.04	Pharm 17.02

Comment

There is very little evidence comparing one antipsychotic with another, and no evidence for superior efficacy of any one antipsychotic in the management of borderline personality disorder.

Studies reviewed of haloperidol versus phenelzine

SOLOFF1993

This is a 5-week three-arm placebo-controlled trial (with a 16-week continuation period) comparing haloperidol and phenelzine in 108 patients with borderline personality disorder (61% with mixed borderline and schizotypal personality disorder). Participants began the study as inpatients. The numbers leaving treatment early are unclear and the study is too old to contact the study authors. The study authors reported superior efficacy for phenelzine over haloperidol and placebo. They were unable to replicate their earlier results for haloperidol.

Studies reviewed of olanzapine versus fluoxetine

ZANARINI2004

This is an 8-week three-arm trial of olanzapine, fluoxetine and combination olanzapine and fluoxetine (see Section 6.3.9) in 45 women with borderline personality disorder. The authors report that olanzapine and combination treatment significantly reduced both depression and aggression, while fluoxetine greatly reduced impulsive aggression and depression with more rapid treatment effects in the combination and olanzapine arms. This may reflect pharmacodynamic rather than effects specific in borderline personality disorder. The results are reported in Section 6.4.

6.3.9   Combination treatment trials

For study characteristics of trials of combination treatment see Table 73.

Table 73: Study characteristics of trials of combination treatment

	Olanzapine versus olanzapine + fluoxetine
No. trials (Total participants)	1 RCT (452)
Study IDs	ZANARINI2004
N/% female	45/100
Mean age	23
Axis I/II disorders	None
Additional intervention	None
Setting	Outpatients
Length of treatment	8 weeks
Length of follow-up	None

Studies reviewed

ZANARINI2004

This is an 8-week three-arm trial of olanzapine, fluoxetine and combination olanzapine and fluoxetine in 45 women with borderline personality disorder. Evidence for efficacy, and most acceptability and tolerability outcomes, was very low quality. There was evidence that those taking combined treatment were on average 1.5 kg lighter than those taking olanzapine alone. The summary evidence profile is in Table 74.

Pharmacological and other physical treatments

Table 74: Summary evidence profile for olanzapine versus olanzapine + fluoxetine (harm data are for olanzapine + fluoxetine versus olanzapine)

Outcome	Aggression	Depression	Leaving treatment early	Leaving treatment early because of side effects	N reporting side effects	Weight
Clinician-rated effect size	SMD = 0.02 (−0.71, 0.76)*	SMD = 0.39 (−0.35, 1.13)*	RD = 0.13 (−0.06, 0.33) 13% versus 0%	RD = 0.07 (−0.1, 0.23) 7% versus 0%	RD = −0.2 (−0.42, 0.02) 80% versus 100%	WMD = −1.5 (−2.91, −0.09)
Quality of evidence	Very low	Very low	Very low	Very low	Very low	Moderate
Number of studies/ participants	(K = 1; n = 29)	(K = 1; n = 29)	(K = 1; n = 31)	(K = 1; n = 31)	(K = 1; n = 31)	(K = 1; n = 29)
Forest plot	Pharm 03.01	Pharm 06.08	Pharm 16.04	Pharm 17.02	Pharm 17.05	Pharm 18.02

*Based on skewed data.

245

Comment

There is one small trial comparing combination treatment (fluoxetine and olanzapine) with monotherapy. This did not demonstrate an advantage for combined fluoxetine and olanzapine treatment over treatment with olanzapine alone.

6.4   ANTIDEPRESSANTS

6.4.1   Introduction

Antidepressants are primarily used to treat depression although some are also licensed for anxiety spectrum disorders such as panic disorder, OCD and PTSD. A small number are licensed for the treatment of neuropathic pain and nocturnal enuresis in children. Depression and symptoms of depression are common in people with borderline personality disorder.

The mode of action of most antidepressants is via inhibition of monoamine reuptake transporters, which results in increased neurotransmission in serotonin and/or noradrenergic pathways. Monoamine-oxidase inhibitors (MAOIs) such as phenelzine inhibit the metabolism of several monoamines including serotonin.

There is some evidence that low serotonin levels may be associated with aggressive behaviour and impulsivity as well as low mood (Young & Leyton, 2002). Thus it has been suggested that serotonergic antidepressants, such as SSRIs and amitriptyline, may ameliorate aggression and impulsivity.

Treatment with antidepressants, most of which have some effect on serotonin pathways, has been linked with an increase in suicidal thoughts and acts (Friedman & Leon, 2007), with young people being most at risk. Although the overall risk is very low, it is not known if people with pre-existing impulse control problems, such as those with borderline personality disorder, are particularly vulnerable.

6.4.2   Placebo-controlled trials

Three placebo-controlled trials met inclusion criteria with one being excluded (see Table 75).

There were sufficient data to combine the placebo-controlled trials on only one outcome measure, self-rated depression scores. This showed that antidepressants were more effective than placebo in reducing depression symptoms (see Table 76).

Studies reviewed of amitriptyline (tricyclic antidepressant)

SOLOFF1989

This is a 5-week three-arm placebo-controlled trial comparing amitriptyline and haloperidol in 90 patients (80%) with borderline and/or schizotypal personality disorder. Participants began the study as inpatients and were discharged after 2 weeks. Several publications were produced from the study, which makes some of the data

Table 75: Study characteristics of placebo-controlled trials of antidepressants

	Amitriptyline	Fluvoxamine	Phenelzine
No. trials (Total participants)	1 RCT (90)	1 RCT (38)	1 RCT (72)
Study IDs	SOLOFF1989	RINNE2002	SOLOFF1993
N/% female	90/76	38/100	72*/76
Mean age	25	29	27
Axis I/II disorders	39% borderline personality disorder/4% schizotypal personality disorder/57% mixed	29% comorbid depression, 21% comorbid dysthymia, 8% comorbid general anxiety disorder, 32% PTSD	61% comorbid schizotypal personality disorder
Additional intervention	Usual group milieu or individual therapies in inpatient unit, biperiden hydrochloride for extrapyramidal symptoms	None	None
Setting	Inpatient	Mixed sample	Inpatients discharged after 2 weeks
Length of treatment	5 weeks	6 weeks	5 weeks
Length of follow-up phase	None	None	16-week continuation
Notes			*Ns for phenelzine and placebo groups only (three-arm trial)

Table 76: Summary evidence profile for antidepressants versus placebo

Symptom	Depression	Leaving treatment early because of side effects	N reporting side effects
Clinician-rated effect size	–	RD = 0.01 (−0.03, 0.06) 1% versus 0%	RD = 0.08 (0.01, 0.15) 21% versus 13%
Quality of evidence	–	Very low	Very low
Number of studies/ participants	–	(K = 3; n = 167)	(K = 3; n = 167)
Forest plot	–	Pharm 16.01	Pharm 17.01
Self-rated effect size	SMD = −0.46 (−0.82, −0.09)*	–	–
Quality of evidence	Low	–	–
Number of studies/ participants	(K = 2; n = 119)	–	–
Forest plot	Pharm 07.01	–	–

*Based on skewed data.

unclear (for example, the number leaving the study early). The final report does not give details on those leaving early apart from those dropping out in the first 2 weeks, while an interim report on the first 64 patients details drop-outs.

The study reports many outcomes that appear to be measuring similar aspects of functioning. Therefore for depression, the HRSD-24 and BDI were extracted, but not the relevant SCL-90 subscales. For anxiety/hostility, the SCL-90 hostility subscale was extracted, but not the relevant IMPS subscales or BDHI. For cognitive/schizo-typal functioning, the IMPS total score was extracted, but not the relevant subscales on either the IMPS or SCL-90. For impulsive/behavioural functioning, the BIS was extracted but not the WSIAP (this was developed for the study) or a self-report test of impulse control.

Amitriptyline was more effective than placebo in reducing depression symptoms. The authors reported that they found no significant interactions based on borderline subtype (borderline personality disorder or schizotypal-borderline) on any outcome measure. See Table 77 for a summary evidence profile.

Comment
Amitriptyline is effective in the treatment of depressive symptoms in people with a diagnosis of borderline personality disorder, although it is not clear if this effect is

Table 77: Summary evidence profile for amitriptyline versus placebo

Symptom	Depression	Hostility	Impulsivity	Leaving treatment early because of side effects	N reporting side effects
Clinician-rated effect size	SMD = −0.53 (−1.06, 0)*	–	SMD = −0.12 (−0.64, 0.4)	RD = 0 (−0.07, 0.07) 0% versus 0%	RD = 0 (−0.07, 0.07) 0% versus 0%
Quality of evidence	Moderate	–	Very low	Very low	Very low
Number of studies/ participants	(K = 1; n = 57)	–	(K = 1; n = 57)	(K = 1; n = 57)	(K = 1; n = 57)
Forest plot	Pharm 06.01	–	Pharm 10.01	Pharm 16.01	Pharm 17.01
Self-rated effect size		SMD = −0.3 (−0.82, 0.22)	–	–	–
Quality of evidence	–	Very low	–	–	–
Number of studies/ participants	–	(K = 1; n = 58)	–	–	–
Forest plot	–	Pharm 09.02	–	–	–

*Based on skewed data.

related to comorbid depression or the borderline personality disorder diagnosis alone. Amitriptyline has side effects such as dry mouth, which some patients may find hard to tolerate. It should also be noted that amitripytline (and most other tricylics) are considerably more toxic in overdose than other antidepressants, notably SSRIs (Buckley & McManus, 2002). Lofepramine and nortriptyline are safer TCAs, and SSRIs are safer still (Buckley & McManus, 2002). However, there is no evidence for the efficacy of these drugs in people with borderline personality disorder. People taking SSRIs tend to report fewer side effects than those taking TCAs (NCCMH, 2005), but the risk of self-harm by overdose in people with borderline personality disorder is so great that the risks of toxicity after overdose are such that in most instances prescription of amitriptyline should be avoided.

Studies reviewed of fluvoxamine (SSRI)

RINNE2002
This is a 6-week placebo-controlled trial of fluvoxamine in 38 women with a diagnosis of borderline personality disorder. It was followed by a 6-week half cross-over phase and then 12 weeks of open-label treatment. A large proportion of the participants had a comorbid axis I disorder. Only data for the first 6 weeks double-blind treatment were extracted. The study reported efficacy outcomes that were excluded by the GDG so no efficacy data were extracted. See Table 78 for a summary evidence profile.

Comment
There is one small trial of an SSRI, but this did not report extractable efficacy data.

Table 78: Summary evidence profile for fluvoxamine versus placebo

Symptom	Efficacy data	Leaving treatment early for any reason	Leaving treatment early because of side effects	N reporting side effects
Clinician-rated effect size	None extractable	RD = −0.06 (−0.23, 0.11) 5% versus 11%	RD = 0.05 (−0.08, 0.18) 5% versus 0%	RD = 0.34 (0.08, 0.61) 90% versus 56%
Quality of evidence	–	Very low	Very low	Very low
Number of studies/ participants	–	(K = 1; n = 38)	(K = 1; n = 38)	(K = 1; n = 38)
Forest plot	–	Pharm 15.01	Pharm 16.01	Pharm 17.01

Studies reviewed of phenelzine (MAOI)

SOLOFF1993

This is a 5-week three-arm placebo-controlled trial (with a 16-week continuation period), comparing haloperidol and phenelzine in 108 patients with borderline personality disorder (61% with mixed borderline and schizotypal personality disorder). Participants began the study as inpatients. The numbers leaving treatment early are unclear and the study is too old to contact the study authors. There was evidence for effectiveness of phenelzine on hostility symptoms, but not on other symptoms. See Table 79 for the summary evidence profile.

Comment

There is some evidence of the efficacy of phenelzine in the treatment of hostility symptoms in people with borderline personality disorder. However, there was no evidence of efficacy in other symptoms.

6.4.3   Trials comparing active treatments

Studies reviewed of olanzapine versus fluoxetine versus fluoxetine plus olanzapine

ZANARINI2004

This is an 8-week three-arm trial of olanzapine, fluoxetine and combination olanzapine and fluoxetine (see below) in 45 women (symptomatic volunteers) with borderline personality disorder and comorbid axis I disorders, primarily depression and anxiety disorders.

There was moderate quality evidence that fluoxetine was more effective than olanzapine in reducing depression symptoms. See Table 80 for the summary evidence profile.

Comment

One small trial compared olanzapine with fluoxetine finding increased efficacy for fluoxetine in depression symptoms. Olanzapine has a propensity to lead to weight gain. There is no other data comparing an antidepressant with another active treatment.

Fluoxetine versus fluoxetine plus olanzapine

There was no effect on symptoms of either treatment, and some evidence of increased weight in participants who took combination treatment. See Table 81 for the study characteristics and Table 82 for the summary evidence profile.

Comment

One small trial compared treatment with an antidepressant (fluoxetine) with combined olanzapine and fluoxetine. There was no evidence of any advantage for either treatment. Olanzapine has a propensity to lead to weight gain.

Table 79: Summary evidence profile for phenelzine versus placebo

Symptom	Depression	Global functioning	Hostility	Impulsivity	Leaving treatment early because of side effects	N reporting side effects
Clinician-rated effect size	SMD = −0.18 (−0.68, 0.32)*	SMD = 0.14 (−0.36, 0.64)	SMD = −0.64 (−1.15, −0.13)*	SMD = 0 (−0.5, 0.5)	RD = 0 (−0.05, 0.05) 0% versus 0%	RD = 0 (−0.05, 0.05) 0% versus 0%
Quality of evidence	Very low	Very low	Moderate	Very low	Very low	Moderate
Number of studies/ participants	(K = 1; n = 62)	(K = 1; n = 62)	(K = 1; n = 62)	(K = 1; n = 62)	(K = 1; n = 72)	(K = 1; n = 72)
Forest plot	Pharm 07.01	Pharm 08.01	Pharm 09.01	Pharm 10.01	Pharm 16.01	Pharm 17.01

*Based on skewed data.

Table 80: Summary evidence table for olanzapine versus fluoxetine

Symptom	Aggression	Depression	Leaving treatment early	Leaving treatment early because of side effects	N reporting side effects	Weight
Clinician-rated effect size	SMD = −0.2 (−0.93, 0.53)*	SMD = 0.73 (−0.03, 1.49)*	RD = 0.07 (−0.1, 0.24) 7% versus 0%	RD = 0.07 (−0.1, 0.24) 7% versus 0%	RD = −0.43 (−0.69, −0.17) 57% versus 100%	WMD = −2.5 (−4.29, −0.72)
Quality of evidence	Very low	Moderate	Very low	Very low	Very low	Moderate
Number of studies/ participants	(K = 1; n = 29)	(K = 1; n = 29)	(K = 1; n = 30)	(K = 1; n = 30)	(K = 1; n = 30)	(K = 1; n = 29)
Forest plot	Pharm 03.01	Pharm 06.08	Pharm 15.02	Pharm 16.02	Pharm 17.02	Pharm 18.01

* Based on skewed data.

253

Table 81: Study characteristics of fluoxetine versus fluoxetine plus olanzapine

	Fluoxetine + olanzapine
No. trials (Total participants)	1 RCT (45)
Study IDs	ZANARINI2004
N/% female	45/100
Mean age (or range if not given)	23
Axis I/II disorders	100% borderline personality disorder 93% mood disorder 51% substance use disorder 49% anxiety disorder 44% eating disorder
Comparisons	Fluoxetine versus olanzapine versus combination
Setting	Symptomatic volunteers
Length of treatment	8 weeks
Length of follow-up	None

6.4.4   Comment on antidepressants

There are three placebo-controlled trials of antidepressants in people with borderline personality disorder, each of a drug from a different class of antidepressant (tricyclic, SSRI and MAOI). There was some efficacy in reducing individual symptoms, notably depression.

There was one trial comparing fluoxetine with olanzapine and with fluoxetine plus olanzapine. There was also no evidence of increased efficacy of either the antidepressant over the antipsychotic or of the antidepressant over combination treatment.

There is insufficient evidence on which to base a recommendation for antidepressants in the general treatment of borderline personality disorder, although there is evidence that they may be helpful in reducing symptoms of depression where these co-exist. These effects may be the consequence of treating comorbid depression, although dissecting drug effects by diagnosis in this way may not be safe.

6.5   OMEGA-3 FATTY ACIDS

6.5.1   Introduction

The omega-3 fatty acids, eicosapentaenoic acid (EPA) and docosahexaenoic acid (DHA) have important biological functions in the CNS; their presence is essential to

Table 82: **Summary evidence profile for olanzapine + fluoxetine versus fluoxetine (harm data is fluoxetine versus olanzapine + fluoxetine)**

Symptom	Aggression	Depression	Leaving treatment early	Leaving treatment early because of side effects	N reporting side effects	Weight
Clinician-rated effect size	SMD = −0.2 (−0.93, 0.53)*	SMD = −0.41 (−1.19, 0.37)	RD = −0.06 (−0.3, 0.18) 15% versus 21%	RD = 0.07 (−0.1, 0.24) 7% versus 0%	RD = −0.23 (−0.56, 0.1) 57% versus 80%	WMD = 1 (−0.39, 2.39)
Quality of evidence	Very low	Very low	Very low	Very low	Very low	Moderate
Number of studies/ participants	(K = 1; n = 29)	(K = 1; n = 26)	(K = 1; n = 39)	(K = 1; n = 29)	(K = 1; n = 29)	(K = 1; n = 26)
Forest plot	Pharm 03.01	Pharm 06.08	Pharm 15.02	Pharm 16.02	Pharm 17.02	Pharm 18.01

* Based on skewed data

255

maintaining the composition of cell membranes and the consequent normal neuronal activity (Fenton *et al.*, 2000).

Reduced levels of omega-3 fatty acids have been found in the red blood cell membranes of people with a number of psychiatric disorders and this led to the theory that omega-3 fatty acid supplements may be beneficial in restoring mental health (Freeman, 2000).

Omega-3 fatty acids have been used to some effect in people with major depressive disorder and bipolar disorder although there are few high-quality RCTs (Freeman *et al.*, 2006). Several RCTs have been conducted in people with schizophrenia with mixed results (for example, Peet *et al.*, 2001; Fenton *et al.*, 2001). Omega-3 fatty acids may have moderating effects on aggression and impulsivity (Garland & Hallahan, 2006).

6.5.2   Omega-3 fatty acids (fish oil) compared with placebo

Studies reviewed

HALLAHAN2007
This is a 12-week placebo-controlled trial of omega-3 fatty acids in 49 people with recurrent self-harm. Enrolment onto the trial followed presentation at an emergency department for a self-harm episode. Just over 81% had a diagnosis of borderline personality disorder at baseline. The mean BDI depression scores at baseline were in the severe range for both groups. However, there was a statistically and clinically significant difference between the treatment and placebo groups at baseline and therefore baseline scores were used as a covariate. In addition, 53% of participants were on psychotropic medication at baseline; all were taking antidepressants with many also taking benzodiazepines. The authors note that the study was not powered to detect differences in self-harm rates.

ZANARINI2003
This is an 8-week placebo-controlled trial of omega-3 fatty acids in 30 women with a diagnosis of borderline personality disorder. It was designed as a pilot study, although a larger trial is yet to be published. The study recruited via newspaper advertisements in Boston in the US. Patients were excluded if they had a serious mental illness but the number with other axis I disorders is not reported. See Table 83 for study characteristics.

Treatment had some effect on aggression and depression symptoms, although the larger HALLAHAN2007 study carried more weight in the meta-analyses and found a larger effect on symptoms than the smaller ZANARINI2003 study. Over half of the patients in this study were taking antidepressants. There was also some evidence of increased self-harm/suicidality among those in the treatment group. See Table 84 for the summary evidence profile.

Comment
There are two small trials of omega-3 fatty acids (fish oils) in the treatment of people with borderline personality disorder. There is some evidence of efficacy in some

Table 83: Study characteristics for placebo-controlled trials of omega-3 fatty acids

	Omega-3 fatty acid
No. trials (Total participants)	2 RCT (79)
Study IDs	HALLAHAN2007 ZANARINI2003
N/% female	(1) 49/65 (2) 30/100
Mean age (or range if not given)	(1) 30 (2) 26
Axis I/II disorders	(1) 82% borderline personality disorder; severe depression at baseline (not diagnosed as major depressive disorder); recurrent self-harm (2) 100% borderline personality disorder; mild depression symptoms at baseline (not diagnosed as major depressive disorder)
Additional intervention	(1) 53% on psychotropic medication (2) None
Setting	(1) A&E presentations following self-harm (2) Community
Length of treatment	8 weeks
Length of follow-up	None

symptoms. In addition, one of the studies has considerable confounding factors and is therefore hard to interpret. There is therefore insufficient evidence on which to base a recommendation for the use of omega-3 fatty acids in the treatment of borderline personality disorder.

6.6   NALOXONE

6.6.1   Introduction

Naloxone is an opioid antagonist that is licensed for the management of opioid over-dose. It has a short half-life and can only be administered by subcutaneous, intramuscular or intravenous injection.

As well as blocking the effects of opioid drugs, naloxone also blocks the effects of naturally occurring endorphins and enkephalins. It is thought that these

Table 84: Summary evidence profile for omega-3 fatty acids versus placebo

Symptom	Aggression	Depression	Self-harm (dichotomous data)	Leaving treatment early	Leaving treatment early because of side effects	N reporting side effects
Clinician-rated effect size	SMD = −0.52 (−1.02, −0.01)*	SMD = −0.52 (−1.02, −0.01)	RD = 0.01 (−0.19, 0.21) 23% versus 27%	RD = −0.08 (−0.24, 0.08) 12% versus 22%	RD = −0.05 (−0.15, 0.05) 0% versus 5%	Significant heterogeneity: use individual study results
Quality of evidence	Moderate	Moderate	Very low	Very low	Very low	–
Number of studies/participants	(K = 2; n = 66)	(K = 2; n = 66)	(K = 2; n = 69)	(K = 2; n = 79)	(K = 2; n = 79)	–
Forest plot	Pharm 03.01	Pharm 06.07	Pharm 12.01	Pharm 15.07	Pharm 16.06	Pharm 17.06
Self-rated effect size	–	SMD = −0.96 (−1.63, −0.3)				
Quality of evidence	–	Moderate				
Number of studies/participants	–	(K = 1; n = 39)				
Forest plot	–	Pharm 07.08				

* Based on skewed data.

substances may be involved in the reinforcement of self-harming behaviour. It has therefore been suggested that naloxone may reduce self-harming behaviour. It may also reduce dissociative symptoms, which could possibly be mediated through opioid pathways.

6.6.2   Naloxone versus placebo

Studies reviewed

PHILIPSEN2004A

This is placebo-controlled cross-over trial of naloxone in nine women with a diagnosis of borderline personality disorder with moderate to severe dissociative symptoms; most (n = 8) experienced concomitant flashbacks. Patients were given naloxone when they were in an acute dissociative state. Pre-crossover data are not given and therefore the trial data have not been input. The study authors report that although dissociative symptoms decreased after administration of naloxone or placebo, there was no advantage for the study drug. See Table 85 for the study characteristics.

Comment

There were no extractable data from the trial. The GDG took the view that naloxone is not an acceptable treatment for people with borderline personality disorder since it has to be injected and excluded the trial.

Table 85: Study characteristics for placebo-controlled trials of naloxone

	Naloxone
No. trials (Total participants)	1 RCT (9)
Study IDs	PHILIPSEN2004A
N/% female	9/100
Mean age	35
Axis I/II disorders	56% PTSD; 33% eating disorders; 11% OCD; 22% major depressive disorder; 22% social phobia; 22% specific phobia
Additional intervention	None
Setting	Inpatients (n = 7); outpatients (n = 2)
Length of treatment	N/A (two injections while patients in dissociative state)
Length of follow-up	None
Notes	Cross-over trial; data not extractable excluded trial

6.7   EFFECT OF TREATMENT ON SYMPTOMS

6.7.1   Introduction

There are relatively few RCTs examining the efficacy of drug treatments in people with borderline personality disorder, and the data for the efficacy of individual drugs is correspondingly weak. However, several studies reported efficacy for individual symptoms, and so the data are examined by symptom. The symptoms reported are based on the outcomes used by the individual studies.

6.7.2   Placebo-controlled trials – overall effect on symptoms

Where there were sufficient data (at least three placebo-controlled trials reporting similar outcomes) trials of different active treatments were combined to show the effect on symptoms of pharmacological treatment.

There were insufficient data for the following symptoms: aggression, anxiety, global function, quality of life, self-harm/suicidality, service use and severe psychopathology. However, there was an effect of treatment on symptoms of anger (clinician-rated) and depression (self-rated), but not on hostility. See Table 86 for the summary evidence profile.

6.7.3   Aggression

Impulsive aggression is a core symptom of borderline personality disorder. It is associated with reduced serotonergic activity in the brain, and therefore drug treatments aim to target this. There are several aspects to aggression, including the subjective state of anger, readiness to react with anger and tendency to direct anger outward.

The clinical-completed modified OAS was reported by several studies, although all reported different outcomes (mean total at endpoint, mean total change score at endpoint, mean total of the last 4 weeks of the trial and the aggression subscale mean endpoint). One study also reported the Aggression Questionnaire which is a self-report scale. The trials were between 8 and 12 weeks long.

Four studies reported measures of aggression (see Table 87).

There were insufficient studies reporting similar outcomes to undertake an analysis of all active treatments versus placebo. In addition, all the reported data were skewed. The quality of evidence for the effectiveness of treatment on aggression symptoms was very low, and so no conclusions can be drawn. See Table 88 for the summary evidence profile.

Comment
There is no evidence for any drug of an effect of treatment on aggression symptoms in a range of settings.

Table 86: Summary evidence profile for the effect on symptoms of any pharmacological treatment versus placebo (where >= 3 studies available)

Symptom	Anger	Depression	Hostility	Impulsiveness	Mental distress
Clinician-rated	SMD = −1.97 (−2.41, −1.52)	SMD = −0.35 (−0.61, −0.08)	SMD = −0.37 (−0.56, −0.19)	SMD = 0.02 (−0.28, 0.32)	SMD (random effects) = −0.12 (−0.42, 0.18)*
Quality of evidence	High	Moderate	High	High	Very low
Number of studies/participants	(K = 3; n = 121)	(K = 5; n = 223)	(K = 5; n = 480)	(K = 3; n = 174)	(K = 3; n = 615)
Forest plot	Pharm 01.03	Pharm 01.06	Pharm 01.09	Pharm 01.10	Pharm 01.11
Self-rated	–	SMD (random effects) = −0.72 (−1.06, −0.38)*	–	–	–
Quality of evidence	–	Low	–	–	–
Number of studies/participants	–	(K = 9; n = 385)	–	–	–
Forest plot	–	Pharm 01.07	–	–	–

* Based on skewed data.

Table 87: Pharmacological studies reporting aggression outcomes

Study ID	Comparison	Population
ELI LILLY #6253	Olanzapine versus placebo	Outpatients
SCHULZ2008	Olanzapine versus placebo	Outpatients
HOLLANDER2001	Divalproex versus placebo	Mixed sample
HOLLANDER2003	Divalproex versus placebo	Outpatients
ZANARINI2003	Omega-3 fatty acids versus placebo	Symptomatic volunteers
ZANARINI2004	Olanzapine versus fluoxetine versus olanzapine + fluoxetine	Symptomatic volunteers with comorbid mood, substance use or anxiety disorders

6.7.4   Anger

The self-report STAXI was reported by several studies, either the individual subscales or the combined subscale total. Data from the state anger subscale were entered. One study also provided follow-up data based on naturalistic follow-up. No conclusions can be drawn from this since the placebo group took medication during the follow-up period (the data are not presented here). The trials were between 8 and 12 weeks long.

Four studies reported measures of anger (see Table 89).

Sufficient studies reporting similar outcomes were available to undertake an analysis of all active treatments versus placebo. This showed that there was high-quality evidence that treatment with drugs reduces anger symptoms, with effective treatments including topiramate (quality of evidence: moderate) and aripiprazole (quality of evidence: moderate). Both studies were in symptomatic volunteers. No data were skewed. The summary evidence profile is in Table 90.

Comment

There is evidence that topiramate and aripiprazole reduce symptoms of anger within 8 to 12 weeks in symptomatic volunteers who meet diagnosis for borderline personality disorder and a comorbid axis I disorder, in particular depression or anxiety. However, these results are based on the studies by Nickel and colleagues (see Section 6.1.6). There was unlikely to be a difference in anger symptoms between outpatients taking olanzapine and those taking placebo. The GDG concluded that there was no evidence for the effectiveness of drug treatments in controlling symptoms of anger in people with borderline personality disorder.

Comparison	Population	Effect size Quality of evidence Number of studies, number of participants Forest plot	
		Endpoint (clinician-rated)	Endpoint (self-rated)
Divalproex versus placebo	Outpatients; includes cluster B and intermittent explosive disorder	SMD = -0.15 (-0.56, 0.27)* Very low (K = 1; n = 91) Pharm 03.01	SMD = -0.54 (-1.89, 0.82)* Very low (K = 1; n = 9) Pharm 03.02
Olanzapine versus fluoxetine	100% axis I disorders (mood, substance use, anxiety, eating disorders); symptomatic volunteers	SMD = -0.2 (-0.93, 0.53)* Very low (K = 1; n = 29) Pharm 03.01	–
Olanzapine versus fluoxetine + olanzapine	100% axis I disorders (mood, substance use, anxiety, eating disorders); symptomatic volunteers	SMD = 0.02 (-0.71, 0.76)* Very low (K = 1; n = 29) Pharm 03.01	–
Fluoxetine versus fluoxetine + olanzapine	100% axis I (mood, substance use, anxiety, eating); symptomatic volunteers	SMD = -0.2 (-0.93, 0.53)* Very low (K = 1; n = 29) Pharm 03.01	–
Olanzapine versus placebo	Outpatients	SMD = 0.04 (-0.12, 0.2) Moderate (K = 2; n = 585) Pharm 03.01	–
Omega-3 fatty acids	Mild depression (no diagnosis); symptomatic volunteers	SMD = -0.52 (-1.02, -0.01)* Low (K = 2; n = 66) Pharm 03.01	–

* Based on skewed data

Table 89: Pharmacological studies reporting anger outcomes

Study ID	Comparison	Population
NICKEL2004	Topiramate versus placebo	Symptomatic volunteers
NICKEL2005	Topiramate versus placebo	Symptomatic volunteers
NICKEL2006	Aripiprazole versus placebo	Symptomatic volunteers
SCHULZ2008	Olanzapine versus placebo	Outpatients
TRITT2005	Lamotrigine versus placebo	Symptomatic volunteers

6.7.5   Anxiety

The clinician-completed HARS and STAI, and the self-completed SCL-90 (anxiety subscale) were reported. One study also provided follow-up data based on naturalistic follow-up. No conclusions can be drawn from this since the placebo group took medication during the follow-up period (the data are not presented here). The trials were between 8 and 24 weeks long.

Three studies reported measures of anxiety (see Table 91).

There were insufficient studies reporting similar outcomes to undertake an analysis of all active treatments versus placebo. None of the data were skewed. There is evidence for the effectiveness of topiramate and aripiprazole (moderate) in symptomatic volunteers. See Table 92 for the summary evidence profile.

Comment
There is evidence that topiramate and aripiprazole reduce symptoms of anxiety within 8 to 12 weeks in symptomatic volunteers who meet threshold for a diagnosis of borderline personality disorder and a comorbid axis I disorder, most commonly depression or anxiety. However, these results are based on the studies by Nickel and colleagues (see Section 6.1.6). There was no evidence of an effect of other drugs (olanzapine and ziprasidone). The GDG concluded that there was no evidence for the effectiveness of drug treatments in controlling symptoms of anxiety in people with borderline personality disorder.

6.7.6   Depression

The clinician-completed HDRS and MADRS, and the self-completed BDI and SCL-90 (depression subscale), were reported. One study also provided follow-up data based on naturalistic follow-up. No conclusions can be drawn from this since the placebo group took medication during the follow-up period and the data are not presented here. Another trial provided data for 16-week follow-up. The trials were between 8 and 24 weeks long. In most studies participants had measurable depression

Table 90: Summary evidence profile for effectiveness of treatment for anger symptoms (all outcomes)

Comparison	Population	Effect size Quality of evidence Number of studies, number of participants Forest plot	
		Endpoint (clinician-rated)	**Follow-up (clinician-rated)**
Topiramate versus placebo	100% axis I (depression, anxiety, OCD, somatoform disorders, eating disorders, substance/alcohol misuse); symptomatic volunteers	SMD (random effects) = −2.67 (−4.41, −0.94) Moderate (K = 2; n = 71) Pharm 04.01	–
Lamotrigine versus placebo	Symptomatic volunteers	SMD = −2.75 (−3.87, −1.62) Moderate (K = 1; n = 27) Pharm 04.01	–
Aripiprazole versus placebo	100% axis I (depression, anxiety, OCD, somatoform disorders); symptomatic volunteers	SMD = −1.78 (−2.43, −1.13) Moderate (K = 1; n = 52) Pharm 04.01	12 months: SMD = −3.84 (−4.94, −2.74) 18 months: SMD = −3.66 (−4.73, −2.6) Low (K = 1; n = 39) Pharm 04.03
Olanzapine versus placebo	Outpatients	SMD = −0.18 (−0.4, 0.04)* Moderate (K = 1; n = 314) Pharm 04.02	–
Any drug compared with placebo (where similar outcome reported by >= 3 studies)	–	SMD (random effects) = −2.36 (−3.1, −1.61) Moderate (K = 4; n = 150) Pharm 04.01	–

* Based on skewed data

265

Table 91: Pharmacological studies reporting anxiety outcomes

Study ID	Comparison	Population
BOGENSCHUTZ 2004	Olanzapine versus placebo	Outpatients
LOEW2006	Topiramate versus placebo	Symptomatic volunteers
NICKEL2006	Aripiprazole versus placebo	Symptomatic volunteers
PASCUAL2008	Zipransidone versus placebo	Outpatients

symptoms, even in trials where major depressive disorder had been specifically excluded, while some trials specifically included only those with comorbid major depressive disorder. Eleven studies reported measures of depression (see Table 93).

There were sufficient studies reporting similar outcomes to undertake an analysis of all active treatments versus placebo. This showed that treatment with drugs is effective for depression symptoms, although it should be noted that although most participants had some depression symptoms not all had been diagnosed with comorbid affective disorder. However, because of skewed data the overall quality grade was low.

Individual drugs that showed an effect include: divalproex (in a mixed sample of participants including symptomatic volunteers with comorbid bipolar II disorder and graded low because of skewed data); topiramate (in symptomatic volunteers with comorbid affective and anxiety disorders); aripiprazole (in symptomatic volunteers with comorbid affective and anxiety disorders); haloperidol (in inpatients with unstable borderline personality disorder and schizotypal personality disorder [50% also with axis I diagnoses] and moderate depression at baseline, also graded low because of skewed data); and amitriptyline (mix of unstable borderline personality disorder and schizotypal personality disorder; moderate depression at baseline). Omega-3 fatty acids (moderate depression; no formal diagnosis) were also effective although the data were skewed. There were few follow-up data. However, one study added a 16-week continuation phase that showed that placebo was more effective after a total of 21 weeks of treatment.

In the available head-to-head trials, fluoxetine is better than olanzapine (100% axis I disorders [mood, substance use, anxiety, eating] graded low because of skewed data). However, after a further 16 weeks of treatment, the placebo group showed fewer depression symptoms. Phenelzine (mix of borderline personality disorder and schizotypal personality disorder, with axis I disorders; moderate depression at baseline) was not effective compared with placebo. See Table 94 for the summary evidence profile.

Comment

There is evidence that a range of drug treatments are effective in reducing depressive symptoms in people with a diagnosis of borderline personality disorder who have

Table 92: Summary evidence profile for effectiveness of treatment for anxiety symptoms

Comparison	Population	Effect size Quality of evidence Number of studies, number of participants Forest plot		
		Endpoint (clinician-rated)	Endpoint (self-rated)	Follow-up (clinician-rated)
Topiramate versus placebo	100% axis I (depression, anxiety, OCD, somatoform disorders, eating disorders, substance/alcohol misuse); symptomatic volunteers	–	SMD = –1.4 (–1.99, –0.81) Moderate (K = 1; n = 56) Pharm 05.03	–
Aripiprazole versus placebo	100% axis I (depression, anxiety, OCD, somatoform disorders); symptomatic volunteers	SMD = –0.73 (–1.29, –0.17) Moderate (K = 1; n = 52) Pharm 05.01	SMD = –1.41 (–2.03, –0.8) Moderate (K = 1; n = 52) Pharm 05.03	12 months: SMD = –2.67 (–3.56, –1.78) 18 months: SMD = –2.42 (–3.27, –1.57) Low (K = 1; n = 39) Pharm 05.02
Olanzapine versus placebo	Outpatients	–	SMD = 0.21 (–0.46, 0.89) Very low (K = 1; n = 34) Pharm 05.03	–
Ziprasidone versus placebo	Outpatients	SMD = –0.11 (–0.62, 0.39) Very low (K = 1; n = 60) Pharm 05.01	–	–

Table 93: Pharmacological studies reporting depression outcomes

Study ID	Comparison	Population	Depression at baseline (instrument)
BOGENSCHUTZ2004	Olanzapine versus placebo	Outpatients	Not given
DELAFUENTE1994	Carbamazepine versus placebo	Inpatients (excluded major depression)	Severe depression (HRSD-24)
FRANKENBURG2002	Divalproex versus placebo	Symptomatic volunteers; comorbid bipolar II (excluded major depression)	High depression scores (SCL-90)
HOLLANDER2001	Divalproex versus placebo	Mixed sample	Mild depression (BDI)
LEOW2006	Topiramate versus placebo	Symptomatic volunteers with comorbid affective/ anxiety disorders	Not given
NICKEL2006	Aripiprazole versus placebo (includes follow-up data)	Symptomatic volunteers with comorbid affective/anxiety disorders	Severe depression (HRSD)
PASCUAL2008	Ziprasidone versus placebo	Outpatients	Moderate depression (HRSD)
SOLOFF1989	Haloperidol versus amitriptyline versus placebo	Inpatients with unstable borderline personality disorder or schizotypal personality disorder or comorbid borderline/ schizotypal personality disorder	Moderate depression (HRSD)
SOLOFF1993	Haloperidol versus phenelzine versus placebo (includes follow-up data)	Inpatients with comorbid depressive disorders	Moderate depression (HRSD)
ZANARINI2003	Omega-3 fatty acids versus placebo	Symptomatic volunteers	Moderate depression (MADRS)
ZANARINI2004	Olanzapine versus fluoxetine versus olanzapine + fluoxetine	Symptomatic volunteers with comorbid mood, substance use or anxiety disorders	Mild depression (MADRS)

Table 94: Summary evidence profile for effectiveness of treatment for depression symptoms

Comparison	Population	Depression at baseline	Effect size Quality of evidence Number of studies, number of participants Forest plot	
			Clinician rated	**Self-rated**
Antipsychotics versus placebo	–	Moderate depression	SMD (random effects) = –0.68 (–1.21, –0.15) Low (K = 3; n = 168) Pharm 06.04	SMD = –0.41 (–0.77, –0.04) Moderate (K = 2; n = 116) Pharm 07.04
Antidepressants versus placebo	–	Moderate depression	–	SMD = –0.46 (–0.82, –0.09)* Low (K = 2; n = 119) Pharm 07.01
Any drug – compared with placebo (where >= 3 studies report similar outcomes)	–	Moderate depression	SMD = –0.35 (–0.61, –0.08) Moderate (K = 5; n = 223) Pharm 01.06	SMD (random effects) =–0.72 (–1.06, –0.38) Low (K = 9; n = 385) Pharm 01.07
Inpatients				
Carbamazepine versus placebo	Inpatients (excluded major depression)	Severe depression	SMD = –0.52 (–1.41, 0.38)* Very low (K = 1; n = 20) Pharm 06.06	SMD = –0.67 (–1.57, 0.24)* Very low (K = 1; n = 20) Pharm 07.07

Continued

Table 94: (*Continued*)

Comparison	Population	Depression at baseline	Effect size Quality of evidence Number of studies, number of participants Forest plot	
			Clinician rated	Self-rated
Haloperidol versus placebo	Inpatients with unstable borderline personality disorder or schizotypal personality disorder or comorbid borderline personality disorder/schizotypal personality disorder	Moderate depression	SMD = −0.05 (−0.42, 0.32) Low (K = 2; n = 114) Pharm 06.03	SMD = −0.49 (−1.02, 0.04)* Low (K = 1; n = 56) Pharm 07.04
Haloperidol versus placebo (follow-up at 21 weeks)	Inpatients with unstable borderline personality disorder or schizotypal personality disorder or comorbid borderline personality disorder/schizotypal personality disorder	Moderate depression	SMD = 0.97 (0.22, 1.71) (favours placebo)* Low (K = 1; n = 32) Pharm 06.05	SMD = 0.64 (−0.08, 1.36)* (favours placebo) Low (K = 1; n = 32) Pharm 07.06
Amitriptyline versus placebo	Inpatients; mix of unstable borderline personality disorder and schizotypal personality disorder; moderate depression at baseline	Moderate depression	SMD = −0.53 (−1.06, 0) Moderate (K = 1; n = 57) Pharm 06.01	–
Phenelzine versus placebo	Inpatients; mix of unstable borderline personality disorder and schizotypal personality disorder; moderate depression at baseline	Moderate depression	SMD = −0.18 (−0.68, 0.32)* Very low (K = 1; n = 62) Pharm 06.01	–
Phenelzine versus placebo (follow-up at 16 weeks)	Inpatients; mix of unstable borderline personality disorder and schizotypal personality disorder; moderate depression at baseline	Moderate depression	SMD = 0.12 (−0.5, 0.75)* Very low (K = 1; n = 40) Pharm 06.02	SMD = −0.15 (−0.77, 0.47)* Low (K = 1; n = 40) Pharm 07.02

Outpatients

		Not given		SMD = −0.45 (−0.23, 1.13) Very low (K = 1; n = 34) Pharm 07.05
Olanzapine versus placebo	Outpatients		–	
Ziprazidone versus placebo	Outpatients	Moderate depression	SMD = −0.31 (−0.82, 0.2) Very low (K = 1; n = 60) Pharm 06.03	SMD = −0.33 (−0.83, 0.18) Very low (K = 1; n = 60) Pharm 07.04
Symptomatic volunteers				
Omega-3 fatty acids	Symptomatic volunteers/presentations at A&E following self-harm	Moderate/severe depression	SMD = −0.52 (−1.02, −0.01)* Low (K = 2; n = 66) Pharm 06.07	SMD = −0.96 (−1.63, 0.3)* Low (K = 1; n = 39) Pharm 07.08
Divalproex versus placebo	Symptomatic volunteers with bipolar II disorder; other study mixed sample	Some depression present	–	SMD = −0.61 (−1.29, 0.07)* Low (K = 2; n = 39) Pharm 07.07
Topiramate versus placebo	Symptomatic volunteers with comorbid affective/anxiety disorders	Not given	–	SMD = −0.51 (−1.04, 0.02) Moderate (K = 1; n = 56) Pharm 07.07
Aripiprazole versus placebo	Symptomatic volunteers with comorbid affective/anxiety disorders	Severe depression	SMD = −1.25 (−1.85, −0.65) Moderate (K = 1; n = 52) Pharm 06.03	SMD = −1.96 (−2.63, −1.29) Moderate (K = 1; n = 52) Pharm 07.03

Continued

Table 94: (*Continued*)

Comparison	Population	Depression at baseline	Effect size Quality of evidence Number of studies, number of participants Forest plot	
			Clinician rated	**Self-rated**
Olanzapine versus fluoxetine	Symptomatic volunteers with comorbid mood, substance use or anxiety disorders	Mild depression	SMD = 0.73 (−0.03, 1.49)* Low (K = 1; n = 29) Pharm 06.08	–
Olanzapine versus fluoxetine + olanzapine	Symptomatic volunteers with comorbid mood, substance use or anxiety disorders	Not given	SMD = 0.39 (−0.35, 1.13)* Very low (K = 1; n = 29) Pharm 06.08	–
Fluoxetine versus fluoxetine + olanzapine	Symptomatic volunteers with comorbid mood, substance use or anxiety disorders	Mild depression	SMD = −0.41 (−1.19, 0.37)* Very low (K = 1; n = 26) Pharm 06.08	–

*Based on skewed data.

some pre-existing depression symptoms (even if no depression diagnosis has been made). However, the trials are all relatively small and many report skewed data. In addition, most are in different drugs, with populations in a range of settings with various levels of depression symptoms at baseline, and it is quite possible that the depressive symptoms were part of a comorbid syndrome.

In inpatients, there is evidence for the effectiveness of amitriptyline, while haloperidol and phenelzine were not effective. In symptomatic volunteers aripiprazole and topiramate showed some effect.

6.7.7   Hostility

Six studies reported measures of hostility as measured by the clinician-rated BDHI and the self-rated SCL-90 hostility subscale (see Table 95).

Table 95: Pharmacological studies reporting hostility outcomes

Study ID	Comparison	Population
DELAFUENTE1994	Carbamazepine versus placebo	Inpatients (excluded major depression)
FRANKENBURG2002	Divalproex versus placebo	Symptomatic volunteers; comorbid bipolar II disorder (excluded major depression)
LEOW2006	Topiramate versus placebo	Symptomatic volunteers with comorbid affective/ anxiety disorders
NICKEL2006	Aripiprazole versus placebo (includes follow-up data)	Symptomatic volunteers with comorbid affective/ anxiety disorders
SOLOFF1989	Haloperidol versus amitriptyline versus placebo	Inpatients with unstable borderline personality disorder or schizotypal personality disorder or comorbid borderline personality disorder/ schizotypal personality disorder
SOLOFF1993	Haloperidol versus phenelzine versus placebo	Inpatients with comorbid depressive disorders

There were sufficient studies reporting similar outcomes to undertake an analysis of all active treatments versus placebo. This showed a small, not statistically significant effect size. Aripiprazole, haloperidol, phenelzine and topiramate showed some effect on reducing hostility (moderate). See Table 96 for the summary evidence profile.

Comment

In symptomatic volunteers aripiprazole and topiramate showed some effect in reducing hostility (results based on the studies by Nickel and colleagues [see Section 6.1.6]), and in inpatients, haloperidol and phenelzine showed some effect. In outpatients, olanzapine was effective. Overall, antipsychotics (haloperidol and olanzapine) showed some effect on symptoms, although this was modest. Carbamazepine and divalproex were not effective although the studies were underpowered.

6.7.8   Impulsivity

Three studies reported measures of impulsivity as measured by the clinician-rated BIS and the self-rated STIC (see Table 97).

There was unlikely to be a difference between antipsychotics and placebo on reducing impulsivity. The evidence for the effect of antidepressants was inconclusive. See Table 98 for the summary evidence profile.

Comment

There was no evidence for the effectiveness of antipsychotics or antidepressants for impulsivity in people with borderline personality disorder.

6.7.9   Borderline personality disorder symptomatology

Two studies reported the ZAN-BPD scale which measures symptoms of borderline personality disorder (see Table 99).

There were insufficient studies reporting similar outcomes to undertake an analysis of all active treatments versus placebo. There was some evidence that haloperidol was effective in reducing impulsivity in inpatients. The summary evidence profile is in Table 100.

Comment

There is no evidence that olanzapine produces a clinically significant reduction in the symptoms of borderline personality disorder compared with placebo, as measured by the ZAN-BPD.

Table 96: Summary evidence profile for effect of treatment on hostility

Comparison	Population	Effect size Quality of evidence Number of studies, number of participants Forest plot	
		Clinician-rated	Self-rated
Anticonvulsants			
Divalproex versus placebo	100% bipolar II disorder	–	SMD = −0.15 (−0.91, 0.61) Very low (K = 1; n = 30) Pharm 09.02
Topiramate versus placebo	100% axis I (depression, anxiety, OCD, somatoform, eating, substance/alcohol misuse); symptomatic volunteers	–	SMD = −3.1 (−3.89, −2.3) Moderate (K = 1; n = 56) Pharm 09.02
Carbamazepine versus placebo	Inpatients	–	SMD = −0.34 (−1.23, 0.54) Very low (K = 1; n = 20) Pharm 09.02
Antipsychotics			
Haloperidol versus placebo	Mix of unstable borderline personality disorder and schizotypal personality disorder (50% with axis I); moderate depression at baseline; inpatients	SMD = −0.18 (−0.69, 0.34) Very low (K = 1; n = 58) Pharm 09.01	SMD = −0.46 (−0.84, −0.09) Moderate (K = 2; n = 114) Pharm 09.02
Haloperidol versus placebo (follow-up at 21 weeks)	Mix of unstable borderline personality disorder and schizotypal personality disorder (50% with axis I); moderate depression at baseline; inpatients	SMD = −0.17 (−0.87, 0.53) Very low (K = 1; n = 32) Pharm 09.01	–

Continued

Table 96: (Continued)

Comparison	Population	Effect size Quality of evidence Number of studies, number of participants Forest plot	
		Clinician-rated	**Self-rated**
Aripiprazole versus placebo	100% axis I (depression, anxiety, OCD, somatoform); symptomatic volunteers	–	SMD = –1.14 (–1.73, –0.55) Moderate (K = 1; n = 52) Pharm 09.02
Olanzapine versus placebo	No stated comorbidities: outpatients	–	SMD = –0.42 (–0.65, –0.2) Moderate (K = 1; n = 314) Pharm 09.02
Antipsychotics versus placebo	Mix of unstable borderline personality disorder and schizotypal personality disorder; moderate depression at baseline; various settings	–	SMD = –0.43 (–0.63, –0.24) High (K = 3; n = 428) Pharm 09.04
Antidepressants			
Amitriptyline versus placebo	Mix of unstable borderline personality disorder and	–	SMD = –0.3 (–0.82, 0.22) Very low

			(K = 1; n = 58) Pharm 09.02
Phenelzine versus placebo	Mix of borderline personality disorder and schizotypal personality disorder with axis I disorders; moderate depression at baseline; inpatients	SMD = −0.64 (−1.15, −0.13) Moderate (K = 1; n = 62) Pharm 09.01	SMD = −0.34 (−0.84, 0.17) Low (K = 1; n = 62) Pharm 09.02
Phenelzine versus placebo (follow-up at 21 weeks)	Mix of borderline personality disorder and schizotypal personality disorder with axis I disorders; moderate depression at baseline ; inpatients	SMD = −0.56 (−1.19, 0.08) Moderate (K = 1; n = 40)	–
Any drug compared with placebo (where >= 3 studies report similar outcomes) (various settings)		SMD = −0.28 (−0.59, 0.03) Very low (K = 4; n = 166)	–

Table 97: Pharmacological studies reporting impulsivity outcomes

Study ID	Comparison	Population
PASCUAL2008	Ziprasidone versus placebo	Outpatients
SOLOFF1989	Haloperidol versus amitriptyline versus placebo	Inpatients with unstable borderline personality disorder or schizotypal personality disorder or comorbid borderline personality disorder/ schizotypal personality disorder
SOLOFF1993	Haloperidol versus phenelzine versus placebo	Inpatients with comorbid depressive disorders

6.8   EFFECT OF TREATMENT ON GENERAL FUNCTIONING AND OTHER OUTCOMES

6.8.1   Global functioning

One study reported global functioning measured by the GAF, both in clinical populations mostly with comorbid depression (see Table 101).

There were insufficient studies reporting similar outcomes to undertake an analysis of all active treatments versus placebo. Haloperidol showed an effect on global functioning (moderate). The summary evidence profile is in Table 102.

Comment
There was some effect on global functioning for haloperidol after 21 weeks of treatment, although only in one small study. There was no evidence for the effectiveness of phenelzine.

6.8.2   Mental distress

Four studies reported measures of mental distress as measured by the GSI, which is calculated from the self-rated SCL-90 (see Table 103). It should be noted that the SCL-90 is made up of nine subscales, several of which are not usually associated with borderline personality disorder symptomatology. Therefore, this measure may have limited validity in this population.

There were insufficient studies reporting similar outcomes to undertake an analysis of all active treatments versus placebo. There was some evidence that aripiprazole

Table 98: Summary evidence table for studies reporting impulsivity outcomes

Comparison	Population	Effect size Quality of evidence Number of studies, number of participants Forest plot	
		Clinician-rated	Self-rated
Antipsychotics			
Antipsychotics versus placebo			
Haloperidol versus placebo	Inpatients, some with comorbid depressive disorders or schizotypal personality disorder	SMD = 0.07 (−0.3, 0.43) Very low (K = 2; n = 114) Pharm 10.01	SMD = 0.18 (−0.34, 0.7) Very low (K = 1; n = 58) Pharm 10.02
Ziprasidone versus placebo	Outpatients	SMD = −0.06 (−0.57, 0.44) Very low (K = 1; n = 60) Pharm 10.01	
Antidepressants			
Amitriptyline versus placebo	Mix of unstable borderline personality disorder and schizotypal personality disorder; moderate depression at baseline; inpatients	SMD = −0.12 (−0.64, 0.4) Very low (K = 1; n = 57) Pharm 10.01	
Phenelzine versus placebo	Mix of borderline personality disorder and schizotypal personality disorder with axis I disorders; moderate depression at baseline; inpatients	SMD = 0 (−0.5, 0.5) Very low (K = 1; n = 62) Pharm 10.01	
Phenelzine versus placebo (follow-up at 21 weeks)	Mix of borderline personality disorder and schizotypal personality disorder with axis I disorders; moderate depression at baseline; inpatients		SMD = 0.26 (−0.24, 0.76) Very low (K = 1; n = 62) Pharm 10.02

Table 99: Pharmacological studies reporting borderline personality disorder symptomatology

Study ID	Comparison	Population
ELI LILLY#6253	Olanzapine versus placebo	Outpatients
SCHULZ2008	Olanzapine versus placebo	Outpatients

Table 100: Summary evidence table for studies reporting borderline personality disorder symptomatology

Comparison	Population	Effect size Quality of evidence Number of studies, number of participants Forest plot
Olanzapine versus placebo	Outpatients	SMD = −0.15 (−0.31, 0.01) Moderate (K = 2; n = 596) Pharm 14.01

Table 101: Pharmacological studies reporting global functioning measures

Study ID	Comparison	Population
SOLOFF1993	Haloperidol versus phenelzine versus placebo	Inpatients with comorbid depressive disorders

was effective in reducing mental distress in symptomatic volunteers. The summary evidence profile is in Table 104.

Comment

In symptomatic volunteers there is some evidence for the effectiveness of aripiprazole in reducing overall mental distress (based on studies by Nickel and colleagues [see Section 6.1.6]). There is no evidence for the effectiveness of phenelzine or haloperidol.

6.8.3   Self-harm and suicide

Four studies reported self-harm rates or suicide attempts (see Table 105).

Table 102: Summary evidence profile for effect of treatment on global functioning

Comparison	Population	Effect size Quality of evidence Number of studies, number of participants Forest plot (all clinician-rated)
Haloperidol versus placebo	Mix of unstable borderline personality disorder and schizotypal personality disorder (50% with axis I); moderate depression at baseline; inpatients	SMD = −0.31 (−0.83, 0.21) Very low (K = 1; n = 58) Pharm 08.01
Haloperidol versus placebo (follow-up at 21 weeks)	Mix of unstable borderline personality disorder and schizotypal personality disorder (50% with axis I) ; moderate depression at baseline; inpatients	SMD = −0.73 (−1.45, 0) Moderate (K = 1; n = 32) Pharm 08.01
Phenelzine versus placebo	Mix of borderline personality disorder and schizotypal personality disorder with axis I disorders; moderate depression at baseline; inpatients	SMD = 0.14 (−0.36, 0.64) Very low (K = 1; n = 62) Pharm 08.01
Phenelzine versus placebo (follow-up at 21 weeks)	Mix of borderline personality disorder and schizotypal personality disorder with axis I disorders; moderate depression at baseline; inpatients	SMD = −0.17 (−0.79, 0.46) Very low (K = 1; n = 40) Pharm 08.01

Table 103: Pharmacological studies reporting mental distress outcomes

Study ID	Comparison	Population
ELI LILLY#6253	Olanzapine versus placebo	Outpatients
SCHULZ2008	Olanzapine versus placebo	Outpatients
NICKEL2006	Aripiprazole versus placebo (includes follow-up data)	Symptomatic volunteers with comorbid affective/ anxiety disorders
SOLOFF1989	Haloperidol versus amitriptyline versus placebo	Inpatients with unstable borderline personality disorder or schizotypal personality disorder or comorbid borderline personality disorder or/ schizotypal personality disorder

Table 104: Summary evidence table for studies reporting mental distress outcomes (all self-rated)

Comparison	Population	Effect size / Quality of evidence / Number of studies, number of participants / Forest plot	
		Endpoint	**Follow-up**
Haloperidol versus placebo	Mix of unstable borderline personality disorder and schizotypal personality disorder (50% with axis I); moderate depression at baseline; inpatients	SMD = 0.23 (−0.28, 0.75)* Very low (K = 1; n = 58) Pharm 11.01	–
Aripiprazole versus placebo	100% axis I (depression, anxiety, OCD, somatoform); symptomatic volunteers	SMD = −1.27 (−1.87, −0.67) Moderate (K = 1; n = 52) Pharm 11.01	12 months: SMD = −2.62 (−3.5, −1.74) 18 months: SMD = −2.22 (−3.04, −1.4) Moderate (K = 1; n = 39) Pharm 11.01
Olanzapine versus placebo	Outpatients	SMD (random effects) = −0.21 (−0.53, 0.1)* Very low (K = 2; n = 557) Pharm 11.01	
Phenelzine versus placebo	Mix of borderline personality disorder and schizotypal personality disorder with axis I disorders; moderate depression at baseline; inpatients	SMD = −0.23 (−0.73, 0.27)* Very low (K = 1; n = 62) Pharm 11.01	–

* Based on skewed data.

Table 105: Pharmacological studies reporting self-harm/suicidality outcomes

Study ID	Comparison	Population
ELI LILLY #6253	Olanzapine versus placebo	Outpatients
HALLAHAN2007	Omega-3 fatty acids versus placebo	A&E presentation following self-harm
SCHULZ2008	Olanzapine versus placebo	Outpatients
ZANARINI2003	Omega-3 fatty acids versus placebo	Symptomatic volunteers

There was little difference in rates of self-harm between those taking omega-3 fatty acids and those taking placebo. This may be because treatment was unlikely to have an effect within the relatively short time frame of this trial. Similarly, there was little difference in the rate of suicide attempts or self-harm between those taking olanzapine and those taking placebo. See Table 106 for the summary evidence profile.

Comment
There is no evidence that drugs reduce the rates of self-harm and/or suicide attempts. There was no evidence for the effect of other drugs on this outcome.

6.8.4   Psychopathology

Two studies reported the Brief Psychiatric Rating Scale (BPRS) which is a general measure of psychopathology (see Table 107).
There was significant heterogeneity so the results of the two studies are reported separately (see Table 108).

Comment
There was evidence that taking placebo improved general psychopathology compared with carbamazepine, while the evidence for the effectiveness of ziprasidone on this outcome was inconclusive.

6.9   EFFECT OF TREATMENT ON ACCEPTABILITY/ TOLERABILITY OUTCOMES

6.9.1   Leaving treatment early for any reason

Leaving treatment early for any reason (that is, study attrition rate) is reported by most studies, although in a few the data were unclear and clarification was sought from authors.

Table 106: Summary evidence profile for self-harm/suicidality outcomes

Comparison	Population	Effect size Quality of evidence Number of studies, number of participants Forest plot		
		Suicide attempts/self-harm	OAS-M suicidality subscale change scores	ZAN-BPD suicidal/self-mutilating behaviour
Olanzapine versus placebo	Outpatients	RD = 0.01 (−0.02, 0.04) 5% versus 3% High (K = 2; n = 608) Pharm 12.02	SMD = −0.26 (−0.43, −0.1) Moderate (K = 2; n = 586) Pharm 12.02	SMD = 0.3 (0.08, 0.52) Moderate (K = 1; n = 314) Pharm 12.02
Omega-3 fatty acids versus placebo	A&E presentation following self-harm/symptomatic volunteers	RD = 0.01 (−0.19, 0.21) 23% versus 27% Very low (K = 2; n = 69) Pharm 12.02	–	–

Table 107: Pharmacological studies reporting psychopathology outcomes

Study ID	Comparison	Population
DE LAFUENTE1994	Carbamazepine versus placebo	Inpatients
PASCUAL2008	Ziprasidone versus placebo	Outpatients

Table 108: Summary evidence profile for psychopathology outcomes (all clinician-rated)

Comparison	Population	Effect size Quality of evidence Number of studies, number of participants Forest plot
Carbamazepine versus placebo	Inpatients	SMD = 1.27 (0.29, 2.25) Moderate (K = 1; n = 20) Pharm 13.01
Ziprasidone versus placebo	Outpatients	SMD = −0.27 (−0.78, 0.24) Very low (K = 1; n = 60) Pharm 13.01

There were no statistically significant differences between the attrition rates in treatment and comparison groups, although for some drugs attrition rates were relatively high (from both the treatment and comparison groups), including for divalproex and olanzapine. See Table 109 for the summary evidence profile.

Comment

None of the calculated effect sizes was statistically significant and in some trials large numbers left from both treatment and placebo groups, while in others relatively few participants did not complete the study protocol. This makes it difficult to draw conclusions about the acceptability of treatment based on this outcome since there are likely to be factors unrelated to the treatments affecting attrition. These may include aspects of the study protocol that are not analogous to care in the NHS. The failure to complete treatment is higher than in most comparable trials in psychiatric disorders and suggests a poorer level of adherence in this population.

Table 109: Summary evidence profile for leaving treatment early for any reason

Comparison	Population	Effect size Quality of evidence Number of studies, number of participants Forest plot
Antidepressants		
Fluvoxamine versus placebo	100% axis I disorders (depression, dysthymia, anxiety, PTSD; mixed sample)	RD = −0.06 (−0.23, 0.11), 5% versus 11% Very low (K = 1; n = 38) Pharm 15.01
Fluoxetine versus fluoxetine + olanzapine	100% axis I disorders (mood, substance use, anxiety, eating); symptomatic volunteers	RD = −0.06 (−0.3, 0.18) , 15% versus 21% Very low (K = 0; n = 39) Pharm 15.02
Antipsychotics		
Olanzapine versus placebo	Outpatient/community	RD (random effects) = −0.01 (−0.16, 0.14) 39% versus 40% Very low (K = 4; n = 833) Pharm 15.03
Aripiprazole versus placebo	100% axis I disorders (depression, anxiety, OCD, somatoform); symptomatic volunteers	RD = 0 (−0.07, 0.07), 0% versus 0% Very low (K = 1; n = 52) Pharm 15.04
Ziprasidone versus placebo	Outpatients	RD = 0.1 (−0.15, 0.35) , 57% versus 47% Very low (K = 1; n = 60) Pharm 15.03
Antipsychotics versus placebo	Various settings	RD (random effects) =0.01 (−0.08, 0.09) 39% versus 38% Very low (K = 6; n = 945) Pharm 15.03
Olanzapine versus fluoxetine	100% axis I disorders (mood, substance use, anxiety, eating);	RD = 0.07 (−0.1, 0.24), 7% versus 0% Very low

Table 109: (*Continued*)

Comparison	Population	Effect size Quality of evidence Number of studies, number of participants Forest plot
	symptomatic volunteers	(K = 1; n = 30) Pharm 15.04
Olanzapine versus fluoxetine + olanzapine	100% axis I disorders (mood, substance use, anxiety, eating); symptomatic volunteers	RD = 0.13 (−0.06, 0.33), 13% versus 0% Very low (K = 1; n = 31) Pharm 15.05
Loxapine versus chlorpromazine	Outpatients	RD = −0.03 (−0.18, 0.13), 13% versus 15% Very low (K = 1; n = 80) Pharm 15.05
Anticonvulsants		
Divalproex versus placebo	Mix of comorbid bipolar II disorder; comorbid PTSD and intermittent explosive disorder; outpatients	RD = 0.03 (−0.09, 0.14), 47% versus 42% (K = 3; n = 292) Very low Pharm 15.06
Topiramate versus placebo	100% axis I disorders (depression, anxiety, OCD, somatoform, eating, substance/alcohol misuse); symptomatic volunteers	RD = −0.04 (−0.13, 0.05), 4% versus 8% Very low (K = 3; n = 131) Pharm 15.06
Lamotrigine versus placebo	Symptomatic volunteers	RD = −0.17 (−0.46, 0.12), 6% versus 22% Very low (K = 1; n = 27) Pharm 15.06
Carbamazepine versus placebo	Inpatients	RD = 0.2 (−0.08, 0.48), 20% versus 0% Very low (K = 1; n = 20) Pharm 15.06
Anticonvulsants versus placebo	Various settings	RD = 0.01 (−0.07, 0.08), 31% versus 30%

Continued

Table 109: (*Continued*)

Comparison	Population	Effect size Quality of evidence Number of studies, number of participants Forest plot
		Very low (K = 8; n = 470) Pharm 15.06
Omega-3 fatty acids	Mild depression (no diagnosis); symptomatic volunteers	RD = 0 (−0.23, 0.23), 10% versus 10% Very low (K = 1; n = 30) Pharm 15.07

6.9.2   Leaving treatment early because of side effects

Leaving treatment early because of side effects is also reported by most studies. However, few comparisons showed a statistically significant effect size, other than for anticonvulsants versus placebo, where placebo was more tolerable. See Table 110 for the summary evidence profile.

Comment

Only one of the calculated effect sizes was statistically significant (anticonvulsants versus placebo) favouring placebo, although in placebo-controlled trials more participants taking the study drug left treatment early because of side effects compared with those taking placebo.

6.9.3   Number of study participants reporting side effects

Most studies also reported the number of participants reporting side effects (regardless of whether they left treatment early). In the divalproex versus placebo studies there were high levels of side effects reported by those both in the treatment and placebo groups, but in most other studies few side effects were reported. Participants taking olanzapine plus fluoxetine reported fewer side effects than those taking olanzapine alone. Fewer of those in the fluoxetine-only group reported side effects. However, the rate of reporting in all four treatment groups in this trial was very high. See Table 111 for the summary evidence profile.

Comment

In some trials a large proportion of participants reported side effects in both treatment and placebo groups, while in other trials reporting levels were much lower. Given this heterogeneity in these data, they are hard to interpret.

Table 110: Summary evidence profile for leaving treatment early because of side effects

Comparison	Population	Effect size Quality of evidence Number of studies, number of participants Forest plot
Antidepressants		
Amitriptyline versus placebo	Mix of unstable borderline personality disorder and schizotypal personality disorder; moderate depression at baseline; inpatients	RD = 0 (−0.07, 0.07) , 0% versus 0% Very low (K = 1; n = 57) Pharm 16.01
Phenelzine versus placebo	Mix of borderline personality disorder and schizotypal personality disorder with axis I disorders; moderate depression at baseline; inpatients	RD = 0 (−0.05, 0.05) , 0% versus 0% Very low (K = 1; n = 72) Pharm 16.01
Fluvoxamine versus placebo	100% axis I disorders (depression, dysthymia, anxiety, PTSD); mixed sample	RD = 0.05 (−0.08, 0.18), 5% versus 0% Very low (K = 1; n = 38) Pharm 16.01
Antidepressants versus placebo	Various settings	RD = 0.01 (−0.03, 0.06) , 1% versus 0% Very low (K = 3; n = 167) Pharm 16.01
Fluoxetine versus fluoxetine + olanzapine	100% axis I disorders (mood, substance use, anxiety, eating); symptomatic volunteers	RD = 0.07 (−0.1, 0.24) , 7% versus 0% Very low (K = 1; n = 29) Pharm 16.02
Antipsychotics		
Olanzapine versus placebo	Outpatient/community	RD (random effects) =0.01 (−0.09, 0.1) 8% versus 11% Very low (K = 4; n = 833) Pharm 16.03
Aripiprazole versus placebo	100% axis I disorders (depression, anxiety, OCD,	RD = 0 (−0.07, 0.07), 0% versus 0%

Continued

Table 110: (*Continued*)

Comparison	Population	Effect size Quality of evidence Number of studies, number of participants Forest plot
	somatoform); symptomatic volunteers	Very low (K = 1; n = 52) Pharm 16.03
Haloperidol versus placebo	Mix of unstable borderline personality disorder and schizotypal personality disorder (50% with axis I); moderate depression at baseline; inpatients	RD = 0.01 (−0.04, 0.06), 2% versus 0% Very low (K = 2; n = 126) Pharm 16.03
Antipsychotics versus placebo	Various settings	RD = 0.00 (−0.04, 0.04), 7% versus 9% Very low (K = 7; n = 1011) Pharm 16.03
Olanzapine versus fluoxetine	100% axis I disorders (mood, substance use, anxiety, eating); symptomatic volunteers	RD = 0.07 (−0.1, 0.24), 7%versus 0% Very low (K = 1; n = 30) Pharm 16.04
Loxapine versus chlorpromazine	Outpatients	RD = −0.05 (−0.14, 0.04), 3% versus 8% Very low (K = 1; n = 80) Pharm 16.04
Olanzapine versus fluoxetine + olanzapine	100% axis I disorders (mood, substance use, anxiety, eating); symptomatic volunteers	RD = 0.07 (−0.1, 0.23), 7% versus 0% Very low (K = 1; n = 31) Pharm 16.04
Anticonvulsants		
Divalproex versus placebo	Mixed outpatients; symptomatic volunteers	RD = 0.09 (0.02, 0.17), 14% versus 5% (K = 3; n = 292) Very low Pharm 16.05
Topiramate versus placebo	100% axis I disorders (depression, anxiety, OCD,	RD = 0 (−0.05, 0.05), 0% versus 0%

Table 110: (*Continued*)

Comparison	Population	Effect size Quality of evidence Number of studies, number of participants Forest plot
	somatoform, eating, substance/alcohol misuse); symptomatic volunteers	Very low (K = 3; n = 131) Pharm 16.05
Lamotrigine versus placebo	Symptomatic volunteers	RD = 0 (−0.15, 0.15), 0% versus 0% (K = 1; n = 27) Very low Pharm 16.05
Carbamazepine versus placebo	Inpatients	RD = 0 (−0.17, 0.17), 0% versus 0% Very low (K = 1; n = 20) Pharm 16.05
Anticonvulsants versus placebo	Various settings	RD = 0.06 (0.01, 0.11), 9% versus 3% Moderate (K = 8; n = 470) Pharm 16.05
Omega-3 fatty acids	Mild depression (no diagnosis); symptomatic volunteers	RD = 0 (−0.14, 0.14), 0% versus 0% (K = 1; n = 30) Very low Pharm 16.06

6.9.4 Weight change

Some studies of anticonvulsants and antipsychotics reported weight gain/loss or mean weight at endpoint. Weights are in kilograms. This was not reported by trials of antidepressants. Those taking olanzapine showed a statistically significant weight gain of 2.72 kg in studies lasting between 12 and 26 weeks. However, there were few data for other drugs. See Table 112 for the summary evidence profile.

Comment
Few data for weight gain were statistically significant other than for olanzapine, which showed an average weight gain of between 1 kg and 2 kg.

Table 111: Summary evidence profile for number of study participants reporting side effects

Comparison	Population	Effect size Quality of evidence Number of studies, number of participants Forest plot
Antidepressants		
Amitriptyline versus placebo	Mix of unstable borderline personality disorder and schizotypal; personality disorder; moderate depression at baseline; inpatients	RD = 0 (−0.07, 0.07), 0% versus 0% Very low (K = 1; n = 57) Pharm 17.01
Phenelzine versus placebo	Mix of borderline personality disorder and schizotypal personality disorder with axis I disorders; moderate depression at baseline; inpatients	RD = 0 (−0.05, 0.05), 0% versus 0% Moderate (K = 1; n = 72) Pharm 17.01
Fluvoxamine versus placebo	100% axis I disorders (depression, dysthymia, anxiety, PTSD); mixed sample	RD = 0.34 (0.08, 0.61), 90% versus 56% Very low (K = 1; n = 38) Pharm 17.01
Antidepressants versus placebo	Various settings	RD = 0.08 (0.01, 0.15), 21% versus 13% Very low (K = 3; n = 167) Pharm 17.01
Fluoxetine versus fluoxetine + olanzapine	100% axis I disorders (mood, substance use, anxiety, eating); symptomatic volunteers	RD = −0.23 (−0.56, 0.1), 57% versus 80% Very low (K = 1; n = 29) Pharm 17.02
Olanzapine versus fluoxetine	100% axis I disorders (mood, substance use, anxiety, eating); symptomatic volunteers	RD = −0.43 (−0.69, −0.17), 57%versus 100% Very low (K = 1; n = 30) Pharm 17.02

Table 111: (*Continued*)

Comparison	Population	Effect size Quality of evidence Number of studies, number of participants Forest plot
Antipsychotics		
Olanzapine versus placebo	Outpatient/community	RD (random effects) =0.1 (−0.05, 0.25) 63% versus 54% Very low (K = 2; n = 488) Pharm 17.03
Haloperidol versus placebo	Mix of unstable borderline personality disorder and schizotypal personality disorder (50% with axis I); moderate depression at baseline; inpatients	RD = 0 (−0.04, 0.04), 0% versus 0% Moderate (K = 2; n = 126) Pharm 17.03
Aripiprazole versus placebo	100% axis I disorders (depression, anxiety, OCD, somatoform); symptomatic volunteers	RD = 0 (−0.07, 0.07), 0% versus 0% Very low (K = 1; n = 52) Pharm 17.03
Antipsychotics versus placebo	Various settings	RD = 0.04 (−0.01, 0.08), 4% versus 0% Moderate (K = 4; n = 218) Pharm 17.03
Loxapine versus chlorpromazine	Outpatients	RD = −0.08 (−0.28, 0.13), 28% versus 35% Very low (K = 1; n = 80) Pharm 17.04
Fluoxetine + olanzapine versus olanzapine	100% axis I disorders (mood, substance use, anxiety, eating); symptomatic volunteers	RD = −0.2 (−0.42, 0.02), 80% versus 100% Very low (K = 1; n = 31) Pharm 17.04

Continued

Table 111: (*Continued*)

Comparison	Population	Effect size Quality of evidence Number of studies, number of participants Forest plot
Anticonvulsants		
Divalproex versus placebo	Various settings; some bipolar II disorder, cluster B and intermittent explosive disorder	RD = 0.1 (0.02, 0.17), 74% versus 74% Very low (K = 3; n = 292) Pharm 17.05
Topiramate versus placebo	100% axis I disorders (depression, anxiety, OCD, somatoform, eating, substance/alcohol misuse); symptomatic volunteers	RD = 0 (−0.06, 0.06), 0% versus 0% Very low (K = 2; n = 86) Pharm 17.05
Lamotrigine versus placebo	Symptomatic volunteers	RD = 0 (−0.1, 0.1), 0% versus 0% Moderate (K = 1; n = 36) Pharm 17.05
Carbamazepine versus placebo	Inpatients	RD = 0 (−0.17, 0.17), 0% versus 0% Very low (K = 1; n = 20) Pharm 17.05
Anticonvulsants versus placebo	Various settings	RD = 0.06 (0.01, 0.12), 51% versus 48% Very low (K = 7; n = 434) Pharm 17.05
Omega-3 fatty acids	Mild depression (no diagnosis); symptomatic volunteers	Considerable heterogeneity – overall result not reportable Pharm 17.06

Table 112: Summary evidence profile for weight change

Comparison	Population	Effect size/ Quality of evidence Number of studies, number of participants Forest plot
Antidepressants		
Fluoxetine versus fluoxetine + olanzapine	100% axis I disorders (mood, substance use, anxiety, eating); symptomatic volunteers	WMD = 1 (−0.39, 2.39) Moderate (K = 1; n = 26) Pharm 18.01
Fluoxetine versus olanzapine	Symptomatic volunteers; mild depression at baseline	WMD = −2.5 (−4.29, −0.72) Moderate (K = 1; n = 29) Pharm 18.01
Antipsychotics		
Olanzapine versus placebo	Outpatient/community	WMD (random effects) =2.96 (2.37, 3.55) Moderate (K = 4; n = 668) Pharm 18.02
Olanzapine versus fluoxetine	100% axis I disorders (mood, substance use, anxiety, eating); symptomatic volunteers	WMD = −2.5 (−4.29, −0.72) Moderate (K = 1; n = 29) Pharm 18.02
Fluoxetine + olanzapine versus olanzapine	100% axis I disorders (mood, substance use, anxiety, eating); symptomatic volunteers	WMD = −1.5 (−2.91, −0.09) Moderate (K = 1; n = 29) Pharm 18.02
Anticonvulsants		
Divalproex versus placebo	Various settings; some bipolar II disorder, cluster B and intermittent explosive disorder	WMD = 1.04 (−0.54, 2.62) Very low (K = 1; n = 30) Pharm 18.03
Topiramate versus placebo	100% axis I disorders (depression, anxiety, OCD, somatoform, eating, substance/alcohol misuse); symptomatic volunteers	WMD = −4.93 (−20.34, 10.48) Very low (K = 3; n = 127) Pharm 18.03
Lamotrigine versus placebo	Symptomatic volunteers	WMD = −1.3 (−9.82, 7.22) Very low (K = 1; n = 27) Pharm 18.03

6.10   SUMMARY OF CLINICAL EVIDENCE REVIEW

Although there are 28 evaluable studies of pharmacological treatments in people with a diagnosis of borderline personality disorder (six of which did not meet inclusion criteria), there are few studies of each individual drug, which makes it difficult to draw firm conclusions. There are no trials of benzodiazepines or of ECT. Also, there are variations in the populations in each study, including inpatients, outpatients and symptomatic volunteers, and those with and without comorbid axis I disorders. This means that there are very few studies for each drug within each setting, and consequently, any calculations have low power. Another problem with this dataset is the large number of outcomes reported by each individual study and the lack of standard outcome rating scales within the research field. This also makes the dataset very hard to analyse. However, a relatively large proportion of the available studies have been published relatively recently, which points to a growing interest in research in this area. This is encouraging for the future.

There was some evidence that pharmacological treatments can help to reduce specific symptoms experienced by people with borderline personality disorder including anger, anxiety, depression symptoms, hostility and impulsivity, although this is largely based on single studies. However, there is no evidence that they alter the fundamental nature of the disorder in either the short or longer term. The evidence is weak, and it is far from clear if the effects found are the consequence of treating comorbid disorders. In addition, no drug has UK marketing authorisation for these indications in people with borderline personality disorder.

There were too few data to assess quality of life outcomes, self-harm/suicidality (except for omega-3 fatty acids) and service use. It was also not possible to explore potential moderators including:

● % population with bipolar diagnoses
● % psychotic or schizotypal
● high dropout rates.

There were few meaningful data regarding harm, so this was difficult to assess. However, it is well known that treatment with olanzapine can lead to weight gain and diabetes and the use of antipsychotics is associated with significant, and in some cases irreversible, long-term harm, such as tardive dyskinesia.

There were no data to suggest that any drug was effective as an overall mood stabiliser in people with borderline personality disorder. There is therefore insufficient evidence for the treatment of borderline personality disorder or of the individual symptoms of borderline personality disorder. However, pharmacological treatments may be appropriate for the treatment of comorbid disorders, such as depression. Comorbidity is discussed in the care pathway (Chapter 8, Section 8.5).

6.11   HEALTH ECONOMIC EVIDENCE

No evidence on the cost effectiveness of pharmacological and other physical treatments for people with borderline personality disorder was identified by the systematic search of the economic literature. Details on the methods used for the systematic review of economic literature are described in Chapter 3.

6.12   CLINICAL PRACTICE RECOMMENDATIONS

6.12.1   The role of drug treatment

6.12.1.1   Drug treatment should not be used specifically for borderline personality disorder or for the individual symptoms or behaviour associated with the disorder (for example, repeated self-harm, marked emotional instability, risk-taking behaviour and transient psychotic symptoms).

6.12.1.2   Antipsychotic drugs should not be used for the medium- and long-term treatment of borderline personality disorder.

6.12.1.3   Drug treatment may be considered in the overall treatment of comorbid conditions (see Section 8.5.13).

6.12.1.4   Review the treatment of people with borderline personality disorder who do not have a diagnosed comorbid mental or physical illness and who are currently being prescribed drugs, with the aim of reducing and stopping unnecessary drug treatment.

6.13   RESEARCH RECOMMENDATION

6.13.1   Mood stabilisers for people with borderline personality disorder

What is the effectiveness and cost effectiveness of mood stabilisers on the symptoms of borderline personality disorder? This should be answered by a randomised placebo-controlled trial, which should include the medium to long-term impact of such treatment. The study should be sufficiently powered to investigate both the effects and side effects of this treatment.

Why this is important
There is little evidence of the effectiveness of pharmacological treatments for people with personality disorder. However, there have been encouraging findings from small-scale studies of mood stabilisers such as topiramate and lamotrigine, which indicates the need for further research. Emotional instability is a key feature of borderline personality disorder and the effect of these treatments on mood and other key features of this disorder should be studied. The findings of such a study would support the development of future recommendations on the role of pharmacological interventions in the treatment of borderline personality disorder.

An additional research recommendation on the development of an agreed set of outcomes measures for borderline personality disorder can be found in Chapter 5.

7.   MANAGEMENT OF CRISES

7.1   INTRODUCTION

People with borderline personality disorder can often present in a crisis; indeed this is characteristic of many people with the disorder. They present with a range of symptoms and behaviours, including behavioural disturbance, self-harm, impulsive aggression, and short-lived psychotic symptoms, as well as with intense anxiety, depression and anger. As a result they can be regular users of psychiatric and acute hospital emergency services.

Frequent crisis presentation may induce complacency in assessors who fail to estimate the risk accurately; the context of a person's regular contact with services in a crisis inoculates them against assessing each presentation in its own right. The challenge is to assess risk and to manage the crisis without acting in ways that are experienced by the patient as invalidating or minimising their problems while, at the same time, fostering autonomy. In particular, assessors need to avoid interventions that might cause harm, including undermining a person's autonomy; this needs to be balanced against the need to intervene. For example, too rapid an admission to hospital may prevent the person from developing skills to manage emotional crises for themselves, and yet refusal to admit the person may endanger them. Assessors need to take into account that the emotional reactivity of patients with borderline personality disorder may mask underlying comorbidities such as depression, while it may also be part of situationally triggered emotional dysregulation that may resolve with limited intervention.

Medication is commonly started when a patient presents in crisis although there is no evidence for the use of any specific drug or combination of drugs in crisis management. In making judgements on the value of psychotropic drugs in the treatment of borderline personality disorder it is important to be aware that there is much prescribing in crisis settings where the imperative to intervene is very strong, which can lead to further prescribing. This has the potential for a dangerous collusion between the patient and the prescriber that should not be fostered if its only gain is short-term satisfaction that is more than offset by long-term adverse effects from continuing prescribed medication. Therefore, when medication is used, it should always be considered in the context of a longer-term treatment plan involving psychological and/or social intervention. Of particular importance is the issue of the patient's capacity to consent to treatment during times of crisis.

7.2   CURRENT PRACTICE

People with borderline personality disorder may present to a range of emergency services, including ambulance services and emergency departments if self-harm or suicide attempts are part of the presentation, or to the police if public disturbance is part of the picture. Families or carers may be involved in such situations and mental health professionals may approach them in helping to manage crises, while ensuring that they are not over-burdened with responsibility. Crisis teams within mental health services may be called, which enables patients to be offered immediate support while assessment of risk and review of treatment takes place. Offering support and regular contact to the patient is probably the commonest intervention offered in a crisis. On the basis of the crisis evaluation, decisions need to be made to admit or not to admit the person to hospital, offer immediate daily contact including home treatment, arrange outpatient care, continue with scheduled treatment, or start more formal treatment.

7.3   REVIEWING THE EVIDENCE BASE

When searching for RCTs of treatments in people with borderline personality disorder (see Chapter 5 and other evidence review chapters for details of the search for RCTs), none was found in which people had been specifically recruited during a crisis period. Since crises can both pass and recur quickly in people with borderline personality disorder, this is not surprising. Also, the nature of crises in this client group means that there are considerable issues of consent in recruiting people to trials.

This chapter is therefore based on the expert opinion of the GDG (see Chapter 3).

7.4   GENERAL MANAGEMENT OF CRISES

The overall aim during the management of a crisis is to help the person to return to a more stable level of mental functioning as quickly as possible without inducing any harmful effects that might prolong the problems. The person's autonomy should be maintained as far as possible, their safety and that of others assured, and their emotions, impulses and behaviours reduced to a manageable level. Supportive and empathic comments are necessary in the first instance and these may be particularly beneficial if the initial contact in the crisis is by telephone. Medication use should be limited, following the general guidance below, and should be only for short-term use. Specific goals of treatment should be set.

Vignette of a service user accessing services during a crisis

Being faced with someone with borderline personality disorder in crisis can unfortunately be perceived as quite a daunting prospect for some people. In my experience, though, it needn't be. Responses don't need to be that profound or from people with a lot of experience of working with this disorder, they just need to be human. Despite this, I have often found that responses to me during such crises were variable and at times unhelpful. However, I have been fortunate

299

enough to have had some very good responses over the period of my disorder that illustrate this point.

I was experiencing a period of extremely low mood. My psychiatrist who had seen me through most of my journey had recently retired, I had been raped about 6 months previously, and after a destructive relationship had also been through a pregnancy and termination. After previously making so much progress, I was deteriorating rapidly in mood. I had cut-off from my psychologist and was withdrawing from work with my CPN. Although most of the time I was too low to care, at other times I was desperate for connectedness and needed to know that someone was aware of how desperate I was feeling.

I made contact with the out-of-hours social work team by telephone. This is a service that deals primarily with emergency child, welfare and older adult issues, but takes over from the adult mental health out-of-hours service after 10pm. Although most of the social workers are Approved Social Workers and have knowledge of the Mental Health Act and the issues associated with it, the majority of them have not had any specific therapeutic training or any specialist personality disorder related training. The point I am making is that none of them was a skilled therapist with experience of people with borderline personality disorder.

I phoned them and got through to one of the duty social workers who helped me to calm myself enough to talk. This was achieved by him remaining calm, reassuring me and not making me feel that I had limited time or needed to rush. A few gentle questions helped, not, what I call, big questions such as 'How can I help?' or 'What's happened?', but smaller questions such as 'I can hear you're upset, how long have you been feeling like this', 'do you know why you're feeling like this?' Big questions such as 'How can I help?' or 'What's wrong?' always feel to me too overwhelming and too difficult to find a starting point.

It only took a few little questions to get me started and to begin to articulate what I was feeling. I hadn't spoken to anyone in days – so I really appreciated not feeling rushed, pressurised into speaking or sensing that the other person was getting frustrated with my inarticulateness. Once I began to speak, it became easier to express my distress with the help of some prompts, some empathy and some help with articulation when I was struggling to express myself. I didn't need much. I just needed a sense of connection to another human being, to feel reassured; I needed to feel that the person cared enough to have some empathy. I didn't need anything done, nor crisis admission or referral (even though I would need a more assertive intervention in the weeks to come, that wasn't what I was looking for or needed at that moment). I didn't even need anyone specialised. I just needed a caring human response, to hear a voice.

We were on the telephone for only about 30 minutes in total, but it was enough to help and to 'hold' me through the night. The social worker gave me the option to ring back again in the night if I needed to, and although I didn't wish to, it helped me to contain my feelings knowing that the option was there. The other useful outcome of this phone contact was the knowledge that there would be some kind of follow-up the next morning. The social worker following my phone call sent a fax to my CPN outlining the details of my contact with a request for my CPN to ring me to check that I was OK and if any further follow-up was needed. Just knowing that a follow-up and human contact were in place for the next day makes such a big difference in helping to contain the intense emotional distress that can occur with this disorder and stopping situations escalating into admission, crises or self-harm. On this occasion and during a number of previous situations I didn't need much from my CPN once he rang; sometimes I would need an extra visit, but on other occasions the knowledge that the phone call was to take place was enough to settle me for the time being. Knowing that I'd have an opportunity to talk about the feelings I was struggling with was enough to enable me to manage until the next scheduled appointment time.

7.4.1 Clinical practice recommendations

Clinical practice recommendations relating to the management of crises in primary care can be found in the care pathway in Chapter 8.

7.4.1.1 When a person with borderline personality disorder presents during a crisis, consult the crisis plan and:
- maintain a calm and non-threatening attitude
- try to understand the crisis from the person's point of view
- explore the person's reasons for distress
- use empathic open questioning, including validating statements, to identify the onset and the course of the current problems
- seek to stimulate reflection about solutions
- avoid minimising the person's stated reasons for the crisis
- refrain from offering solutions before receiving full clarification of the problems
- explore other options before considering admission to a crisis unit or inpatient admission
- offer appropriate follow-up within a time frame agreed with the person.

7.5 PHARMACOLOGICAL MANAGEMENT OF CRISES

7.5.1 Drug treatment during crises

It is recognised that drug treatments are often considered part of the emergency management of crises, sometimes including self-harm and violence, however no specific treatments for borderline personality disorder or for particular symptom clusters are recommended.

Moreover, no drug has UK marketing authorisation for the treatment of borderline personality disorder so the continued prescribing of medication in people with borderline personality disorder should be undertaken with caution and normal prescribing practice for patients at risk of self-harm should be taken into account. Prescribing should, wherever possible, be limited to the short-term management of crises using sedatives (or to the treatment of comorbid conditions). Some advice is available on the use of medication off licence – see 'Use of licensed medicines for unlicensed applications in psychiatric practice' published by the Royal College of Psychiatrists (http://www.rcpsych.ac.uk/files/pdfversion/cr142.pdf).

There is no evidence that people with borderline personality disorder, or other personality disorders, need higher doses of drugs than other patients. Dosage should be kept within the normal therapeutic range.

Drugs prescribed during a crisis may be continued inadvertently after the symptoms that presented during the crisis have subsided. This may lead to service users taking more than one drug for an extended period of time – there is evidence that people with borderline personality disorder are prescribed inappropriate combinations and an excessive number of psychotropic drugs at any one time (Sansone *et al.*, 2003; Zanarini *et al.*, 2004a). Any patient, whatever their current diagnosis, who describes a treatment history of polypharmacy with limited beneficial response should have their diagnosis reviewed with consideration given to the possibility of borderline personality disorder.

7.5.2   Clinical practice recommendations

7.5.2.1   Before starting short-term drug treatments for people with borderline personality disorder during a crisis (see recommendation 7.5.2.2):
- ● ensure that there is consensus among prescribers and other involved professionals about the drug used and that the primary prescriber is identified
- ● establish likely risks of prescribing, including alcohol and illicit drug use
- ● take account of the psychological role of prescribing (both for the individual and for the prescriber) and the impact that prescribing decisions may have on the therapeutic relationship and the overall care plan, including long-term treatment strategies
- ● ensure that a drug is not used in place of other more appropriate interventions
- ● use a single drug
- ● avoid polypharmacy whenever possible.

7.5.2.2   Short-term use of sedative medication may be considered cautiously as part of the overall treatment plan for people with borderline personality disorder in a crisis.[14] The duration of treatment should be agreed with them, but should be no longer than 1 week.

---

[14]Sedative antihistamines are not licensed for this indication and informed consent should be obtained and documented.

7.5.2.3   When prescribing short-term drug treatment for people with borderline personality disorder in a crisis:
- choose a drug (such as a sedative antihistamine[15]) that has a low side-effect profile, low addictive properties, minimum potential for misuse and relative safety in overdose
- use the minimum effective dose
- prescribe fewer tablets more frequently if there is a significant risk of overdose
- agree with the person the target symptoms, monitoring arrangements and anticipated duration of treatment
- agree with the person a plan for adherence
- discontinue a drug after a trial period if the target symptoms do not improve
- consider alternative treatments, including psychological treatments, if target symptoms do not improve or the level of risk does not diminish
- arrange an appointment to review the overall care plan, including pharmacological and other treatments, after the crisis has subsided.

7.5.2.4   After a crisis has resolved or subsided, ensure that crisis plans, and if necessary the overall care plan, are updated as soon as possible to reflect current concerns and identify which treatment strategies have proved helpful. This should be done in conjunction with the person with borderline personality disorder and their family or carers if possible, and should include:
- a review of the crisis and its antecedents, taking into account environmental, personal and relationship factors
- a review of drug treatment, including benefits, side effects, any safety concerns and role in the overall treatment strategy
- a plan to stop drug treatment begun during a crisis, usually within 1 week
- a review of psychological treatments, including their role in the overall treatment strategy and their possible role in precipitating the crisis.

7.5.2.5   If drug treatment started during a crisis cannot be stopped within 1 week, there should be a regular review of the drug to monitor effectiveness, side effects, misuse and dependency. The frequency of the review should be agreed with the person and recorded in the overall care plan.

7.6   MANAGEMENT OF INSOMNIA

7.6.1   Introduction

Although insomnia can be a problem for people with borderline personality disorder, there is nothing specific to its management in relation to the disorder. Therefore, general advice relevant to anyone with sleep problems can be given, including advice on sleep hygiene, such as avoiding activity or caffeine near to bedtime.

---

[15]Ibid.

7.6.2 Clinical practice recommendation

7.6.2.1 Provide people with borderline personality disorder who have sleep problems with general advice about sleep hygiene, including having a bedtime
routine, avoiding caffeine, reducing activities likely to defer sleep (such as
watching violent or exciting television programmes or films), and employing activities that may encourage sleep.

7.6.3 Short-term management of sleep disturbance

Some people with borderline personality disorder have found the occasional use of
sedative antihistamines useful when sleep disturbance has been associated with
emotional instability.

There is also a NICE Technology Appraisal on the use of newer hypnotic drugs in
managing insomnia (NICE, 2004b). This recommended:

1.1 When, after due consideration of the use of non-pharmacological measures,
hypnotic drug therapy is considered appropriate for the management of severe
insomnia interfering with normal daily life, it is recommended that hypnotics
should be prescribed for short periods of time only, in strict accordance with their
licensed indications.

1.2 It is recommended that, because of the lack of compelling evidence to distinguish
between zaleplon, zolpidem, zopiclone or the shorter acting benzodiazepine
hypnotics, the drug with the lowest purchase cost (taking into account daily
required dose and product price per dose) should be prescribed.

1.3 It is recommended that switching from one of these hypnotics to another should
only occur if a patient experiences adverse effects considered to be directly
related to a specific agent. These are the only circumstances in which the drugs
with the higher acquisition costs are recommended.

1.4 Patients who have not responded to one of these hypnotic drugs should not be
prescribed any of the others.

7.6.4 Clinical practice recommendation

7.6.4.1 For the further short-term management of insomnia follow the recommendations in 'Guidance on the use of zaleplon, zolpidem and zopiclone for
the short-term management of insomnia' (NICE technology appraisal
guidance 77). However, be aware of the potential for misuse of many of
the drugs used for insomnia and consider other drugs such as sedative
antihistamines.

8. THE CONFIGURATION AND ORGANISATION OF SERVICES

8.1 INTRODUCTION

Concerns have repeatedly been expressed about the quality of services for people with personality disorder. In 2003, the Department of Health in England highlighted the problems that many people with personality disorder face when trying to access appropriate care in primary or secondary services (Department of Health, 2003). Consequently, the department set standards for delivering services to people with personality disorder in England that aimed to ensure that people with the disorder (including borderline personality disorder) would be able to access general and specialist mental health services. Mental health trusts in England are now expected to take responsibly for meeting the needs of people with personality disorder with an emphasis placed on local expertise, suitable skills and multi-agency working (Department of Health, 2006).

However, a significant challenge for the NHS is that the evidence on which to base recommendations for guiding the development of services for people with personality disorder is poor. General principles, based on expert opinion, provide an approach to working with people with personality disorder (Holmes, 1999; Bateman & Tyrer, 2004) and suggest how general mental health services can work more effectively with people with such problems (Sampson *et al.*, 2006). However, research conducted in this field has generally focused on delivering a specific treatment and not service configuration or organisation. To address this problem the Department of Health in England funded a number of new services for people with personality disorder and commissioned research aimed at identifying organisational, therapeutic and other factors that service users and providers believe result in high quality care for people with personality disorders (Crawford *et al.*, 2007).

Lessons learned from the evaluation of these new services suggest that because of the complexity of personality disorder most services should offer more than one type of intervention, make efforts to encourage patient choice and active participation, have a coherent model for understanding personality disorder, have clear systems of communication, make sure the person with a personality disorder is valued within the service, and ensure that services have facilities to help a person in a crisis (Crawford *et al.*, 2008).

This clinical guideline builds on these findings and makes recommendations for service configuration and organisation for the treatment and care of people with borderline personality disorder. A systematic review of the evaluable evidence was undertaken. Where possible, current evidence for service provision for people with borderline personality disorder that could help service providers and practitioners determine what type of services maximise effectiveness and safety and minimise harm for the delivery of specific treatments will be presented.

The chapter begins by reviewing the evidence on specialist services (including community-based) in the medium- and long-term management of people with borderline personality disorder. The following section describes a patient pathway for borderline personality disorder that is similar to other guidelines as it follows the stepped care and chronic care models of service delivery (as recommended in the depression and bipolar disorder guidelines [NICE, 2004c; 2006a]). As described in previous guidelines (for example, NICE, 2004c), the stepped care model recommends offering the least restrictive and least costly intervention that will be effective for the problem the individual presents with (Davison, 2000). The chronic care model requires co-operation between primary and secondary care so that care is shared effectively.

The following sections will review the available clinical evidence on the risk of suicide and effectiveness of inpatient care for people with borderline personality disorder before exploring the needs of their families or carers. Finally, the chapter will explore whether special considerations are required for young people with borderline personality disorder.

8.1.1   Topics considered

This chapter looks at the different types of services involved in the delivery of care for people with borderline personality disorder, in particular:
● the role of specialist services
● risk factors for suicide
● the role of inpatient care
● a care pathway for people with borderline personality disorder
● special considerations for people with learning disabilities.

8.1.2   Reviewing the evidence base

In order to make recommendations about services for people with borderline personality disorder, the GDG asked a series of clinical questions, which are reproduced in the reviews that follow. For all reviews summary study characteristics and descriptions of the studies are given in tables below but more information is available in Appendix 16. Similarly, summary evidence profiles are given in tables below with the full profiles in Appendix 18 and the forest plots in Appendix 17. Reviewed studies are referred to by first author surname in capitals plus year of publication. Full references for these studies are in Appendix 16.

8.2   THE ROLE OF SPECIALIST SERVICES

In order to make recommendations on the role of specialist services for people with borderline personality disorder the GDG asked two linked clinical questions:
● What type of services maximise effectiveness and safety and minimise harm (taking into account long-term outcomes) for the delivery of specific treatments for people with borderline personality disorder?

● What is the role of specialist services (including community-based) in the medium- and long-term management of people with borderline personality disorder?

The most appropriate research design to answer these questions is the RCT, and therefore the evidence base reviewed comprised all available RCTs undertaken in people with a diagnosis of borderline personality disorder. However, since for some more recently developed therapies there are no RCTs, evidence from non-randomised trials was sought.

8.2.1 Evidence search

The review team undertook a search for all RCTs in borderline personality disorder. This did not yield any studies that specifically made comparisons of services in this client group. The review team therefore checked the literature for serious mental illness that had been reviewed for the NICE guideline on schizophrenia (NCCMH, 2002) and updated for the NICE guideline on bipolar disorder (NCCMH, 2006). None of the studies included in this review involved high percentages of people with a diagnosis of borderline personality disorder (although a number of studies did not report axis II diagnoses) (see Table 113). The review team therefore undertook a new search for RCTs in this area in any personality disorder.

Table 113: Studies of specialist services reviewed by the NICE guideline on bipolar disorder showing percentage with comorbid personality disorder

Assertive community treatment	
Assertive community treatment versus case management	
BUSH1990	5% personality disorder
DRAKE1998	No mention of personality disorder
ESSOCK1995	No axis II
JERRELL1995	Axis I only
MORSE1997	Axis I only
QUINLIVAN1995	Primary axis I diagnosis only
Assertive community treatment versus hospital-based rehabilitation	
CHANDLER1997	No mention of personality disorder
DECANGAS1994	Personality disorder in exclusion criteria
LAFAVE1996	17% personality disorder by DSM-III-R

Continued

Table 113: (*Continued*)

MARX1973	20% other diagnosis covering a wide range, including sociopathic personalities
Assertive community treatment versus standard care	
ABERG1995	88% schizophrenia, 12% psychotic illness
AUDINI1994	No axis II
BOND1988	No personality disorder
BOND1990	5% personality disorder
DEKKER2002	'Majority suffered schizophrenia, but many also had personality disorder'
FEKETE1998	20% other, for example personality disorder
HAMPTON1992	42% schizophrenia
HERINCKX1997	No mention of personality disorder
LEHMAN1997	Axis I only
MORSE1992	Axis I only
QUINLIVAN1995	Primary axis I diagnosis only
ROSENHECK1993	8% personality disorder
TEST1991	Personality disorder
Crisis resolution and home treatment teams (CRHTTs) **CRHTTs versus standard care (all included in Cochrane review, JAY2004)**	
FENTON1979	Schizophrenia, psychoses or neurosis only
FENTON1998	Comorbid axis II disorder among patients without schizophrenia or schizoaffective or bipolar disorder – 20% (Note, only 3% of total participants did not have schizophrenia, schizoaffective or bipolar disorder)
HOULT1981	30% other – no more detail
JOHNSON2005	13% personality disorder
MUIJEN1992	15% other – no more detail
PASAMANICK1964	100% schizophrenia
STEIN1980	50% schizophrenia, no more detail

Continued

Table 113: (*Continued*)

Community mental health teams (CMHTs) CMHTs + intensive case management versus CMHTs	
MALM2001	100% schizophrenia
CMHTs versus standard care	
TYRER1998	16% other – no further detail
CMHTs versus standard community care	
MERSON1992	1% personality disorder (n = 1)
Home-based approach versus casemanagement + outpatient rehabilitation	
SELLWOOD1999	100% schizophrenia
Day hospitals Day hospitals versus admission	
CREED1990	10% personality disorder
CREED1997	Personality disorder in exclusion criteria
DICK1985A	Participants admitted as emergencies with personality disorder were discussed with the ward team. 42% other – no further detail
HERZ1971	9% personality disorder
KRIS1965	Psychotic illness – no further detail
SLEDGE1996A	9% other – no further detail
Day hospital versus outpatient care	
LINN1979	100% schizophrenia
MELTZOFF1966	91% schizophrenia, 4% affective disorders, no further detail
TYRER1979	No mention of personality disorder
WELDON1979	100% schizophrenia
Transitional day hospital versus outpatient care (on discharge)	
GLICK1986	No mention of personality disorder

The review team then undertook a search for any RCT in this topic area for any personality disorder (see Table 114). Details of the search strings used are in Appendix 7.

Table 114: Databases searched and inclusion/exclusion criteria for RCTs of services for people with a personality disorder

Electronic databases	MEDLINE, EMBASE, PsycINFO, CINAHL, Cochrane Library
Date searched	Database inception to March 2008
Update searches	None undertaken
Study design	RCT
Patient population	People with a diagnosis of any personality disorder according to DSM or similar criteria
Treatments	Assertive outreach, CRHTTs, CMHTs, home treatment, partial hospitalisation/day hospital, residential psychotherapy, inpatient psychotherapy, care planning, case management, service organisation, service delivery, health services
Outcomes	Any

No studies were found that were relevant. The GDG therefore developed a care pathway for people with borderline personality disorder based on expert consensus (see section 8.5).

8.3   RISK FACTORS FOR SUICIDE IN PEOPLE WITH BORDERLINE PERSONALITY DISORDER

8.3.1   Introduction

Suicide attempts are a defining feature of borderline personality disorder and form part of the diagnostic criteria. Suicide attempts differ from self-harm, which has a different pattern and purpose, for example, to relieve negative emotions. Self-harm, such as superficial cutting to the arms, is usually not intended to be fatal, although cutting can, of course, be serious. Suicide attempts, however, refer to acts that have suicidal intent.

A relatively large proportion of people with a diagnosis of borderline personality disorder complete suicide, with some estimates as high as 10% (Paris, 2004a) and 49% in inpatients (Fyer *et al.*, 1988). However, identifying those at high risk is difficult.

8.3.2 Reviewing the evidence base

In order to make recommendations relating to the risk of suicide in people with borderline personality disorder, the GDG decided to review relevant cohort studies.

Information on the search undertaken and the summary study characteristics and descriptions of the studies found are given in tables below but more information is available in Appendix 16. Similarly, summary evidence profiles are given in tables below with the full profiles in Appendix 18 and the forest plots in Appendix 17. Reviewed studies are referred to by first author surname in capitals plus year of publication. Full references for these studies are in Appendix 16.

8.3.3 Evidence search and overview of studies found

The electronic databases searched are given in Table 115. Details of the search strings used are in Appendix 7.

Table 115: Databases searched and inclusion/exclusion criteria for studies of risk factors for suicide in people with borderline personality disorder

Electronic databases	MEDLINE, EMBASE, PsycINFO
Date searched	Database inception to August 2007
Update searches	March 2008
Study design	Cohort studies
Patient population	Adults over the age of 18 years with a diagnosis of borderline personality disorder according to DSM or similar criteria

Both studies specifically of people with borderline personality disorder and studies including non-specific psychiatric diagnoses were included. Some studies included only those with a recent suicide attempt and some compared those with a suicide attempt with those without. A few studies were of young people; these are reviewed in a separate section below. See Table 116 for the summary study characteristics.

Studies that did not look at specific risk factors were excluded. CHANCE2000 was not relevant because it is a psychodynamically-oriented study looking at relational patterns in inpatients with borderline personality disorder comparing those who had made a suicide attempt with those who had not.

311

Table 116: Summary study characteristics of studies of risk factors for suicide in people with borderline personality disorder

	General psychiatric populations or non-specific personality disorder	Studies of people with depression with and without comorbid borderline personality disorder	Studies comparing suicidality in those with borderline personality disorder and those without	Studies of people with borderline personality disorder
No. trials (Total participants)	4 studies (1756)	2 studies (260)	1 study (180)	5 studies (684)
Study IDs	(1) BARBER1998 (2) YEN2004 (3) YEN2005 (4) ZISOOK1994	(1) CORBITT1996 (2) SOLOFF2000	BERK2007	(1) BRODSKY1997 (2) FYER1988 (3) LINKS2007 (4) PARIS1989 (5) SOLOFF1994
N/% female	(1) 135/51 (2) 621/64 (3) 489/NA (4) 1000/52	(1) 102/55 (2) 158/65	180/57	(1) 214/unclear (2) 180/81 (3) 82/83 (4) 100/NA (5) 108/76
Mean age (or range if not given)	(1) 38 (2) NA (3) 18–45 (4) 34	(1) 18–64 (2) 32	34	(1) unclear (2) 29 (3) 33 (4) NA (5) 27

Axis I/II disorders	(1) 40% major depressive disorder; 27% schizophrenia; 15% bipolar disorder; 13% substance misuse; 4% other axis I disorders; 79% no axis II disorder; 13% borderline personality disorder; 8% other personality disorder (2) 20% borderline personality schizotypal personality disorder; 26% borderline personality disorder; 23% avoidant personality disorder; 23% obsessive-compulsive personality disorder; 15% major depressive disorder (control group) (3) Personality disorder (4) Major depressive disorder 17%; dysthymia 10%; bipolar disorder 4%; schizophrenia 15%; substance misuse 6%; anxiety 5%; borderline personality disorder 7% (others not given)	(1) 100% major depressive disorder; 29% borderline personality disorder; 17% cluster B (not borderline personality disorder); 11% other personality disorder (2) 13% disorder; 31% borderline personality disorder + major depressive disorder; 49% major depressive disorder	36% borderline personality disorder	(1)–(5) borderline personality disorder
Setting	(1) Randomly selected general psychiatric admissions; US (2) NA (3) Outpatients or past patients (4) All comers at a psychiatric outpatient clinic; US	(1) Inpatients (2) Inpatients	Emergency department patients following suicide attempt	(1)–(3) Inpatients (4) Former outpatients (5) Inpatients

Continued

Table 116: (*Continued*)

	General psychiatric populations or non-specific personality disorder	Studies of people with depression with and without comorbid borderline personality disorder	Studies comparing suicidality in those with borderline personality disorder and those without	Studies of people with borderline personality disorder
Suicidality	(1) 53% reported ≥ suicide attempt (2) 15.3% suicidal behaviour; 9.3% suicide attempt (3) 13% suicide attempt during 3-year follow-up period (4) 53% reported ≥ suicide attempt	(1) 90% of those with borderline personality disorder had made a suicide attempt in the past (2) Lifetime history of suicide attempts: 72% borderline personality disorder only; 86% comorbid major depressive disorder; 35% major depressive disorder only	>1 suicide attempt	(1) Details not given (2) 19% no history of suicidal behaviour; 32% had made suicidal gestures; 49% had made serious attempts (3) Previous suicide attempt (50%) (4) Completed suicide group (5) 70/81 admitted previous suicide attempt(s) (data not taken from all participants)

NA = not available.

8.3.4 Studies of general psychiatric populations or non-specific personality disorder

Study descriptions

BARBER1998

This is a US-based study of 135 people chosen at random from adult psychiatric admissions to a psychiatric division of a university medical centre. The study aimed to collect information about aborted suicide attempts using a 30-minute semi-structured interview based on a questionnaire devised for the study. Diagnoses were determined from hospital records after discharge.

Factors that were statistically significantly associated with aborted suicide attempts included younger age (mean 35 years compared with mean 41 years) and borderline personality disorder.

YEN2004

This 2-year prospective study of 621 people is part of the Collaborative Longitudinal Personality Disorders Study (Gunderson *et al.*, 2000). The study included people with a range of personality disorders and a control group of people with major depressive disorder and no personality disorder. The largest group had a diagnosis of borderline personality disorder and were the focus of this paper. Just over 15% of the sample (n = 95) reported suicidal behaviour and 9.3% (n = 58) made a suicide attempt. People with borderline personality disorder made up 79% and 78% of these groups.

The authors found that suicidal behaviour was predicted by affective instability, identity disturbance and impulsivity, but not by major depressive disorder, substance use disorder or childhood sexual abuse. Suicide attempts were predicted by affective instability and childhood sexual abuse.

YEN2005

This study followed 489 participants for 3 years. All participants had a diagnosis of a personality disorder (schizotypal; borderline personality disorder; avoidant; obsessive-compulsive) and were compared with a comparison group of people with major depressive disorder but no personality disorder. Sixty-one people made a suicide attempt; 24 of these people made multiple attempts. All reported at least one negative life event, with those relating to love-marriage or crime-legal factors being positively associated with suicide attempts. The study did not give results for different personality disorders separately so it is unclear whether the findings apply specifically to people with a diagnosis of borderline personality disorder.

ZISOOK1994

This is a US-based study of 1000 consecutive attendances at a psychiatric outpatient clinic. Participants' past suicidal behaviour was assessed using a self-report questionnaire. DSM-III-R diagnoses were made based on a psychiatric interview.

The study found that patients with borderline personality disorder and comorbid major depressive disorder were most likely to have current thoughts of death, wishes to be dead, thoughts of suicide and plans for suicide. Patients with border-line personality disorder were the most likely of all diagnostic groups to have made suicide attempts and, of those who made attempts, to have made the most attempts.

Clinical summary

These studies of general psychiatric populations or people with non-specified personality disorder confirm the higher prevalence of suicidal thoughts and attempts in people with borderline personality disorder compared with people with other psychiatric diagnoses. This helps to establish the diagnosis as a risk factor in itself. Also, negative life events seem to be related to suicide attempts in those with a personality disorder, particularly those relating to love-marriage or crime-legal factors.

8.3.5   Studies of people with depression with and without comorbid borderline personality disorder

Study descriptions

CORBITT1996

This study recruited 102 patients with depression admitted to a university-based private psychiatric hospital in the US. All patients admitted to the hospital were screened for major depressive disorder (DSM-III-R) and those that met criteria were asked to participate in the study. Participants were aged between 18 and 64 years, with just over half being female. Mean baseline HRSD scores were 29.6 (SD 7.4). Axis II disorders were assessed towards the end of the admission period. Suicidality was assessed in a structured interview. Patients with comorbid borderline personality disorder and those without were then compared.

Compared with those with other personality disorders and those with no person-ality disorder, those with comorbid borderline personality disorder were more likely to have made three or more suicide attempts and to have been younger when they made their first attempt. They were also more likely to have had a higher severity of suicidal ideation before the index hospitalisation (measured retrospectively), to have been younger at their first psychiatric admission and to be women.

SOLOFF2000

This study recruited participants from consecutive admissions to an adult inpatient service including only those with a diagnosis of borderline personality disorder and/or major depressive disorder. Data on suicidal behaviour were collected using a semi-structured interview. The study included 158 people, 20% with borderline personality disorder, 31% with borderline personality disorder plus comorbid major depressive disorder, and 49% with major depressive disorder only. The major depres-sive disorder only group were significantly older than the other two groups (mean 41 years versus 26 years and 30 years respectively).

The group with comorbid borderline personality disorder and major depressive disorder had a higher number of lifetime suicide attempts than the other groups, although the difference was not statistically significant (lifetime history of suicide attempts: 72% borderline personality disorder only; 86% comorbid major depressive disorder; 35% major depressive disorder only). There were more attempts among all those with borderline personality disorder regardless of comorbidity compared with those with major depressive disorder only, and they also reported their first suicide attempt at an earlier age.

Clinical summary

These studies show that a diagnosis of borderline personality disorder which is comorbid with major depressive disorder is itself a risk factor for making a suicide attempt.

8.3.6   Studies comparing suicidality in those with borderline personality disorder with those without

Study description

BERK2007

This study examined patients who had made a recent suicide attempt (recruited in an emergency department) comparing those with a diagnosis of borderline personality disorder with those without. In all 180 people were recruited, of whom 36% (n = 65) had a diagnosis of borderline personality disorder. Baseline measures were taken up to 3 weeks after the index suicide attempt using both clinician-rated and self-rated measures, with psychiatric diagnoses made using SCID for DSM-IV. The trial was part of an RCT of CT (Brown *et al.*, 2005).

The study found that those with a diagnosis of borderline personality disorder showed greater overall psychopathology than those without, including increased depression and hopelessness, and more axis I diagnoses, particularly bipolar I disorder and PTSD. In addition, this group had more psychiatric hospitalisations and had received more psychiatric treatment than those without a diagnosis of borderline personality disorder. They were also more likely to have experienced childhood physical and sexual abuse, have had more lifetime suicide attempts and report feelings of regret that the suicide attempt had failed. They also had poorer problem-solving skills.

8.3.7   Clinical summary

This study confirms that those with a diagnosis of borderline personality disorder who make a suicide attempt are likely to have greater psychopathology than others making a suicide attempt.

8.3.8   Studies of people with borderline personality disorder

Study descriptions

BRODSKY1997

This study examines pooled data from two studies of newly admitted inpatients with borderline personality disorder in order to generate sufficient data to examine suicidality. Axis I diagnoses were determined using DSM-III-R based on structured clinical interviews, while axis II diagnoses were determined by the Personality Disorder Examination in one study and DSM-III-R in the other. A detailed history of suicidal behaviour was taken.

The study reported that in people with borderline personality disorder, when lifetime depression and substance abuse were controlled for, impulsivity and the presence of a history of abuse significantly correlated with the number of previous suicide attempts.

FYER1988

This study reported on 180 patients who were selected by reviewing the records of consecutive inpatients who had been given a diagnosis of borderline personality disorder. All data were collected by chart review.

The study found that 65% had a concurrent affective disorder, 70% concurrent substance use disorder and 43% had dual diagnoses. In addition, 19% had no history of suicidal behaviour, 32% had made suicidal gestures and 49% had made serious attempts. Those with dual diagnoses had a higher rate of serious attempts and a lower rate of suicidal gestures than those with no concurrent diagnosis. Those with concurrent affective disorder tended to have a higher rate of serious attempts than either those with no concurrent disorder and those with a substance use disorder. Fewer of those with a concurrent substance use disorder, but no affective disorder, had made suicidal gestures compared with those with no concurrent diagnosis.

LINKS2007

This study recruited participants with a diagnosis of borderline personality disorder who had made at least two suicide attempts (one in the previous 2 years) and followed them prospectively for 1 month. Potential participants were specifically excluded if they had current major depressive disorder, a psychotic disorder, active substance dependence, cyclothymia or bipolar I disorder.

The study used experience sampling methodology to sample subjective experience randomly using devices such as telephone bleepers and pagers to contact participants who were then asked to complete various measures. These included affective instability, which was measured in various ways such as present or absent based on SCID-II affective instability item and affect lability based on the subscale of the Dimensional Assessment of Personality Pathology - Basic Questionnaire. Suicide ideation was measured using the Scale for Suicide Ideation and suicide behaviour using the Suicidal Behaviors Questionnaire.

The study found a positive correlation between negative mood intensity and suicidal ideation and behaviour.

318

PARIS1989

This study compared 100 patients from a 15-year follow-up of people with borderline personality disorder with 14 people who had completed suicide who had been part of the original study (and therefore had had a diagnosis of borderline personality disorder). The study used the Diagnostic Index for Borderlines (DIB) and collected demographic variables.

The study found no difference between the groups (those with completed suicide and those without) on the DIB subscales of social adaptation, impulse-action, affects or interpersonal relations. It found that those who had completed suicide had lower psychosis scores and had made more previous suicide attempts. There was no significant difference in prevalence of affective disorder. The completed suicide group were more likely to have had higher education. There was no difference for sex, age or marital status.

SOLOFF1994

This was a study of inpatients who had a diagnosis of borderline personality disorder. The data relating to self-harm and suicidal behaviour were collected as part of a larger study in the form of semi-structured interviews.

The study compared those who self-harmed with those who did not. It found that self-harm was significantly associated with younger age and greater borderline personality disorder symptomatology. It was also associated with greater suicidal ideation and recent suicide attempts. It did not find that results varied in the presence of major depressive disorder.

Clinical summary

These studies show the particular factors associated with suicidality in people with borderline personality disorder. These include impulsivity, presence of a history of abuse, comorbid affective disorder and dual diagnosis (affective disorder and substance use disorder). Self-harm was also associated with greater suicidal ideation and recent suicide attempts. Those completing suicide tended to have made more previous suicide attempts and were more likely to have had higher education.

8.3.9   Overall clinical summary for risk factors for suicide

Given that suicidal ideation is a diagnostic criterion for borderline personality disorder, it is not surprising that borderline personality disorder itself is a risk factor for suicide attempts, particularly when comorbid with major depressive disorder. Those people who complete suicide who have a diagnosis of borderline personality disorder tend to have made more previous suicide attempts. Patients are likely to have greater psychopathology than other people who attempt suicide, including impulsivity, presence of a history of abuse, comorbid affective disorder and dual diagnosis (affective disorder and substance use disorder).

These findings suggest that the presence of comorbid affective disorders should be carefully assessed in patients with a diagnosis of borderline personality disorder.

It may be appropriate to consider admission for patients with a diagnosis of border-line personality disorder following a suicide attempt, but the assessing clinician should consider that such a response might inadvertently increase the risk in the longer term by decreasing the patient's capacity to manage their own risk.

While risks to self and others must not be dismissed, it is also important to distin-guish between long-term risks and acute ones. Failure to do so can lead to an exag-gerated and inappropriate response to long-term risks, inconsistencies in the service that is offered, and may undermine a person's care plan. Following episodes of self-harm or a suicide attempt clinicians should follow existing NICE guidance (CG16) (NCCMH, 2004).

8.3.10   Clinical practice recommendation

8.3.10.1   Follow the recommendations in 'Self-harm' (NICE clinical guideline 16) to manage episodes of self-harm or attempted suicide.

8.4   THE ROLE OF INPATIENT SERVICES

8.4.1   Introduction

People with borderline personality disorder have been shown to be high users of inpa-tient services (Bender *et al.*, 2001). However, despite frequent use of inpatient admis-sions in the management and treatment of people with borderline personality disorder, the effectiveness of admission as an intervention is uncertain. This is largely because of the lack of good quality evidence evaluating the impact inpatient care has on the outcome of borderline personality disorder.

8.4.2   Reviewing the evidence base

In order to make recommendations about the role of inpatient care in the treatment of borderline personality disorder the GDG asked two clinical questions:
● What is the role of inpatient (acute, forensic) care in the management of people with borderline personality disorder?
● Is long-term inpatient care in the treatment of borderline personality disorder effective?

8.4.3   Evidence search

Since no RCTs comparing inpatient care with other forms of care in people with borderline personality disorder were identified in the general search for RCTs under-taken at the beginning of the guideline development process (described elsewhere, for example, Chapter 6), the review team undertook an additional search for any primary research study. The electronic databases searched are given in Table 117. Details of the search strings used are in Appendix 7.

**Table 117: Databases searched and inclusion/exclusion criteria
for studies of inpatient care**

Electronic databases	MEDLINE, EMBASE, PsycINFO, CINAHL, Cochrane Library
Date searched	Database inception to August 2007
Update searches	March 2008
Study design	None specified
Patient population	People with a diagnosis of borderline personality disorder according to DSM or similar criteria
Topic	Inpatient care
Outcomes	None specified

Five studies were found, of which three were included (see Table 118).

Table 118: Inpatient studies

	Inpatient studies
No. trials (Total participants)	5 studies
Study ID	(1) ANTIKAINEN1992 (2) ANTIKAINEN1994 (3) ANTIKAINEN1995
N /% female	(1) 66/42 (2) 66/44 (3) 62/40
Mean age	(1)–(2) 32 (3) 36
Setting	(1)–(3) Inpatients, Finland

Two studies were excluded because they did not contain any data (JAKUBCZYK2001; JONES1989).

8.4.4　Review of inpatient studies

Study descriptions

ANTIKAINEN1992
This study, carried out in a specialised psychiatric ward of a hospital in Finland, reported the impact of an inpatient programme on depression and anxiety symptoms in 66 patients. There were 38 male and 28 female inpatients with a mean age of 32 (range 15 to 56 years). The authors report that 32% had a diagnosis of borderline or other personality disorder. The treatment programme consisted of dynamic psychotherapy and psychopharmacological treatment. Patients received 45 minutes of individual dynamic psychotherapy and group therapy sessions twice a week. In addition psychotropic drugs were used in accordance with clinical practice. Patients were in hospital for an average of 88 days (range 21 to 296 days) and participated in an average of 25 therapy sessions during this period. The authors report significant reductions in anxiety, depression and other psychiatric symptoms including suicidal thoughts.

ANTIKAINEN1994
This study was carried out in a psychiatric ward of a hospital in Finland specialising in the psychotherapeutic treatment of borderline personality disorders. The study aimed to identify factors predicting the outcome of psychiatric hospital treatment in 66 patients. There were 37 male and 29 female inpatients with a mean age of 32 (range 15 to 56 years). Participants' baseline diagnoses are not reported, however the authors report that at the end of treatment 29% of participants had a personality disorder diagnosis. The treatment programme consisted of individual and group therapy sessions twice a week, including family members when necessary, ward meetings, committees and creative activities. Psychotropic medication was also used in accordance with clinical practice. Patients were in hospital for an average of 88 days (range 21 to 296 days). The outcome reported in this study was depressive symptoms as measured by the BDI and HDRS. A significant association was found between 14 variables and the outcome of treatment. For example, a good outcome was associated with suicidality and tension expressed by the patient on admission, whereas a poor outcome was associated with expressed delusions. The authors also report that participants taking benzodiazepines showed a better outcome as measured by the BDI and HDRS.

ANTIKAINEN1995
This study reports a 3-year follow-up of inpatients treated on a psychiatric ward in Finland specialising in the psychotherapeutic treatment of borderline personality disorder. Sixty-two patients were included in this study, 37 male and 25 female, with a mean age of 36 years at baseline. The authors report that 32% of patients were diagnosed with borderline or other personality disorder. The treatment

programme consisted of individual and group therapy sessions twice a week, including family members when necessary, ward meetings, committees and creative activities. Psychotropic medication was also used in accordance with clinical practice. Patients were in hospital for an average of 91 days (range 21 to 296 days). This study reports the long-term effectiveness of inpatient treatment on symptoms of depression and anxiety. Forty-two participants completed the 3-year follow-up assessment. The authors report a significant decline in symptoms of depression and anxiety at discharge, as measured by the BDI and HDRS, which was maintained at follow-up.

Clinical summary

It is difficult to draw any concrete conclusions and make any firm recommendations based on the findings of the above studies. All of the papers reviewed evaluate a specialist inpatient treatment for people with borderline personality disorder and come from one treatment programme in Finland. It is therefore different from many standard inpatient units in the UK. The studies used symptoms of depression and anxiety as their main outcome variable and it is impossible to determine whether the intervention was effective at treating borderline personality disorder. The lack of a comparison control group compounds the problem.

To date the literature on inpatient treatment for borderline personality disorder is based largely on expert opinion. Several experts have not only dismissed the therapeutic impact that non-specialist hospitalisation has on borderline personality disorder but have gone as far as suggesting that inpatient admission actually has a negative outcome (Paris, 2004b; Krawitz & Watson, 2000). Despite this being an intuitive argument other experts have cautioned against this assumption, as there is no conclusive evidence to suggest that hospitalisation is harmful (Bateman & Tyrer, 2004). There is, however, general expert consensus within the literature that long admissions in standard psychiatric inpatients units are unlikely to be helpful in the treatment of borderline personality (Krawitz & Watson, 2000; Bateman & Tyrer, 2004; Fagin, 2004). The expert consensus view proposes that if non-specialist inpatient units are needed then they should be brief and focus on crisis management (Fagin, 2004). There is some empirical evidence that tentatively suggests that brief planned admissions are at least no more harmful than standard treatment (Van Kessel *et al.*, 2002).

There is little empirical evidence to draw on to answer the clinical questions regarding inpatient care. There is no evidence that long-term hospitalisation is effective in the treatment of borderline personality disorder. There is also no evidence to support the assumption that admission to hospital is harmful for people with borderline personality disorder. The scant evidence and expert opinion suggests that most effective treatment of borderline personality disorder occurs in outpatient settings and if hospitalisation is required it is for crisis management and treatment of clinical symptoms rather than the treatment of borderline personality disorder. Admission to inpatient units is further considered in the section on the care pathway below.

8.4.5   Clinical practice recommendations

Clinical practice recommendations relating to admission follow the relevant section in the care pathway below.

8.5   CARE PATHWAY

8.5.1   Introduction

Since no studies had been found that were relevant to answering clinical questions on the role of specialist services (see section 8.2), the GDG developed a care pathway for people with borderline personality disorder based on expert consensus. An important issue in providing services for people with borderline personality disorder is to support staff in their work, since this client group can be challenging to work with. The GDG therefore considered the following clinical question as part of their consensus work on a care pathway:

● How can healthcare professionals involved in the care of people with borderline personality disorder best be supported?

This was answered based on the consensus view of the GDG and is discussed below in the section on teamwork and communication. Staff support is also included in the recommendations on psychological interventions in Chapter 5.

8.5.2   General principles to be considered when working with people with borderline personality disorder

Experiences of people with borderline personality disorder (see also Chapter 4), their relatives and friends, and those of healthcare professionals, suggest that in addition to the type of interventions that are offered, careful consideration also needs to be given to the manner in which these are delivered. The general principles outlined here aim to promote a constructive therapeutic relationship and balance efforts to meet a person's needs while promoting self-efficacy. These general principles are important throughout primary, secondary and specialist services.

Active participation
People with borderline personality disorder often find it hard to cope at times of crisis, and may look to others to take responsibility for their needs. While service providers may feel under pressure to try to do this, this approach may inadvertently undermine a person's limited capacity to care for themselves. It is therefore important to try to ensure that people with borderline personality disorder remain actively involved in finding solutions to their problems, even during crises.

An assumption of capacity
While people with borderline personality disorder may struggle to make informed choices, especially at times of crisis, efforts to coerce a person to do what others feel is in their best interests may also undermine a person's limited self efficacy. Instead,

324

it may be helpful for family and carers to encourage the person to think about the options they have and consider the impact of the choices they make on themselves and others.

Being consistent and reliable

People with borderline personality disorder may find it difficult to trust and engage with others, possibly because of previous experiences of neglect or abuse. Therefore, a consistent approach by service providers is essential to providing a sound basis for delivering help and support. Being reliable, for instance, by doing what one says one will do and avoiding false assurances or promises, may help to build trust, contain anxiety and support the development of a therapeutic relationship. Conversely, making changes to the service a person receives, such as cancelling appointments or changing a key worker without sufficient notice, may provoke a deterioration in mental health.

Teamwork and communication

Many people with borderline personality disorder try to cope with interpersonal difficulties by seeing people in extreme terms, for example, as either trustworthy or untrustworthy, or as either wholly good or wholly bad. This is also called 'splitting' and it can make it difficult to deliver a consistent treatment approach when different healthcare professionals, either working in different teams or within the same team, are involved. Regular communication between those providing services can help guard against this tendency to 'split' and help ensure that a coherent service is delivered.

Complex treatment programmes are delivered by a team of mental health professionals; therefore, effective teamwork is important in this context. People with borderline personality disorder are emotionally challenging and disagreements in the team may become polarised, making it hard for individuals not to blame each other for management or treatment difficulties. In these circumstances, leadership of a team is essential. Leadership is given rather than taken or assumed, for example because of professional identity. The qualities of a good leader are not specific to any one professional group. Leadership requires a willingness on the part of a team to assign the responsibility of leadership to a member of the team whom they collectively respect as well as that member being willing to undertake the leadership role. The natural tendency for team members to want to make an individual contribution has to become subordinate to the team itself. In order to achieve this, teams should adopt an interative process to generate consensus about all aspects of their work, including clinical decision-making structures, support mechanisms, risk management (including regular review to make sure that the team has not been inoculated against risk or become overly risk averse), levels of supervision and training requirements, and overall patient care.

Realistic expectations

People with borderline personality disorder tend to experience gradual rather than sudden improvement in symptoms. Therefore, helping service users set realistic short- as well as long-term goals may help them see that progress is possible. Equally mental health professionals need to accept a realistic rate of change.

8.5.3   Clinical practice recommendations

8.5.3.1   Work in partnership with people with borderline personality disorder to develop their autonomy and promote choice by:
- ensuring they remain actively involved in finding solutions to their problems, including during crises
- encouraging them to consider the different treatment options and life choices available to them, and the consequences of the choices they make.

8.5.3.2   Teams working with people with borderline personality disorder should review regularly the team members' tolerance and sensitivity to people who pose a risk to themselves and others. This should be reviewed annually (or more frequently if a team is regularly working with people with high levels of risk).

8.5.4   Primary care

In addition to attending to the physical health needs of people with borderline personality disorder, primary care workers may encounter people with the disorder when they present with emotional distress, episodes of self-harm and psychosocial crises. An awareness of borderline personality disorder and the principles that underpin its management may help primary care services to contain a person within a primary care setting and also guide decisions about when to refer to secondary care.

Awareness of borderline personality disorder
People with borderline personality disorder may present to primary care with emotional distress, including anxiety, fear of abandonment and feelings of emptiness. Other indications of the disorder include recurrent presentations with psychosocial crises, long-standing suicidal ideation, repeated self-harm, and marked interpersonal problems with reduced social functioning. In addition to helping guide the management of people with borderline personality disorder, an awareness of this disorder may help ensure that inappropriate strategies such as polypharmacy are avoided. Many people with borderline personality disorder experience other intra-psychic and interpersonal problems such as impulsivity, sensitivity to criticism and dependence on others; these factors can readily lead to unnecessary and sometimes risky prescription of drugs.

8.5.5   Clinical practice recommendation

8.5.5.1   If a person presents in primary care who has repeatedly self-harmed or shown persistent risk-taking behaviour or marked emotional instability, consider referring them to community mental health services for assessment for borderline personality disorder. If the person is younger than 18 years, refer them to CAMHS for assessment.

Assessment

Assessment of people with borderline personality disorder is challenging because it can be difficult to interpret marked fluctuations in mental state that many people experience but that also define the condition. Consequently, more than one meeting is generally required. Collateral information from family members or significant others can help to develop a better understanding of the interpersonal problems experienced by people with this disorder.

People with borderline personality disorder experience high levels of emotional distress, including symptoms of anxiety and depression, and fluctuations in mental state. The fluctuating nature of a person's mental distress can help distinguish this condition from other mental disorders.

People with borderline personality disorder have high rates of other mental health-related problems, such as eating disorders and substance misuse, and a full assessment is important in order to identify further treatment. If a person with borderline personality disorder appears to have several comorbid disorders, it may be helpful to refer them to a specialist and develop a treatment plan that addresses the person's core difficulties. Care is required to avoid offering inconsistent or inappropriate treatment.

When assessing risk it is important to include specific enquiry about self-harm and suicidal ideation. Risk posed to others is less frequent, but impulse aggression and violence can sometimes occur. The welfare of dependent children should also be considered.

Assessment of precipitating factors that may have led to deterioration in mental health may reveal important factors in the person's social environment that are amenable to change. By enquiring about such precipitants, people with borderline personality disorder may be helped to think about actions that may reduce the likelihood of future crises.

The way in which someone with borderline personality disorder reacts to primary care workers, and the feelings that workers have about the person (such as frustration, anger or hopelessness), may provide helpful insights into the interpersonal problems that the person with borderline personality disorder experiences in other settings.

Management

People with borderline personality disorder may present to primary care in crisis and at such times a person's coping strategies may be at their most fragile. Enquiring about whether the person has experienced similar episodes and trying to find out how the person managed to get through these may be helpful. If the person is living with a family member, partner, or other person, obtaining consent to discuss the situation with them and involving their help may alleviate a crisis and reduce long-term risk.

Social problems, such as housing or financial difficulties, may play a central role in maintaining a person's mental distress; providing information about how a person can access social services and other sources of advice, such as the Citizens Advice Bureau or debt counselling, may be of considerable value.

While pressure from the service user to 'do something' may lead professionals to consider prescribing medication, a crisis is not a favourable time in which to start a new long-term prescription of psychotropic mediation. Encouraging service users to identify and implement small changes that can help them get through the crisis are indicated (see Chapter 7).

The offer of a follow-up appointment within a few days of the crisis may contain the person's anxiety and help to reassure them that others are willing to support them through a crisis. A clearer picture of the precipitants of a crisis may emerge during the follow-up meeting. This meeting can also be a good opportunity for encouraging the person to consider how they might avoid a future crisis and what they can do to try to cope better when these occur.

8.5.6   Clinical practice recommendation

8.5.6.1   When a person with an established diagnosis of borderline personality disorder presents to primary care in a crisis:
- assess the current level of risk to self or others
- ask about previous episodes and effective management strategies used in the past
- help to manage their anxiety by enhancing coping skills and helping them to focus on the current problems
- encourage them to identify manageable changes that will enable them to deal with the current problems
- offer a follow-up appointment at an agreed time.

When to refer
Most people with borderline personality disorder can be managed within primary care – isolated crises do not in themselves indicate a need for referral to secondary care services. Some people with borderline personality disorder have contact with multiple services, and consideration should be given to the support that is already being provided before they are referred to another service.

Referral to secondary care should be considered when there is uncertainty about diagnosis. Specific indicators include repeated self-harm, persistent risk-taking and marked emotional instability. Risk of harm to self or others is an important indication for referral to secondary care services (see also the NICE self-harm guideline [NCCMH, 2004]). When the diagnosis is established and the person is motivated to change, consideration should be given to direct referral to psychological treatment services.

Where dedicated personality disorder services exist they should be able to provide advice and support for those working with people with personality disorder in primary care. They may also be willing to take referrals directly from primary care, without the need for assessment by generic mental health teams.

8.5.7   Clinical practice recommendation

8.5.7.1   Consider referring a person with diagnosed or suspected borderline personality disorder who is in crisis to a community mental health service when:
- their levels of distress and/or the risk to self or others are increasing

- their levels of distress and/or the risk to self or others have not subsided despite attempts to reduce anxiety and improve coping skills
- they request further help from specialist services.

8.5.8 Emergency medical services

People who repeatedly present to emergency medical services following self-injury and other forms of self-harm are likely to have borderline personality disorder. Awareness of this disorder and of the availability of local services is therefore important. An assessment based on history and a mental state examination should include assessment of comorbid mental health disorders and substance misuse problems and may be enhanced by interviewing a family member or significant other. Psychological treatments for people with borderline personality disorder may be helpful in the management of repeated self-harm (see Chapter 5). See the NICE guideline on self-harm for recommendations on the treatment and management of self-harm in emergency departments (NICE, 2004b).

8.5.9 Secondary care

Secondary care services are well placed to understand the extent of the interpersonal problems experienced by a person with borderline personality disorder and to assess their mental health and social needs. They should also be able to provide psychologically-informed management of the person's problems and work with the person to design and implement an appropriate care plan. Where indicated, secondary care services can facilitate referral to psychological or specialist personality disorder services and may be able to support the work of such services by coordinating care and providing additional support at times of crisis. A community mental health service, such as a CMHT, should be responsible for routine assessment, treatment and management of people with borderline personality disorder.

Assessment
When assessing borderline personality disorder in secondary care it is important to take a full history, which may need to include an assessment of comorbid mental disorders, such as substance misuse and eating disorders. A full assessment of personality functioning, coping strategies, strengths and vulnerabilities should be included.

The assessment process can be distressing for people with borderline personality disorder. Therefore it is important that questions about early childhood are handled sensitively as it may reveal experiences of neglect or abuse, and that support is provided to the person during this process. Similarly care should be taken when discussing diagnosis. Widespread misunderstanding of the label 'personality disorder' means that some services prefer to use other terms, such as 'interpersonal problems' and 'complex cases' to describe this condition. Where the term borderline personality disorder is used, time needs to be taken to explain its meaning, the available treatment options and the prognosis (see also Chapter 4).

Useful questions to ask when assessing the difficulties of a person with borderline personality disorder are listed in Text Box 4. The quality of an assessment can be enhanced by conducting more than one interview and by obtaining collateral information from a person who knows the service user well. The assessment should also take into account the possible risks posed to self and others, including the welfare of dependent children.

Text Box 4: Questions and issues to consider when assessing someone who may have borderline personality disorder.*

1. The presence of suicidal ideation and or repeated self-harm: 'Do you ever think that you do not care whether you live or died/ feel that life is not worth living?'
2. Tendency to form intense unstable relationships: as evidenced by personal, marital and psychosexual history.
3. Fear of abandonment: established by asking questions about relationships that have ended and steps taken by the service user to try to prevent this from happening.
4. Emotional lability: 'Do you experience big changes in your emotions and the way that you feel or do you generally keep on an even keel?'
5. Poor sense of self: as evidenced by frequent changes in appearance and/or behaviour.
6. Impulsiveness: 'Are you someone who likes to take time and weigh up the options before making a decision or do you often act on the spur of the moment?'
7. Emptiness and boredom: 'How easy do you find it to occupy your self? Do you ever experience feelings of emptiness or boredom?'
8. Problems coping with crises: 'When was the last time you were in crisis? How did you try to cope with the problems that you faced at this time?'

*Note: It is important to assess the presence of borderline personality disorder in the context of personality as a whole. This should include questions about personal strengths as well as weaknesses and be based on a full history and mental state examination.

In order to involve the person actively in the management of their borderline personality disorder, it is important that the assessment includes information about how the service user sees their problems and possible steps that the service user can take to manage them.

8.5.10   Clinical practice recommendations

8.5.10.1   Community mental health services (community mental health teams, related community-based services, and tier 2/3 services in CAMHS) should be responsible for the routine assessment, treatment and management of people with borderline personality disorder.

8.5.10.2   When assessing a person with possible borderline personality disorder in community mental health services, fully assess:

- psychosocial and occupational functioning, coping strategies, strengths and vulnerabilities
- comorbid mental disorders and social problems
- the need for psychological treatment, social care and support, and occupational rehabilitation or development
- the needs of any dependent children.

Risk management

Because people with borderline personality disorder often experience suicidal ideation, it is important to distinguish acute from chronic risks. Suicidal ideation and self-harm may arise for a variety of reasons. They may represent an attempt to manage unbearable feelings, to end a dissociated state, to elicit care, to express anger and punish someone, or as an attempt to end life.

Chronic risk refers to the long-term risk of self-harm and suicide inherent in borderline personality disorder. Acute risks are those which may arise in the context of crises and further increase the risk of suicidal behaviour. A chronic risk may be made acute by the response of services. Service users may be at more risk when practitioners are seen to be 'giving up', particularly if this is at the end of a series of attempts to help them.

In addition to self-harm, people with borderline personality disorder may undertake other high-risk behaviour such as evoking negative responses from others or high-risk sexual behaviour. It is important that these risks are identified and the level of risk posed to the service user and others assessed. Risk assessment should always be undertaken in the context of a needs assessment.

Factors that may trigger heightened risk to self or others should be documented as part of a risk management plan, which should be shared with others involved in the person's care. It is important to involve the person actively in the development of this plan, for instance by helping them try to identify alternatives to high risk behaviour and to think about the consequences of their actions. Efforts to persuade or coerce the person into pursuing an alternative course of action may be counterproductive. The plan should address both chronic and acute risks and be explicitly related to the overall treatment plan to ensure continuity and coherence.

Because risk factors and triggers vary among people with borderline personality disorder, it is important that a clinician is cautious when assessing a service user who is not well known to them. It is also important to avoid being over-controlling or dismissive, and to underestimate the seriousness of the risk, particularly in people who undergo frequent suicidal crises. It is, therefore, also important to involve other clinicians in managing risk, as well as the service user. Team working is very important and should be supported by adequate supervision.

8.5.11   Clinical practice recommendations

8.5.11.1   Risk assessment in people with borderline personality disorder should:
- take place as part of a full assessment of the person's needs
- differentiate between long-term and more immediate risks
- identify the risks posed to self and others, including the welfare of any dependent children.

8.5.11.2   Agree explicitly the risks being assessed with the person with borderline personality disorder and develop collaboratively risk management plans that:
- address both the long-term and more immediate risks
- relate to the overall long-term treatment strategy
- take account of changes in personal relationships, including the therapeutic relationship.

8.5.11.3   When managing the risks posed by people with borderline personality disorder in a community mental health service, risks should be managed by the whole multidisciplinary team with good supervision arrangements, especially for less experienced team members. Be particularly cautious when:
- evaluating risk if the person is not well known to the team
- there have been frequent suicidal crises.

Psychologically-informed management

Psychologically-informed management involves helping a person with borderline personality disorder reach a better understanding of their emotions and feelings and develop healthy coping strategies. Encouraging the person to make changes could help to mitigate the impact of their difficulties. For instance, helping someone to identify and pursue pleasurable activities may start to help them to counter chronic feelings of emptiness or low self-esteem.

When developing a care plan it is important to involve the person with borderline personality disorder with support and advice from a multi-disciplinary team. It is useful to include a crisis plan in which triggers for crises and steps that service users can take at these times are specified. In preparing the care plan it is also helpful to set short- and long-term goals that the service user would like to achieve. It is important that these goals are realistic and that the steps that the service user and others may need to take in order to try to achieve these goals are clearly specified. In order for service providers to help ensure that the services provided are appropriate for the service user's needs, the care plan needs to be regularly reviewed (it may be beneficial to include significant others in the review if the service user agrees).

People with borderline personality disorder may be in contact with a variety of health and social care professionals as well as people working in voluntary sector organisations. Because service users may sometimes try to manage the difficulties they have with interpersonal relationships through 'splitting' (seeing people as entirely good or entirely bad), it is helpful to have regular review meetings to bring all those involved in the care plan together. Professionals also need to be aware of their own tendency to 'split' from other professionals and the person with borderline personality disorder or their family or carer, and to ensure collaborative working relationships with all involved in the care of the service user. Through sharing information and agreeing a care plan the disruption that splitting can result in can be minimised.

In the light of these concerns it is important that when more than one service is involved in the provision of care for people with borderline personality disorder, and especially when psychological treatments have also started, that the care programme approach (CPA) is used to ensure effective coordination of services and to reduce the unhelpful tendency towards splitting.

8.5.12   Clinical practice recommendations

8.5.12.1   Teams working with people with borderline personality disorder should develop comprehensive multidisciplinary care plans in collaboration with the service user (and their family or carers, where agreed with the person). The care plan should:
- identify clearly the roles and responsibilities of all health and social care professionals involved
- identify manageable short-term treatment aims and specify steps that the person and others might take to achieve them
- identify long-term goals, including those relating to employment and occupation, that the person would like to achieve, which should underpin the overall long-term treatment strategy; these goals should be realistic, and linked to the short-term treatment aims
- develop a crisis plan that identifies potential triggers that could lead to a crisis, specifies self-management strategies likely to be effective and establishes how to access services (including a list of support numbers for out-of-hours teams and crisis teams) when self-management strategies alone are not enough
- be shared with the GP and the service user.

8.5.12.2   Teams should use the CPA when people with borderline personality disorder are routinely or frequently in contact with more than one secondary care service. It is particularly important if there are communication difficulties between the service user and healthcare professionals, or between healthcare professionals.

The management of comorbidities
Comorbidity of major psychiatric disorders in borderline personality disorder is widely reported in the literature, with mood disorders, anxiety disorders, eating disorders and drug and alcohol dependence being particularly common. This may lead to problems in

diagnosis as some of the features of these disorders are inextricably linked to those of personality disorder. In general terms, psychiatric symptoms show particular character-istics when they are linked to borderline personality disorder compared with how they are expressed in independent psychiatric disorders. They tend to be short-lived and can fluctuate rapidly, they are likely to occur primarily in the context of interpersonal stress and they respond swiftly to structured interventions, such as admission or other envi-ronmental modification. The diagnosis of both borderline personality disorder and a comorbid disorder should therefore be reviewed before treatment is initiated, particu-larly if any diagnosis was made during an emergency presentation.

Any psychiatric symptoms that are integral to borderline personality disorder should be treated as part of that disorder. However, if a comorbid disorder is present, clinicians should assess the severity of it and follow the appropriate treatment guide-lines. Patients with comorbid axis I and axis II disorders should receive best treatment for both disorders. The treating clinician may need to consider referral to another clinician or service for appropriate treatment of the comorbid disorder depending on their own training and experience, the context of treatment for borderline personality disorder and the severity and type of the comorbid disorder. For example, people with borderline personality disorder that is comorbid with a major psychosis, a severe eating disorder or substance dependence on Class A drugs are likely to require addi-tional expertise if they are to have the best chance of improvement. Under these circumstances clinicians are advised to ensure appropriate arrangements are made for co-ordinated care with agreement on responsibilities and roles. If a comorbid disor-der is diagnosed in the initial assessment of a person with borderline personality disorder, it may be most appropriate to refer them for treatment for the axis I disor-der before commencing treatment for borderline personality disorder. However, if a person is already engaged in treatment for borderline personality disorder and a comorbid axis I disorder develops or becomes apparent during the course of treat-ment, a care co-ordinator should keep in contact with the person while they are receiving treatment for the axis I disorder so that they can continue with treatment for borderline personality disorder when appropriate.

The situation is more complex if the comorbid disorder includes predominant depression, PTSD or anxiety symptoms. In many patients these problems are best treated within a psychotherapeutic treatment programme for borderline personality disorder itself and no additional psychotherapy offered. If medication is required, integrating prescribing within the treatment programme may prevent inappropriate prescription of drugs.

8.5.13   Clinical practice recommendations

8.5.13.1   Before starting treatment for a comorbid condition in people with border-line personality disorder, review:
● the diagnosis of borderline personality disorder and that of the comor-bid condition, especially if either diagnosis has been made during a crisis or emergency presentation

- the effectiveness and tolerability of previous and current treatments; discontinue ineffective treatments.

8.5.13.2   Treat comorbid depression, post-traumatic stress disorder or anxiety within a well-structured treatment programme for borderline personality disorder.

8.5.13.3   Refer people with borderline personality disorder who also have major psychosis, dependence on alcohol or Class A drugs, or a severe eating disorder to an appropriate service. The care coordinator should keep in contact with people being treated for the comorbid condition so that they can continue with treatment for borderline personality disorder when appropriate.

8.5.13.4   When treating a comorbid condition in people with borderline personality disorder, follow the NICE clinical guideline for the comorbid condition.

Discharge to primary care

Fears of abandonment and previous experiences of unsatisfactory endings mean that many people with borderline personality disorder find the ending of treatment or discharge from a service especially challenging (see also Chapter 4). Therefore when discharging a service user back to primary care services, it is important that time is taken to discuss this well in advance with the person, and where available, their family or carer. The decision about when to refer back to primary care will depend on the severity of the person's disorder, the presence of comorbid axis I disorder, the level of social functioning and the response to input from secondary care. When considering discharge it is useful to agree a care plan beforehand specifying the steps the service user can take to try to manage their distress and cope with future crises. This should be communicated to the primary care clinician.

8.5.14   Clinical practice recommendation

8.5.14.1   When discharging a person with borderline personality disorder from secondary care to primary care, discuss the process with them and, whenever possible, their family or carers beforehand. Agree a care plan that specifies the steps they can take to try to manage their distress, how to cope with future crises and how to re-engage with community mental health services if needed. Inform the GP.

Referral for psychological treatment

It is important to consider referral for psychological treatment for all people with borderline personality disorder, but not all should be referred. Factors to be considered when making this decision are the views of the service user, the severity of the disorder and the extent of their use of other services. Service users' views are paramount. Ideally the service user should have some understanding of the nature of their problems, a desire to engage in psychological treatment and an ability to think about what they would like to try to achieve with the help of treatment. In reality many people with borderline personality disorder have ambivalent feelings about having psychological treatment and those delivering psychological treatments to people with this condition will be used to working with this ambivalence. Service users should be given written material about the treatments being considered and their effectiveness to help in making an informed decision. Referral of those with high levels of disturbance and poor motivation to change may therefore still be indicated.

For people with lower levels of disturbance and higher levels of social functioning, developing a better understanding of the steps they can take to resolve their problems without prolonged input from services may be preferable. The opinion of those providing psychological treatments may be helpful in making a decision about whether or not to refer. It would be helpful for those providing psychological treatments to make sure that they can assist in this way and are able to offer clear information to the service user about the process of referral. Unrealistic expectations about what will be provided or what psychological treatments can achieve can be unhelpful. A new care plan may be agreed that details the service user's role and responsibilities, as well as those of care providers.

It is also important to be aware that service users may find the assessment process distressing, therefore it may be beneficial if arrangements for support during this period were agreed in advance of the referral. Once the assessment has been completed a new care plan may be agreed that specifies the role and responsibilities of the service user, those delivering psychological treatment and other health and social care providers.

8.5.15 Clinical practice recommendations

8.5.15.1 When considering a psychological treatment for a person with borderline personality disorder, take into account:
- the choice and preference of the service user
- the degree of impairment and severity of the disorder
- the person's willingness to engage with therapy and their motivation to change
- the person's ability to remain within the boundaries of a therapeutic relationship
- the availability of personal and professional support.

8.5.15.2 Before offering a psychological treatment for a person with borderline personality disorder or for a comorbid condition, provide the person with written material about the psychological treatment being considered. For people who have reading difficulties, alternative means of presenting the information should be considered, such as video or DVD. So that the person can make an informed choice, there should be an opportunity for them to discuss not only this information but also the evidence for the effectiveness of different types of psychological treatment for borderline personality disorder and any comorbid conditions.

8.5.15.3   When providing psychological treatment to people with borderline personality disorder as a specific intervention in their overall treatment and care,
use the CPA to clarify the roles of different services, professionals providing psychological treatment and other healthcare professionals.

8.5.15.4   When providing psychological treatment to people with borderline personality disorder, monitor the effect of treatment on a broad range of
outcomes, including personal functioning, drug and alcohol use, self-harm,
depression and the symptoms of borderline personality disorder.

The role of psychological treatment
Please refer to Chapter 5.

Role of drug treatment
Considerations and recommendations about the role of drug treatment are described in
Chapters 6 and 7. Service users should be given written material about the treatments
being considered and their effectiveness to help in making an informed decision.

8.5.16   Clinical practice recommendations

8.5.16.1   When considering drug treatment for any reason for a person with borderline personality disorder, provide the person with written material about
the drug being considered. This should include evidence for the drug's
effectiveness in the treatment of borderline personality disorder and for any
comorbid condition, and potential harm. For people who have reading
difficulties, alternative means of presenting the information should be
considered, such as video or DVD. So that the person can make an
informed choice, there should be an opportunity for the person to discuss
the material.

Use of inpatient services
While every effort should be made to avoid admission to inpatient units, circumstances may arise when a period of inpatient care is indicated. These circumstances
include diagnostic uncertainty and the short-term management of acute risk.
Diagnostic uncertainty may arise when a marked affective component or evidence of
psychotic symptoms suggest that there may be an axis I disorder that needs treatment.
When problems are so severe that further assessment cannot be undertaken safely in
the community, it may beneficial to consider an inpatient assessment. Service users
should be referred to a CRHTT when admission is being considered.

   While inpatient treatment is not suitable for the treatment of chronic risks associated with borderline personality disorder, there may be circumstances in which acute
risks cannot be safely managed in a community setting. As with other aspects of service delivery for people with borderline personality disorder, it is important that service users are actively involved in decisions about the use of inpatient treatment and
where possible the admission planned and the length of the admission agreed in

advance. In keeping with the aim of actively involving service users in their management, admission to hospital on a voluntary basis is preferable. A decision to treat the person against their will may undermine their fragile ability to look after themselves. Where compulsory treatment is used in extreme circumstances, it is vital that management on a voluntary basis is resumed at the earliest opportunity. Service users who experience recurrent admissions should have a care programme review.

8.5.17   Clinical practice recommendations

8.5.17.1   Before considering admission to an acute psychiatric inpatient unit for a person with borderline personality disorder, first refer them to a crisis resolution and home treatment team or other locally available alternative to admission.

8.5.17.2   Only consider people with borderline personality disorder for admission to an acute psychiatric inpatient unit for:
- the management of crises involving significant risk to self or others that cannot be managed within other services, or
- detention under the Mental Health Act (for any reason).

8.5.17.3   When considering inpatient care for a person with borderline personality disorder, actively involve them in the decision and:
- ensure the decision is based on an explicit, joint understanding of the potential benefits and likely harm that may result from admission
- agree the length and purpose of the admission in advance
- ensure that when, in extreme circumstances, compulsory treatment is used, management on a voluntary basis is resumed at the earliest opportunity.

8.5.17.4   Arrange a formal CPA review for people with borderline personality disorder who have been admitted twice or more in the previous 6 months.

Support for service providers and reflective practice
It is important that those involved in providing secondary care services to people with borderline personality disorder have an opportunity to reflect on their practice. Reflective practice may be enhanced through independent supervision from a person not directly involved in the day-to-day workings of the team. Those providing supervision need to encourage reflection on the impact the work has on the practitioner and whether he or she is responding in ways that are counter-therapeutic.

8.5.18   Specialist services

Introduction
A number of specialist services for people with personality disorder have been established following an initiative from the Department of Health (2003), which carries the expectation that all trusts will develop expertise in this area. Specialist personality

disorder services are based on the same general principles for working with person-ality disorder described above, but have additional expertise. Nonetheless, where such services are available, decisions about referral should follow the principles outlined above in the section on referral to psychological treatment.

Current practice
Many trusts now have specialised personality disorder services, which receive most of their referrals from other services within the same trust (that is, they are tertiary services). Many other trusts have no such specialised services, and people with personality disorder then have access either to general secondary services or, if secondary services cannot cope, they rely on regional or national services, including therapeutic communities and forensic services. Those within secondary care will receive the usual range of services (community based, outpatient, day patient and inpatient). Only a small minority of those with borderline personality disorder are treated outside CMHTs. In fact, roughly 40% of the people who use CMHTs have a diagnosis of personality disorder and many of those will have a diagnosis of border-line personality disorder.

Consequences of current service arrangements
There is little doubt that the anxieties and uncertainties of mental healthcare profes-sionals who have not been trained to evaluate or work with people with borderline personality disorder often mean that uninformed treatment may be given to those with the diagnosis. Also, admission to hospital may be used inappropriately, with the significant possibility that this may lead to long-term harm. Staff in these settings need access to training and specialist help in the management of borderline personal-ity disorder and this can be provided by specialist services, but with the emphasis that most people with this condition will continue to be managed in non-specialist community services. In other words, the added value of specialist services within trusts may be in the support, training, consultation and advice that they provide for generalist services (CMHTs in the main), rather than the specialist service they will provide for a small handful of people with more severe forms of personality disorder.

The evidence
Many approaches for delivering specialist services have been developed. Such serv-ices are generally offered over periods of years rather than months, but the value of interventions of differing length has not been established. Service models include intensive outpatient treatment and day hospital-based care, but the GDG was unable to find an evidence base on which to recommend one model over another (see above), although inpatient services are generally not indicated because of greater cost.

Views of the GDG
It was the view of the GDG that specialist services should not be restrictive and should offer more than one type of intervention to meet the predominantly complex needs of service users and allow for flexibility and choice to be exercised, especially in the absence of any clear evidence that one treatment or a type of service provision

is more advantageous than another. The limited availability of such services for people with personality disorder suggests they should focus on the treatment of those with severe personality disorder who have greater impaired functioning and may have high levels of risk. In addition, they are likely to have high levels of service utilisation. Education and training, as provided by specialist services, are needed to support the work of general mental health services together with case consultations and opportunities for reflective practice. Specialist services can contribute to the development of training programmes on diagnosis and management (as well as the implementation of this guideline) for professionals who have contact with people with borderline personality disorder. Training should also address problems around stigma and discrimination as these apply to people with borderline personality disorder.

The effects and cost effectiveness of specialist services compared with high-quality secondary care have not been examined, nor has the impact of the development of specialist services on the willingness or ability of secondary care services to work effectively with people with personality disorder. Although specialisation is a common development in many medical services, the limited number of patients that can be treated at any one time by a specialist service, and the high co-occurrence of personality disorder with most mental illnesses, mean that most of those with borderline personality disorder will continue to be seen in CMHTs and primary care only.

Summary

This guideline recommends a care pathway to organise and integrate the provision of care for this guideline. The main place of treatment for these disorders will continue to be the CMHT, but in order that the staff working in these teams can be more confident and competent at dealing with the complex problems of people with borderline personality disorder, a specialist personality disorder service should be set up in each trust to provide a core of expertise as well as a referral source and training setting to help those people who present with the most challenging problems.

8.5.19   Clinical practice recommendations

8.5.19.1   Mental health professionals working in secondary care services, including community-based services and teams, CAMHS and inpatient services, should be trained to diagnose borderline personality disorder, assess risk and need, and provide treatment and management in accordance with this guideline. Training should also be provided for primary care healthcare professionals who have significant involvement in the assessment and early treatment of people with borderline personality disorder. Training should be provided by specialist personality disorder teams based in mental health trusts (see recommendation 8.5.19.3).

8.5.19.2   Mental health professionals working with people with borderline personality disorder should have routine access to supervision and staff support.

8.5.19.3   Mental health trusts should develop multidisciplinary specialist teams and/or services for people with personality disorders. These teams should have specific expertise in the diagnosis and management of borderline personality disorder and should:

- provide assessment and treatment services for people with borderline personality disorder who have particularly complex needs and/or high levels of risk
- provide consultation and advice to primary and secondary care services
- offer a diagnostic service when general psychiatric services are in doubt about the diagnosis and/or management of borderline personality disorder
- develop systems of communication and protocols for information sharing among different services, including those in forensic settings, and collaborate with all relevant agencies within the local community including health, mental health and social services, the criminal justice system, CAMHS and relevant voluntary services
- be able to provide and/or advise on social and psychological interventions, including access to peer support, and advise on the safe use of drug treatment in crises and for comorbidities and insomnia
- work with CAMHS to develop local protocols to govern arrangements for the transition of young people from CAMHS to adult services
- ensure that clear lines of communication between primary and secondary care are established and maintained
- support, lead and participate in the local and national development of treatments for people with borderline personality disorder, including multi-centre research
- oversee the implementation of this guideline
- develop and provide training programmes on the diagnosis and management of borderline personality disorder and the implementation of this guideline (see 8.5.19.4)
- monitor the provision of services for minority ethnic groups to ensure equality of service delivery.
  The size and time commitment of these teams will depend on local circumstances (for example, the size of trust, the population covered and the estimated referral rate for people with borderline personality disorder).

8.5.19.4 Specialist teams should develop and provide training programmes that cover the diagnosis and management of borderline personality disorder and the implementation of this guideline for general mental health, social care, forensic and primary care providers and other professionals who have contact with people with borderline personality disorder. The programmes should also address problems around stigma and discrimination as these apply to people with borderline personality disorder.

8.5.19.5 Specialist personality disorder services should involve people with personality disorders and families or carers in planning service developments, and in developing information about services. With appropriate training and support, people with personality disorders may also provide services, such as training for professionals, education for service users and families or carers, and facilitating peer support groups.

8.6   RESEARCH RECOMMENDATION

8.6.1   Developing a care pathway

8.6.1.1   What is the best care pathway for people with borderline personality disorder?

A mixed-methods cohort study examining the care pathway of a representative sample of people with borderline personality disorder should be undertaken. Such a study should include consideration of factors that should guide referral from primary to secondary care services, and examine the role of inpatient treatment. The study should examine the effect that people with borderline personality disorder and service-level factors have on the transfer between different components of care and include collection and analysis of both qualitative and quantitative data.

Why is this important

The development of a care pathway for people with borderline personality disorder would help to ensure that available resources are used effectively and that services are suited to their needs. Service provision for people with borderline personality disorder varies greatly in different parts of the country, and factors that should be considered when deciding the type and intensity of care that people receive are poorly understood. A cohort study in which qualitative and quantitative data from service users and providers are collected at the point of transfer to and from different parts of the care pathway would help to inform the decisions that people with borderline personality disorder and healthcare professionals have to make about the type of services that people receive.

8.7   SPECIAL CONSIDERATIONS FOR PEOPLE WITH LEARNING DISABILITIES

8.7.1   Introduction

There has been a lack of conceptual clarity about the diagnosis of personality disorders for people with learning disabilities highlighted by a significant blurring of the boundaries between personality, psychiatric and behaviour disorders for this population.

A review of prevalence studies revealed a wide variation in the prevalence of borderline personality disorder among people with learning disabilities, from 1 to 91% in community settings and 22 to 92% in hospital populations (Alexander & Coorey, 2003). Although the justification for this remains unclear, methodological flaws have been attributed to these large variable figures of prevalence (Torr, 2003).

Characteristics of borderline personality disorder, such as impulsivity and affective lability, are also common features associated with learning disabilities (Alexander & Coorey, 2003). Flynn and colleagues (2002) found links between the diagnosis of personality disorder in adults with learning disabilities and childhood sexual abuse.

DC-LD, the diagnostic criteria for people with learning disabilities (Royal College of Psychiatrists, 2001), recommends that, because of developmental delay in people with learning disabilities, the diagnosis of personality disorder should not be made until at least 21 years of age. In addition DC-LD requires the initial confirmation of personality disorder unspecified, before progressing to more specific types of personality disorder. Personality disorder requires that the characteristics must not be a direct consequence of the person's learning disabilities and also states specifically that there must be associated significant problems in occupational and/or social functioning. People with severe learning disabilities may not be capable of developing maladaptive thoughts and processing information about social environment for the diagnosis of a personality disorder to be made. Conversely it is possible that behaviour patterns attributed to a personality disorder in those with mild or moderate learning disabilities might be viewed as a behaviour disorder in those with severe or profound learning disabilities. Moreland and colleagues (2008) in a conceptual study argue that the validity of a personality disorder diagnosis in people with learning disabilities is fraught with problems and is derived from research on the general population without having been integrated with research conducted within the population of learning disabilities. They suggest that there are grounds to be cautious with the current diagnostic process and to question its clinical validity.

8.7.2   Databases searched and inclusion/exclusion criteria

Studies were sought from the citations downloaded in the search for RCTs undertaken in people with borderline personality disorder, which are described in the other evidence chapters. Since no studies were found, an additional search for any primary research in people with learning disabilities and borderline personality disorder was undertaken. This search was broadened to search for studies on any personality disorder. Information about the databases searched and the inclusion/exclusion criteria used are in Table 119.

**Table 119: Databases searched and inclusion/exclusion
criteria for clinical evidence**

Electronic databases	Medline, EMBASE, PsycINFO, CINAHL
Date searched	Database inception to 2 April 2008
Study design	Any primary research design
Patient population	Personality disorder plus learning disability
Interventions	Any
Outcomes	Any relevant outcomes

8.7.3 Studies considered

No relevant studies were found from the search undertaken. The GDG included a member with specific expertise in this client group who advised on recommendations for consensus opinion.

8.7.4 Clinical evidence summary

There is very little information relating to personality disorder and response to treatment and management (Lindsay, 2007). Case studies have described pharmacological and behaviour interventions in three individuals with borderline personality disorder and learning disabilities (Mavromatis, 2000) and Wilson (2001) postulated a four-stage model based upon DBT. However, the evidence base is yet to emerge. In view of this, there is no reason why people with borderline personality disorder who have mild learning disabilities should not be treated in the same way as other people with a diagnosis of borderline personality disorder and have full access to mainstream services. Clinicians should have access to specialist advice when assessing and diagnosing borderline personality disorder in people with mild learning difficulties. Those with moderate or severe learning difficulties should not normally be diagnosed with borderline personality disorder, but, if their behaviour and symptoms suggest borderline personality disorder, they should be referred for specialist assessment and treatment.

8.7.5 Clinical practice recommendations

8.7.5.1   When a person with a mild learning disability presents with symptoms and behaviour that suggest borderline personality disorder, assessment and diagnosis should take place in consultation with a specialist in learning disabilities services.

8.7.5.2   When a person with a mild learning disability has a diagnosis of borderline personality disorder, they should have access to the same services as other people with borderline personality disorder.

8.7.5.3   When care planning for people with a mild learning disability and borderline personality disorder, follow the Care Programme Approach (CPA). Consider consulting a specialist in learning disabilities services when developing care plans and strategies for managing behaviour that challenges.

8.7.5.4   People with a moderate or severe learning disability should not normally be diagnosed with borderline personality disorder. If they show behaviour and symptoms that suggest borderline personality disorder, refer for assessment and treatment by a specialist in learning disabilities services

8.8 SPECIAL CONSIDERATIONS FOR PEOPLE FROM BLACK AND MINORITY ETHNIC GROUPS

Studies examining the prevalence of personality disorder have generally included insufficient numbers of people from black and minority ethnic (BME) communities to explore whether this influences the likelihood of having a personality disorder (Coid *et al.*, 2006). As a result we do not know if the prevalence of borderline personality disorder is higher or lower among people from BME communities in the UK.

Cross-sectional surveys of people in contact with general and forensic mental health services suggest that the proportion of people from BME communities who are given a diagnosis of personality disorder may be lower than that among the British white population (Tyrer *et al.*, 1994; Singleton *et al.*, 1998). However it is not known whether this is the result of lower prevalence or whether healthcare staff are less likely to make this diagnosis among people from BME groups. A case-vignette study among 220 forensic psychiatrists in the UK found some evidence to support the view that doctors are less likely to make a diagnosis of antisocial personality disorder among people from Afro-Caribbean backgrounds, but the same study did not find evidence of cultural bias in the diagnosis of borderline personality disorder (Mikton & Grounds, 2007).

Prospective data collected from a sample of 547 people with personality disorder in North America demonstrated Hispanic and African American patients were less likely to receive individual and group psychotherapy or to receive psychotropic medication (Bender *et al.*, 2007). In Britain, people who are referred to residential personality disorder services from BME communities may be less likely to be offered a service (Geraghty & Warren, 2003). Data collected from people referred to 11 community-based services for adults with personality disorder in England has shown that people from BME communities are less likely to be taken on by specialist personality disorder services and may be more likely to drop out of them (Crawford *et al.*, 2007).

In summary, we do not know if the prevalence of borderline personality disorder varies among different BME groups in the UK. However there is some evidence to suggest that people with personality disorder from these communities are less likely to receive treatment for their disorder.

8.8.1 Clinical practice recommendations

8.8.1.1 Ensure that people with borderline personality disorder from black and minority ethnic groups have equal access to culturally appropriate services based on clinical need.

8.8.1.2 When language is a barrier to accessing or engaging with services for people with borderline personality disorder, provide them with:
● information in their preferred language and in an accessible format
● psychological or other interventions in their preferred language
● independent interpreters.

9.   YOUNG PEOPLE WITH BORDERLINE PERSONALITY DISORDER

9.1   INTRODUCTION

This guideline uses the term 'young people' to refer to those aged under 18 years as people of this age prefer this descriptor to the term 'adolescent'.

There are very few studies of the prevalence of borderline personality disorder in young people, but two suggest that the disorder affects between 0.9 to 3% of the community population of those aged under 18 years (Lewinsohn *et al.*, 1997; Bernstein *et al.*, 1993). Employing lower symptom thresholds results in an increase to between 10.8 to 14% (Bernstein *et al.*, 1993; Chabrol *et al.*, 2001). Chanen and colleagues (2004) cite data suggesting a prevalence rate of 11% in adolescent outpatients. A more recent study by the same group suggests a rate of 22% in outpatients (Chanen *et al.*, 2008b). Grilo and colleagues (2001) report a prevalence rate of 49% in adolescent inpatients. Further studies are needed before firm conclusions can be drawn about prevalence.

Adolescence is a period of major developmental transitions – physically, psychologically and socially. During this period young people experience emotional distress, frequent interpersonal disruptions and challenges in establishing a sense of identity. Consequently, young people with borderline personality disorder may experience a minimisation or dismissal of their difficulties from staff, their families or from their wider social circle, who attribute their problems to the typical stresses and strains of the adolescent transition. This may preclude access to appropriate help for their difficulties. However, many clinicians are reluctant to diagnose borderline personality disorder in young people because of a number of factors: uncertainties about whether personality disorder can be diagnosed in this age group; the appropriateness of the diagnosis at a time of major developmental change characterised by some of the behaviours within the diagnosis; and possible negative consequences of the diagnostic label. Many clinicians also do not believe that making the diagnosis will add to their understanding of the young person, their difficulties or the treatment plan.

Given the concerns about diagnosing young people with borderline personality disorder, the current approach to diagnosis and conceptualisation of the problems presented by young people with borderline personality disorder is highly variable. Consequently, treatment strategies are also inconsistent. While assessing the behaviours that would form a diagnosis of borderline personality disorder, healthcare professionals often do not conceptualise the problems as borderline personality disorder or make a formal diagnosis. In some circumstances clinicians may use an axis I diagnosis rather than a diagnosis of borderline personality disorder because of concerns about the person living with the diagnosis (Chanen *et al.*, 2007a). In addition, because young people with borderline personality disorder often have multiple comorbidities, clinicians tend to focus on the assessment and treatment of axis I disorders. Because of the complexity and comorbidity of the problems, some young people will receive a multitude of interventions with varying degrees of coordination. In these circumstances, the absence of coordination and a failure to involve other systems around the young person (for example, family and school) may limit the effectiveness of interventions. Other young people will receive less frequent interventions. In some cases, either the service or the individual practitioner experiences frequent demands and requests for help from the young person, their family or other services involved and the intensity of service required may exceed the capacity of either the individual practitioner or the service.

Deciding on the main goals of treatment often presents a challenge given the complexity of the difficulties and the limited nature of the evidence base for working with young people with borderline personality disorder. Frequently interventions focus exclusively and sometimes unhelpfully on the assessment and management of risk to the exclusion of treatment of the disorder or comorbid disorders. Current practice includes a range of different psychological and pharmacological treatments. Psychological treatments currently offered may include CBT, DBT, CAT, family therapy, psychodynamic psychotherapy, counselling, treatments derived from attachment theory and non-specific talking therapies. Pharmacological treatments currently prescribed may include SSRIs, mood stabilisers and low-dose neuroleptics, either with the intention of treating a comorbid condition (for example, an SSRI for depression) or of addressing specific symptoms (for example, a neuroleptic to reduce impulsivity). Some services will utilise the CPA for young people with borderline personality disorder, but others will not. Irrespective of the treatment offered, healthcare professionals may have difficulty remaining appropriately focused on the goals of treatment in the presence of multiple comorbidities and social or family problems. The emotional lability of the young person with borderline personality disorder, and the motivational fluctuations that often accompany it, can lead professionals unintentionally away from the pre-determined focus of the intervention.

There are potential risks associated with intervention. The most common risk, which can occur both in outpatient and inpatient treatment, is the reinforcement of problematic behaviours, leading to deterioration in functioning. Young people may then require more intensive treatment and, in a small proportion of people, this can lead to expensive out-of-area placements and/or placements with higher levels of security. Young people with borderline personality disorder and a history of childhood trauma may also deteriorate if trauma therapy that involves repeated and/or in-depth exposure to the trauma is embarked upon before their more impulsive behaviours are stabilised.

Young people with borderline personality disorder may also be known to social services either as a result of child protection concerns or because the young person is designated a 'child in need'. Young people in these circumstances, as well as receiving routine services, may also live in foster placements, therapeutic foster placements or residential settings. They may also come to the attention of the Youth Justice Service or be in prison as a result of impulsive behaviours that are antisocial or criminal in nature. Some young people with borderline personality disorder may have a statement of special educational need and/or may find it difficult to access standard educational settings.

This chapter considers first the diagnosis of borderline personality disorder and its stability in young people. The assessment of young people with borderline personality disorder is then considered, including which assessment tools may assist clinicians in identifying borderline personality disorder in young people. As with adult patients, the assessment and management of suicide risk frequently forms a major focus of the work and this chapter reviews the evidence for suicide risk in young people with borderline personality disorder. Treatment options are then reviewed. The chapter concludes with a care pathway and associated recommendations.

9.2   DIAGNOSIS

DSM-IV allows for all personality disorders, with the exception of antisocial personality disorder, to be diagnosed in young people with certain caveats (APA, 1994). To diagnose a personality disorder in a young person the maladaptive personality traits must be assessed as pervasive and persistent and not limited to periods of an axis I disorder or to a specific developmental stage (APA, 1994). The criteria for diagnosing borderline personality disorder are the same in young people as for adults. As a degree of emotional lability, interpersonal instability and identity confusion are more typical in adolescence, however, assessing clinicians must establish that the severity and intensity of these behaviours exceed what is typical for young people before concluding that the criterion is present. Sub-cultural differences in the prevalence of the behaviours must also be considered. ICD-10 also allows for a diagnosis of emotionally unstable personality disorder, borderline type, to be made in young people using the same criteria as for adults (World Health Organization, 1992). However, it states that, in general for personality disorders, it is 'unlikely that the diagnosis of personality disorder will be appropriate before the age of 16 or 17 years'. Defining the beginning and end of the adolescent stage of development varies across cultures. Using a chronological age to demarcate the stage can present difficulties as young people of the same chronological age may differ greatly in their levels of developmental maturity. For this same reason using a specific age as the lower limit to define when to consider the recommendations in this guideline is problematic. The GDG and the specialist advisors decided, therefore, that rather than using age as a criterion, the recommendations in this chapter would apply to young people post-puberty and that it would be highly unusual to consider the diagnosis in young people under the age of 13.

Both the research literature and clinicians use a variety of terms to refer to young people who present with behaviours consistent with a diagnosis of borderline personality disorder. Often, when referring to young people a qualifying term is added to the borderline personality disorder diagnosis. The most commonly used qualifiers include 'possible', 'putative', 'tentative', 'emerging' and 'emergent'. The guideline does not use any of these qualifying terms but rather refers to those aged under 18 years who meet criteria for the disorder as 'young people with borderline personality disorder'. The view of the guideline group was that the use of qualifying terms most likely stems from concerns about whether or not it is possible to make the diagnosis in young people and/or concerns about the negative effects of labelling. Concerns about labelling are legitimate and apply equally regardless of age. To mitigate these concerns the GDG recommends that the diagnosis only be employed following a thorough assessment and that it should be used to inform an appropriate treatment plan and not as justification for refusing or limiting access to services.

9.3   STABILITY OF THE DIAGNOSIS OF BORDERLINE PERSONALITY DISORDER IN YOUNG PEOPLE

9.3.1   Introduction

One concern over the appropriateness of the diagnosis of borderline personality disorder in young people is its stability, particularly at a time of major developmental change during which some of the features that constitute the disorder are present, albeit at lower levels of intensity. The issue of stability of the diagnosis is important because it has an impact on the identification, diagnosis and treatment of borderline personality disorder in young people.

9.3.2   Reviewing the evidence base

The most appropriate research design to establish whether the borderline personality disorder diagnosis is stable in young people is the prospective cohort study. The evidence base reviewed, therefore, comprised all available prospective studies undertaken in young people in whom a diagnosis of borderline personality disorder had been made either at baseline or at follow-up. Review studies focusing on borderline personality disorder in young people were also sought to ascertain the state of the available literature and to check that the relevant references had been identified by the search strings used.

The summary study characteristics and descriptions of the studies are given in Table 121, but more information is available in Appendix 16. Reviewed studies are referred to by first author surname in capitals plus year of publication.

9.3.3   Evidence search and overview of studies found

The electronic databases searched are given in Table 120. Details of the search strings used are in Appendix 7.

Studies of young people diagnosed with borderline personality either at baseline or at follow-up were included. Forty-four prospective cohort papers were found from searches of electronic databases, of which 33 were excluded. The most common reasons for exclusion were that there were no useable data, no longitudinal data were

Table 120: Databases searched and inclusion/exclusion criteria for studies of stability of diagnosis of borderline personality disorder in young people

Electronic databases	MEDLINE, EMBASE, PsycINFO
Date searched	Database inception to September 2007
Update searches	May 2008
Study design	Prospective and quasi-prospective cohort studies
Population	Young people aged under 18 years who were assessed both before the age of 18 and in adulthood, with at least one of the assessments being for borderline personality disorder according to DSM or similar criteria

reported or there were no data reported for borderline personality disorder specifically (further information about both included and excluded studies can be found in Appendix 16).

Eighteen of the 44 prospective studies found from the searches reported data from the Children in the Community Study (see for example Cohen *et al.*, 2005). This study followed-up a randomly selected sample of 976 children recruited in 1975. Despite the fact that this is a prospective study with a large sample size, a considerable limitation of the dataset is that the study began before the diagnosis of borderline personality disorder in DSM-III. Therefore, the study authors retrospectively applied a diagnostic instrument to identify borderline personality disorder using an algorithm for scoring items from self-report questionnaires and structured interviews conducted by trained lay interviewers. This study has therefore been excluded from the analysis below.

In addition, a number of studies were found that reported data for cluster B personality disorders but did not report any data specifically for borderline personality disorder. These studies were also excluded from the analysis because it cannot be assumed that the stability of different cluster B personality disorders is similar. This is illustrated by Chanen and colleagues (2004) who report that the stability of different cluster B personality disorders ranges from 0% for histrionic and narcissistic to 100% for antisocial in a sample of young people over a 2-year period.

9.3.4 Prospective longitudinal short follow-up studies of borderline personality disorder

Study descriptions

CHANEN2004

This is a 2-year prospective study of 101 young people drawn from an adolescent outpatient service in Australia. Participants were assessed using the SCID-II at baseline

Table 121: Summary study characteristics of included studies of the stability of borderline personality disorder in young people

	Prospective longitudinal short follow-up studies of borderline personality disorder	Quasi-prospective studies of developmental antecedents of borderline personality disorder	Children with disruptive and/or emotional disorders followed-up as young people
No. trials (Total participants)	3 prospective longitudinal studies (158)	3 quasi-prospective studies (210)	5 prospective studies (784)
Study IDs	(1) CHANEN2004 (2) GARNET1994 (3) MEIJER1998	(1) HELGELAND2004 (2) LOFGREN1991 (3) ZELKOWITZ2007	(1) FISCHER2002 (2) HELGELAND2005 (3) HELLGREN1994 (4) RAMKLINT2003 (5) REY1995
N/% female	(1) 101/63 (2) 21/52 (3) 36/50	(1) 132/53 (2) 19/26 (3) 59/19	(1) 239/10 (2) 130/53 (3) 112/37 (4) 158/60 (5) 145/44
Age range (mean age) (where given)	(1) 15–18 (16) (2) 15–19 (17) (3) (15)	(1) 12–18 (15) (2) 6–10 (3) 7–12	(1) 4–12 (2) 12–18 (15) (3) 7–7 (7) (4) 10–17 (14) (5) 12–16 (14)
Setting	(1) Outpatients; Australia (2) Inpatients; US (3) Inpatients; Holland	(1) Inpatients; Norway (2) Inpatients; US (3) Inpatients; Canada	(1) Not reported; US (2) Inpatients; Norway (3) Community; Sweden (4) Inpatients; Sweden (5) Adolescent Unit; Australia
Length of follow-up	(1)–(2) 2 years (3) 3 years	(1) 28 years (2) 10–20 years (3) 5–7 years	(1) 14 years (2) 28 years (3) 9 years (4) 16 years (5) 14 years

and 97 were re-interviewed 2 years later by interviewers who were blind to the baseline assessment. At baseline, 11 participants met the criteria for borderline personality disorder. At the 2-year follow-up, six participants who had met the criteria at baseline no longer did, eight new cases of borderline personality disorder were diagnosed and four people who met the criteria at baseline retained the diagnosis 2 years later. The overall proportion of enduring cases of borderline personality disorder over 2 years was 40%.

GARNET1994

This is a US-based study of 21 inpatients with borderline personality disorder. Participants were contacted 2 years following discharge. Symptoms were assessed using the Personality Disorder Examination at baseline and again at follow-up by raters who were blind to the baseline diagnosis. At the 2-year follow-up, seven participants retained the diagnosis of borderline personality disorder and 14 no longer met the criteria; the overall proportion of enduring cases in this sample was 33%.

The authors also examined the ability of baseline criteria for borderline personality disorder to predict the diagnosis of borderline personality disorder at the 2-year follow-up. For the subgroup of participants who were diagnosed with borderline personality disorder both at baseline and at follow-up, the most stable symptoms were emptiness or boredom (100% agreement between baseline and follow-up), inappropriate and intense anger (86% agreement), affective instability (71% agreement), identity disturbance (71% agreement) and suicidal behaviours (67% agreement). The least stable symptoms were impulsiveness (57% agreement) and unstable intense relationships (50% agreement).

MEIJER1998

This Dutch study followed-up 36 inpatients, 14 with borderline personality disorder and 22 without. The Diagnostic Interview for Borderline Patients was administered to all participants at baseline and at the 3-year follow-up by raters who were blind to baseline diagnosis. At the 3-year follow-up, two people who met the criteria for borderline personality disorder at baseline retained their diagnosis. Twelve people no longer met the criteria but it was reported that some borderline symptoms were still present. There were no new cases of borderline personality disorder in the sample. Overall the proportion of enduring cases was 21%. The authors report the most persistent symptoms were conflict about giving and receiving care, dependency and masochism, and 'areas or periods of special achievement'.

Clinical summary

These prospective longitudinal studies of the stability of borderline personality disorder in young people over a period of 2 to 3 years suggest that the stability of this disorder is between 21 and 40%. However, it should be noted that all the studies have very small sample sizes, with only 46 people with borderline personality disorder at baseline across the three studies.

9.3.5   Quasi-prospective studies of developmental antecedents of borderline personality disorder

Study descriptions

HELGELAND2004

This is a Norwegian quasi-prospective study investigating the developmental antecedents of borderline personality disorder in 25 participants with borderline personality disorder compared with 107 controls. Baseline diagnosis was determined on the basis of medical records and follow-up interview after 28 years. At follow-up, SCID-I and SIDP-IV were administered by raters who were blind to the baseline diagnosis. Twenty-five participants met the criteria for borderline personality disorder at some point in their life; of these 16 met at least five of the borderline personality disorder criteria at follow-up, while nine with a history of lifetime borderline personality disorder no longer met at least five of the criteria. Overall 64% of people with a history of borderline personality disorder met the diagnostic criteria at follow-up.

LOFGREN1991

This US study followed up 19 children who had been diagnosed with borderline personality disorder in the preceding 10 to 20 years. These children had been identified with borderline personality disorder at baseline according to the criteria of Bemporad and colleagues (1982, 1987). At follow-up participants were assessed using the SCID and unstructured clinical interviews. Three of the 19 participants met the diagnostic criteria for borderline personality disorder at follow-up. A further 13 met the criteria for a personality disorder other than borderline. Overall the proportion of enduring cases was 16% in this sample.

ZELKOWITZ2007

This Canadian study followed up 59 young people who had been treated in a child psychiatric day hospital 5 to 7 years earlier. The child version of the Retrospective Diagnostic Interview for Borderlines was used to review participants' medical charts; on this basis 28 participants were diagnosed with borderline pathology of childhood while 31 participants who did not have a history of borderline pathology of childhood served as the comparison group. Borderline personality disorder was assessed at follow-up with the Diagnostic Interview for Borderlines. At follow-up, five participants met the criteria for a current diagnosis of borderline personality disorder and 23 participants who had a history of borderline pathology of childhood did not. Overall 18% of people who were diagnosed with borderline pathology of childhood met the diagnostic criteria for borderline personality disorder at follow up.

Clinical summary

These quasi-prospective studies of the antecedents of borderline personality disorder in children and young people suggest that the stability of the diagnosis over a longer period of time is less clear; the proportion of participants who retained the diagnosis for borderline personality disorder at follow-up varied from between 16 and 64%.

9.3.6 Children with disruptive and/or emotional disorders followed-up as young people

Study descriptions

FISCHER2002

This US study followed up 147 participants diagnosed as hyperactive in childhood and 73 matched community controls. Participants were originally assessed at age 4 to 12 years; this study followed them up an average of 14 years later. At follow-up, SCID-NP (non-patient edition), including SCID-II, was administered. Two out of 73 (3%) of participants in the control group, and 20 out of 147 (14%) of those in the hyperactive group, were diagnosed with borderline personality disorder. Borderline personality disorder was one of the most common diagnoses in the hyperactive group.

Data are also presented for comorbidities in the hyperactive group: having major depressive disorder, passive-aggressive personality disorder or histrionic personality disorder significantly increased the likelihood of having borderline personality disorder. Likewise, having borderline personality disorder was a significant risk for major depressive disorder, passive-aggressive personality disorder, histrionic personality disorder and antisocial personality disorder. In addition, severity of conduct disorder at adolescent follow-up significantly predicted risk for borderline personality disorder.

HELGELAND2005

This Norwegian quasi-prospective study assessed personality disorders in adulthood in a group of participants who were admitted to an adolescent unit 28 years earlier with emotional and/or disruptive behaviour disorders. One hundred and thirty participants were re-diagnosed based on hospital records and were interviewed with the SIDP-IV at 28 years, follow-up by a rater who was blind to the baseline diagnosis. Young people with disruptive behaviour disorders were significantly more likely to have borderline personality disorder in adulthood than those with emotional disorders: at follow-up, two out of 45 (4%) participants with emotional disorder in adolescence, and 22 out of 85 (26%) participants with disruptive disorder in adolescence, were diagnosed with borderline personality disorder.

HELLGREN1994

This Swedish study followed-up 56 children at age 16 years who had deficits in attention, motor control and perception at age 7 years and compared them with 45 control children. The Personality Disorder Examination was administered at follow-up. Psychiatric disorders and personality disorders were more common in participants who had deficits in attention, motor control and perception as children compared with the controls. Three out of 13 (23%) participants who had severe deficits in attention, motor control and perception as children, and 5 out of 26 (19%) participants who had mild deficits in attention, motor control and perception as children, were diagnosed with borderline personality disorder at follow-up. Two out of 11 (18%) participants who had motor control/perception dysfunction only and three out of six (50%) who had attention deficits only as children had borderline personality disorder at follow-up compared with four out of 45 (9%) participants in the control group.

RAMKLINT2003

This Swedish study assessed personality disorders in a group of 158 former psychiatric inpatients. Childhood and adolescent axis I disorders were obtained from medical records and coded into DSM-IV diagnoses. Participants were followed up an average of 16 years later and personality disorders in adulthood were assessed using the DSM-IV and ICD-10 Personality Questionnaire (DIP-Q). At follow-up, 50 of the 158 (32%) participants were diagnosed with borderline personality disorder. The authors report that childhood and adolescent depression and substance-related disorders were significant risk factors for borderline personality disorder in adulthood.

REY1995

This Australian study followed up 145 young adults who had been diagnosed with a variety of emotional and disruptive disorders during adolescence, an average of 14 years earlier. The Personality Disorder Examination was administered at follow-up and a total of 11 of the 145 (8%) participants were diagnosed with borderline personality disorder in adulthood. Of these, nine out of 80 (11%) participants who had a disruptive disorder in adolescence were diagnosed with borderline personality disorder at follow-up; three had an adolescent diagnosis of attention deficit hyperactivity disorder (ADHD), one had oppositional disorder, two had conduct disorder and three had conduct disorder and ADHD. Two out of 65 (3%) participants who had an emotional disorder in adolescence were diagnosed with borderline personality disorder at follow-up; both had an adolescent diagnosis of dysthymic disorder.

Clinical summary
These studies of children with disruptive and/or emotional disorders followed up in adolescence or adulthood report a higher incidence of borderline personality disorder at follow-up for participants who were diagnosed with a disruptive disorder in childhood (between 11 and 26%).

9.3.7   Overall clinical summary for stability of the diagnosis of borderline personality disorder in young people

Table 122 summarises the stability statistics for each of the studies described above. Limited evidence makes it difficult to draw any firm conclusions regarding the stability of the diagnosis of borderline personality disorder in young people. There is some evidence that the diagnosis is stable in between 21 and 40% of young people over a 2- to 3-year period; the picture becomes less clear, however, over longer follow-up periods, partly due to the fact that the diagnosis of borderline personality disorder was only introduced in 1980 with DSM-III. A follow-up time of 2 to 3 years is insufficient to establish stability or instability.

This limited evidence on the stability of the borderline personality disorder diagnosis in young people has led some commentators to argue for its instability

Table 122: Summary stability data for borderline personality disorder in young people

Prospective longitudinal short (2-3 years) follow-up studies of borderline personality disorder in adolescence

Study ID	N baseline	N follow-up	Length of follow-up (years)	N borderline personality disorder at baseline (T1)	N borderline personality disorder at follow-up (T2)	N borderline personality disorder present T1, absent T2	N borderline personality disorder absent T1, present T2 (new cases)	N borderline personality disorder present T1 & T2 (enduring cases)	% enduring cases
CHANEN2004	101	97	2	11	12	6	8	4	40
GARNET1994	21	21	2	21	7	14	0	7	33
MEIJER1998	36	36	3	14	2	12	0	2	21

Quasi-prospective studies of developmental antecedents of borderline personality disorder using medical records

Study ID	N baseline	N follow-up	Length of follow-up(years)	N borderline personality disorder at follow-up	N borderline personality disorder in past but not at follow-up	% people with borderline personality disorder in past diagnosed with the disorder at follow-up
HELGELAND2004	132	132	28	16	9	64
LOFGREN1991	19	19	10–20	3	16	16
ZELKOWITZ2007	59	–	5–7	5	23	18

Children with disruptive/emotional disorders followed up as young people/young adults

Study ID	N baseline	N follow-up	Length of follow-up (years)	Disruptive disorder in adolescence total N	Disruptive disorder in adolescence with borderline personality disorder at follow-up	Emotional disorder in adolescence total N	Emotional disorder in adolescence with borderline personality disorder at follow-up	Total N with disorder in adolescence and borderline personality disorder at follow-up	% of those with disorder in adolescence that have disorder at follow-up
FISCHER2002	239	220	14	147	20	–	–	20	14
HELGELAND2005	130	130	28	85	22	45	2	24	19
HELLGREN1994	112	101	9	56	13	–	–	13	23
RAMKLINT2003	158	158	16	75	OR = 0.99*	28	OR = 2.91*	50	34
REY1995	145	145	14	80	9	65	2	11	8

*Odds ratios adjusted for age, sex and presence of other childhood disorders.

(Becker *et al.*, 2002) and others to argue that the diagnosis is stable over time (Bradley *et al.*, 2005a). It may be that there are different sub-groups of young people who receive a diagnosis of borderline personality disorder, some of whom will recover more rapidly and others who will experience more enduring difficulties. Some young people with the diagnosis may experience a reduction in symptoms as they develop and mature or in response to positive changes in their family or social environment. Further research into the developmental course of young people with the diagnosis, or symptoms and behaviours suggestive of the disorder, is warranted. One recent study conducted in the US with adults reported that the prognosis of the disorder was more positive than was previously believed (Zanarini *et al.*, 2003) and it may be that even those young people with a stable diagnosis over 2 years (Garnet *et al.*, 1994) may go on to recover over a longer time period. Given the limitations of the evidence base and the size of the stability estimates in the studies that are available, healthcare professionals should exercise caution in making the diagnosis of borderline personality disorder in young people especially given the stigma associated with the diagnosis. Assessment issues are discussed further in section 9.5.

9.4   SUICIDE RISK IN YOUNG PEOPLE WITH BORDERLINE PERSONALITY DISORDER

9.4.1   Risk factors for suicide in young people with borderline personality disorder or symptoms of borderline personality disorder

A separate review of factors associated with suicide in young people with symptoms of borderline personality disorder or borderline personality disorder was undertaken. Personality disorder in this age group may not be stable, therefore different factors are likely to be important compared with risk factors in adults.

Nine studies of suicide in young people with borderline personality disorder were found. Two of these were excluded (see below). See Table 123 for a summary of the characteristics of the included studies.

Studies that did not look at specific risk factors were excluded (CRUMLEY1981; FRIEDMAN1989).

9.4.2   Studies of general psychiatric populations

Study descriptions

BRENT1993
This US study compared 37 psychiatric inpatients aged between 13 and 19 years who had made a suicide attempt in the year prior to admission with 29 inpatients who had never made a suicide attempt. The sample was not consecutive but was frequency matched (the term is not explained by the authors) with a previously gathered sample of young people who had completed suicide on age, gender and primary psychiatric diagnosis. Despite this, the never-attempted group contained

Table 123: Summary study characteristics of studies of risk factors for suicide in young people with borderline personality disorder

	General psychiatric populations or non-specific personality disorder	Studies comparing those with major depressive disorder with those with borderline personality disorder
No. trials (Total participants)	4 observational studies (188)	2 observational studies (125)
Study IDs	(1) BRENT1993 (2) RUNESON1991 (3) STONE1992 (4) YOUNG1995	(1) HORESH2003A (2) HORESH2003B
N/% female	(1) 66/39 (2) 58/28 (3) 9/56 (4) 55/53	(1) 60/55 (2) 65/77
Age range (mean)	(1) 13–19 (16) (2) 15–29 (23) (3) 15–20 (18) (4) 14–18 (16)	(1) *(17) (2) 13–18 (15)
Axis I/II disorders	(1) Any affective disorder: suicide attempter group 86.5%, control group 55.2%; substance misuse: 29.7%, 37.9%; ADHD 5.4%, 34.5%; any personality disorder 81.1%, 58.6%; borderline personality disorder or trait 32.4%, 10.3% (2) Major depression 22%; schizophrenia 14%; adjustment disorder 14%; borderline personality disorder 33%; antisocial personality disorder 16% (3) 5 had borderline personality disorder; 4 psychosis (1 bipolar; 4 schizoaffective); comorbidities not given	(1) Major depressive disorder 33%; borderline personality disorder 33%; no diagnosis (control group) 33% (2) Borderline personality disorder 51%; major depressive disorder 49%

Continued

Table 123: (*Continued*)

	General psychiatric populations or non-specific personality disorder	Studies comparing those with major depressive disorder with those with borderline personality disorder
	(4) Borderline personality disorder 38%; narcissistic personality disorder 9%; antisocial personality disorder 4%; personality disorder not otherwise specified 35%	
Setting	(1) Inpatients (2) 79% had previous psychiatric care in 2 years before suicide (3)–(4) Inpatients	(1) Outpatients (2) Inpatients
Suicidality	(1) 56% recent suicide attempt (2)–(3) all completed suicide (4) 69% suicidal	(1) 100% recent suicide attempt (2) 26% recent suicide attempt

*Not available but described as adolescents.

more boys than the group of young people who had attempted suicide (90% and 38% respectively), which also comprised more young people with affective illness. The study compared the two groups on various factors. As well as finding that those who had attempted suicide were more likely to be girls and to have an affective illness (notably major depressive disorder, bipolar disorder mixed state and bipolar spectrum disorder), the study found that this group was less likely to have diagnoses of conduct disorder or ADHD. They were more likely to have a personality disorder (81.1% versus 58.6%), particularly cluster C disorders (70.3% versus 48.3%). There were more patients with borderline personality disorder or borderline traits (32.4%, 10.3%), and this group were more likely to have made a previous attempt.

RUNESON1991
This study reports on 58 consecutive suicides among young people and young adults (aged 15 to 29 years) completed between 1984 and 1987 in Sweden. Data were collected in semi-structured interviews with relatives. In some cases relevant healthcare professionals were also interviewed. In 69% of cases psychiatric records

were consulted. Diagnoses were made by consensus based on DSM-III-R criteria. Of the total 58 cases, 21 were given a diagnosis of borderline personality disorder. There was a relatively high rate of depressive disorders (42% in the borderline personality disorder group, 56% in the non-borderline personality disorder group).

Those given a borderline personality disorder diagnosis were more likely to have had absent or divorced parents, and to have been exposed to alcohol and drug misuse by their first-degree relatives. They were also more likely to have had more than two jobs, to have had financial problems, to have been homeless and to have received a court sentence. Unfortunately, these data are not broken down by age, so may be dominated by those over 18 years.

STONE1992

This is a report of a study following a cohort of patients admitted to the New York State Psychiatric Institute between 1963 and 1976. The authors reported on the nine patients who completed suicide as young people (aged 20 years or younger). Five of these had a diagnosis of borderline personality disorder (DSM-III criteria) and four presented with a psychosis.

The study found that those who had completed suicide were more likely to experience traumatic life events than others, particularly those with borderline personality disorder. This group were also more likely to have experienced parental brutality than those with psychosis.

YOUNG1995

This US study looked at the families of 55 young people aged 14 to 18 years who had been admitted to an adolescent and family treatment unit. Patients were admitted following self-harm, dangerous drug use, suicidal behaviour, treatment-resistant eating disorders, depression and OCD. Based on DSM-III-R diagnoses, 21 were diagnosed with borderline personality disorder. Of these, 29% had a comorbid eating disorder, 33% major affective disorder, 19% PTSD and none had OCD. There were 16 girls and 5 boys. Fifty-seven per cent had an intact family, 24% were adopted, 19% had parents who were divorced or separated and 24% had parents who had remarried. Of those with borderline personality disorder, 66% were suicidal, all had shown self-destructive behaviour and 67% were aggressive. Data were collected in a 2-hour standardised family assessment between 2 and 5 weeks after admission.

The study compared the young people's views with those of their parents, making comparisons between those with borderline personality disorder and those without. It reported that young people with borderline personality disorder who were more suicidal tended to see themselves as more alienated from their parents, more socially isolated and with poorer overall functioning than others. Their parents, however, did not see their children in the same way, which the study authors believe illustrates the young people's alienation. Within the group of those with borderline personality disorder, those who were more self-destructive (such as self-harming or running away) tended to see themselves as more socially isolated than other young people.

Clinical summary

It is not surprising that many of the studies reviewed found that young people with borderline personality disorder or traits of borderline personality disorder are more likely to attempt suicide than others since suicidal behaviour is a diagnostic criterion of the disorder. However, the studies help to emphasise the fact that young people with borderline personality disorder are at risk. In addition, those who are suicidal are more likely to feel alienated from their families and more socially isolated than others. Those completing suicide are also more likely to have experienced traumatic events and parental brutality, absence or divorce.

9.4.3   Studies comparing people with depression with those with borderline personality disorder

Study descriptions

HORESH2003A

This study looked at suicidality in 40 young people referred to an outpatient clinic following a suicide attempt. It was undertaken in Israel and compared those with major depressive disorder (n = 20) with those with borderline personality disorder (n = 20). These groups were further compared with a control group (n = 20) who had no psychiatric diagnosis or suicide attempts and who were matched on age and sex. Those with comorbid borderline personality disorder and major depressive disorder were excluded. Participants were interviewed within a month of the index admission.

The study found that young people with depression had statistically significantly higher BDI depression scores than those with borderline personality disorder, who in turn had statistically significantly higher scores than those in the control group. On a suicide risk scale, both the major depression and borderline personality disorder groups had significantly higher scores than the control group. This pattern was the same for the number of serious life events. Those with borderline personality disorder had experienced significantly more sexual abuse events than either of the other groups: 30% compared with 5% of those with major depressive disorder and 5% of the control group.

HORESH2003B

This study, also conducted in Israel, looked at 65 young people with either major depressive disorder (n = 32) or borderline personality disorder (n = 33). Some of the young people in each group had made a recent (that is, within 30 days of assessment) suicide attempt (n = 17), and some had never attempted suicide (n = 16). Comorbid disorders among those with borderline personality disorder included major depressive disorder (n = 10), dysthymia (n = 11) and conduct disorder (n = 3).

The study found that among those with a diagnosis of borderline personality disorder, those with a recent suicide attempt were more impulsive, while those with major depressive disorder with a recent suicide attempt had higher intent scores than those with a recent suicide attempt and borderline personality disorder.

Clinical summary

These studies confirm that those with borderline personality disorder who make a suicide attempt are likely to have increased depressive symptoms compared with those with no psychiatric diagnosis. However, these symptoms are unlikely to meet diagnosis for major depressive disorder. Young people who made a suicide attempt were also more likely to have suffered sexual abuse. However, a diagnosis of borderline personality disorder does not necessarily imply someone will make a suicide attempt, but it appears that those who do are likely to be more impulsive than those who do not.

9.4.4   Overall clinical summary suicide risk studies

There are relatively few studies of risk factors for suicide in young people with borderline personality disorder or traits. Young people with borderline personality disorder who attempt suicide are likely to have some depression symptoms and to be more impulsive. Young people with borderline personality disorder completing suicide are more likely to have experienced traumatic events and parental brutality, absence or divorce. These findings indicate that, as with adults, assessment and management of suicide risk is likely to form part of the treatment plan.

9.5   ASSESSMENT

9.5.1   Reviewing the evidence base

In order to make recommendations about identification of borderline personality disorder in young people, the GDG asked the following clinical questions:

- What can help clinicians identify features of borderline personality disorder in young peoples?
- Are there tools/assessments which clinicians can use to assist in the identification / assessment process?
- Are there tools/assessments which can be used in tier 1?

The questions regarding assessment were addressed by a group of special advisors (see Appendix 3).

9.5.2   Identifying the young person with borderline personality disorder

There are a number of clinical features that may indicate to the clinician the need to assess for borderline personality disorder as part of a comprehensive clinical assessment. These are:

- frequent suicidal/self-harming behaviours
- marked emotional instability
- increasing intensity of symptoms

- multiple comorbidities
- non-response to established treatments for current symptoms
- high level of functional impairment (Chanen *et al.*, 2007a).

Questionnaire measures may also provide a useful screen to indicate that a comprehensive assessment is required. Chanen and colleagues (2008b) evaluated four screening measures for borderline personality disorder in an outpatient sample of young people: the McLean Screening Instrument for borderline personality disorder (MSI-borderline personality disorder); the Borderline Personality Questionnaire (BPQ); items from the IPDE; and the borderline personality disorder items from the SCID-II. All four measures performed well. The BPQ had the highest diagnostic accuracy and highest test – re-test reliability; it is also the longest of the four measures although administering and scoring can be completed within 15 minutes.

The criteria for diagnosing borderline personality disorder are the same in young people as for adults (with the caveats as indicated above in section 9.2). Diagnosing borderline personality disorder in young people can be assisted by a structured clinical interview and should be conducted as part of a comprehensive clinical assessment leading to a clear formulation of the young person's difficulties. The diagnosis of borderline personality disorder in a young person should only be made after a comprehensive and rigorous assessment has been completed by a practitioner knowledgeable about the adolescent period and skilled in the assessment of mental health problems in this age group. Such an assessment should also include a developmental family history with the young person's family or carers. Detailed and comprehensive assessments are important in all areas of mental health but are especially so when the diagnosis carries a significant likelihood of stigmatisation. To assist with the assessment, clinicians may use the questions from the SCID-II or the Shedler & Westen Assessment Procedure - Adolescents, which is a Q-sort technique based on a structured diagnostic interview that was specifically developed for the assessment of personality disorder in young people (Westen & Shedler, 2007). This latter assessment may be suitable in some specialist services but is likely to be too time consuming for most settings. None of these measures is suitable for use by tier 1 staff because such measures need to be part of a comprehensive diagnostic and clinical assessment.

Both the diagnostic criteria and retrospective studies indicate that borderline personality disorder develops in late adolescence/young adulthood, yet the diagnosis is made rarely at first presentation. Non-diagnosis early in the course of the disorder may relate to valid concerns about the appropriateness of diagnosing it during this developmental stage, concerns about misdiagnosis, the iatrogenic effects of diagnosis and/or to a failure to conceptualise the problems as belonging to a personality disorder. Given that a diagnosis of borderline personality disorder in adolescence predicts both axis I and axis II problems in adulthood (Cohen *et al.*, 2007; Daley *et al.*, 1999; Johnson *et al.*, 1999b), failure to consider it early may mean that appropriate early interventions to ameliorate the difficulties for this group of young people are not offered. This may become increasingly important as more efficacious treatments for borderline personality disorder are developed.

9.6   TREATMENT

9.6.1   Review of the evidence base

In relation to treatment for young people, the GDG asked the following clinical question:
● What interventions and care processes are effective in improving outcomes or altering the developmental course for people under the age of 18 with borderline personality disorder or borderline symptoms?

In order to address this question, the reviews of the literature of adults with borderline personality disorder were scanned to ascertain whether any studies had been conducted in young people. This yielded one study of CAT (CHANEN2008), but there was no effect for CAT compared with manualised 'good practice' other than for reducing self-harm and general functioning (see Chapter 5 for the data for this study). No study of a pharmacological intervention was found in young people aged under 18 years. This is not surprising because not only does no drug have marketing authorisation for the treatment of people with borderline personality disorder, but also few psychotropic drugs have marketing authorisation for young people aged under 18 for any indication.

In the absence of high-quality evidence, the GDG and its special advisors (see Appendix 3) agreed that both the general principles and the recommendations for treatment for adults described elsewhere in this guideline could be applied to young people.

9.6.2   Issues of consent to treatment for young people

It is desirable to gain informed consent from both the young person and their parents before treatment starts, not least because the success of any treatment approach significantly depends upon the development of a positive therapeutic alliance between the young person, the family and the professionals. In most outpatient settings consent is usually straightforward as the young person will generally have a choice to accept or decline treatment. Nonetheless, information about the potential risks and benefits of the intervention being offered should be given.

There may be times when professionals consider inpatient admission to be necessary, but either the young person or the family do not consent. In the Mental Health Act 2007 (HMSO, 2007), there have been some changes to the law regarding young people aged under 18 years. If a young person aged 16 or 17 years has capacity to give or refuse treatment, it is no longer possible for the person with parental authority to overrule the young person's wishes. However, for those aged under 16 years, a 'Gillick-competent' young person can still be admitted against his or her wishes with the consent of someone with parental authority. While the use of parental consent is legal, it is generally good practice to consider the use of other appropriate legislation, usually the Mental Health Act, for prolonged periods of admission as it includes safeguards such as the involvement of other professionals, a time limit and a straightforward procedure for appeals and regular reviews.

On the other hand, a young person aged under 16 years has the right to consent to treatment if deemed 'Gillick competent'. If the person with parental authority objects, these objections must be considered but will not necessarily prevail.

Alternative legislation includes using a care order (Section 31) under the Children Act 1989 (HMSO, 1989) or a specific issue order (Section 8). Both of these options normally involve social services and can be time consuming. Another more rapid alternative to the Children Act is to apply for a Wardship Order, which in an emergency can be organised by telephone.

9.6.3   Involvement of family and carers

The role of the family in the treatment of young people with borderline personality disorder is critical to consider. Issues within the family, both past and present, are likely to be highly relevant to the development or maintenance (or both) of the young person's problems. Where modification of problematic family interactions is possible, it is likely to have a significant positive effect on outcome. It may also be the first opportunity some parents have had to consider and address some of their own particular problems. Severity of parental mental health problems also can impact adversely on treatment outcome. Where there are extreme family problems, however, working collaboratively with the family of the young person may prove impossible. Likewise, it may be difficult to form a meaningful therapeutic alliance with parents whose parenting style provokes child protection concerns.

9.7   SERVICE CONFIGURATION

9.7.1   Configuration of CAMHS

Interventions for young people with borderline personality disorder will usually be provided by specialist CAMHS, but some young people are helped significantly by non-specialist healthcare, social or educational services. In order to recognise the different levels of interventions for many mental health problems in children and young people, CAMHS has been organised into four main levels, or tiers, of delivery (NHS Health Advisory Service, 1995; Department of Health, 2004) (see Text box 5).

9.8   SUGGESTED CARE PATHWAY FOR YOUNG PEOPLE
WITH BORDERLINE PERSONALITY DISORDER

Available evidence for a care pathway for young people with borderline personality disorder was minimal. The care pathway in this guideline was drawn up in consultation with experts and from extrapolation from the adult care pathway.

Text box 5: Structure of CAMHS' tiers

Tier 1	● Provide primary or direct contact with young people, primarily for reasons other than mental health, including primary care/general practice, counselling and psychotherapy, general paediatrics, social services, health visitors and schools. ● First point of contact with the child/family with mental health problems. ● Draw on specialist CAMHS personnel who can consult and advise them about working with children and young people in their care who either have, or are at risk of developing, a mental health problem.
Tier 2	● Specialist CAMHS professionals working in a community-based setting alongside tier 1 workers, working in primary care, schools and other relevant community settings such as social services. ● Work as a part of a team, with tier 1 staff, built around the individual child. ● Able to provide fairly rapid assessment and treatment to children within tier 1 settings, as well as consultation/support to tier 1 workers. ● Able to help identify those children needing referral to more specialist services. ● Ideally organised into multidisciplinary teams, with good links to tier 3 services, thereby facilitating a more seamless transition across tiers. ● Sometimes, tier 2 services are provided by the voluntary sector (for example, some but not all adolescent counselling and psychotherapy services).
Tier 3	● Comprise multidisciplinary teams of specialist CAMHS professionals working in (secondary care) specialist CAMHS facilities (for example, Child and Family Consultation Services or Hospital Liaison Teams). ● The NSF for Children's Services states that all Primary Care Trust/Local Health Board areas should have at least one (or access to one) comprehensive tier 3 multidisciplinary CAMHS team providing specialist co-ordinated assessments and interventions, and offering the full range of appropriate psychological and pharmacological treatments. ● Offer outreach services to those young people who are housebound or otherwise unable to access tier 3 services based in secondary care facilities, or to work in conjunction with outpatient treatment plans (for example, monitoring of

Text box 5: *(Continued)*

		medication). Emergency services with 24-hour availability should also be in place in all localities.
	●	Provide consultation and training to tier 1 workers and refer when necessary to tier 4 services.
Tier 4	●	Highly specialised tertiary CAMHS that provide multidisciplinary services for very severe mental health problems, or for those who need very intensive treatment or supervision. These services vary in how they are organised.
	●	Includes highly specialist outpatient treatment (for example, crisis intervention and intensive home-based therapies).
	●	Referrals to tier 4 services usually come from tier 3 CAMHS professionals, and service users are usually discharged back to tier 3 services or outreach services after the tier 4 intervention.

9.8.1 General principles to be considered when working with young people with borderline personality disorder

As with adults, both the type of interventions offered to the young person with borderline personality disorder and the manner of delivery are equally important. The general principles outlined for adults that aim to promote a constructive therapeutic relationship are also applicable, with some caveats, to young people. There are some additional principles for working with young people with borderline personality disorder that are also important and are outlined below.

Active participation
Young people with borderline personality disorder find coping with the developmental challenges of adolescence difficult and consequently struggle to function effectively at home, at school and with their peer group. Frequently, their experiences in childhood, as well as causing distress and difficulty, have also failed to prepare them for adolescence. Given these difficulties and the age of the young person, service providers frequently attempt to take responsibility for the young person or strongly encourage parents or carers to do so. This presents particular challenges as the developmental task for young people is to separate and individuate from parents/carers and to develop a degree of autonomy. Young people with borderline personality disorder often attempt to become autonomous in the absence of key capacities to exercise autonomy safely, which increases anxiety in families/carers and professionals alike. Encouraging active participation in this context presents challenges but is highly important. Promoting active engagement in decision making (for example, outlining treatment options, highlighting the consequences of certain behaviours or choices and evaluating the benefits and disadvantages of behaviour change) may assist in developing and maintaining the therapeutic alliance.

An assumption of capacity

In working with adults, assuming that the person has capacity is important. With young people a key goal of treatment may be developing capacity. In working with young people with borderline personality disorder professionals must balance the developing autonomy and capacity of the young person with the responsibility of parents and carers. Professionals need to be familiar with the various legal frameworks surrounding consent in young people to manage this balance effectively.

Experienced and well-trained professionals

Young people with borderline personality disorder often form intense relationships with adults endeavouring to help them. In this context, professionals require the ability to balance validation and nurturing with limit setting around both the frequency and type of contact with the young person. Frequently the intensity and extremity of emotional and behavioural disturbance in these young people, combined with the contextual variability in their functioning, results in different staff members or groups of staff having widely differing views of the nature of the young person's problems. This can lead to major conflict between staff, which is often referred to as 'splitting'. Staff must have the capacity to reflect on this process rather than act upon emotions generated by it and maintain collaborative working relationships both with the young person, their family or support system and other professionals engaged with the young person. Staff must avoid lone working, especially in the absence of supervision. Professionals should be alert to circumstances where young people who are hard to engage form intense relationships with tier 1 staff where such staff are inadequately trained to manage the difficulties arising in the helping relationship. Such circumstances warrant consultation from more specialist services (tiers 2 and 3).

Teamwork and communication

Young people frequently see other people and circumstances in extreme terms. This tendency is exacerbated for young people with borderline personality disorder. Regular communication among professionals helps to ensure a consistent treatment approach. Clear leadership with an established and open decision-making hierarchy can ensure that disagreements in teams about treatment planning and delivery are handled sensitively and effectively.

Monitoring the type and intensity of treatment

Often young people with borderline personality disorder receive either uni-modal interventions or multiple uncoordinated interventions. Frequently each additional crisis leads to the addition of new interventions or the involvement of new staff or services. Too little but also too much treatment may be unhelpful. Careful monitoring of the impact of interventions is, therefore, warranted. Young people with borderline personality disorder who also meet criteria for a diagnosis of PTSD present a particular clinical dilemma, especially if the young person is highly unstable (for example, where there is frequent, severe suicidal/self-harming behaviour, severe substance misuse or other severe psychopathology). In such circumstances trauma processing work or exploratory approaches may be contra-indicated until a reduction in risk or increase in emotional stability has been achieved. With other young people interventions to address the trauma may facilitate a reduction in risk and an increase in stability. Consequently, professionals should consider carefully whether to offer trauma-focused work and how best to do so safely where the young person presents with high levels of risk. As with all interventions, effectiveness must be reviewed regularly.

Realistic expectations
Improvements in the symptoms and functioning of young people with borderline personality disorder, as with adults, tend to be gradual rather than sudden. Therefore, setting realistic goals for progress in both the short and long term can assist young people in remaining motivated. Professionals must also guard against becoming demoralised about slow rates of change.

Being consistent and reliable
As with adults, young people with borderline personality disorder may find engaging with others difficult because of previous or indeed current experiences of abuse and neglect. Providing a consistent approach to the service user provides a sound basis for developing other therapeutic interventions. Consistency can be promoted by providing regular appointment times, being clear about how to access the service in times of crisis, having a clear theoretical model/approach and explaining reasons for certain professional responses.

Multi-agency response
Many young people with borderline personality disorder have needs that span health, social care and education. Coordinating a multi-agency response for these young people is often exceptionally difficult. Often, the presence of one agency in the care of the young person reduces the likelihood of involvement, or in some cases precipitates the withdrawal, of another agency. Withdrawal by one agency when the young person has identified needs that are their responsibility is unhelpful. Those involved with the young person will need to decide which agency is taking responsibility and ensure mechanisms are in place for clear multi-agency communication that do not compromise a young person's rights to a confidential service, and minimise confusion, particularly for young people who often have disturbed interpersonal communications.

There are some groups of young people with borderline personality disorder who find it especially difficult to access services, for example, those who are homeless and/or substance dependent. Professionals may need to be creative and flexible in attempting to engage these young people.

Management of acute and chronic risks
As with adults, young people with borderline personality disorder may experience high levels of suicidal ideation and repeated self-harm. Therefore working with young people with borderline personality disorder necessarily requires active engagement in the management of both chronic and acute exacerbations of risk. Acute and chronic risks may require different approaches. For example, a service

may provide time-limited increased support during a period of heightened acute risk. Yet in response to a less severe increase in risk, the same service may promote more active engagement of the young person in problem solving rather than providing more service input. Professionals must carefully consider strategies to manage acute and chronic risks and develop these in the care plan as appropriate.

Staff and services need to be able to not under- or overreact to crises. Staff must remain alert to the potential dangers of reinforcing behavioural escalations with increased input and involvement and to the risk of withdrawing prematurely during periods of apparent stability and calm. Staff must also take care not to ignore or minimise risks. Failure to respond appropriately to high-risk behaviours may also result in behavioural escalations that cannot be ignored. In general terms, a comprehensive treatment plan to address the needs of the young person facilitates taking a considered approach to risk management. Because striking the right balance in managing risk is difficult, all changes in service input must be carefully considered both with the young person and their family/support system and with other professionals (for example, the treating team or clinical supervisor).

Focusing interventions solely on risk may lead to inappropriate early withdrawal when risk decreases but also may mean that significant interpersonal issues remain unaddressed, possibly leading to later deterioration. Services must structure interventions to provide ongoing intervention and treatment beyond crisis periods.

Involvement of family /carers

Many young people with borderline personality disorder continue to live with their parents. Even for young people no longer with parents, they live in circumstances where significant others may be legally responsible for them. Family or carer involvement in treatment is an essential component of working with young people with borderline personality disorder. The nature and type of family involvement, however, needs careful consideration. Rarely are family relationships unproblematic and in many cases may contribute significantly to the difficulties of the young person. Equally the levels of difficulty for the young person frequently have an adverse impact on the family's capacity to function effectively. When young people with borderline personality disorder are engaging in risky behaviours, professionals need to consider carefully the balance of maintaining confidentiality regarding the young person with ensuring families and carers have enough relevant information to make informed decisions about safety and the amount of autonomy to give the young person. Involvement of the young person in this decision making process is helpful as is an attitude of honesty about the reasons for certain responses by professionals.

9.8.2   Child and adolescent mental health services

Tier 1

Professionals in tier 1 are most likely to encounter young people with borderline personality disorder as a consequence of interpersonal difficulties (for example, bullying at school), as a result of self-harm, or in association with family difficulties.

Tier 1 professionals are unlikely to be involved in diagnosing borderline personality disorder, rather they are involved in providing for the service user's physical health-care, social and educational needs. An awareness of borderline personality disorder and the principles underpinning its management may contextualise the difficulties of the young person with borderline personality disorder and help tier 1 professionals continue to provide routine services to this vulnerable group of young people. Awareness of borderline personality disorder may prevent inappropriate dismissal of the difficulties presented by the young person and encourage more flexible approaches to meeting the young person's needs. For tier 1 professionals to be able to fulfil these roles they will need appropriate training. Training programmes for tier 1 staff may require modification to cover borderline personality disorder or behaviours suggestive of the diagnosis. In order for professionals to contextualise appropriately the difficulties of these young people an understanding of personality and personality development will also be beneficial. This training may be most effectively targeted at services that have young people with higher rates of mental health concerns (for example, key stage 4 pupil referral units). Following appropriate training, tier 1 professionals may be involved in the sensitive detection of borderline type difficulties. Such identified concerns should lead to referral to or consultation with tier 2 professionals.

Tier 2
Tier 2 professionals provide consultation and training to tier 1 professionals in regard to all mental health problems. Tier 2 professionals therefore require an awareness of the problems of young people with borderline personality disorder and the general principles of intervention in order to intervene effectively in collaboration with tier 1 professionals. Tier 2 professionals may also be involved in early identification of borderline personality disorder in young people and determining whether more specialist assessment and intervention from tier 3 is warranted. Young people presenting with serious suicidal behaviour and repeated self-harm combined with deterioration in functioning either at home or at school should be referred to tier 3 for assessment. Significant family difficulties alongside behavioural concerns also require more specialist assessment. Referral to social services either under Section 47 (Child Protection) or Section 17 (Child in Need) of the Children Act 2004 (HMSO, 2004) may also be required alongside referral to tier 3.

Tier 2 professionals may consider low-intensity coping or skills interventions focusing on emotional regulation and alternatives to self-harm for young people with sub-threshold symptoms of borderline personality disorder where risk is low and functioning is maintained. In the absence of a robust evidence base caution should be exercised in using such interventions and professionals should remain alert for signs of deterioration.

Tier 2 professionals, alongside colleagues in tier 1, often have significant involvement with young people with borderline personality disorder who either refuse referral to tier 3 in the first instance or who do not engage with tier 3 services. While tier 3 services may need to expand the range and type of interventions to engage more effectively this hard-to-reach group of young people, services may also need to develop capacity to provide more extensive consultation and supervision to tier 2 staff supporting these young people.

Tier 3

Tier 3 services can provide a comprehensive assessment of the young person with borderline personality disorder. Tier 3 services must ensure that they consider borderline personality disorder along with other diagnostic possibilities in formulating the young person's difficulties and be aware that young people assessed and treated at Tier 3 frequently have multiple comorbidities. The management of comorbidities in young people is no different from that for adults (see Chapter 8).

Given that most young people with borderline personality disorder live with their families, with foster parents, or in social services' residential placements, involving carers in treatment may be helpful, although no studies evaluating such treatment appear to have been undertaken. Some treatment programmes (for example, DBT-A, an adapted form of DBT for young people) have specific treatment modalities involving the family. Other programmes (for example, some home-based treatment models) work entirely with the family. In some treatment models intervention may focus primarily on developing the capacity of families or carers to support the young person with borderline personality disorder therapeutically. Such interventions may be especially important when the young person does not consent to or is unmotivated to have treatment, although evaluation studies do not appear to have been undertaken.

As many young people with borderline personality disorder require a multi-agency response, clarity about the responsibilities of each agency facilitates the delivery of care. Agencies must strive to collaborate to provide coordinated care. Different thresholds for entry into services can compromise this objective, for example, tier 3 professionals may have concerns about a young person's social care that may not meet social service thresholds for intervention. This can reduce the effectiveness of therapeutic interventions as tier 3 staff become involved in trying to coordinate or meet social care needs. Likewise social services may find accessing specialist therapy services for some of the young people they care for difficult because tier 3 staff consider that the young person's social care needs are not met sufficiently to enable therapeutic work to begin. Failure to engage at all with the young person in these circumstances may prevent the success of social service interventions to improve the young person's social care. Professionals need to work flexibly and creatively around these tensions over service thresholds. Respecting the validity of the principles leading to the development of thresholds while trying to meet the needs of the young person is required in these circumstances.

Tier 3 teams must develop sub-teams of professionals with expertise in the management of young people with borderline personality disorder. Such professionals must also have the capacity to provide consultation and training to tier 2 staff. In some areas the specialist borderline personality disorder provision may be nested within tier 3, in others it may be stand alone. There is no evidence to support one model over the other. Where the breadth of services offered for young people with borderline personality disorder is wide and the level of intensity and expertise in the service is high, these services may be more appropriately considered tier 4 services.

Healthcare professionals in tier 3 should also follow the recommendations for adults in Chapters 5, 6 and 7.

Tier 4

For young people with borderline personality disorder tier 4 services comprise inpatient services, specialist outpatient services and home-based treatment teams. There is an extremely limited evidence base for the effectiveness of treatment in these settings.

Inpatient services. There are several circumstances in which healthcare professionals consider admission of people with borderline personality disorder to inpatient services: to manage an acute crisis, to treat chronic risk, to treat the borderline personality disorder itself or to treat a comorbid condition. Admissions for the management of acute risk should be clearly linked to an acute exacerbation of risk, be time-limited and have clear goals. Admission may also be required when risk is high and the motivation of the client to collaborate in treatment is very low or non-existent. The aim of such admissions is to ensure that the client is 'just community ready'. Transfer back to the community is clearly facilitated in circumstances where the young person is effectively engaged in a structured outpatient programme.

Factors warranting consideration for admission by a tier 4 team for treatment of borderline personality disorder, other axis I difficulties or chronic risk include repeated self-harm combined with a significant deterioration in functioning and a reduced capacity of either the family or community team to manage the young person. Caution should be exercised in these circumstances, however, because admission to a general purpose adolescent unit with a mixed client group can lead to an escalation of risk and deterioration in symptoms and functioning. The consistent application of the general principles of treatment delivery with this client group, and the application of a structured model of intervention during admission, may mitigate the potential damaging effects of admission.

Adolescent units offering treatment for chronic risk, borderline personality disorder or other diagnoses must have the following characteristics:

● A clearly defined treatment programme.
● A sub-team of professionals with training and expertise in the management of borderline personality disorder.
● Clear leadership and decision making structures in both the main team and the sub-team.
● A clear theoretical model/therapeutic approach to the treatment of borderline personality disorder that all staff in the sub-team know thoroughly and staff in the main team are aware of and support.
● An ability to tolerate and take therapeutic risks, in particular the capacity to discharge young people who remain at high risk of suicide.
● A system of monitoring of outcomes to ensure that deterioration is noted early and strategies implemented to resolve the problem.
● Attention to the mix of clients on the unit. There may be specific contraindications for mixing young people with acute psychosis and those with borderline personality disorder in a single treatment programme. Both groups of young people may be adversely affected by the problems of the other, and the requirements of treatment programmes for these two groups differ so widely that staff may experience extreme difficulty in applying flexibly the different approaches needed.

Admission of young people for the management of acute risk alongside those in treatment for a broader range of difficulties may also present challenges; separating young people admitted for a crisis from those in a more comprehensive treatment programmes may prove more effective.

Specialist outpatient services and home-based treatment teams   Home-based treatment teams for young people are in the early stages of development in the UK and consequently their place in the treatment of borderline personality disorder has yet to be established. Like inpatient services, existing teams frequently manage acute risk and attempt to address chronic risk and/or low functioning patients.

Services are likely to take different forms depending on whether their focus is on acute or chronic problems. When focused on acute risk, services usually combine characteristics of assertive outreach and crisis intervention with intensive case management. These services have proved effective both when tier 3 treatment has been disrupted and as a mechanism for organising an effective outpatient intervention plan. Typically services have a capacity for rapid and intensive engagement lasting no more than a few weeks, followed by client/family-centred intensive case management.

Services focused on chronic risk and/or low functioning are characterised by a stronger psychotherapy focus, a longer duration of treatment and an active engagement phase pre-treatment. These services have also been used as step-down from inpatient care or when inpatient stays have become ineffective. This type of intervention might be considered when parenting has become distorted by the client's presentation and family relationships are undermining individually-focused treatment plans.

In most cases, psychoeducational work with parents is required before implementing more intensive interventions that may often be experienced as intrusive. These forms of home-based treatment are best avoided where there are longstanding concerns about parental capacity.

Home-based treatment services, regardless of whether they focus on the treatment of acute or chronic issues, share a number of characteristics: they require experienced staff with expertise in borderline personality disorder and a team structure that allows a high level of supervision and the effective management of risk in the community; each is likely to offer time-limited treatment but of different durations; and each is likely to balance limit setting with developing autonomy. Services need to differentiate clearly between interventions for the young person, and those involving parents, family, and the wider system, and to focus primarily on the management of risk and the promotion of functioning rather than longer-term behavioural change.

In the case of services focused on chronic presentation, staff will require broad-based and sophisticated psychotherapy skills and teams will need to operate according to a clear theoretical model.

9.8.3   Transition to adult services

The transition to adult services for young people is often marked by a series of discontinuities in terms of personnel, frequency of treatment (often less intense in adult services) and treatment approach, and often a failure to recognise and adapt treatment to developmental stage. This can be particularly difficult for the young person with borderline personality disorder, who is likely to find endings and beginnings especially challenging. In such circumstances the CPA and joint working between adult mental health services and CAMHS may facilitate the transition. Flexible working around age-limit cut-offs is also likely to be helpful in promoting smooth transitions.

Many young people who have been treated by CAMHS will not meet the referral criteria for adult mental health services, either because the services do not accept people with a personality disorder or because the service does not consider their difficulties to be severe enough to warrant intervention. This latter scenario can be particularly frustrating for young people and CAMHS staff alike, who may have worked together successfully to reduce the intensity and severity of problematic behaviours and are now seeking treatment for the young person for current comorbidities or to consolidate treatment gains. In some circumstances this can be a major disincentive for young people in transition to adult services to work on their difficulties constructively.

Protocols with adult mental health services need to be in place to ensure the smooth transition of young people to adult services when they turn 18 years old. Such protocols need to ensure that access criteria to adult services are consistent with young people who have been previously treated by CAMHS. Commissioners of CAMHS and adult mental health should collaborate to identify service gaps and explore service models, for example, jointly commissioned services across the age range, to address the needs of young people in transition from CAMHS to adult mental health services. In exceptional circumstances where no age appropriate services are available for young people, adult services need protocols in place for young people admitted to adult wards. These protocols should include liaison with and involvement of CAMHS.

9.9   OVERALL CLINICAL SUMMARY

Young people present to services with patterns of behaviour and functioning consistent with a diagnosis of borderline personality disorder. Both DSM-IV and ICD-10 allow clinicians to diagnose borderline personality disorder in young people with certain caveats. There is very little evidence of the effectiveness of treatments for young people with borderline personality disorder (with the exception of the study by CHANEN2008), which is not surprising given the relatively small evidence base in adults.

Given the limited evidence base, however, there is no reason why the recommendations developed for adults should not be adopted for the treatment and management of young people with borderline personality disorder, with additional recommendations relating to issues specific to young people, such as the structure of services and the presence of parents or other carers. Clearly further research into the treatment of borderline personality disorder in young people is required.

9.10   CLINICAL PRACTICE RECOMMENDATIONS

Clinical practice recommendations for young people also appear elsewhere in the guideline where they apply to other evidence review chapters.

9.10.1.1   Young people with a diagnosis of borderline personality disorder, or symptoms and behaviour that suggest it, should have access to the full range of treatments and services recommended in this guideline, but within CAMHS.

9.10.1.2   CAMHS professionals working with young people with borderline personality disorder should:
- balance the developing autonomy and capacity of the young person with the responsibilities of parents or carers
- be familiar with the legal framework that applies to young people, including the Mental Capacity Act, the Children Acts and the Mental Health Act.

9.10.1.3   CAMHS and adult healthcare professionals should work collaboratively to minimise any potential negative effect of transferring young people from CAMHS to adult services. They should:
- time the transfer to suit the young person, even if it takes place after they have reached the age of 18 years
- continue treatment in CAMHS beyond 18 years if there is a realistic possibility that this may avoid the need for referral to adult mental health services.

9.10.1.4   NHS trusts providing CAMHS should ensure that young people with severe borderline personality disorder have access to tier 4 specialist services if required, which may include:
- inpatient treatment tailored to the needs of young people with borderline personality disorder
- specialist outpatient programmes
- home treatment teams.

10. SUMMARY OF RECOMMENDATIONS

GUIDANCE

10.1 GENERAL PRINCIPLES FOR WORKING WITH PEOPLE WITH BORDERLINE PERSONALITY DISORDER

10.1.1 Access to services

10.1.1.1 People with borderline personality disorder should not be excluded from any health or social care service because of their diagnosis or because they have self-harmed.

10.1.1.2 Young people with a diagnosis of borderline personality disorder, or symptoms and behaviour that suggest it, should have access to the full range of treatments and services recommended in this guideline, but within CAMHS.

10.1.1.3 Ensure that people with borderline personality disorder from black and minority ethnic groups have equal access to culturally appropriate services based on clinical need.

10.1.1.4 When language is a barrier to accessing or engaging with services for people with borderline personality disorder, provide them with:

- information in their preferred language and in an accessible format
- psychological or other interventions in their preferred language
- independent interpreters.

10.1.2 Borderline personality disorder and learning disabilities

10.1.2.1 When a person with a mild learning disability presents with symptoms and behaviour that suggest borderline personality disorder, assessment and diagnosis should take place in consultation with a specialist in learning disabilities services.

10.1.2.2 When a person with a mild learning disability has a diagnosis of borderline personality disorder, they should have access to the same services as other people with borderline personality disorder.

10.1.2.3 When care planning for people with a mild learning disability and borderline personality disorder, follow the Care Programme Approach (CPA). Consider consulting a specialist in learning disabilities services when developing care plans and strategies for managing behaviour that challenges.

10.1.2.4 People with a moderate or severe learning disability should not normally be diagnosed with borderline personality disorder. If they show behaviour and symptoms that suggest borderline personality disorder, refer for assessment and treatment by a specialist in learning disabilities services.

10.1.3   Autonomy and choice

10.1.3.1   Work in partnership with people with borderline personality disorder to develop their autonomy and promote choice by:
● ensuring they remain actively involved in finding solutions to their problems, including during crises
● encouraging them to consider the different treatment options and life choices available to them, and the consequences of the choices they make.

10.1.4   Developing an optimistic and trusting relationship

10.1.4.1   When working with people with borderline personality disorder:
● explore treatment options in an atmosphere of hope and optimism, explaining that recovery is possible and attainable
● build a trusting relationship, work in an open, engaging and non-judgemental manner, and be consistent and reliable
● bear in mind when providing services that many people will have experienced rejection, abuse and trauma, and encountered stigma often associated with self-harm and borderline personality disorder.

10.1.5   Involving families or carers

10.1.5.1   Ask directly whether the person with borderline personality disorder wants their family or carers to be involved in their care, and, subject to the person's consent and rights to confidentiality:
● encourage family or carers to be involved
● ensure that the involvement of families or carers does not lead to withdrawal of, or lack of access to, services
● inform families or carers about local support groups for families or carers, if these exist.
10.1.5.2   CAMHS professionals working with young people with borderline personality disorder should:
● balance the developing autonomy and capacity of the young person with the responsibilities of parents or carers
● be familiar with the legal framework that applies to young people, including the Mental Capacity Act, the Children Acts and the Mental Health Act.

10.1.6   Principles for assessment

10.1.6.1   When assessing a person with borderline personality disorder:
● explain clearly the process of assessment
● use non-technical language whenever possible

- explain the diagnosis and the use and meaning of the term borderline personality disorder
- offer post-assessment support, particularly if sensitive issues, such as childhood trauma, have been discussed.

10.1.7 Managing endings and supporting transitions

10.1.7.1 Anticipate that withdrawal and ending of treatments or services, and transition from one service to another, may evoke strong emotions and reactions in people with borderline personality disorder. Ensure that:
- such changes are discussed carefully beforehand with the person (and their family or carers if appropriate) and are structured and phased
- the care plan supports effective collaboration with other care providers during endings and transitions, and includes the opportunity to access services in times of crisis
- when referring a person for assessment in other services (including for psychological treatment), they are supported during the referral period and arrangements for support are agreed beforehand with them.

10.1.7.2 CAMHS and adult healthcare professionals should work collaboratively to minimise any potential negative effect of transferring young people from CAMHS to adult services. They should:
- time the transfer to suit the young person, even if it takes place after they have reached the age of 18 years
- continue treatment in CAMHS beyond 18 years if there is a realistic possibility that this may avoid the need for referral to adult mental health services.

10.1.8 Managing self-harm and attempted suicide

10.1.8.1 Follow the recommendations in 'Self-harm' (NICE clinical guideline 16) to manage episodes of self-harm or attempted suicide.

10.1.9 Training, supervision and support

10.1.9.1 Mental health professionals working in secondary care services, including community-based services and teams, CAMHS and inpatient services, should be trained to diagnose borderline personality disorder, assess risk and need, and provide treatment and management in accordance with this guideline. Training should also be provided for primary care healthcare professionals who have significant involvement in the assessment and early treatment of people with borderline personality disorder. Training should be provided by specialist personality disorder teams based in mental health trusts (see recommendation 10.5.1.1).

10.1.9.2 Mental health professionals working with people with borderline personality disorder should have routine access to supervision and staff support.

10.2 RECOGNITION AND MANAGEMENT IN PRIMARY CARE

10.2.1 Recognition of borderline personality disorder

10.2.1.1 If a person presents in primary care who has repeatedly self-harmed or shown persistent risk-taking behaviour or marked emotional instability, consider referring them to community mental health services for assessment for borderline personality disorder. If the person is younger than 18 years, refer them to CAMHS for assessment.

10.2.2 Crisis management in primary care

10.2.2.1 When a person with an established diagnosis of borderline personality disorder presents to primary care in a crisis:
● assess the current level of risk to self or others
● ask about previous episodes and effective management strategies used in the past
● help to manage their anxiety by enhancing coping skills and helping them to focus on the current problems
● encourage them to identify manageable changes that will enable them to deal with the current problems
● offer a follow-up appointment at an agreed time.

10.2.3 Referral to community mental health services

10.2.3.1 Consider referring a person with diagnosed or suspected borderline personality disorder who is in crisis to a community mental health service when:
● their levels of distress and/or the risk to self or others are increasing
● their levels of distress and/or the risk to self or others have not subsided despite attempts to reduce anxiety and improve coping skills
● they request further help from specialist services.

10.3 ASSESSMENT AND MANAGEMENT BY COMMUNITY MENTAL HEALTH SERVICES

10.3.1 Assessment

10.3.1.1 Community mental health services (community mental health teams, related community-based services, and tier 2/3 services in CAMHS) should be responsible for the routine assessment, treatment and management of people with borderline personality disorder.

10.3.1.2   When assessing a person with possible borderline personality disorder in community mental health services, fully assess:

- psychosocial and occupational functioning, coping strategies, strengths and vulnerabilities
- comorbid mental disorders and social problems
- the need for psychological treatment, social care and support, and occupational rehabilitation or development
- the needs of any dependent children.[16]

10.3.2   Care planning

10.3.2.1   Teams working with people with borderline personality disorder should develop comprehensive multidisciplinary care plans in collaboration with the service user (and their family or carers, where agreed with the person). The care plan should:

- identify clearly the roles and responsibilities of all health and social care professionals involved
- identify manageable short-term treatment aims and specify steps that the person and others might take to achieve them
- identify long-term goals, including those relating to employment and occupation, that the person would like to achieve, which should underpin the overall long-term treatment strategy; these goals should be realistic, and linked to the short-term treatment aims
- develop a crisis plan that identifies potential triggers that could lead to a crisis, specifies self-management strategies likely to be effective and establishes how to access services (including a list of support numbers for out-of-hours teams and crisis teams) when self-management strategies alone are not enough
- be shared with the GP and the service user.

10.3.2.2   Teams should use the CPA when people with borderline personality disorder are routinely or frequently in contact with more than one secondary care service. It is particularly important if there are communication difficulties between the service user and healthcare professionals, or between healthcare professionals.

---

[16]See the May 2008 Social Care Institute for Excellence research briefing 'Experiences of children and young people caring for a parent with a mental health problem'. Available from www.scie.org.uk/publications/briefings/files/briefing24.pdf

10.3.3 Risk assessment and management

10.3.3.1 Risk assessment in people with borderline personality disorder should:
- take place as part of a full assessment of the person's needs
- differentiate between long-term and more immediate risks
- identify the risks posed to self and others, including the welfare of any dependent children.

10.3.3.2 Agree explicitly the risks being assessed with the person with borderline personality disorder and develop collaboratively risk management plans that:
- address both the long-term and more immediate risks
- relate to the overall long-term treatment strategy
- take account of changes in personal relationships, including the therapeutic relationship.

10.3.3.3 When managing the risks posed by people with borderline personality disorder in a community mental health service, risks should be managed by the whole multidisciplinary team with good supervision arrangements, especially for less experienced team members. Be particularly cautious when:
- evaluating risk if the person is not well known to the team
- there have been frequent suicidal crises.

10.3.3.4 Teams working with people with borderline personality disorder should review regularly the team members' tolerance and sensitivity to people who pose a risk to themselves and others. This should be reviewed annually (or more frequently if a team is regularly working with people with high levels of risk).

10.3.4 Psychological treatment

10.3.4.1 When considering a psychological treatment for a person with borderline personality disorder, take into account:
- the choice and preference of the service user
- the degree of impairment and severity of the disorder
- the person's willingness to engage with therapy and their motivation to change
- the person's ability to remain within the boundaries of a therapeutic relationship
- the availability of personal and professional support.

10.3.4.2 Before offering a psychological treatment for a person with borderline personality disorder or for a comorbid condition, provide the person with written material about the psychological treatment being considered. For people who have reading difficulties, alternative means of presenting the information should be considered, such as video or DVD. So that the person can make an informed choice, there should be an opportunity for them to discuss not only this information but also the evidence for the effectiveness of different types of psychological treatment for borderline personality disorder and any comorbid conditions.

10.3.4.3 When providing psychological treatment for people with borderline personality disorder, especially those with multiple comorbidities and/or severe impairment, the following service characteristics should be in place:

- an explicit and integrated theoretical approach used by both the treatment team and the therapist, which is shared with the service user
- structured care in accordance with this guideline
- provision for therapist supervision.

Although the frequency of psychotherapy sessions should be adapted to the person's needs and context of living, twice-weekly sessions may be considered.

10.3.4.4 Do not use brief psychological interventions (of less than 3 months' duration) specifically for borderline personality disorder or for the individual symptoms of the disorder, outside a service that has the characteristics outlined in 10.3.4.3.

10.3.4.5 For women with borderline personality disorder for whom reducing recurrent self-harm is a priority, consider a comprehensive dialectical behaviour therapy programme.

10.3.4.6 When providing psychological treatment to people with borderline personality disorder as a specific intervention in their overall treatment and care, use the CPA to clarify the roles of different services, professionals providing psychological treatment and other healthcare professionals.

10.3.4.7 When providing psychological treatment to people with borderline personality disorder, monitor the effect of treatment on a broad range of outcomes, including personal functioning, drug and alcohol use, self-harm, depression and the symptoms of borderline personality disorder.

10.3.5   The role of drug treatment

10.3.5.1 Drug treatment should not be used specifically for borderline personality disorder or for the individual symptoms or behaviour associated with the disorder (for example, repeated self-harm, marked emotional instability, risk-taking behaviour and transient psychotic symptoms).

10.3.5.2 Antipsychotic drugs should not be used for the medium- and long-term treatment of borderline personality disorder.

10.3.5.3 Drug treatment may be considered in the overall treatment of comorbid conditions (see section 10.3.6).

10.3.5.4 Short-term use of sedative medication may be considered cautiously as part of the overall treatment plan for people with borderline personality disorder in a crisis.[17] The duration of treatment should be agreed with them, but should be no longer than 1 week (see section 10.3.7).

---

[17]Sedative antihistamines are not licensed for this indication and informed consent should be obtained and documented.

10.3.5.5   When considering drug treatment for any reason for a person with borderline personality disorder, provide the person with written material about the drug being considered. This should include evidence for the drug's effectiveness in the treatment of borderline personality disorder and for any comorbid condition, and potential harm. For people who have reading difficulties, alternative means of presenting the information should be considered, such as video or DVD. So that the person can make an informed choice, there should be an opportunity for the person to discuss the material.

10.3.5.6   Review the treatment of people with borderline personality disorder who do not have a diagnosed comorbid mental or physical illness and who are currently being prescribed drugs, with the aim of reducing and stopping unnecessary drug treatment.

10.3.6   The management of comorbidities

10.3.6.1   Before starting treatment for a comorbid condition in people with border-line personality disorder, review:
   ● the diagnosis of borderline personality disorder and that of the comor-bid condition, especially if either diagnosis has been made during a crisis or emergency presentation
   ● the effectiveness and tolerability of previous and current treatments; discontinue ineffective treatments.

10.3.6.2   Treat comorbid depression, post-traumatic stress disorder or anxiety within a well-structured treatment programme for borderline personality disorder.

10.3.6.3   Refer people with borderline personality disorder who also have major psychosis, dependence on alcohol or Class A drugs, or a severe eating disorder to an appropriate service. The care coordinator should keep in contact with people being treated for the comorbid condition so that they can continue with treatment for borderline personality disorder when appropriate.

10.3.6.4   When treating a comorbid condition in people with borderline personality disorder, follow the NICE clinical guideline for the comorbid condition.

10.3.7   The management of crises

Principles and general management of crises

10.3.7.1   When a person with borderline personality disorder presents during a crisis, consult the crisis plan and:
   ● maintain a calm and non-threatening attitude
   ● try to understand the crisis from the person's point of view
   ● explore the person's reasons for distress
   ● use empathic open questioning, including validating statements, to identify the onset and the course of the current problems

Summary of recommendations

- seek to stimulate reflection about solutions
- avoid minimising the person's stated reasons for the crisis
- refrain from offering solutions before receiving full clarification of the problems
- explore other options before considering admission to a crisis unit or inpatient admission
- offer appropriate follow-up within a time frame agreed with the person.

Drug treatment during crises

10.3.7.2 Before starting short-term drug treatments for people with borderline personality disorder during a crisis (see recommendation 10.3.5.4):
- ensure that there is consensus among prescribers and other involved professionals about the drug used and that the primary prescriber is identified
- establish likely risks of prescribing, including alcohol and illicit drug use
- take account of the psychological role of prescribing (both for the individual and for the prescriber) and the impact that prescribing decisions may have on the therapeutic relationship and the overall care plan, including long-term treatment strategies
- ensure that a drug is not used in place of other more appropriate interventions
- use a single drug
- avoid polypharmacy whenever possible.

10.3.7.3 When prescribing short-term drug treatment for people with borderline personality disorder in a crisis:
- choose a drug (such as a sedative antihistamine[18]) that has a low side-effect profile, low addictive properties, minimum potential for misuse and relative safety in overdose
- use the minimum effective dose
- prescribe fewer tablets more frequently if there is a significant risk of overdose
- agree with the person the target symptoms, monitoring arrangements and anticipated duration of treatment
- agree with the person a plan for adherence
- discontinue a drug after a trial period if the target symptoms do not improve
- consider alternative treatments, including psychological treatments, if target symptoms do not improve or the level of risk does not diminish
- arrange an appointment to review the overall care plan, including pharmacological and other treatments, after the crisis has subsided.

---

[18]Sedative antihistamines are not licensed for this indication and informed consent should be obtained and documented.

386

Follow-up after a crisis

10.3.7.4   After a crisis has resolved or subsided, ensure that crisis plans, and if necessary the overall care plan, are updated as soon as possible to reflect current concerns and identify which treatment strategies have proved helpful. This should be done in conjunction with the person with borderline personality disorder and their family or carers if possible, and should include:

- a review of the crisis and its antecedents, taking into account environmental, personal and relationship factors
- a review of drug treatment, including benefits, side effects, any safety concerns and role in the overall treatment strategy
- a plan to stop drug treatment begun during a crisis, usually within 1 week
- a review of psychological treatments, including their role in the overall treatment strategy and their possible role in precipitating the crisis.

10.3.7.5   If drug treatment started during a crisis cannot be stopped within 1 week, there should be a regular review of the drug to monitor effectiveness, side effects, misuse and dependency. The frequency of the review should be agreed with the person and recorded in the overall care plan.

10.3.8   The management of insomnia

10.3.8.1   Provide people with borderline personality disorder who have sleep problems with general advice about sleep hygiene, including having a bedtime routine, avoiding caffeine, reducing activities likely to defer sleep (such as watching violent or exciting television programmes or films), and employing activities that may encourage sleep.

10.3.8.2   For the further short-term management of insomnia follow the recommendations in 'Guidance on the use of zaleplon, zolpidem and zopiclone for the short-term management of insomnia' (NICE technology appraisal guidance 77). However, be aware of the potential for misuse of many of the drugs used for insomnia and consider other drugs such as sedative antihistamines.

10.3.9   Discharge to primary care

10.3.9.1   When discharging a person with borderline personality disorder from secondary care to primary care, discuss the process with them and, whenever possible, their family or carers beforehand. Agree a care plan that specifies the steps they can take to try to manage their distress, how to cope with future crises and how to re-engage with community mental health services if needed. Inform the GP.

10.4   INPATIENT SERVICES

10.4.1.1   Before considering admission to an acute psychiatric inpatient unit for a person with borderline personality disorder, first refer them to a crisis resolution and home treatment team or other locally available alternative to admission.

10.4.1.2   Only consider people with borderline personality disorder for admission to an acute psychiatric inpatient unit for:
- the management of crises involving significant risk to self or others that cannot be managed within other services, or
- detention under the Mental Health Act (for any reason).

10.4.1.3   When considering inpatient care for a person with borderline personality disorder, actively involve them in the decision and:
- ensure the decision is based on an explicit, joint understanding of the potential benefits and likely harm that may result from admission
- agree the length and purpose of the admission in advance
- ensure that when, in extreme circumstances, compulsory treatment is used, management on a voluntary basis is resumed at the earliest opportunity.

10.4.1.4   Arrange a formal CPA review for people with borderline personality disorder who have been admitted twice or more in the previous 6 months.

10.4.1.5   NHS trusts providing CAMHS should ensure that young people with severe borderline personality disorder have access to tier 4 specialist services if required, which may include:
- inpatient treatment tailored to the needs of young people with borderline personality disorder
- specialist outpatient programmes
- home treatment teams.

10.5   ORGANISATION AND PLANNING OF SERVICES

10.5.1   The role of specialist personality disorder services within trusts

10.5.1.1   Mental health trusts should develop multidisciplinary specialist teams and/or services for people with personality disorders. These teams should have specific expertise in the diagnosis and management of borderline personality disorder and should:
- provide assessment and treatment services for people with borderline personality disorder who have particularly complex needs and/or high levels of risk
- provide consultation and advice to primary and secondary care services
- offer a diagnostic service when general psychiatric services are in doubt about the diagnosis and/or management of borderline personality disorder

- develop systems of communication and protocols for information sharing among different services, including those in forensic settings, and collaborate with all relevant agencies within the local community including health, mental health and social services, the criminal justice system, CAMHS and relevant voluntary services
- be able to provide and/or advise on social and psychological interventions, including access to peer support, and advise on the safe use of drug treatment in crises and for comorbidities and insomnia
- work with CAMHS to develop local protocols to govern arrangements for the transition of young people from CAMHS to adult services
- ensure that clear lines of communication between primary and secondary care are established and maintained
- support, lead and participate in the local and national development of treatments for people with borderline personality disorder, including multi-centre research
- oversee the implementation of this guideline
- develop and provide training programmes on the diagnosis and management of borderline personality disorder and the implementation of this guideline (see 10.5.1.2)
- monitor the provision of services for minority ethnic groups to ensure equality of service delivery.

The size and time commitment of these teams will depend on local circumstances (for example, the size of trust, the population covered and the estimated referral rate for people with borderline personality disorder).

10.5.1.2   Specialist teams should develop and provide training programmes that cover the diagnosis and management of borderline personality disorder and the implementation of this guideline for general mental health, social care, forensic and primary care providers and other professionals who have contact with people with borderline personality disorder. The programmes should also address problems around stigma and discrimination as these apply to people with borderline personality disorder.

10.5.1.3   Specialist personality disorder services should involve people with personality disorders and families or carers in planning service developments, and in developing information about services. With appropriate training and support, people with personality disorders may also provide services, such as training for professionals, education for service users and families or carers, and facilitating peer support groups.

RESEARCH RECOMMENDATIONS

10.6   DEVELOPMENT OF AN AGREED SET OF OUTCOMES MEASURES

What are the best outcome measures to assess interventions for people with borderline personality disorder? This question should be addressed in a three-stage process using formal consensus methods involving people from a range of backgrounds, including service users, families or carers, clinicians and academics. The outcomes chosen should be valid and reliable for this patient group, and should include measures of quality of life, function and symptoms for both service users and carers.

The three-stage process should include: (1) identifying aspects of quality of life, functioning and symptoms that are important for service users and families/carers; (2) matching these to existing outcome measures and highlighting where measures are lacking; (3) generating a shortlist of relevant outcome measures to avoid multiple outcome measures being used in future. Where measures are lacking, further work should be done to develop appropriate outcomes.

Why this is important
Existing research examining the effects of psychological and pharmacological interventions for people with borderline personality disorder has used a wide range of outcomes measures. This makes it difficult to synthesise data from different studies and to compare interventions. Also, outcomes do not always adequately reflect patient experience. Agreeing outcome measures for future studies of interventions for people with borderline personality disorder will make it easier to develop evidence-based treatment guidelines in the future.

10.7   PSYCHOLOGICAL THERAPY PROGRAMMES FOR PEOPLE WITH BORDERLINE PERSONALITY DISORDER

What is the relative efficacy of psychological therapy programmes (for example, mentalisation-based therapy, dialectical behaviour therapy or similar approach) delivered within well structured, high-quality community-based services (for example, a day hospital setting, or a community mental health team) compared with high-quality community care delivered by general mental health services without the psychological intervention for people with borderline personality disorder?

This question should be answered using a randomised controlled design which reports medium-term outcomes (including cost effectiveness outcomes) of at least 18 months' duration. They should pay particular attention to the training and supervision of those providing interventions in order to ensure that systems for delivering them are both robust and generalisable.

Why this is important
Research suggests that psychological therapy programmes, such as dialectical behaviour therapy and mentalisation-based therapy as delivered in the studies reviewed for this guideline, may benefit people with borderline personality disorder. However, trials are relatively small, and research is generally at an early stage of development with studies tending to examine interventions delivered in centres of excellence. In addition, few trials have included large numbers of men. Pragmatic trials comparing psychological therapy programmes with high-quality outpatient follow-up by

community mental health services would help to establish the effectiveness, costs and cost effectiveness of these interventions delivered in generalisable settings. The effect of these interventions among men and young people should also be examined.

10.8 OUTPATIENT PSYCHOSOCIAL INTERVENTIONS

What is the efficacy of outpatient psychosocial interventions (such as cognitive analytic therapy, cognitive behavioural therapy, schema-focused therapy, and transference focused therapy) for people with less severe (fewer comorbidities, higher level of social functioning, more able to depend on self-management methods) borderline personality disorder? This question should be answered using randomised controlled trials which report medium-term outcomes (for example, quality of life, psychosocial functioning, employment outcomes and borderline personality disorder symptomatology) of at least 18 months. They should pay particular attention to training and supervision of those delivering interventions.

Why this is important
The evidence base for the effectiveness of psychosocial interventions for people with personality disorder is at an early stage of development. Data collected from cohort studies and case series suggest that a variety of such interventions may help people with borderline personality disorder. Trials of these interventions would help to develop a better understanding of their efficacy. They should examine the process of treatment delivery in an experimental study, and explore logistical and other factors that could have an impact on the likelihood of larger scale experimental evaluations of these interventions succeeding.

10.9 MOOD STABILISERS

What is the effectiveness and cost effectiveness of mood stabilisers on the symptoms of borderline personality disorder? This should be answered by a randomised placebo-controlled trial which should include the medium to long-term impact of such treatment. The study should be sufficiently powered to investigate both the effects and side effects of this treatment.

Why this is important
There is little evidence of the effectiveness of pharmacological treatments for people with personality disorder. However, there have been encouraging findings from small-scale studies of mood stabilisers such as topiramate and lamotrigine, which indicates the need for further research. Emotional instability is a key feature of borderline personality disorder and the effect of these treatments on mood and other key features of this disorder should be studied. The findings of such a study would support the development of future recommendations on the role of pharmacological interventions in the treatment of borderline personality disorder.

10.10   DEVELOPING A CARE PATHWAY

What is the best care pathway for people with borderline personality disorder?

A mixed-methods cohort study examining the care pathway of a representative sample of people with borderline personality disorder should be undertaken. Such a study should include consideration of factors that should guide referral from primary to secondary care services, and examine the role of inpatient treatment. The study should examine the effect that people with borderline personality disorder and service-level factors have on the transfer between different components of care and include collection and analysis of both qualitative and quantitative data.

Why this is important

The development of a care pathway for people with borderline personality disorder would help to ensure that available resources are used effectively and that services are suited to their needs. Service provision for people with borderline personality disorder varies greatly in different parts of the country, and factors that should be considered when deciding the type and intensity of care that people receive are poorly understood. A cohort study in which qualitative and quantitative data from service users and providers are collected at the point of transfer to and from different parts of the care pathway would help to inform the decisions that people with borderline personality disorder and healthcare professionals have to make about the type of services that people receive.

11.   APPENDICES

Appendix 1: Scope for the development of the clinical guideline   392

Appendix 2: Declarations of interests by GDG members   399

Appendix 3: Special advisers to the Guideline Development Group   413

Appendix 4: Stakeholders and experts who submitted comments
in response to the consultation draft of the guideline   414

Appendix 5: Researchers contacted to request information about
unpublished or soon-to-be published studies   416

Appendix 6: Clinical questions   417

Appendix 7: Search strategies for the identification of clinical studies   419

Appendix 8: Clinical study data extraction form   422

Appendix 9: Quality checklists for clinical studies and reviews   426

Appendix 10: Outcomes   440

Appendix 11: Pharmacology peer reviewer consultation table   463

Appendix 12: Search strategies for the identification of health
economics evidence   491

Appendix 13: Quality checklist for economic studies   493

Appendix 14: Data extraction form for economic studies   496

Appendix 15: Evidence tables for economic studies   499

Appendix 16: Study characteristics tables   on CD

Appendix 17: Clinical evidence forest plots   on CD

Appendix 18: GRADE evidence profile tables   on CD

APPENDIX 1:
SCOPE FOR THE DEVELOPMENT OF THE
CLINICAL GUIDELINE

Final Version

14 March 2007

GUIDELINE TITLE

Borderline personality disorder: treatment and management

Short title

Borderline personality disorder (BPD)

BACKGROUND

The National Institute for Health and Clinical Excellence ('NICE' or 'the Institute') has commissioned the National Collaborating Centre for Mental Health to develop a clinical guideline on borderline personality disorder for use in the NHS in England and Wales. This follows referral of the topic by the Department of Health (see appendix [to the Scope, p. 400]). The guideline will provide recommendations for good practice that are based on the best available evidence of clinical and cost effectiveness.

The Institute's clinical guidelines will support the implementation of National Service Frameworks (NSFs) in those aspects of care where a framework has been published. The statements in each NSF reflect the evidence that was used at the time the framework was prepared. The clinical guidelines and technology appraisals published by the Institute after an NSF has been issued will have the effect of updating the framework.

NICE clinical guidelines support the role of healthcare professionals in providing care in partnership with patients, taking account of their individual needs and preferences, and ensuring that patients (and their families/carers, where appropriate) can make informed decisions about their care and treatment.

CLINICAL NEED FOR THE GUIDELINE

Borderline personality disorder is characterised by a pattern of instability of interpersonal relationships, self-image and affects, and by marked impulsivity. Its diagnosis does not imply any specific cause.

Estimates of the prevalence of borderline personality disorder vary between 0.7 and 2% in the general population. It is estimated to be present in 20% of inpatients in psychiatric wards and between 10 and 30% of outpatients. It is a disorder predominantly diagnosed in women (75%); although, again, estimates vary and most of these studies have been in clinical populations, where women predominate as they are more likely to seek treatment. Other estimates indicate that the rate in men (1%) is two and a half times that in women (0.4%). The prevalence of borderline personality disorder is particularly high in the prison population; in England and Wales it is estimated to be 23% among male remand prisoners, 14% among sentenced male prisoners and 20% among female prisoners.

Borderline personality disorder is defined descriptively in terms of its associated impairments. ICD-10 uses the term emotionally unstable personality disorder, dividing this into two variants (impulsive type and borderline type) both of which share the general theme of impulsiveness and lack of self-control. The impulsive variant is characterised by a tendency to conflict and outbursts of anger or violence, difficulty in maintaining any course of action that offers no immediate reward, and instability of mood; the borderline variant is characterised by disturbances of self-image, a tendency to unstable relationships, efforts to avoid abandonment, and threats or acts of self-harm (including suicide). In DSM-IV, borderline personality disorder is defined more broadly to include all of the features of the borderline variant of emotionally unstable personality disorder and most of the criteria for the impulsive variant. DSM-IV also defines all personality disorders as axis II disorders. Borderline personality disorder is defined as a cluster B disorder ('dramatic, emotional or erratic' type) along with antisocial, histrionic and narcissistic personality disorders. There is substantial comorbidity of borderline personality disorder with common mental disorders such as depressive illness, the range of anxiety disorders or substance misuse disorders.

There is some divergence between ICD-10 and DSM-IV as to whether borderline/emotionally unstable personality disorder can be diagnosed in those younger than 18 years, and this may lead to uncertainties about the usage of the diagnosis in young people. In ICD-10 the disorder comes within the overall grouping of disorders of adult personality and behaviour, but DSM-IV specifies that borderline personality disorder can be diagnosed in those younger than 18 if the features of the disorder have been present for at least 1 year.

Specific causes of borderline personality disorder have not been identified. Although the processes that lead to its development remain a matter of debate, it appears likely that borderline personality disorder develops through the accumulation and interaction of multiple factors, including temperament, childhood and adolescent experiences, and other environmental factors. One common factor in people with borderline personality disorder is history of traumatic events during childhood and adolescence, in particular physical, sexual and emotional abuse, neglect, hostile conflict, and early parental loss or separation. However, the association with childhood and adolescent trauma is neither ubiquitous in borderline personality disorder nor unique to this personality disorder. Other psychosocial and demographic factors associated with the disorder may reflect the consequences of the disorder on the individual's life rather than causal processes. A role for genetic factors mediating the response to environmental factors and life events has been postulated, but the evidence is sparse. Neurobiological mechanisms have also been proposed on the basis of neuroimaging data, but it is unknown whether any biological dysfunction associated with borderline personality disorder is a cause or consequence of the disorder. Neuropsychological impairments associated with borderline personality disorder appear to be different from other personality disorders and show specific impairments of memory and emotional processing.

Borderline personality disorder can be a seriously disabling condition and often takes a huge toll on the individual. People with borderline personality disorder usually develop signs and symptoms of the disorder in adolescence or early adulthood. They may experience difficulties such as considerable changes in mood, lack of confidence, impulsive and self-injurious behaviour, substance use, excessive sensitivity and fears of rejection and criticism. As a consequence it is hard for people with borderline personality disorder to develop mature and lasting relationships or to function successfully in the home, educational settings and the workplace. Failures in these areas accentuate feelings of rejection, depressive moods and self-destructive impulses. As a result of their difficulty in controlling their impulses and emotions, and also their often distorted perceptions of themselves and others, people with borderline personality disorder may experience enormous pain and evoke high levels of anxiety in those around them. Suicide is a particular risk in borderline personality disorder, with up to one in ten people with borderline personality disorder committing suicide. The impact of the disorder on the individual is often exacerbated by presence of comorbid conditions such as affective disorders and substance misuse.

In general, the impact of the disorder and the risk of suicide is greatest in early adulthood. The short- to medium-term outcome is poor, however longer term follow-up is more positive. Although most people with borderline personality disorder still have significant morbidity; for example, some long-term studies of borderline personality disorder indicate that only 50% of women and 25% of men diagnosed with the condition gain stability and satisfactory relationships characterised by intimacy.

People with borderline personality disorder use mental health services at higher rates than people from other mental health diagnostic groups, except for people with schizophrenia. They tend to make heavy demands on services, having frequent contact with mental health and social services, accident and emergency departments, GPs and the criminal justice system, and are likely to be high-cost, persistent, and intensive users of mental health services.

It should be noted that a separate guideline on antisocial personality disorder is being developed in parallel to the development of the borderline personality disorder guideline. Beyond the differences in the diagnostic criteria for borderline personality disorder and antisocial personality disorder, there are good grounds for developing two separate guidelines for these disorders, rather than one unified guideline on personality disorders, as there are marked differences in the populations the guidelines will address in terms of their interaction with services. People with borderline personality disorder tend to be treatment seeking and at high risk of self-harm and suicide, whereas people with antisocial personality disorder tend not to seek treatment, are likely to come into contact with services via the criminal justice system and their behaviour is more likely to be a risk to others. Nevertheless, it is acknowledged that people with either of these diagnoses may present with some symptoms and behaviour normally associated with the other diagnosis.

THE GUIDELINE

The guideline development process is described in detail in two publications that are available from the NICE website (see 'Further information'). 'The guideline development process: an overview for stakeholders, the public and the NHS' describes how organisations can become involved in the development of a guideline. 'The guidelines manual' provides advice on the technical aspects of guideline development.

This document is the scope. It defines exactly what this guideline will (and will not) examine, and what the guideline developers will consider. The scope is based on the referral from the Department of Health (see appendix [to the Scope, p. 400]). The areas that will be addressed by the guideline are described in the following sections.

POPULATION

Groups that will be covered:
- adults (aged 18 years and older) with a diagnosis of borderline personality disorder
- people younger than 18 years with borderline symptoms, or putative borderline personality disorder
- people with borderline personality disorder and a learning disability.

HEALTHCARE SETTING

The guideline will cover the care provided within primary, community, secondary and specialist healthcare services within the NHS. The guideline will include specifically:
- care in general practice and NHS community care
- hospital outpatient, day and inpatient care, including secure hospitals
- primary/secondary interface of care
- the transition from child and adolescent services to adult services
- care in prisons and the transition from prison health services to NHS services
This is an NHS guideline. It will comment on the interface with other services such as: prison health services, forensic services, social services and the voluntary sector. It will not include recommendations relating to the services exclusively provided by these agencies, except insofar as the care provided in those institutional settings is provided by NHS healthcare professionals, funded or contracted by the NHS.

Appendix 1

CLINICAL MANAGEMENT – AREAS THAT WILL BE COVERED BY THE GUIDELINE

- Early identification of borderline personality disorder: clarification and confirmation of diagnostic criteria currently in use, and therefore the diagnostic factors that trigger the use of this guideline.
- Treatment pathways.
- The full range of treatment and care normally made available by the NHS, including art and music therapy.
- All common psychological interventions currently employed in the NHS, including dynamic psychotherapy and cognitive behavioural treatments.
- The appropriate use of pharmacological interventions, including initiation and duration of treatment, management of side effects and discontinuation. Note that guideline recommendations will normally fall within licensed indications; exceptionally, and only where clearly supported by evidence, use outside a licensed indication may be recommended. The guideline will assume that prescribers will use a drug's summary of product characteristics to inform their decisions for individual patients. Nevertheless, where pharmacological interventions are commonly utilised off-licence in treatment strategies for people with BPD in the NHS, the evidence underpinning their usage will be critically evaluated.
- Combined pharmacological and psychological treatments.
- Therapeutic communities.
- The therapeutic environment, including team and individual professional's functioning and how they are influenced by working with this client group.
- Treatment of people younger than 18 years for borderline symptoms, or putative borderline personality disorder, in so far as the treatment may alter the level of impairment, risk or progression to adult borderline personality disorder.
- Management of common comorbidities in people with borderline personality disorder, as far as these conditions affect the treatment of borderline personality disorder.
- Management of borderline personality disorder in individuals who also have a learning disability.
- Sensitivity to different beliefs and attitudes of different races and cultures.
- The role of the family/carers in the treatment and support of people with borderline personality disorder (with consideration of choice, consent and help), and support that may be needed by families/carers themselves.
- The guideline development group will take reasonable steps to identify ineffective interventions and approaches to care. When robust and credible recommendations for repositioning the intervention for optimal use, or changing the approach to care to make more efficient use of resources, can be made, they will be clearly stated. When the resources released are substantial, consideration will be given to listing such recommendations in the 'Key priorities for implementation' section of the guideline.

CLINICAL MANAGEMENT – AREAS THAT WILL NOT BE COVERED BY THE GUIDELINE

- Treatments not normally available in the NHS.
- The separate management of comorbid conditions.

STATUS

Scope

This is the consultation draft of the scope. The consultation period is 21 November – 19 December 2006.

The guideline will cross-refer to relevant clinical guidance[19] issued by the Institute, including:

- Schizophrenia: Core interventions in the treatment and management of schizophrenia in primary and secondary care (2002)
- Depression: The management of depression in primary and secondary care (2004)
- Anxiety: Management of generalised anxiety disorder and panic disorder (2004)
- Self-harm: The short-term physical and psychological management and secondary prevention of self-harm in primary and secondary care (2004)
- Post-traumatic stress disorder: Management of PTSD in adults in primary, secondary and community care (2005)
- Obsessive-compulsive disorder: Core interventions in the treatment of obsessive-compulsive disorder and body dysmorphic disorder (2005)
- Violence: The short-term management of disturbed/violent behaviour in in-patient psychiatric settings and emergency departments (2005)
- Bipolar disorder: The management of bipolar disorder in adults, children and adolescents, in primary and secondary care (2006)
- Drug misuse: Opioid detoxification (2007)
- Drug misuse: Psychosocial interventions (2007)
- Attention deficit hyperactivity disorder: Diagnosis and management of ADHD in children, young people and adults (2008)
- Antisocial personality disorder: Treatment, management and prevention (2009).

GUIDELINE

The development of the guideline recommendations will begin in January 2007.

---

[19]Since the Scope was issued some of the guideline titles had changed during development; the titles have been corrected here to reflect those changes.

FURTHER INFORMATION

Information on the guideline development process is provided in:
- An overview for stakeholders, the public and the NHS (2006 edition)
- The guidelines manual (2006 edition).

These booklets are available as PDF files from the NICE website (http://www.nice.org.uk/page.aspx?o=guidelinesmanual). Information on the progress of the guideline will also be available from the website.

APPENDIX – REFERRAL FROM THE DEPARTMENT OF HEALTH

The Department of Health asked the Institute to develop a guideline:

> *'... for the evidence-based primary and secondary care treatment of adults diagnosed with borderline personality disorder and to consider which settings are most appropriate for which interventions. Where appropriate evidence related to those with learning disability should be included.'*

APPENDIX 2:

DECLARATIONS OF INTERESTS BY GDG MEMBERS

With a range of practical experience relevant to borderline personality disorder in the GDG, members were appointed because of their understanding and expertise in healthcare for people with borderline personality disorder and support for their families/carers, including: scientific issues; health research; the delivery and receipt of healthcare, along with the work of the healthcare industry; and the role of professional organisations and organisations for people with borderline personality disorder and their families/carers.

To minimise and manage any potential conflicts of interest, and to avoid any public concern that commercial or other financial interests have affected the work of the GDG and influenced guidance, members of the GDG must declare as a matter of public record any interests held by themselves or their families which fall under specified categories (see below). These categories include any relationships they have with the healthcare industries, professional organisations and organisations for people with borderline personality disorder and their families/carers.

Individuals invited to join the GDG were asked to declare their interests before being appointed. To allow the management of any potential conflicts of interest that might arise during the development of the guideline, GDG members were also asked to declare their interests at each GDG meeting throughout the guideline development process. The interests of all the members of the GDG are listed below, including interests declared prior to appointment and during the guideline development process.

CATEGORIES OF INTEREST

- **Paid employment**
- **Personal pecuniary interest:** Financial payments or other benefits from either the manufacturer or the owner of the product or service under consideration in this guideline, or the industry or sector from which the product or service comes. This includes holding a directorship, or other paid position; carrying out consultancy or fee paid work; having shareholdings or other beneficial interests; receiving expenses and hospitality over and above what would be reasonably expected to attend meetings and conferences.
- **Personal family interest:** Financial payments or other benefits from the healthcare industry that were received by a member of your family.
- **Non-personal pecuniary interest:** Financial payments or other benefits received by the GDG member's organisation or department, but where the GDG member has not personally received payment, including fellowships and other support provided by the healthcare industry. This includes a grant or fellowship or other payment to sponsor a post, or contribute to the running costs of the department; commissioning of research or other work; contracts with, or grants from, NICE.

● **Personal non-pecuniary interest:** These include, but are not limited to, clear opinions or public statements you have made about borderline personality disorder, holding office in a professional organisation or advocacy group with a direct interest in borderline personality disorder, other reputational risks relevant to borderline personality disorder.

Declarations of interest	
Professor Peter Tyrer – Chair, Guideline Development Group	
Employment	Professor of Community Psychiatry, Imperial College London
Personal pecuniary interest	None
Personal family interest	None
Non-personal pecuniary interest	Principal investigator (PI) for:
	2005–2006 The effect of nidotherapy on antisocial behaviour and attitudes to intervention (National Programme for Forensic Mental Health); £70,688
	2002–2007 National Coordinating Centre for Health Technology Assessment (NCCHTA) for a randomised trial – Neuroleptics for Aggressive Challenging Behaviour in Intellectual Disability (NACHBID); £630,943
	2000–2006 IMPALOX study into the assessment of dangerous and severe personality disorder (DSPD) programme in England (Home Office); £743,276
	1999–2000 Study on the feasibility of carrying out an RCT of therapeutic community treatment for severe personality disorder at the Henderson Hospital (High Security Commissioning Board R&D); £13,200
	Secondary investigator for:
	Two projects concerned with the evaluation of new forensic services for personality disorder (PI-Dr Paul Moran) and on new services for personality disorder in general psychiatric services (PI-Dr Mike Crawford)
Personal non-pecuniary interest	None

Continued

Declarations of interest (*Continued*)	
Professor Anthony Bateman	
Employment	Consultant Psychiatrist, Barnet, Enfield, and Haringey Mental Health NHS Trust and Visiting Professor University College London
Personal pecuniary interest	2003–2004 Consultancy for Eli Lilly on the development of a protocol for an RCT of olanzapine in borderline personality disorder; $2000 Authored books on mentalisation-based therapy for borderline personality disorder
Personal family interest	None
Non-personal pecuniary interest	2004–2007 Borderline Personality Disorder Research Foundation, grant for the study of mentalisation-based therapy for borderline personality disorder; $420,000 2004–2006 Eli Lilly: study of olanzapine in borderline personality disorder – money received for patient participation; total received by hospital £60,000 2003–2005 Wyeth Pharmaceuticals: research grant – depression and personality disorder in primary care; £25,000 2003–2005 London Development Centre – personality disorder training; £56,000 Barnet, Enfield and Haringey MHT is developing links with pharmaceutical industry for drug trials. Run training courses on mentalisation-based therapy for borderline personality disorder; monies earned go to employer
Personal non-pecuniary interest	Developed and interested in dynamic processes and mentalisation-based therapy for borderline personality disorder. Continuing research and in receipt of research grants for outcomes in borderline personality disorder using mentalisation-based therapy from Borderline Personality Disorder Research Foundation (BPDRF)

Continued

Declarations of interest (*Continued*)	
Professor Nick Bouras	
Employment	Professor Emeritus of Psychiatry, Health Service and Population Research Department, Institute of Psychiatry, King's College London
	Honorary Consultant Psychiatrist, South London and Maudsley NHS Foundation Trust
Personal pecuniary interest	None
Personal family interest	None
Non-personal pecuniary interest	Special Trustees: South London and Maudsley NHS Foundation Trust, Guy's and St Thomas' Charity, European Union on Stigma and Mental Illness
Personal non-pecuniary interest	None
Ms Jenifer Clarke-Moore (2007)	
Employment	Consultant Nurse, Gwent Healthcare NHS Trust
Personal pecuniary interest	None
Personal family interest	None
Non-personal pecuniary interest	2006 Research fellowship to evaluate an education/training programme for working with people with a personality disorder; £9,000
Personal non-pecuniary interest	None
Dr Mike Crawford	
Employment	Reader in Mental Health Services Research, Imperial College London; Honorary Consultant Psychiatrist Central and North West London NHS Foundation Trust
Personal pecuniary interest	None
Personal family interest	None
Non-personal pecuniary interest	None
Personal non-pecuniary interest	None

Continued

Declarations of interest (*Continued*)	
Ms Victoria Green	
Employment	Research Assistant, Dartington Social Research Unit, Dartington, Totnes, Devon
Personal pecuniary interest	None
Personal family interest	None
Non-personal pecuniary interest	None
Personal non-pecuniary interest	None
Dr Rex Haigh	
Employment	Consultant Psychiatrist, Berkshire Healthcare NHS Foundation Trust
Personal pecuniary interest	2002 – present Project Lead for Community of Communities Quality Improvement Network, Royal College of Psychiatrists' Research and Training Unit
	Honorarium approx £10,000 p.a. to research budget at Nottingham University Personality Disorder Institute
	Seconded 2 days per week to the Department of Health National Personality Disorder Development Programme until March 2010
Personal family interest	None
Non-personal pecuniary interest	None
Personal non-pecuniary interest	Board/executive committee member of several relevant charitable and not-for-profit organisations:
	Trustee – Community Housing and Therapy (registered charity); Trustee – Association of Therapeutic Communities; Association of Therapeutic Communities (registered charity); Borderline UK Board (not for profit limited company); Personality Plus Board (community interest company); Exclusion Link (community interest company) – all as unpaid voluntary work

Continued

Declarations of interest (*Continued*)	
Mr Dennis Lines	
Employment	Semi-retired
Personal pecuniary interest	None
Personal family interest	None
Non-personal pecuniary interest	None
Personal non-pecuniary interest	None
Dr David Moore	
Employment	General Practitioner, Nottinghamshire County Teaching Primary Care Trust
Personal pecuniary interest	None
Personal family interest	None
Non-personal pecuniary interest	None
Personal non-pecuniary interest	None
Dr Paul Moran	
Employment	Clinical Senior Lecturer, Institute of Psychiatry, King's College London
	Honorary Consultant Psychiatrist, South London and Maudsley Foundation Trust
Personal pecuniary interest	None
Personal family interest	None
Non-personal pecuniary interest	2008–2011 Medical Research Council – Joint crisis plans for people with personality disorder; £423,152
	2008 Department of Health – 18-month follow-up of men admitted to pilot services for people with personality disorder in adult forensic settings; £7,000
	2006–2009 Wellcome Trust: Training fellowship – Common mental disorders among women victims of trafficking returned to Moldova; £75,726

Declarations of interest (*Continued*)	
	2005–2007 NHS Service Delivery and Organisation Research and Development Programme – an evaluation of pilot services for people with personality disorder in adult forensic settings; £196,440
	2005–2007 Nuffield Foundation – The relative effects of maternal personality disorder and depression on infant development at 18 months; £110,702
	2003–2005 Foundation for the Study of Infant Deaths – the impact of maternal personality disorder and depression on early infant care; £93,000
	2005–2007 NHS Service Delivery and Organisation Research and Development Programme – Learning the lessons: an evaluation of pilot community services for adults with personality disorder; £286,076
	2003–2004 Department of Health – The impact of personality disorder on the needs and pathways to psychiatric care of mentally ill inpatients; £39, 987
	2001–2005 National Programme on Forensic Mental Health; Department of Health – Access to treatment for people with severe personality disorder; £186,073
Personal non-pecuniary interest	None
Professor Glenys Parry	
Employment	Professor of Applied Psychological Therapies, Centre for Psychological Services Research, University of Sheffield Consultant Clinical Psychologist, Sheffield Health and Social Care Foundation Trust
Personal pecuniary interest	None
Personal family interest	None

Continued

Declarations of interest (*Continued*)	
Non-personal pecuniary interest	2005–2009 Sheffield Health and Social Research Consortium – Psychological treatments for severe and complex mental health problems/ personality disorders: SPeDi trial – a randomised controlled trial; £120,607
	2005 Association for Cognitive Analytic Therapy – Feasibility study of a practice research network in cognitive analytic therapy; £14,000
	1996–2001 The Mental Health Foundation – a method for identifying key psychotherapeutic competencies in personality disorder; £70,000
Personal non-pecuniary interest	2006 Member of HTA-funded technology appraisal team: Psychological therapies including dialectical behaviour therapy for borderline personality disorder: a systematic review and preliminary economic evaluation
	2005 Member of technology appraisal team for NICE guideline on computerised cognitive behavioural therapy
	Member of the following professional associations: British Psychological Society; Division of Clinical Psychology; UKCP; American Psychological Association (foreign affiliate); Association for Cognitive Analytic Therapy (trainer and supervisor in cognitive analytic therapy); Society for Psychotherapy Research
Mrs Carol Paton	
Employment	Chief Pharmacist, Oxleas NHS Foundation Trust
Personal pecuniary interest (non-specific)	2008 Advisory board for Eli Lilly relating to products currently subject to clinical trials (depot IM olanzapine and novel drugs in phase 2 studies), none of which are currently licensed or intended to treat borderline personality disorder; consultancy not exceeding £3000 p.a
	2007 Advisory board and consultancy for Eli Lilly for duloxetine; consultancy not exceeding £3000 p.a

Declarations of interest (*Continued*)	
	2004–2005 Bristol-Myers Squibb £1250; consultancy (psychosis)
	2004–2005 Eli Lilly; £2500 consultancy (psychosis and depression)
	2003–2004 Eli Lilly; £1500 consultancy (psychosis)
Personal family interest	None
Non-personal pecuniary interest	None
Personal non-pecuniary interest	2007–2008 NICE GDG member for depression (update) guideline
	2003–2004 NICE GDG member for depression guideline
	2004–2005 Specialist advisor for NICE depression in children guideline
	2004–2005 Specialist advisor for NICE Violence guideline
	2007 Attendance at European College of Neuropsychopharmacology sponsored by Janssen
Dr Mark Sampson	
Employment	Clinical Psychologist, Manchester Mental Health and Social Care Trust
Personal pecuniary interest	None
Personal family interest	None
Non-personal pecuniary interest	None
Personal non-pecuniary interest	Accredited cognitive behavioural therapist and cognitive analytic therapist (practitioner level)
Dr Michaela Swales	
Employment	Consultant Clinical Psychologist, North Wales NHS Trust and Bangor University
Personal pecuniary interest	None

Declarations of interest *(Continued)*	
Personal family interest	Husband is the managing director of, and major shareholder in, Integral Business Support Ltd, a company that is the sole UK provider of training in dialectical behaviour therapy (DBT) a treatment covered by the guideline
	Director of the British Isles Training Team that provides training in DBT to mental health professionals and healthcare organisations throughout the UK and Eire. This role is part of Dr Swales' university appointment as a lecturer-practitioner within the school of Psychology, University of Wales, Bangor. The School of Psychology receives the income from the DBT training outlined above. This income funds a secretary for Dr Swales at the university, training for clinicians in the local NHS Trust (Conwy and Denbighshire NHS Trust) and has at times funded a psychology assistant post in the clinical service in which Dr Swales is employed (Conwy and Denbighshire NHS Trust). British Isles Training Team is also in possession of a licence to deliver the training from the American Training Company BTech LLC
	The School of Psychology is also in receipt of a grant from Economic and Social Research Council under the Knowledge Transfer Programme to further develop training in DBT and increase dissemination of the treatment. The grant was awarded over 3 years to the School of Psychology working jointly with Integral Business Support Ltd (see section above on personal family interest); £104,707. The company partner will contribute £50,760 to the project over the 3-year period
	Written a book on DBT due for publication September 2008
Personal non-pecuniary interest	Regular presentations at conferences on DBT

Declarations of interest *(Continued)*	
Dr Angela Wolff	
Employment	West London Mental Health Trust
Personal pecuniary interest	None
Personal family interest	None
Non-personal pecuniary interest	None
Personal non-pecuniary interest	None

National Collaborating Centre for Mental Health	
Dr Tim Kendall – Facilitator, Guideline Development Group	
Employment	Joint Director, NCCMH
	Deputy Director, Royal College of Psychiatrists' Research and Training Unit
	Consultant Psychiatrist and Medical Director, Sheffield Health and Social Care Foundation Trust
Personal pecuniary interest	None
Personal family interest	None
Non-personal pecuniary interest	NICE – annual grant to develop guidelines; c£1,200,000
	Economic and Social Research Council – funding for attendance at a 2-day symposium on evidence-based medicine in psychiatry at the London School of Economics; funding for attendance at a symposium on problems with the evidence base in the pharmaceutical industry at Nottingham University
Personal non-pecuniary interest	On behalf of the NCCMH, met with Jan Balmer of Association of the British Pharmaceutical Industry to discuss Department of Health/industry proposals for developing

National Collaborating Centre for Mental Health (*Continued*)	
	implementation tools for the schizophrenia guideline.
	Expressed views on a number of news and current affairs television and radio programmes on the following topics: the role of selective publishing in the pharmaceutical industry; improving access to psychological therapies; use of Seroxat in children and adults; use of SSRIs in adults; use of antipsychotics for the treatment of dementia; use of cholinesterase inhibitors for the treatment of dementia
Ms Linda Bayliss (2008)	
Employment	Research Assistant, NCCMH
Personal pecuniary interest	None
Personal family interest	None
Non-personal pecuniary interest	None
Personal non-pecuniary interest	None
Ms Rachel Burbeck	
Employment	Systematic Reviewer, NCCMH
Personal pecuniary interest	None
Personal family interest	None
Non-personal pecuniary interest	None
Personal non-pecuniary interest	None
Ms Elizabeth Costigan (2007)	
Employment	Project Manager, NCCMH
Personal pecuniary interest	None
Personal family interest	None
Non-personal pecuniary interest	None

National Collaborating Centre for Mental Health (*Continued*)	
Personal non-pecuniary interest	None

Ms Sarah Hopkins (2007–2008)

Employment	Project Manager, NCCMH
Personal pecuniary interest	None
Personal family interest	None
Non-personal pecuniary interest	None
Personal non-pecuniary interest	None

Mrs Farheen Jeeva (2008)

Employment	Health Economist, NCCMH
Personal pecuniary interest	None
Personal family interest	None
Non-personal pecuniary interest	None
Personal non-pecuniary interest	None

Dr Ifigeneia Mavranezouli (2008)

Employment	Senior Health Economist, NCCMH
Personal pecuniary interest	None
Personal family interest	None
Non-personal pecuniary interest	None
Personal non-pecuniary interest	None

Ms Poonam Sood (2007)

Employment	Research Assistant, NCCMH
Personal pecuniary interest	None

National Collaborating Centre for Mental Health *(Continued)*	
Personal family interest	None
Non-personal pecuniary interest	None
Personal non-pecuniary interest	None
Ms Sarah Stockton	
Employment	Information Scientist, NCCMH
Personal pecuniary interest	None
Personal family interest	None
Non-personal pecuniary interest	None
Personal non-pecuniary interest	None
Dr Clare Taylor	
Employment	Editor, NCCMH
Personal pecuniary interest	None
Personal family interest	None
Non-personal pecuniary interest	None
Personal non-pecuniary interest	None
Mr Loukas Xaplanteris (2007)	
Employment	Health Economist, NCCMH
Personal pecuniary interest	None
Personal family interest	None
Non-personal pecuniary interest	None
Personal non-pecuniary interest	None

APPENDIX 3:

SPECIAL ADVISORS TO THE GUIDELINE DEVELOPMENT GROUP

Dr Andrew Cotgrove	Cheshire and Wirral Partnership NHS Trust
Professor Kate Davidson	University of Glasgow
Ms Jane Dudley	South West London and St George's Mental Health NHS Trust and The British Association of Art Therapy
Professor Edzard Ernst	Peninsula Medical School
Professor Roger Mulder	University of Otago
Professor John Oldham	The Menninger Clinic
Professor Kenneth Silk	University of Michigan Health System
Professor Paul Soloff	University of Pittsburgh
Dr Alison Wood	Bolton Salford & Trafford Mental Health NHS Trust

APPENDIX 4:

STAKEHOLDERS AND EXPERTS WHO SUBMITTED COMMENTS IN RESPONSE TO THE CONSULTATION DRAFT OF THE GUIDELINE

STAKEHOLDERS

Arts Psychotherapies Services
Association for Cognitive Analytic Therapy (ACAT)
Association for Family Therapy and Systemic Practice
Association of Adult Psychotherapists
Association of Professional Music Therapists
Association of Psychoanalytic Psychotherapy in the NHS
Association of Therapeutic Communities
Barnsley PCT
Berkshire Healthcare NHS Trust
Bournemouth and Poole PCT
Bright
British Association for Psychopharmacology
British Association of Art Therapists
British Association of Drama Therapists
British Psychological Society
Cassel Hospital
College of Occupational Therapists
Department of Health
Derbyshire Mental Health Services NHS Trust
Enfield Borough in Barnet, Enfield, and Haringey Mental Health Trust
Henderson Hospital Services
Hertfordshire Partnership NHS Trust
Leeds PCT
Leicestershire Partnership Trust
Managed Clinical Network for Personality Disorder, Leicestershire Partnership Trust
Mental Health Foundation
Mersey Care NHS Trust
Milton Keynes PCT
Mind
National Coordinating Centre for Health Technology Assessment (NCCHTA)
National Network For Safeguarding Children Leads in Mental Health Trusts in England
NHS Direct
NHS Quality Improvement Scotland
Northumberland Tyne & Wear NHS Trust

Orygen Research Centre
Oxfordshire and Buckinghamshire Mental Health Partnership NHS Trust
Partnerships in Care
Royal College of Nursing
Royal College of Paediatrics and Child Health
Royal College of Psychiatrists
Royal Liverpool Children's NHS Trust
Sainsbury Centre for Mental Health
Sheffield Health and Social Care Foundation Trust
Somerset Partnership NHS and Social Care Trust
South London and Maudsley NHS Foundation Trust
Sussex Partnership NHS Trust
Tavistock and Portman Foundation Trust
Tees, Esk & Wear Valleys NHS Trust
UK Council for Psychotherapy
UK Psychiatric Pharmacy Group (UKPPG)
University of Liverpool
West London Mental Health NHS Trust

EXPERTS

Dr Andrew Chanen
Dr Jean Cottraux
Dr Jane Garner
Professor Sigmund Karterud
Dr Ian Kerr
Dr Eileen Vizard

APPENDIX 5:
RESEARCHERS CONTACTED TO REQUEST
INFORMATION ABOUT UNPUBLISHED OR
SOON-TO-BE PUBLISHED STUDIES

Dr Allan Abbass
Dr Helen Andrea
Dr Dawn Bales
Dr Nick Bendit
Professor Donald Black
Dr Gregory Carter
Dr Andrew Chanen
Dr Susan Clarke
Dr John Clarkin
Dr Jean Cottraux
Dr Hans Eriksson
Professor Peter Fonagy
Professor Paul Links
Professor Roel Verheul

APPENDIX 6:

CLINICAL QUESTIONS

No.	Clinical question/subsidiary questions

Reliable identification and assessment of borderline personality disorder

1   What can help clinicians identify features of borderline personality disorder in young people?

2a   Are there tools/assessments that could be used?

2b   Are there tools/assessments that could be used in primary care?

Treatment options for people with borderline personality disorder

3   What interventions and care processes are effective in improving outcomes or altering the developmental course for people aged under 18 years with borderline symptoms or putative borderline personality disorder (that is, would meet diagnosis if over 18)?

4   For people with borderline personality disorder, which treatments are associated with improvement in mental state and quality of life, reduction in self-harm, service use, and risk-related behaviour, and/or improved social and personal functioning while minimising harms?

4a   Which psychological therapy is most effective? (CBT, mentalisation, behaviour therapy, psychodynamic, CAT, group therapy, family therapy, schema-focused therapy, transference-focused and DBT, miscellaneous)

4b   Which psychosocial therapy is most effective?

4c   Which pharmacological therapies maximise benefits while minimising harms? (+ comorbidities)

4d   Combined therapy: psychological therapy + medication

4e   Therapeutic communities

4f   Arts therapies

4 g   Complementary therapies

5   Are treatment options altered in the presence of common comorbidities (depression, psychosis, anxiety disorders, bipolar disorder, substance use disorder, other axis II disorders)?

5a   How should complex and severe borderline personality disorder be managed, including management strategies (over a period of time) and multiple comorbidities?

6   How should the treatment of common comorbidities (depression, psychosis, anxiety disorders, bipolar disorder, substance use disorder, other axis II disorders) be altered in the presence of borderline personality disorder?

Service configuration for people with borderline personality disorder

7   What type of services maximise effectiveness and safety and minimise harm (taking into account long-term outcomes) for the delivery of specific treatments for people with borderline personality disorder? (for example,

day hospitals, inpatient, therapeutic communities, use of enhanced care programming, team-based or individual-based care, partial hospitalisation)

7a What is the role of inpatient (acute, forensic) care in the management of people with borderline personality disorder?

7b What is the role of specialist services (including community-based) in the medium- and long-term management of people with borderline personality disorder?

7c Is long-term inpatient care in the treatment of borderline personality disorder effective?

7d Are particular therapies suited for particular service settings?

7e How should healthcare professionals from other healthcare settings care for people with borderline personality disorder? (primary care, A&E, crisis services, crisis houses, acute care)

8 How should NHS services interface with each other and with non-NHS services for people with borderline personality disorder? (including the transition from adolescent to adult services)

9 Which treatment pathways, care processes and clinical principles (case management, care coordination, CPA, and so on) maximise the effectiveness of care and reduce harm?

10 How can healthcare professionals involved in the care of people with borderline personality disorder best be supported? (supervision, training, case loads and so on)

Family/carers of people with borderline personality disorder

11 Do families (including children) and families/carers of people with borderline personality disorder have specific care needs?

11a If so, what specific interventions should be offered?

12 Do family or carers, through their behaviour, styles of relating and relationships, influence clinical and social outcomes or well-being for people with borderline personality disorder?

12a If so, what interventions should be offered?

Special groups with borderline personality disorder

13 How should treatment and service configurations be adapted for people with borderline personality disorder who have learning disabilities? How should this take into account the severity of learning disability?

14 How should treatment and service configurations be adapted for people with borderline personality disorder who are from an ethnic minority?

15 How should treatment and service configurations be adapted for people with borderline personality disorder who are planning a pregnancy, pregnant or breastfeeding?

Service user and family/carer experience

16 What is the experience of people with borderline personality disorder of care in different settings?

17 What is the experience of families/carers of people with borderline personality disorder of care in different settings?

APPENDIX 7:
SEARCH STRATEGIES FOR THE
IDENTIFICATION OF CLINICAL STUDIES

1. Guideline topic search strategies

    a. MEDLINE, EMBASE, PsycINFO, CINAHL – Ovid interface

1 (borderline state or borderline person$).sh.
2 borderline$.mp. and exp personality disorders/
3 (borderline$ adj3 (disorder$ or person$ or PD$1 or state$)).tw. or (borderline$ and personalit$).mp.
4 (borderline$ and cluster b).mp.
5 (emotion$ adj2 (instabil$ or unstable) adj3 (character$ or difficult$ or disorder$ or dysfunction$ or PD or person$1 or personalit$ or state$)).tw.
6 or/1–5
7 (multiple personality disorder$ or personality disorder$).sh.
8 (personalit$ adj (disorder$ or dysfunction$)).tw.
9 (dsm and (axis and II)).mp.
10 or/7–9
11 or/6,10

    b. Cochrane Database of Systematic Reviews, Database of Abstracts of Reviews of Effects, Cochrane Central Register of Controlled Trials – Wiley Interscience interface

1 MeSH descriptor Borderline Personality Disorder, this term only
2 (borderline*)
3 MeSH descriptor Personality Disorders explode all trees
4 (#2 AND #3)
5 (borderline* near/3 (disorder* or person* or PD* or state*)) or (borderline* and personalit*)
6 (borderline* and cluster near/1b)
7 (emotion* near/2 (instabil* or unstable) near/3 (character* or difficult* or disorder* or dysfunction* or PD or person* or state*))
8 (#1 OR #4 OR #5 OR #6 OR #7)
9 MeSH descriptor Multiple Personality Disorder, this term only
10 MeSH descriptor Personality Disorders, this term only
11 (personalit* near/1 (disorder* or dysfunction*))
12 (dsm and (axis and II))

13 (#9 OR #10 OR #11 OR #12)
14 (#8 OR #13)

2. Systematic review search filters

a. MEDLINE, EMBASE, PsycINFO, CINAHL – Ovid interface

1 cochrane library/or exp literature searching/or exp literature review/or exp review literature/or systematic review/or meta analysis/or meta-analysis as topic/
2 ((systematic or quantitative or methodologic$) adj5 (overview$ or review$)).mp.
3 (metaanaly$ or meta analy$ or metasynthesis or meta synthesis).mp.
4 (research adj (review$ or integration)).mp.
5 reference list$.ab.
6 bibliograph$.ab.
7 published studies.ab.
8 relevant journals.ab.
9 selection criteria.ab.
10 (data adj (extraction or synthesis)).ab.
11 (handsearch$ or ((hand or manual) adj search$)).tw.
12 (mantel haenszel or peto or dersimonian or der simonian).tw.
13 (fixed effect$ or random effect$).tw.
14 ((bids or cochrane or index medicus or isi citation or psyclit or psychlit or scisearch or science citation or (web adj2 science)) and review$).mp.
15 (systematic$ or meta$).pt. or (literature review or meta analysis or systematic review).md.
16 (pooled or pooling).tw.
17 or/1–16

3. RCT search filters

a. MEDLINE, EMBASE, PsycINFO, CINAHL – Ovid interface

1 exp clinical trials/or exp clinical trial/or exp controlled clinical trials/
2 exp crossover procedure/or exp cross over studies/or exp crossover design/
3 exp double blind procedure/or exp double blind method/or exp double blind studies/or exp single blind procedure/or exp single blind method/or exp single blind studies/
4 exp random allocation/or exp randomization/or exp random assignment/or exp random sample/or exp random sampling/
5 exp randomized controlled trials/or exp randomized controlled trial/or randomized controlled trials as topic/
6 (clinical adj2 trial$).tw.

7 (crossover or cross over).tw.
8 (((single$ or doubl$ or trebl$ or tripl$) adj5 (blind$ or mask$ or   dummy)) or (singleblind$ or doubleblind$ or trebleblind$)).tw.
9 (placebo$ or random$).mp.
10 (clinical trial$ or random$).pt. or treatment outcome$.md.
11 animals/not (animals/and human$.mp.)
12 (animal/or animals/) not ((animal/and human/) or (animals/and humans/))
13 (animal not (animal and human)).po.
14 (or/1–10) not (or/11–13)

APPENDIX 8:

CLINICAL STUDY DATA EXTRACTION FORM

Topic Area:			Report reference ID:	
Comparisons:			**Total N**	
Ref List checked		Rev Man	Study Dbase	
Data Checked		Reference Manager updated	Excluded (record reason in Notes below)	
Randomised?		**Blind?**		
Age:		Young/Elderly (mean age over 65) Mean Age % women		
Setting:		In/Out/Mixed/Primary Care (80% patients)		
Analysis:		Completer/ITT (continuous data)		
Diagnosis			% comorbid Axis I	
			% comorbid Axis II	
Mean baseline				

Completed by:				Study reference ID:			
1 TREATMENT GROUP:					**N randomised:**		
Leaving study early (any reason)		**Leaving study early (side effects)**		**Side effects (total)**			
n	*N*	*n*	*N*	*n*	*N*	*n*	*N*

Continous data

	n	*Mean*	*SD*	*n*	*Mean*	*SD*	*n*	*Mean*	*SD*	*n*	*Mean*	*SD*
	n	*Mean*	*SD*	*n*	*Mean*	*SD*	*n*	*Mean*	*SD*	*n*	*Mean*	*SD*
	n	*Mean*	*SD*	*n*	*Mean*	*SD*	*n*	*Mean*	*SD*	*n*	*Mean*	*SD*
	n	*Mean*	*SD*	*n*	*Mean*	*SD*	*n*	*Mean*	*SD*	*n*	*Mean*	*SD*

Trial length:
Interventions (dose):
1
2
3

Appendix 8

Dichotomous data

	n	N	n	N	n	N	n	N
	n	N	n	N	n	N	n	N
	n	N	n	N	n	N	n	N

2 TREATMENT GROUP:				N randomised:			
Leaving study early (any reason)		Leaving study early (side effects)		Side effects (total)			
n	N	n	N	n	N	n	N

Continous data

	n	Mean	SD	n	Mean	SD	n	Mean	SD	n	Mean	SD
	n	Mean	SD	n	Mean	SD	n	Mean	SD	n	Mean	SD
	n	Mean	SD	n	Mean	SD	n	Mean	SD	n	Mean	SD
	n	Mean	SD	n	Mean	SD	n	Mean	SD	n	Mean	SD

Dichotomous data

	n	N	n	N	n	N	n	N
	n	N	n	N	n	N	n	N
	n	N	n	N	n	N	n	N

APPENDIX 9:

QUALITY CHECKLISTS FOR CLINICAL STUDIES AND REVIEWS

The methodological quality of each study was evaluated using dimensions adapted from SIGN (SIGN, 2001). SIGN originally adapted its quality criteria from checklists developed in Australia (Liddel *et al.*, 1996). Both groups reportedly undertook extensive development and validation procedures when creating their quality criteria.

Quality Checklist for a Systematic Review or Meta-Analysis			
Study ID:			
Guideline topic:		**Key question no:**	
Checklist completed by:			
SECTION 1: INTERNAL VALIDITY			
In a well-conducted systematic review:		**In this study this criterion is:** (*Circle one option for each question*)	
1.1	The study addresses an appropriate and clearly focused question.	Well covered Adequately addressed Poorly addressed	Not addressed Not reported Not applicable
1.2	A description of the methodology used is included.	Well covered Adequately addressed Poorly addressed	Not addressed Not reported Not applicable
1.3	The literature search is sufficiently rigorous to identify all the relevant studies.	Well covered Adequately addressed Poorly addressed	Not addressed Not reported Not applicable
1.4	Study quality is assessed and taken into account.	Well covered Adequately addressed Poorly addressed	Not addressed Not reported Not applicable
1.5	There are enough similarities between the studies selected to make combining them reasonable.	Well covered Adequately addressed Poorly addressed	Not addressed Not reported Not applicable
SECTION 2: OVERALL ASSESSMENT OF THE STUDY			
2.1	How well was the study done to minimise bias? *Code* $++, +$ *or* $-$		

Notes on the use of the methodology checklist: systematic reviews and meta-analyses

Section 1 identifies the study and asks a series of questions aimed at establishing the internal validity of the study under review – that is, making sure that it has been carried out carefully and that the outcomes are likely to be attributable to the intervention being investigated. Each question covers an aspect of methodology that research has shown makes a significant difference to the conclusions of a study.

For each question in this section, one of the following should be used to indicate how well it has been addressed in the review:

● well covered
● adequately addressed
● poorly addressed
● not addressed (that is, not mentioned or indicates that this aspect of study design was ignored)
● not reported (that is, mentioned but insufficient detail to allow assessment to be made)
● not applicable.

**1.1   THE STUDY ADDRESSES AN APPROPRIATE AND
          CLEARLY FOCUSED QUESTION**

Unless a clear and well-defined question is specified in the report of the review, it will be difficult to assess how well it has met its objectives or how relevant it is to the question to be answered on the basis of the conclusions.

**1.2   A DESCRIPTION OF THE METHODOLOGY USED IS
          INCLUDED**

One of the key distinctions between a systematic review and a general review is the systematic methodology used. A systematic review should include a detailed description of the methods used to identify and evaluate individual studies. If this description is not present, it is not possible to make a thorough evaluation of the quality of the review, and it should be rejected as a source of level-1 evidence (though it may be useable as level-4 evidence, if no better evidence can be found).

**1.3   THE LITERATURE SEARCH IS SUFFICIENTLY RIGOROUS
          TO IDENTIFY ALL THE RELEVANT STUDIES**

A systematic review based on a limited literature search – for example, one limited to MEDLINE only – is likely to be heavily biased. A well-conducted review should as a minimum look at EMBASE and MEDLINE and, from the late 1990s onward, the

Cochrane Library. Any indication that hand searching of key journals, or follow-up of reference lists of included studies, were carried out in addition to electronic database searches can normally be taken as evidence of a well-conducted review.

1.4   STUDY QUALITY IS ASSESSED AND TAKEN INTO ACCOUNT

A well-conducted systematic review should have used clear criteria to assess whether individual studies had been well conducted before deciding whether to include or exclude them. If there is no indication of such an assessment, the review should be rejected as a source of level-1 evidence. If details of the assessment are poor, or the methods are considered to be inadequate, the quality of the review should be down-graded. In either case, it may be worthwhile obtaining and evaluating the individual studies as part of the review being conducted for this guideline.

1.5   THERE ARE ENOUGH SIMILARITIES BETWEEN THE STUDIES SELECTED TO MAKE COMBINING THEM REASONABLE

Studies covered by a systematic review should be selected using clear inclusion criteria (see question 1.4 above). These criteria should include, either implicitly or explicitly, the question of whether the selected studies can legitimately be compared. It should be clearly ascertained, for example, that the populations covered by the studies are comparable, that the methods used in the investigations are the same, that the outcome measures are comparable and the variability in effect sizes between studies is not greater than would be expected by chance alone.

Section 2 relates to the overall assessment of the paper. It starts by rating the methodological quality of the study, based on the responses in Section 1 and using the following coding system:

+ +	All or most of the criteria have been fulfilled. Where they have not been fulfilled, the conclusions of the study or review are thought **very unlikely** to alter.
+	Some of the criteria have been fulfilled. Those criteria that have not been fulfilled or not adequately described are thought **unlikely** to alter the conclusions.
−	Few or no criteria fulfilled. The conclusions of the study are thought **likely** or **very likely** to alter.

Quality checklist for an RCT	
Study ID:	
Guideline topic:	**Key question no:**
Checklist completed by:	
SECTION 1: INTERNAL VALIDITY	

In a well-conducted RCT study:		**In this study this criterion is:** *(Circle one option for each question)*	
1.1	The study addresses an appropriate and clearly focused question.	Well covered Adequately addressed Poorly addressed	Not addressed Not reported Not applicable
1.2	The assignment of subjects to treatment groups is randomised.	Well covered Adequately addressed Poorly addressed	Not addressed Not reported Not applicable
1.3	An adequate concealment method is used.	Well covered Adequately addressed Poorly addressed	Not addressed Not reported Not applicable
1.4	Subjects and investigators are kept 'blind' about treatment allocation.	Well covered Adequately addressed Poorly addressed	Not addressed Not reported Not applicable
1.5	The treatment and control groups are similar at the start of the trial.	Well covered Adequately addressed Poorly addressed	Not addressed Not reported Not applicable
1.6	The only difference between groups is the treatment under investigation.	Well covered Adequately addressed Poorly addressed	Not addressed Not reported Not applicable
1.7	All relevant outcomes are measured in a standard, valid and reliable way.	Well covered Adequately addressed Poorly addressed	Not addressed Not reported Not applicable
1.8	What percentage of the individuals or clusters recruited into each treatment arm of the study dropped out before the study was completed?		
1.9	All the subjects are analysed in the groups to which they were randomly allocated (often referred to as intention-to-treat analysis).	Well covered Adequately addressed Poorly addressed	Not addressed Not reported Not applicable

1.10	Where the study is carried out at more than one site, results are comparable for all sites.	Well covered Adequately addressed Poorly addressed	Not addressed Not reported Not applicable

SECTION 2: OVERALL ASSESSMENT OF THE STUDY

2.1	How well was the study done to minimise bias? *Code + + , + or –*		

Notes on the use of the methodology checklist: RCTs

Section 1 identifies the study and asks a series of questions aimed at establishing the internal validity of the study under review – that is, making sure that it has been carried out carefully and that the outcomes are likely to be attributable to the intervention being investigated. Each question covers an aspect of methodology that research has shown makes a significant difference to the conclusions of a study.

For each question in this section, one of the following should be used to indicate how well it has been addressed in the review:

- well covered
- adequately addressed
- poorly addressed
- not addressed (that is, not mentioned or indicates that this aspect of study design was ignored)
- not reported (that is, mentioned but insufficient detail to allow assessment to be made)
- not applicable.

1.1   THE STUDY ADDRESSES AN APPROPRIATE AND CLEARLY FOCUSED QUESTION

Unless a clear and well-defined question is specified, it will be difficult to assess how well the study has met its objectives or how relevant it is to the question to be answered on the basis of its conclusions.

1.2   THE ASSIGNMENT OF SUBJECTS TO TREATMENT GROUPS IS RANDOMISED

Random allocation of patients to receive one or other of the treatments under investigation, or to receive either treatment or placebo, is fundamental to this type of study. If there is no indication of randomisation, the study should be rejected. If the

432

description of randomisation is poor, or the process used is not truly random (for example, allocation by date or alternating between one group and another) or can otherwise be seen as flawed, the study should be given a lower quality rating.

1.3   AN ADEQUATE CONCEALMENT METHOD IS USED

Research has shown that where allocation concealment is inadequate, investigators can overestimate the effect of interventions by up to 40%. Centralised allocation, computerised allocation systems or the use of coded identical containers would all be regarded as adequate methods of concealment and may be taken as indicators of a well-conducted study. If the method of concealment used is regarded as poor, or relatively easy to subvert, the study must be given a lower quality rating, and can be rejected if the concealment method is seen as inadequate.

1.4   SUBJECTS AND INVESTIGATORS ARE KEPT 'BLIND' ABOUT TREATMENT ALLOCATION

Blinding can be carried out up to three levels. In single-blind studies, patients are unaware of which treatment they are receiving; in double-blind studies, the doctor and the patient are unaware of which treatment the patient is receiving; in triple-blind studies, patients, healthcare providers and those conducting the analysis are unaware of which patients receive which treatment. The higher the level of blinding, the lower the risk of bias in the study.

1.5   THE TREATMENT AND CONTROL GROUPS ARE SIMILAR AT THE START OF THE TRIAL

Patients selected for inclusion in a trial should be as similar as possible, in order to eliminate any possible bias. The study should report any significant differences in the composition of the study groups in relation to gender mix, age, stage of disease (if appropriate), social background, ethnic origin or comorbid conditions. These factors may be covered by inclusion and exclusion criteria, rather than being reported directly. Failure to address this question, or the use of inappropriate groups, should lead to the study being downgraded.

1.6   THE ONLY DIFFERENCE BETWEEN GROUPS IS THE TREATMENT UNDER INVESTIGATION

If some patients receive additional treatment, even if of a minor nature or consisting of advice and counselling rather than a physical intervention, this treatment is a potential confounding factor that may invalidate the results. If groups are not treated equally, the study should be rejected unless no other evidence is available. If the study is used as evidence, it should be treated with caution and given a low quality rating.

1.7 ALL RELEVANT OUTCOMES ARE MEASURED IN A STANDARD, VALID AND RELIABLE WAY

If some significant clinical outcomes have been ignored, or not adequately taken into account, the study should be downgraded. It should also be downgraded if the measures used are regarded as being doubtful in any way or applied inconsistently.

1.8 WHAT PERCENTAGE OF THE INDIVIDUALS OR CLUSTERS RECRUITED INTO EACH TREATMENT ARM OF THE STUDY DROPPED OUT BEFORE THE STUDY WAS COMPLETED?

The number of patients that drop out of a study should give concern if the number is very high. Conventionally, a 20% drop-out rate is regarded as acceptable, but this may vary. Some regard should be paid to why patients drop out, as well as how many. It should be noted that the drop-out rate may be expected to be higher in studies conducted over a long period of time. A higher drop-out rate will normally lead to downgrading, rather than rejection, of a study.

1.9 ALL THE SUBJECTS ARE ANALYSED IN THE GROUPS TO WHICH THEY WERE RANDOMLY ALLOCATED (OFTEN REFERRED TO AS INTENTION-TO-TREAT ANALYSIS)

In practice, it is rarely the case that all patients allocated to the intervention group receive the intervention throughout the trial, or that all those in the comparison group do not. Patients may refuse treatment, or contraindications arise that lead them to be switched to the other group. If the comparability of groups through randomisation is to be maintained, however, patient outcomes must be analysed according to the group to which they were originally allocated, irrespective of the treatment they actually received. (This is known as intention-to-treat analysis.) If it is clear that analysis is not on an intention-to-treat basis, the study may be rejected. If there is little other evidence available, the study may be included but should be evaluated as if it were a non-randomised cohort study.

1.10 WHERE THE STUDY IS CARRIED OUT AT MORE THAN ONE SITE, RESULTS ARE COMPARABLE FOR ALL SITES

In multi-site studies, confidence in the results should be increased if it can be shown that similar results have been obtained at the different participating centres.

Section 2 relates to the overall assessment of the paper. It starts by rating the methodological quality of the study, based on the responses in Section 1 and using the following coding system:

++	All or most of the criteria have been fulfilled. Where they have not been fulfilled, the conclusions of the study or review are thought **very unlikely** to alter.
+	Some of the criteria have been fulfilled. Those criteria that have not been fulfilled or not adequately described are thought **unlikely** to alter the conclusions.
−	Few or no criteria fulfilled. The conclusions of the study are thought **likely** or **very likely** to alter.

Quality checklist for a cohort study[*]	
Study ID:	**Relevant questions:**
Guideline topic:	
Checklist completed by:	
SECTION 1: INTERNAL VALIDITY	
In a well conducted cohort study:	**In this study the criterion is:** (*Circle one option for each question*)
1.1	The study addresses an appropriate and clearly focused question.	Well covered Not addressed Adequately addressed Not reported Poorly addressed Not applicable
SELECTION OF SUBJECTS	
1.2	The two groups being studied are selected from source populations that are comparable in all respects other than the factor under investigation.	Well covered Not addressed Adequately addressed Not reported Poorly addressed Not applicable
1.3	The study indicates how many of the people asked to take part did so, in each of the groups being studied.	Well covered Not addressed Adequately addressed Not reported Poorly addressed Not applicable
1.4	The likelihood that some eligible subjects might have the outcome at the time of enrolment is	Well covered Not addressed Adequately addressed Not reported Poorly addressed Not applicable

435

	assessed and taken into account in the analysis.		
1.5	What percentage of individuals or clusters recruited into each arm of the study dropped out before the study was completed?		
1.6	Comparison is made between full participants and those lost to follow-up, by exposure status.	Well covered Adequately addressed Poorly addressed	Not addressed Not reported Not applicable
ASSESSMENT			
1.7	The outcomes are clearly defined.	Well covered Adequately addressed Poorly addressed	Not addressed Not reported Not applicable
1.8	The assessment of outcome is made blind to exposure status.	Well covered Adequately addressed Poorly addressed	Not addressed Not reported Not applicable
1.9	Where blinding was not possible, there is some recognition that knowledge of exposure status could have influenced the assessment of outcome.	Well covered Adequately addressed Poorly addressed	Not addressed Not reported Not applicable
1.10	The measure of assessment of exposure is reliable.	Well covered Adequately addressed Poorly addressed	Not addressed Not reported Not applicable
1.11	Evidence from other sources is used to demonstrate that the method of outcome assessment is valid and reliable.	Well covered Adequately addressed Poorly addressed	Not addressed Not reported Not applicable
1.12	Exposure level or prognostic factor is assessed more than once.	Well covered Adequately addressed Poorly addressed	Not addressed Not reported Not applicable
CONFOUNDING			
1.13	The main potential confounders are identified and taken into account in the design and analysis.	Well covered Adequately addressed Poorly addressed	Not addressed Not reported Not applicable
STATISTICAL ANALYSIS			
1.14	Have confidence intervals been provided?		

SECTION 2: OVERALL ASSESSMENT OF THE STUDY	
2.1	How well was the study done to minimise the risk of bias or confounding, and to establish a causal relationship between exposure and effect? *Code + +, + or –*	

*A cohort study can be defined as a retrospective or prospective follow-up study. Groups of individuals are defined on the basis of the presence or absence of exposure to a suspected risk factor or intervention. This checklist is not appropriate for assessing uncontrolled studies (for example, a case series where there is no comparison [control] group of patients).

Notes on the use of the methodology checklist: cohort studies

The studies covered by this checklist are designed to answer questions of the type 'What are the effects of this exposure?' It relates to studies that compare a group of people with a particular exposure with another group who either have not had the exposure or have a different level of exposure. Cohort studies may be prospective (where the exposure is defined and subjects selected before outcomes occur) or retrospective (where exposure is assessed after the outcome is known, usually by the examination of medical records). Retrospective studies are generally regarded as a weaker design, and should not receive a 2+ + rating.

Section 1 identifies the study and asks a series of questions aimed at establishing the internal validity of the study under review – that is, making sure that it has been carried out carefully, and that the outcomes are likely to be attributable to the intervention being investigated. Each question covers an aspect of methodology that has been shown to make a significant difference to the conclusions of a study.

Because of the potential complexity and subtleties of the design of this type of study, there are comparatively few criteria that automatically rule out use of a study as evidence. It is more a matter of increasing confidence in the likelihood of a causal relationship existing between exposure and outcome by identifying how many aspects of good study design are present and how well they have been tackled. A study that fails to address or report on more than one or two of the questions considered below should almost certainly be rejected.

For each question in this section, one of the following should be used to indicate how well it has been addressed in the review:
- well covered
- adequately addressed
- poorly addressed
- not addressed (that is, not mentioned or indicates that this aspect of study design was ignored)
- not reported (that is, mentioned but insufficient detail to allow assessment to be made)
- not applicable.

1.1 THE STUDY ADDRESSES AN APPROPRIATE AND CLEARLY FOCUSED QUESTION

Unless a clear and well-defined question is specified, it will be difficult to assess how well the study has met its objectives or how relevant it is to the question to be answered on the basis of its conclusions.

1.2 THE TWO GROUPS BEING STUDIED ARE SELECTED FROM SOURCE POPULATIONS THAT ARE COMPARABLE IN ALL RESPECTS OTHER THAN THE FACTOR UNDER INVESTIGATION

Study participants may be selected from the target population (all individuals to which the results of the study could be applied), the source population (a defined subset of the target population from which participants are selected) or from a pool of eligible subjects (a clearly defined and counted group selected from the source population). It is important that the two groups selected for comparison are as similar as possible in all characteristics except for their exposure status or the presence of specific prognostic factors or prognostic markers relevant to the study in question. If the study does not include clear definitions of the source populations and eligibility criteria for participants, it should be rejected.

1.3 THE STUDY INDICATES HOW MANY OF THE PEOPLE ASKED TO TAKE PART DID SO IN EACH OF THE GROUPS BEING STUDIED

This question relates to what is known as the participation rate, defined as the number of study participants divided by the number of eligible subjects. This should be calculated separately for each branch of the study. A large difference in participation rate between the two arms of the study indicates that a significant degree of selection bias may be present, and the study results should be treated with considerable caution.

1.4 THE LIKELIHOOD THAT SOME ELIGIBLE SUBJECTS MIGHT HAVE THE OUTCOME AT THE TIME OF ENROLMENT IS ASSESSED AND TAKEN INTO ACCOUNT IN THE ANALYSIS

If some of the eligible subjects, particularly those in the unexposed group, already have the outcome at the start of the trial, the final result will be biased. A well-conducted study will attempt to estimate the likelihood of this occurring and take it into account in the analysis through the use of sensitivity studies or other methods.

1.5 WHAT PERCENTAGE OF INDIVIDUALS OR CLUSTERS RECRUITED INTO EACH ARM OF THE STUDY DROPPED OUT BEFORE THE STUDY WAS COMPLETED?

The number of patients that drop out of a study should give concern if the number is very high. Conventionally, a 20% drop-out rate is regarded as acceptable, but in observational studies conducted over a lengthy period of time a higher drop-out rate is to be expected. A decision on whether to downgrade or reject a study because of a high drop-out rate is a matter of judgement based on the reasons why people drop out and whether drop-out rates are comparable in the exposed and unexposed groups. Reporting of efforts to follow up participants that drop out may be regarded as an indicator of a well-conducted study.

1.6 COMPARISON IS MADE BETWEEN FULL PARTICIPANTS AND THOSE LOST TO FOLLOW-UP BY EXPOSURE STATUS

For valid study results, it is essential that the study participants are truly representative of the source population. It is always possible that participants who drop out of the study will differ in some significant way from those who remain part of the study throughout. A well-conducted study will attempt to identify any such differences between full and partial participants in both the exposed and unexposed groups. Any indication that differences exist should lead to the study results being treated with caution.

1.7 THE OUTCOMES ARE CLEARLY DEFINED

Once enrolled in the study, participants should be followed until specified end points or outcomes are reached. In a study of the effect of exercise on the death rates from heart disease in middle-aged men, for example, participants might be followed up until death, reaching a predefined age or until completion of the study. If outcomes and the criteria used for measuring them are not clearly defined, the study should be rejected.

1.8 THE ASSESSMENT OF OUTCOME IS MADE BLIND TO EXPOSURE STATUS

If the assessor is blinded to which participants received the exposure, and which did not, the prospects of unbiased results are significantly increased. Studies in which this is done should be rated more highly than those where it is not done or not done adequately.

1.9 WHERE BLINDING WAS NOT POSSIBLE, THERE IS SOME RECOGNITION THAT KNOWLEDGE OF EXPOSURE STATUS COULD HAVE INFLUENCED THE ASSESSMENT OF OUTCOME

Blinding is not possible in many cohort studies. In order to assess the extent of any bias that may be present, it may be helpful to compare process measures used on the participant groups – for example, frequency of observations, who carried out the observations and the degree of detail and completeness of observations. If these process measures are comparable between the groups, the results may be regarded with more confidence.

1.10 THE MEASURE OF ASSESSMENT OF EXPOSURE IS RELIABLE

A well-conducted study should indicate how the degree of exposure or presence of prognostic factors or markers was assessed. Whatever measures are used must be sufficient to establish clearly that participants have or have not received the exposure under investigation and the extent of such exposure, or that they do or do not possess a particular prognostic marker or factor. Clearly described, reliable measures should increase the confidence in the quality of the study.

1.11 EVIDENCE FROM OTHER SOURCES IS USED TO DEMONSTRATE THAT THE METHOD OF OUTCOME ASSESSMENT IS VALID AND RELIABLE

The inclusion of evidence from other sources or previous studies that demonstrate the validity and reliability of the assessment methods used should further increase confidence in study quality.

1.12 EXPOSURE LEVEL OR PROGNOSTIC FACTOR IS ASSESSED MORE THAN ONCE

Confidence in data quality should be increased if exposure level or the presence of prognostic factors is measured more than once. Independent assessment by more than one investigator is preferable.

1.13 THE MAIN POTENTIAL CONFOUNDERS ARE IDENTIFIED AND TAKEN INTO ACCOUNT IN THE DESIGN AND ANALYSIS

Confounding is the distortion of a link between exposure and outcome by another factor that is associated with both exposure and outcome. The possible presence of confounding factors is one of the principal reasons why observational studies are not more highly rated as a source of evidence. The report of the study should indicate which potential confounders have been considered and how they have been assessed or allowed for in the analysis. Clinical judgement should be applied to consider whether all likely confounders have been considered. If the measures used to address confounding are considered inadequate, the study should be downgraded or rejected, depending on how serious the risk of confounding is considered to be. A study that does not address the possibility of confounding should be rejected.

1.14   HAVE CONFIDENCE INTERVALS BEEN PROVIDED?

Confidence limits are the preferred method for indicating the precision of statistical results and can be used to differentiate between an inconclusive study and a study that shows no effect. Studies that report a single value with no assessment of precision should be treated with caution.

Section 2 relates to the overall assessment of the paper. It starts by rating the methodological quality of the study, based on the responses in Section 1 and using the following coding system:

+ +	All or most of the criteria have been fulfilled. Where they have not been fulfilled, the conclusions of the study or review are thought **very unlikely** to alter.
+	Some of the criteria have been fulfilled. Those criteria that have not been fulfilled or not adequately described are thought **unlikely** to alter the conclusions.
−	Few or no criteria fulfilled. The conclusions of the study are thought **likely** or **very likely** to alter.

APPENDIX 10:
OUTCOMES

A large number of outcomes are reported by intervention studies in people with borderline personality disorder no doubt because of the multi-symptom nature of the disorder, and the fact that the diagnosis does not include core symptoms as is the case for other mental disorders, such as depression. The problem is compounded by the large number of rating scales available to measure each outcome, including both clinician- and self-rated versions. The problem is further exacerbated by the relatively low number of studies undertaken in people with borderline personality disorder.

To address these problems, the GDG drew up a list of outcomes reported in RCTs reviewed by two existing systematic reviews, one of pharmacological treatments (Binks *et al.*, 2006a) and the other of psychological treatments (Binks *et al.*, 2006b). Each outcome was then allocated to a category (for example, symptoms – depression, harm, general psychiatric morbidity). The outcomes reported within each category were then examined to assess whether they could be combined in meta-analysis. This was done by examining the scales (where relevant publications were available and/or using handbook published by the APA [2000]) to assess how many items they had in common. This was undertaken initially for those outcomes reported in the pharmacological studies. A special advisor with expertise in undertaking trials in people with borderline personality disorder was appointed to advise with this process (see Appendix 3).

The following general rules were adopted when deciding whether to include or exclude a rating scale. The scale had to have been published in a peer-reviewed journal (including validation data), and it had to report an outcome relevant to the guideline. When deciding whether to combine scales in meta-analysis, the following additional rules were adopted: clinician-rated scales were not combined with self-report scales, and the items in the scale had to fairly closely match another scale to be combined.

As studies were reviewed by the GDG that were not included in the existing systematic reviews used to draw up the initial outcome lists, additional outcomes were added to the master list. These were assessed in the same way. Note that dichotomous outcomes based on simple events counts, such as number of episodes of self-harm, were not part of this exercise.

The list of outcomes is in Table 124 together with some notes. Table 125 shows scales arranged by category (domain) with notes on whether they were considered combinable in meta-analysis. Table 126 suggests a possible ranking of the outcomes.

Table 124: Outcomes reported by RCTs reviewed for the guideline

Scale	Self-report (s)	Notes	Category	Comment
ADI (Atypical Depression Inventory)		Based on unpublished scale (Quitkin, F., unpublished scale, 1983)	Symptoms – depression	Not extracting – atypical depression
AIAQ (Anger, Irritability, and Assault Questionnaire)		Coccaro et al., 1991 Three subscales (anger, irritability and assault) adapted from BDHI. There are few studies of validity although it is based on previously published tests one of which is not well known (ALS) and the other has been criticised for the psychometric properties of its subscales (BDHI) (APA, 2000)	Aggression	Useable
AIMS (Abnormal Involuntary Movement Scale)		Guy, 1976 Well-known scale for measuring effects of psychotropic medication, usually antipsychotics	Harm	Useable
AOS (Acting Out Scale)		Cowdry & Gardner, 1988 Drawn from the literature on borderline personality disorder classifies episodes of behavioural dyscontrol into no acting out plus three categories: mild acting-out	Behaviours – acting out	Not extracted as does not appear to be a published scale

Continued

Table 124: (*Continued*)

Scale	Self-report (s)	Notes	Category	Comment
		(exaggerated demanding, angry outburst, suicidal threats), moderate acting out (throwing objects, physical violence without the intention of causing injury, head or arms banging), and severe acting-out (suicidal acts, physical violence with the intention to cause injury)		
AQ (Aggression Questionnaire)	s	Buss & Perry, 1992 Comprises physical aggression, verbal aggression, anger and hostility – adaptation of the BDHI into 29-item Likert scale in an attempt to improve the psychometric properties of the BDHI (Higher is worse)	Symptoms – aggression	Well validated scale. Cannot combine with SCL-90 hostility as only 3/6 items on the SCL-90 map onto AQ items
BAI (Beck Anxiety Inventory)	s	Beck *et al.*, 1988 Good for monitoring change with treatment. Does not assess worry or focus on other DSM-IV symptoms of GAD, therefore not a specific measure for generalised anxiety; does not discriminate well among anxiety disorders or	Symptoms – anxiety	Useable

Scale		Description	Category	Comments
BARNES (Barnes Akathisia Scale)		distinguish anxiety disorders from anxious depression (APA) Barnes, 1989 Well-known scale for measuring effects of psychotropic medication, usually antipsychotics	Harm	Useable
BDHI (Buss Durkee Hostility Inventory)		Buss & Durkee, 1957 'Hostility' used as general term for aggression including emotional, attitudinal and behavioural aspects of aggression – current studies use more specific definitions of hostility and aggression (Higher is worse)	Symptoms – hostility	Original hostility scale – reformed to form the AQ (see above). Useable
BDI (Beck Depression Inventory)	s	Beck *et al.*, 1961 Well-established scale Norms: 12.56 (9.93) (college students) Cut-offs: 0–9 minimal; 10–16 mild; 17–29 moderate; 30–63 severe	Symptoms – depression	Correlates with SCL-90-R depression subscale (r = 0.22 for outpatients; 0.73 to 0.8 for other patient groups). Useable
BHS (Beck Hopelessness Scale)		Beck, 1988 Well-established scale	Symptoms – hopelessness	Useable
BIS (Barratt Impulsiveness Scale)	s	Barratt, 1965 Different versions available - BIS-II – intended for ages >=13.	Symptoms – impulsiveness	Trait-like measure, possibly measuring obsessionality Useable

Continued

445

Table 124: (*Continued*)

Scale	Self-report (s)	Notes	Category	Comment
		Correlates with BDHI and with Anger Out scale of the STAXI. Best suited for use in research with other measures; not useful in individual clinical assessment. Norms: 64.94 (10.19) (college students); general psychiatric patients 69.74 (11.54) (Higher is worse)		
BPDSI (Borderline Personality Disorder Severity Index) [semi-structured interview]		Arntz *et al.*, 2003 Assesses frequency of borderline symptoms in previous 3 months – nine sections to correspond to DSM-IV criteria – only two used in Van den Bosch *et al.* (2002) and Rinne *et al.* (2002) (impulsiveness scales) Eleven questions: buying things impulsively, unsafe sex, sex with unknown persons, gambling, excessive use of alcohol/soft drugs, use of hard drugs, binge eating, shoplifting, reckless driving, other potentially dangerous impulsive behaviours	Symptoms – impulsiveness	Not extracting – turns each DSM-IV criteria into a Likert scale therefore not independent of diagnosis and somewhat tautological

BPRS (Brief Psychiatric Rating Scale)		Overall & Gorham (1982; latest version, 1988) Designed to assess change in severity of psycho-pathology, particularly symptom change in people with psychotic illness, based on existing scales, Multidimensional Scale for Rating Psychiatric Patients and IMPS	Severe psycho-pathology	Not relevant to borderline personality disorder symptoms; may be relevant to axis I comorbidity
Borderline Syndrome Index	s	Floru *et al.*, 1975; Johnson, 1981 Borderline psychopathologic symptoms	General psychiatric morbidity	Not used – only reported by excluded study (Serban & Siegel, 1984)
BSI (Brief Symptom Inventory)	s	Derogatis, 1993 Derived from SCL-90 to reflect psychological symptom patterns, 53-item Likert scale, nine symptom dimensions.	General psychiatric morbidity	Useable
BSSI (Beck Scale for Suicide Ideation)	s	Beck & Steer, 1991 Scored 0–38; 21 items on 3-point Likert scale Correlates with BHS, BDI and HRSD	Behaviours – suicidal ideation	Useable
CGI (Clinical Global Impressions Scale)		Guy, 1976 Weak measure as based on subjective opinion	Global functioning	Not extracted
CGI-I (Clinical Global Impressions – Improvement Scale)		Original scale by Guy, 1976 Rated 1 to 7. 1 = very much improved.	Global functioning	Unpublished scale – not useable

Continued

447

Table 124: (*Continued*)

Scale	Self-report (s)	Notes	Category	Comment
		Based on the nine DSM-IV borderline personality disorder criteria and on the CGI. This version seems to have been developed specifically for one study (Bogenschuzt & George, 2004) and is not published		
DES (Dissociative Experiences Scale)	s	Bernstein & Putnam (1986 and version II, 1993) APA Handbook describes it as a quick, reliable and valid screening measure for the detection of high levels of dissociation – although it does not generate a DSM-IV diagnosis; not validated in under 16s although adolescent version (A-DES) available	Symptoms – dissociation	Not extracted – not relevant to core borderline personality disorder symptomatology
EuroQOL		The EuroQol Group (1990) Five domains (mobility; self-care; usual activity; pain; anxiety/depression) (three response options per domain), plus a visual analogue scale (thermometer score excluded) (Higher is better)	Quality of life	Useable

EuropASI (European Addiction Severity Index)	McLellan et al., 1980 Seven areas: medical status, employment and support, drug use, alcohol use, legal status, family or social status, psychiatric status based on previous 30 days. Useful as tool to guide initial assessment and treatment planning for patients seeking inpatient or outpatient treatment for substance misuse. Adolescent version available. Not suitable for people with schizophrenia as makes assumptions about self-sufficiency	Behaviours – substance use	Not extracted
GAF (Global Assessment of Functioning)	APA, 1987 Established scale	Global functioning	Useable
Global Adjustment Scale	See SHI (below)	Social functioning	Useable
GAS (Global Assessment Scale)	Endicott et al., 1976 Evaluates overall functioning on a scale from 1 to 100. (Higher is better) Norms: over 70 Outpatients: 31 to 70; inpatients 1 to 40	Global functioning	Useable

Continued

Table 124: (*Continued*)

Scale	Self-report (s)	Notes	Category	Comment
GSA (Global Social Adjustment)		See SHI (below)	Social functioning	
GSI (Global Severity Index)	s	Index from SCL-90 (also BSI) – essentially a mean of all items. Calculated as follows: sums of nine symptom dimensions and additional items added together and divided by number of responses (53 if all answered) Given that most of the subscales of the SCL-90 are not relevant to borderline personality disorder symptomatology, GSI and total SCL-90 may not be useful measures Norms (raw scores/T scores): outpatients 1.32/50: adult non-patients 0.3/53; inpatients 1.19/53; adolescent non-patients 0.83/52	Global functioning (mental distress)	Useable
HADS (Hospital Anxiety and Depression Scale)	s	Zigmond & Snaith, 1983 Designed to screen for depression/anxiety in medically ill patients – 14 items rated on 4-point Likert-type scales	Symptoms – depression/ anxiety	Useable

HAM-D (or HRSD; Hamilton Depression Scale)	Hamilton, 1960 Clinician-rated depression scale; well established	Symptoms – depression	Useable: combine with MADRS
HARS (Hamilton Anxiety Rating Scale)	Hamilton, 1959 A 21-item scale, initially designed as indicator of severity of anxiety neurosis, which is no longer a psychiatric term. Does not focus on symptoms of GAD (DSM-IV definition) – for example, worry which is key feature of GAD is less emphasised than phobic symptoms, and symptoms of autonomic arousal, which are no longer part of definition of GAD feature prominently	Symptoms – anxiety	Useable
HDQ (Hysteroid Dysphoria Questionnaire)	Unpublished scale		Not extractable - not published scale
HRQ (Helping Relationship Questionnaire)			Not relevant
IMPS (Inpatient Multidimensional Rating Scale)	Lorr & Klett, 1966 Used in Soloff *et al.*, 1993 to measure symptom severity (schizoptypal functioning) at baseline; used as basis for BPRS	Symptoms – schizotypal, psychoticism	Not extracting – schizotypal functioning not relevant to borderline personality disorder

Continued

451

Table 124: *(Continued)*

Scale	Self-report (s)	Notes	Category	Comment
IIP (Inventory of Interpersonal Problems – circumflex version)	s	Horowitz *et al.*, 1988; Alden *et al.*, 1990 Assesses nature of dysfunctional interpersonal problems – eight areas: domineering, vindictive, cold, socially aviodant, nonassertive, exploitable, overly nurturant, intrusive – higher is worse	Social functioning	Not used
LPC (Lifetime Parasuicide Count)		Comtois & Linehan, 1999 Frequency and subsequent medical treatment of self-mutilating behaviours Scale does not give a count of number of episodes/acts – more of a composite measure of overall 'parasuicidality' in period under review. Relies on client recall	Behaviours – parasuicide	Not useable
MADRS (Montgomery and Asberg Depression Rating Scale)		Montgomery & Asberg, 1979 Clinician-rated depression scale; well-established	Symptoms – depression	Useable

Continued

OAS-M (Overt Aggression Scale – Modified)		Coccaro *et al.*, 1991; Yudofsky, 1986 Original scale was an observer-rated scale for inpatients. Then modified version scale for outpatients. Added items from the Schedule for Affective Disorders and Schizophrenia (SADS) for irritability and suicidality. Validation study done on male psychiatric patients with mood disorders, personality disorder or both. Includes three domains: aggression, irritability, suicidality. 25-item, semi-structured interview with nine subscales. Suicidality items make it difficult to call this an aggression scale. Aggression subscale (used in one study) is original scale. Nature of items better suited to environment in which rater can observe behaviour rather than assess them in clinical interview (Higher is worse)	Symptoms–aggression	Useable
OAS-R and MOAS (McLean Hospital Overt Aggression Symptom Checklist – Revised)	s	Modified version of the Yudofsky (1986) scale. Turned into a self-rated scale and added suicidality items (Teicher *et al.*, 1989)	Symptoms – aggression	Not extractable – not published scale

453

Table 124: (*Continued*)

Scale	Self-report (s)	Notes	Category	Comment
PAI (Psychiatric Assessment Interview)		Appears to have been developed for a particular study (Serban & Siegel, 1984) – no reference available	General psychiatric morbidity	Not extractable from the only study in which it is reported (Serban & Siegel, 1984); also study excluded from review
PANSS (Positive and Negative Syndrome Scale)		Kay *et al.*, 1987 Measures severity of psychopathology in people with psychotic disorders. Items include those from BPRS plus some from Psychopathology Rating Schedule (Singh & Kay, 1975)	General psychiatric morbidity	Not relevant to borderline personality disorder symptomatology
PDQ-DSM-IV (Personality Diagnostic Questionnaire, DSM-IV version)	s	Hyler, 1994 APA handbook assesses PDQ-4 – assume similar to this – best used as screening instrument as high false-positive rate and best used with Clinical Significance Scale, which is a brief interview	Diagnosis	Not extracted
PDRS (Personality Disorder Rating Scale)		Scale designed specifically for study (Salzman *et al.*, 1995)	General psychiatric functioning	Not published scale
PHI (Parasuicide History Interview)		Linehan *et al.*, 1989, 1990 Semi-structured interview assesses	Behaviours - parasuicide	Useable

[now the Suicide Attempt & Self-Injury Interview]		nature and frequency of parasuicidal behaviour since last assessment		
POMS (Profile of Mood States)	s	McNair *et al.*, 1971 Evaluates multiple emotional and behavioural states (for example, vitality and anxiety) – not in APA (Higher is worse)	General psychiatric morbidity	Only used in a study which has been excluded
RLISC (The Reasons for Living Inventory, Survival and Coping Scale).		Linehan *et al.*, 1983 Only used in one study (Linehan, 1991) and data not reported	Suicidal ideation	Not extracted
SAS-I (Social Adjustment Scale – Interview)		Weissman & Bothwell, 1976 Adapted to form SHI Covers functioning at work, social and leisure activities, relationships with extended family, marital role as a spouse, role as a parent, role as a member of the family unit Covers previous 2 months	Social functioning	Useable
SAS-SR (Social Adjustment Scale-Self-Report)	s	Cooper *et al.*, 1982 Modified version used in Bateman & Fonagy, 1999, also modified in Linehan *et al.*, 1991 Scored yes/no rather than on a scale as for interview version	Social functioning	Useable

Continued

Table 124: (*Continued*)

Scale	Self-report (s)	Notes	Category	Comment
SAS-SR LIFE (Social Adjustment Scale – Longitudinal Interview Follow-up)	s	Keller *et al.*, 1987 Modified for Linehan (1991)	Social functioning	Not extracted
SCID-II BPD (Structured Clinical Interview for DSM-IV – borderline personality disorder) Dimensional score		Derived by summing nine SCID-II items scored 1 (absent), 2 (subthreshold), 3 (present). Scores range from 9 to 27. Designed specifically for study (Chanen *et al.*, 2008a)	Diagnosis	Not extracted
SCL-90 (Symptom Checklist-90)	s	Derogatis *et al.*, 1974 Nine subscales (somatisation, obsessive-compulsiveness, interpersonal relationships, depression, general anxiety, anger and hostility, phobic anxiety, paranoid ideation, psychoticism). Includes GSI, which is total means – indicator of respondent's distress level, combining information about numbers of symptoms and intensity of symptoms; Positive Symptom Distress Index – pure intensity measure corrected for number of symptoms, PST relevant number of symptoms	General psychiatric morbidity	Useable – including some individual scales other than: phobic anxiety; obsessive-compulsive; somatisation; paranoid thinking; psychotic – not relevant to borderline personality disorder

456

	No information found on correlation of hostility subscale with AQ but items did not match so were not combined		As for SCL-90
SCL-90-R (Symptom Check List 90 – Revised)	Derogatis, 1994 Intended as a quick screening instrument, as measure of the outcome/status of psychopathology – nine constructs: somatisation, obsessive-compulsiveness, interpersonal relationships, depression, general anxiety, anger and hostility, phobic anxiety, paranoid ideation, psychoticism. Contains only minor reviews of SCL-90 Scores given either as raw scores or t-values	General psychiatric morbidity	
SFQ (Social Functioning Questionnaire)	Tyrer, *et al.*, 2005 (Higher is worse)	Social functioning	Useable
SHI (Social History Interview)	Weissman & Bothwell, 1976 Adaptation of the psychosocial functioning portion of the SAS and the LIFE base schedule allowed for determination of GSA and Global Adjustment Scale scores	Social functioning	Useable

Continued

Table 124: (*Continued*)

Scale	Self-report (s)	Notes	Category	Comment
Simpson-Angus scale		Simpson & Angus, 1970 Well-established scale reporting side effects of psychotropic medication particularly antipsychotics	Harm	Useable
SNOOP (Systematic Nurses' Observation of Psychopathology)		Hargreaves, 1968	General psychiatric morbidity	Only reported in one study and data not extractable (Leone, 1982)
Social and Occupational Functioning Assessment Scale		Goldman *et al.*, 1992	Global functioning	Useable
SSHI (Suicide and Self Harm Inventory)		Only used by one study (Linehan *et al.*, 1991) and data not reported. Also Bateman & Fonagy, 1999, but may be different scale. Not validated or published in peer-review journal	Behaviours – suicidal ideation	Useable
SSI (Scale for Suicide Ideators)		Schotte & Clum, 1982	Behaviours – suicidal ideators	Only used in one study (Linehan *et al.*, 1991)
Schizotypal Symptom Inventory		George & Soloff, 1986	Symptoms – schizotypal symptoms	Not being used – reported in studies with patients with schizotypal personality disorder not borderline personality disorder

Continued

STAI (Spielberger State-Trait Anxiety Inventory)	s	Spielberger et al., 1970 (Higher is worse)	Symptoms – anxiety	Trait items seem to measure depression as well as anxiety (Bieling et al., 1998). Therefore a weak measure of anxiety
STAS-T (Spielberger State-Trait Anger Scale)		Spielberger et al., 1983	Symptoms – anger	Predecessor of STAXI
STAXI (Spielberger Anger Expression Scale/State-Trait Anger Expression Inventory)	s	Spielberger et al., 1983 Assesses components of anger – state-trait dimension. Distinguishes general propensity to experience angry feelings (trait) and level of anger experienced in present moment (state). 44 items making up eight subscales – no total score, just individual scales: S-anger/T-anger scored 10 to 40 AX/In, AX/Out, AX/CON scored 8 to 32 AX/EX calculated by formula from 0 to 72 Cut-off for normal = 40 T-anger correlates with BDHI and Minnesota Multiphasic Personality Inventory	Symptoms – anger	State and trait subscales correlate State subscale more useful because of short-term nature of trials
STIC (Self Report Test of Impulse Control)	s	Lazzaro et al., 1969 Described as 'trait measure of impulse control' in Soloff et al., 1993 which used it (along with two other measures of impulsivity)	Symptoms – impulsivity	Reported by only one study which also reports the BIS so not extracted

Table 124: (*Continued*)

Scale	Self-report (s)	Notes	Category	Comment
		Well-validated scale, correlates negatively with the BIS (Higher is better)		
TBR (Target Behaviour Ratings)		Unpublished scale; scored 0 to 8 for each of target behaviours – anger, impulsive behaviour, emotional instability, frequency of parasuicide (Turner, 2000)	Symptoms/ behaviours – as reported	Not extractable – not published scale
THI (Treatment History Interview)		Linehan & Heard (1987)	Social functioning	Not extracted
WSIAP (Ward Scale of Impulse Action Patterns)		Adapted for study from other sources (Soloff et al., 1989)	Global functioning Impulsivity	Not a published scale
WHO QoL (World Health Organization Quality of Life Assessment)		The WHOQOL group (1998) (Higher scores indicate better QOL)	Quality of life	Useable
Youth/Young Adult Self-Report		Achenbach, 1991; 1997	Used for internalising and externalising psycho-pathology	Not relevant and reported in only one study (Chanen et al., 2008a)

Table 125: Rating scales by domain with notes on possibility of combining scales in meta-analysis

Domain	Scales	Notes
Acting out	AOS	No information available – single scale
Aggression	AQ (s) MOAS (s) OAS-M	Scales are not suitable for combining as there is little overlap between them
Anger	POMS anger subscale (s) Spielberger Anger Expression Scale/STAXI (s)	Combine STAXI-trait anger with SCL-90 anger subscale? Look very similar
Hostility	BDHI POMS anger subscale (s) PCL-90 hostility scale (s) STAS-T Spielberger Anger Expression Scale/STAXI (s)	Combine STAXI-trait anger with SCL-90 anger subscale? Look very similar
Anxiety	BAI (s) HARS SCL-90 anxiety subscale (s) STAI	Have no information about the STAI; BAI combinable with SCL-90 (both self-report)? BAI and HARS seem to measure different things
Depression	ADI BDI (s) HRSD MADRS POMS depression subscale (s) SCL-90 depression subscale (s)	Not interested in atypical depression BDI is self-report therefore do not combine with scales that are not, but combine with POMS and SCL-90? Some overlap between BDI and SCL-90. Able to combine HRSD and MADRS
Dissociation	DES	Single measure
General functioning	CGI GAF GAS	CGI usually considered a weak outcome so do not extract – combine the other two?

Continued

Table 125: *(Continued)*

Domain	Scales	Notes
General psychiatric morbidity	Borderline Syndrome Index BPRS BSI PANSS PDRS POMS Psychiatric Assessment Interview SCL-90	Several seem to be aimed at measuring psychotic symptoms Several derivations of others (BSI, SCL-90, IMPS) Some seem to be created for the study Combine: BPRS and PANSS BSI, SCL-90 and IMPS
Impulsiveness	SNOOP BIS(s) BPDSI (impulsiveness subscale) STIC (s)	Little available information about these scales, so hard to judge these. Ward Scale was adapted for the study (Soloff *et al.*, 1993) so can not use
Service use	WSIAP THI	No information available – single scale
Social functioning	IIP (s) SAS – LIFE (provides GAS scores) (s) SAS – Interview SHI (results in GSA based on SAS)	Used in modified forms in studies Not combinable: mix of self-rated and clinician-rated
Substance use	EuropASI	Only BSSI in APA. SSI was adapted for a particular study (Soloff *et al.*, 1993) and RLISC only used by one study (Linehan *et al.*, 1991) and data not reported
Suicidal ideation	BSSI RLISC	
Suicide/self-harm Impulsiveness	SSI BPDSI (parasuicide subscale) LPC PHI	Little information available Can not add together because of different definitions of parasuicide/self-harm

S = self-report

Table 126: Proposed ranking of the outcomes – by importance

Outcome category	Example outcomes	Rating scales
High importance		
Social functioning	Social adjustment, interpersonal functioning, vocational status	IIP, SHI (results in GSA based on SAS), SAS – LIFE, SAS – Interview
'Mental distress'		
User experience	Acceptability (leaving treatment early), quality of life, experience of care	
Medium importance		
Service use	Inpatient admission, length of inpatient stay, number of A&E attendances	THI
Global state [vague measure, but useful to triangulate the others]	Overall functioning	CGI, CGI-I, GAF, GAS
Behaviours	Acting out, para-suicide, suicide, self-harm and substance use	***Acting out*** AOS ***Parasuicide, suicide and self-harm*** BPDSI (parasuicide subscale), LPC, PHI, SSHI ***Substance use*** EuropASI
Harm	Side effects, side effect symptoms (for example, extrapyramidal symptoms), death (completed suicide, road traffic accidents, accidental self-poisoning)	AIMS, BARNES, Simpson-Angus scale

Proposed taxonomy for outcomes – by importance [consider ranking them]: (*Continued*)

Outcome category	Example outcomes	Rating scales
Symptoms	Depression, anxiety, irritability, suicidal ideation, dissociation, anger, general psychiatric morbidity	***Depression (core symptom)*** ADI, BDI (s), HRSD, MADRS ***Impulsiveness (core symptom)*** BIS, BPDSI (impulsiveness subscale), STIC, WSIAP ***Suicidal ideation*** BSSI, RLISC, SSI ***Hopelessness*** BHS ***Anxiety*** BAI, HARS, STAI ***Dissociation*** DES ***Anger and Hostility*** BDHI, Spielberger Anger Expression Scale/STAXI, STAI ***Aggression*** AQ (s), OAS-M, MOAS ***Schizotypal features*** Schizotypal Symptom Inventory ***General psychiatric morbidity*** BPRS, BSI, Borderline Syndrome Index, IMPS, Psychiatric Assessment Interview, PANSS, PDRS, POMS, SCL-90, SNOOP
Low importance		
Overall diagnosis	Meeting (or not meeting) diagnosis based on DSM-IV or ICD-10 or similar	DIB, SCID-I and SCID-II (DSM-III-R or DSM-IV), IPDE

APPENDIX 11:
PHARMACOLOGY PEER REVIEWER
CONSULTATION TABLE

Please see tables on pages 466–492.

Peer Reviewer	Section	Comments	Developer's Response
Paul Soloff	General (also 6.13)[20]	1. The available literature on borderline personality disorder does not lend itself to meta-analysis. This is acknowledged, in part, in Section 6.13.1 ('This has prevented any meaningful meta-analysis or comparison between trials and treatments.') The limitations of both the database and the method of analysis should be stated in the Introduction, as the conclusions of the study are severely compromised by use of meta-analysis on such data. 2. By virtue of selection rules, the analysis excludes important studies from consideration, including well-crafted RCT trials which had real impact on the field (for example, Cowdry & Gardner, 1988). 3. Given the acknowledged inadequacy of the database for meta-analysis, it would be helpful to supplement the meta-analysis with a review and discussion of excluded RCT studies, relevant open-label studies, and studies of dimensional constructs found in borderline personality disorder (for example	We agree that the available literature does not lend itself to meta-analysis because of the relatively few studies and because of the lack of common outcomes. However, meta-analysis is the method of choice and we have used it as far as possible, calculating simple effect sizes where only single studies are available. We do not use lower levels of analysis to underpin recommendations relating to efficacy, but these can be used to develop research recommendations. The Cowdry & Gardner (1988) study is small and tells us very little as all the effects are short-term ones; furthermore it is compromised by carry-over effects. We feel it is of pioneering interest only. It also used a cross-over design, which is difficult to use in meta-analysis. We use the SIGN grade to indicate the methodological quality of studies.

[20]Please note that the section numbers correspond to the numbers in the consulation draft of Chapter 6 and may not correspond precisely to the published version.

466

| | | These are in the study characteristics tables in the guideline appendix. We apologise if these were not sent to you with the chapter. See http://www.sign.ac.uk/ for further details of the SIGN methodology.

Regarding dimensional constructs, this is a very good point. However, we chose not to do this because of the dangers of producing apparent coherence where this may not exist. Where there is evidence of a diagnosable comorbidity (for example, depression), we recommend that this should be treated as a priority. The Coccaro & Kavousi (1997) study is more relevant to antisocial personality disorder (for which we are also developing a guideline). |
|---|---|---|
| | | Coccaro and Kavousi's [1997] study of fluoxetine for impulsive-aggression.) The APA guideline project dealt with the heterogeneity of study methods by use of a grading system of confidence in method (for example, A = RCT, B = open label, etc). This could be used for studies in a supplement or appendix to the main analysis. |
| | 6.1 Introduction | 'These data are not surprising . . . immediate action is expected.' This is an editorial opinion for which there is no empirical support. | Thank you, we have amended this sentence. |
| Paul Soloff | | |

Continued

467

Peer Reviewer	Section	Comments	Developer's Response
Paul Soloff	6.1.2 placebo effect	'Drug trials with people with borderline personality disorder are particularly prone to the placebo effect.' Another editorial opinion with no empirical support. Compared to other psychiatric disorders? Placebo effect is prominent in most drug trials with psychiatric subjects, not limited to borderline personality disorder.	Thank you, we have amended this sentence.
Paul Soloff	6.1.3	'outcomes . . . do not directly measure symptoms making up the diagnosis . . . aggression and depression.' Please clarify sentence and intent. Aggression is a target symptom because it is a dimensional trait in borderline personality disorder. Depression is measured because it is part of affective dysregulation, a key dimension in borderline personality disorder. Since you do discuss symptom-specific treatments later in the text, it would be useful to acknowledge that a symptom-specific approach to drug trials for the borderline personality disorder syndrome will involve outcome measurements defined for the symptom, not the borderline personality disorder syndrome as a whole.	We agree and have amended the sentence.

Paul Soloff	6.2.1 para.4.	'Impulsive aggression … mediated by lithium.' Mediated? Wrong word.	Thank you, we have amended the text
Paul Soloff	6.2.2 carbamaze-pine comment	'insufficient evidence …' Cowdry & Gardner (1988) found carbamazepine useful against behavioural dyscontrol in an RCT four drug cross-over study. (Should be noted though excluded by selection criteria.)	We disagree and consider this trial unhelpful. Also, we do not discuss excluded studies in the discussion of the evidence.
Paul Soloff	6.3.3	'A sensitivity analysis was undertaken removing one study.' Define 'sensitivity analysis' and why Soloff 1993 was excluded.	The methodology is explained in a separate methods chapter (which we did not send you – apologies for this). The effect size calculated for the outcome in question for the Soloff 1993 trial was clearly an outlier compared with other trials in the analysis and therefore was removed.
Paul Soloff	6.3.3 comment	'there is no evidence for the use of low dose haloperidol as a mood stabiliser … therefore insufficient evidence … to recommend its use in the management of borderline person-ality disorder…' Haloperidol is not a mood	Thank you, we have amended the sentence.

Continued

Peer Reviewer	Section	Comments	Developer's Response
		stabiliser, nor intended as a mood stabiliser in any pharm study. Its target symptoms are cognitive-perceptual, anger, hostility, impulsivity. This statement, and conclusion, are grossly incorrect.	
Paul Soloff	6.3.6 comment	Re. Aripiprazole: 'there is no evidence for its use as a mood stabiliser… insufficient evidence.' Same critique as above. Statement and conclusion are grossly incorrect.	Thank you, we have removed the sentence.
Paul Soloff	6.4.4. comment on antidepressants	… 'there is no evidence of efficacy of these drugs as mood stabilisers in people with borderline personality disorder'. Why the emphasis on mood stabilisers? (see above). The target symptom for TCA, SSRI and MAOI trials is primarily depression.	Thank you, we have removed the sentence.
Paul Soloff	6.5.2 omega-3 fatty acids comment	'… there is no evidence for use as a mood stabiliser.' Why is this the major target symptom for consideration of use in borderline personality disorder? (see above). Because a drug is not a mood stabiliser, do you discount its use in borderline personality disorder?	Thank you, we have removed the sentence.

Paul Soloff	6.7.3 aggression comment	'... no evidence for any drug of an effect of treatment on aggression.' A discussion of Coccaro and Kavousi (1997) would be helpful here as they showed efficacy for fluoxetine in an RCT targeting impulsive-aggression in personality disorder subjects (many, though not all borderline personality disorder). We treat dimensions within the borderline personality disorder syndrome.	Your point about dimensional constructs is a good one. However, we choose not to do this because of the dangers of producing apparent coherence where this may not exist. Where there is evidence of a diagnosable comorbidity (for example, depression), we recommend that this should be treated as a priority. The Coccaro & Kavousi (1997) study is more relevant to antisocial personality disorder (for which we are also developing a guideline).
Paul Soloff	6.11 Summary 6.12 recommend-ations	'There was evidence that pharmacological treatments can help reduce ... anger, anxiety, depression symptoms, hostility and impulsivity. *This is the result supported by your meta-analysis*, yet you recommend (6.12) 'Pharmacological treatments should not routinely be offered ...' To the extent that this analysis purports to be evidence-based, you must acknowledge the positive	Thank you, we have amended the conclusion to reflect our findings and consequent recommendations more accurately. Although there is some evidence it is too weak to support recommendations in a national guideline.

Continued

Peer Reviewer	Section	Comments	Developer's Response
		findings of your own analysis in your recommendations!!	
Paul Soloff	Table 56 Drugs	Because of the limitations of the database and of your analytic method, the drugs identified as 'showing some effects' are unlikely to be first-line choices for clinicians (for example, topiramate for anger and anxiety, AMI for depression, haloperidol for impulsivity).	Thank you. We recommend the treatment of comorbidities but the data are not strong enough to recommend the treatment of traits. We had some concerns about the topiramate and aripiprazole studies by study group led by Nickel because they were very positive compared with other studies. Since this research group had completed a large number of very positive studies across a wide range of disorders (including non-psychiatric disorders) we therefore did not include these studies when drawing up our overall conclusions about the dataset.
Paul Soloff	6.14 Management of crises	'There is no evidence for the use of specific medication in the crisis management . . .' This sweeping generalisation quickly loses meaning when we look at specific symptoms presented in crisis settings, for example	Thank you, we have substantially amended this paragraph to make our meaning clearer. We found no evidence that supports the use of any specific drug or drugs in the crisis

		anger, hostility, anxiety, impulsivity, all of which may respond to medication acutely administered, even in borderline personality disorder (for example, a low dose neuroleptic). Perhaps this is spelled out in NICE CG25 but should be stated here as well.	management of people with borderline personality disorder.
Paul Soloff	General 6.12	Because of the severe limitations imposed by your choice of method, many useful clinical studies are not considered. Helpful treatments identified by the meta-analysis are ignored in your recommendation. As currently constructed, the guideline can not be called evidence-based. It is my personal opinion that the limitations in method and bias in interpretation result in a guideline which is not clinically meaningful.	Thank you, but we feel that the limitations are in the data (that is, paucity of well-conducted RCTs) rather than in our methods. The recommendations will reflect the lack of good evidence and acknowledge the poor evidence base.
Roger Mulder	General	In general I think the report is very good. It systematically evaluates the limited data available, summarises the weak evidence or the lack of evidence and makes appropriate recommendations.	Thank you.

Continued

473

Peer Reviewer	Section	Comments	Developer's Response
Roger Mulder	Opening paragraph	The opening paragraph is very appropriate in that it emphasises that patients with borderline personality disorder are receiving medications whether or not there is an evidence base for doing this. It could be further emphasised in the final section that the high rates of prescribing coupled with poor evidence base make it ethically imperative that large randomised control trials with agreed outcome measures are instituted as soon as possible.	Thank you, we will be making several research recommendations along the lines you suggest.
Roger Mulder	Page 3	On page 3 under the heading 'diagnosis' there is a comment that some trials exclude participants with any comorbid axis I disorder. I wonder whether there needs to be a comment that some trials do not specify whether they exclude axis I disorders or not, making interpretation difficult. I also think it is reasonable to say that in the final sentence 'this may reduce generalisability since most (rather than many) people with borderline personality disorder have also an axis I disorder'.	Thank you, we have amended the paragraph.

Roger Mulder	Page 5	On page 5 the databases searched were last updated in July 2007. There obviously has to be a final date but I wonder whether consideration should be given to a recent randomised control trial of ziprasidone since this is one of the largest that has been undertaken to this point. The reference is Carlos Pascual *et al.* (2008) *Journal of Clinical Psychiatry*, Jan30:e1–e6.	Thank you, this is a good point. We update all the searches every 6 months and for the last time about 6 weeks before we hand in the draft guideline to NICE. We had not updated the chapter with the latest round of updates. We will look at the Pascual *et al.* (2008) study.
Roger Mulder	Page 33	On page 33 the statement that there is insufficient evidence to base a recommendation for antidepressants in the treatment of borderline personality disorder is somewhat at odds with the Cochrane review conclusion which states 'antidepressants, in particular, may be helpful.' It would be useful to include some comment to explain these differences or are we better to leave the evidence as it stands?	Thank you. We are unable to find this in the Cochrane review. However, we found very few significant findings for antidepressants. The updated Cochrane review (of which we were given sight of a pre-publication copy) concluded that there was a limited evidence base to justify intervening with drugs in people with borderline personality disorder. We have made it clearer in the chapter that we are talking about treating the disorder not depression.

Continued

Peer Reviewer	Section	Comments	Developer's Response
Roger Mulder	Page 33	With regard to the effects of antidepressants on mood in patients with borderline personality disorder, would it be worthwhile to include literature on treatment of mood disorders in patients who have comorbid borderline personality disorder? These generally confirm the fact that effective treatment of mood symptoms in the context of borderline personality disorder is possible.	Thank you. This is very difficult to do systematically and we consider that we have used all relevant studies of people with a diagnosis of borderline personality disorder. Also, it is very easy for us to suggest that when drug effects are being shown that this is a consequence of treating a comorbid disorder, but of course we cannot dissect drug effects by diagnosis in this way.
Roger Mulder	Clinical summary	In the summary of clinical evidence review would it be worth putting some comment about the possibility that enrolment, assessment, and treatment in a randomised control trial regardless of which medication was used might be helpful for patients with borderline personality disorder? This would acknowledge the potentially helpful effects of a structured model of intervention with systematic follow up. While I am unaware of specific data to support this, the high placebo response rate in some trials gives it some credibility.	Thank you, we have discussed this issue in the introduction to the chapter (under 'placebo effect').

Continued

Roger Mulder	Comorbidity	In general the question of comorbidity is a can of worms and it is difficult to know where the boundaries are. One can arguably include treatment of comorbid alcohol and drug disorders which are common and clearly influence the outcome. In addition, should comment be made about what DSM-IV calls 'transient, stress-related paranoid ideation or severe dissociative symptoms' and the use of pharmacological treatments. Personally I think this would make it unwieldy.	We agree. Also, transient paranoid symptoms can only be mentioned if studies target these symptoms from the outset, but none of them do. The treatment of comorbid alcohol and drug disorders is not covered by this guideline although we mention this very important issue where appropriate (for example, in the chapter considering the evidence for psychological treatments where there are some studies specifically in this population).
Roger Mulder	General	Finally, I wonder whether the issue of informed consent needs to be considered. Given the fact that the treatments have a very poor evidence base and the potential for harm is quite high, should more formal consent be obtained in some way? This might even be useful in agreeing on target symptoms, avoiding polypharmacy, monitoring the response carefully, and discontinuing drugs if there is no response to the agreed on target symptoms.	Thank you, this is a very good point which we will discuss and include where appropriate.

Appendix 11

Peer Reviewer	Section	Comments	Developer's Response
Roger Mulder	General	Overall, I think the guidelines are very good. The fact that many borderline patients receive multiple medications with such a weak evidence base is concerning but hardly the guideline committee's fault.	Thank you.
Ken Silk	6.1	2nd paragraph: 'This subdivision of symptoms in BPD . . .'. There is some rationale for this. The first comes from the paper by Siever and Davis in American Journal of Psychiatry (December 1991) where they propose these four dimensions underlying the pathophysiology (biology) of personality disorders, and the second comes from Soloff's (1998) paper, 'Symptom-oriented psychopharmacology for personality disorders'. *Journal of Practical Psychiatry and Behavioural Health*, 4, 3-11. These 'latter' ideas were then incorporated into Soloff's algorithms for psychopharmacology of borderline personality disorder published in *Bulletin of the Menninger Clinic and Psychiatric Clinics of North America* (April 2000).	Thank you – these suggestions relate to personality disorders as a whole rather than specifically borderline personality disorder. As far as we are aware, no one in clinical practice or nosology has ever suggested splitting borderline personality disorder in this way.

Ken Silk	6.1.1	Polypharmacy: Zanarini has data for five or six or more simultaneously taken medications. If there is to be a strong proviso against polypharmacy, then Zanarini's data of four or five or six simultaneous drugs might be worth discussing in a bit more detail here.	Thank you, we have added more data from the Zanarini paper to the chapter to make this clearer.
Ken Silk	6.1.2	Range of symptoms: might want to bring in the polythetic nature of the diagnosis and/or some of the factor analyses (that is, from the CLPS study [Sanislow]).	Thank you. We will consider this – it may be more appropriate in the introduction to the guideline rather than here.
Ken Silk	6.1.2	Recruited through advertisement patients: in our PET study, most of our subjects who met borderline personality disorder came from advertisements, and probably 50% were treatment naïve (that is, were able to keep functioning and not have someone drag them for treatment because they were so annoying to others even though they had emotional lability, anger, devaluation, etc).	Thank you.
Ken Silk	6.1.2	Subjects recruited from primary care settings: there is an interesting editorial by	Thank you.

Continued

479

Peer Reviewer	Section	Comments	Developer's Response
		J. Craig Nelson in the *American Journal of Psychiatry* (2008) on why the results from the STAR*D study of depression may differ from other more controlled trials. Many of the STAR*D subjects were recruited from primary care settings and were permitted to have greater 'comorbidities' than subjects in other clinical trials, but these STAR*D subjects may more accurately reflect 'real clinical life'. (Anxious depression and response to treatment. *American Journal of Psychiatry, 165*, 297–299).	
Ken Silk	6.1.2	Therapeutic alliance. See: 1. Waldinger, R. J. & Gunderson, J. G. (1984) Completed psychotherapies with borderline patients. *American Journal of Psychotherapy, 38*, 190–202. 2. Waldinger, R. S. & Frank, A. F. (1989) Clinicians' experiences in combining medication and psychotherapy in the treatment of borderline patients. *Hospital and Community Psychiatry, 40*, 712–718.	Thank you for the references. We have added some text on the importance of therapeutic alliance.

3. Smith, J. M. (1989) Some dimensions of transference in combined treatment. In *The Psychotherapist's Guide to Pharmacotherapy* (ed J. M. Ellison), pp. 79–94. Chicago: Year Book Medical Publishers.
4. Chiles, J. A., Carlin, A. S., Benjamin, G. A. H., *et al.* (1991) A physician, a nonmedical psychotherapist, and a patient: the pharmacotherapy-psychotherapy triangle. In *Integrating Pharmacotherapy and Psychotherapy* (ed B. D. Beitman & G. L. Klerman), pp. 105–118. Washington DC: American Psychiatric Press.
5. Beitman, B. D., Chiles, J. & Carlin, A. (1984) The pharmacotherapy-psychotherapy triangle: psychiatrist, non-medical psychotherapist and patient. *Journal of Clinical Psychiatry, 45*, 458–459.
6. Adelman, S. A. (1985) Pills as transitional objects: a dynamic understanding of the use of medication in psychotherapy. *Psychiatry, 48*, 246–253.

Peer Reviewer	Section	Comments	Developer's Response
Ken Silk	6.1.6	Funding bias: You found that no funding source favoured active treatment which is at variance from what is published in literature. Any thoughts?	We have brought this to the attention of the relevant journal and have written to the relevant authors. The matter is being further investigated and we felt that we could not include these studies when drawing up our overall conclusions about the dataset.
Ken Silk	6.2.1	Lithium is mentioned but no studies reviewed. Perhaps they didn't make the cut though there is the Links study (1990). Also: Sheard, M. H., *et al.* (1976) The effect of lithium on impulsive aggressive behavior in man. *American Journal of Psychiatry, 133,* 1409–1413.	Thank you, but the Links study is a cross-over trial which we can not use in meta-analyses, and the Sheard study is for the antisocial personality disorder guideline.
Ken Silk	6.2.2	The Cowdry & Gardner (1988) study found that carbamazepine increased depression in borderline personality disorder. See Gardner, D. L. & Cowdry, R. W. (1986) Development of melancholia during carbamazepine treatment in borderline personality disorder. *Journal of Clinical Psychopharmacology,*	Thank you, the Cowdry & Gardner (1988) is small and tells us very little because all the effects are short-term ones; furthermore it is compromised by carry-over effects. We feel it is of pioneering interest only. It also used a cross-over design.

		236-9. There is growing concern that there may be some Stevens-Johnson syndrome risk with carbamazepine.	
Ken Silk	6.2.3	Valproate 'may be effective in reducing depressive symptoms in people with BPD'. Based on two studies with an N = 39? This is curious, because I know of little evidence in any clinical population that valproate reduces depression. It may have some impact on acute mania and may be has some effectiveness in preventing mania, but little evidence for an antidepressant effect.	Thank you, we have amended the paragraph.
Ken Silk	6.2.5	Topiramate: Klaus Lieb and Thomas Rinne report that it is the only medication recommended for borderline personality disorder in the guidelines in the Netherlands. Not sure that this is true, but I believe that this was reported on at the ISSPD [The International Society for the Study of Personality Disorders] in The Hague.	Thank you but we found no good evidence for topiramate in this population. Since drug trials of this size are usually expensive to undertake, the GDG undertook some investigations to uncover the funding source and succeeded in discovering that this research group had completed a large number of very positive studies across a wide range of disorders (including

Continued

Peer Reviewer	Section	Comments	Developer's Response
			non-psychiatric disorders). We therefore did not include this and other studies by this research group when drawing up our overall conclusions about the dataset.
Ken Silk	6.3.5	Soloff 1993. 'The study is too old to contact the study authors.' Soloff is alive and well and knowing him he still has the data and he may be able to answer your question. I agree that dose of haloperidol in borderline personality disorder should be lower than dose for psychotic disorders, but I have been accused when using very low doses of haloperidol of using homeopathic doses.	Thank you, but we assume that if the study is more than 5 years old the authors are unlikely to remember the necessary details (and may not have the data since this is the limit of the requirement of most journals regarding retaining data) to answer queries accurately. This is a policy we adopt across all the guidelines we produce.
Ken Silk	6.3.6	For both the haloperidol and the aripiprazole conclusions, you say there is little evidence for its effectiveness in borderline personality disorder. But since borderline personality disorder is a heterogeneous disorder, then one might want to go back and reemphasise that some medications may be helpful with some specific symptoms of borderline	Thank you, this relates to the issues of comorbidity and whether individual symptom dimensions can be treated separately. It is very easy for us to suggest that when drug effects are being shown that this is a consequence of treating a comorbid disorder, but of course we cannot dissect

		personality disorder. It does appear that the antipsychotics, both first- and second-generation, do have some moderate impact on anxiety, depression and hostility and perhaps impulsivity. These in turn may mitigate some of the expression of borderline personality disorder and modify some of the interpersonal chaos these patients tend to find themselves in. But there will NOT be any medication that will treat borderline personality disorder because we do not really know what borderline personality disorder is other than when it meets the DSM criteria set.	drug effects. Looking at the evidence for individual symptoms regardless of diagnosis is very difficult to do systematically; we believe that we have considered all relevant studies of people with a diagnosis of borderline personality disorder. We have made some changes to the overall clinical summary. There is no evidence that drugs alter the fundamental nature of the disorder in either the short or longer term.
Ken Silk	6.3.8	In the Zanarini trial of olanzapine versus the olanzapine-fluoxetine combination, the combination did no better than olanzapine alone. But in this study, if I am correct, there was some effectiveness for olanzapine in terms of rate of improvement.	Thank you. We didn't look at rate of improvement as we did not think it was of any significance. This was only an 8-week trial and early improvement is unlikely to be due to change in personality.
Ken Silk	6.4.2	In discussing TCAs, the note that TCAs are more toxic seems understated. They are significantly more toxic than SSRIs, and	Thank you, we have amended the sentence.

Continued

Peer Reviewer	Section	Comments	Developer's Response
		thus should be used with extreme caution in labile suicidal patients.	
Ken Silk	6.4.3	In discussing antidepressants in borderline personality disorder, it might be useful to have a very brief discussion as to the nature of depression in borderline personality disorder. While people with borderline personality disorder have major depressive episodes, very often what people perceive of as depression in borderline personality disorder is not major depression but dysthymia, loneliness, emptiness. The reader should be cautioned against interpreting these latter affects with true depression and then falling into polypharmacy in trying to beat water out of the non-majorly depressed depressed stone.	Thank you, we will include this in the analysis of the data by outcome later in the chapter (section on depression).
Ken Silk	6.5.2	I might say that there is some intriguing evidence that omega-3 fatty acids may have some impact on depression in borderline personality disorder (the above paragraph by me notwithstanding).	Thank you.

Ken Silk	6.7.6	While a variety of different drugs and drug categories may be somewhat helpful in reducing the depression in borderline personality disorder especially when there is comorbid affective disorder, what stands out is that SSRIs are really not among the group of medications that are somewhat effective. This is an intriguing finding because I think that SSRIs are probably the drugs that are most frequently utilised in an attempt to relieve the depression in borderline personality disorder.	Thank you, this is what we found.
Ken Silk	6.11	I like Table 56 very much but am still sceptical about divalproex and depression.	Thank you, we have amended this table in the light of your comment and also in light of other factors. We are also considering whether it is helpful and may remove it for the final draft of the guideline.
Ken Silk	6.12	Very good.	Thank you.
Ken Silk	6.14	Very important. Patients often wind up on polypharmacy because of repeated crises.	Thank you.

Continued

Peer Reviewer	Section	Comments	Developer's Response
Ken Silk	6.17.1	You make the statement that one should 'discontinue ineffective medication following a reasonable trial'. I might suggest something stronger. If a medication is ineffective after a reasonable period of time, then it should be discontinued before trying a different medication. There is little in the psychiatric literature except for some recent but not very powerful findings from the STAR*D study that augmenting one medication with another results in better clinical outcome. Psychiatric medications are not benign and side effects are not uncommon. Weight gain to a greater or lesser extent is often common save for topiramate and zisprasidone. It is unwise to try augmenting one medication with another if the only definitive result might be weight gain (there is a Zanarini paper on this). Also, we are often dealing with people who have poor self-esteem and a poor body image and to help these people gain weight does not help their overall self-esteem.	Thank you, we have amended the recommendation to include this point.

John Oldham	General		
John Oldham	6.1	Congratulations on an in-depth and highly informative document.	Thank you.
		Is the definition of borderline personality disorder utilised here that of DSM-IV? (This may be defined earlier in the guideline.) A pertinent reference to add is Bender, D. S., Dolan, R. T., Skodol, A. E., *et al.* (2001) Treatment utilization by patients with personality disorders. *American Journal of Psychiatry, 158,* 295–302.	Thank you. Yes, DSM-IV has been used. It is defined in the introduction to the guideline which we did not send you. Thank you for the reference suggestion. The paper does not give specific figures for polypharmacy so we have not included it here.
		Do not agree with statement that the 'main purpose of this classification appears to be to justify pharmacotherapy in the form of . . .'. There are RCTs of different drugs, many of which are itemised later, targeting predominant symptom patterns, reflecting the significant heterogeneity in the DSM polythetic definition of borderline personality disorder.	The justification for this separation is based on a psychobiological theory of personality pathology (Siever & Davis, 1991) that has been used pragmatically in assisting drug treatment but which has no satisfactory evidence base. We have added this to this section. Siever, L. J. & Davis, K. L. (1991) A psychobiological perspective on the personality disorders. *American Journal of Psychiatry, 148,* 1647–1658.

Continued

Peer Reviewer	Section	Comments	Developer's Response
John Oldham	6.1.2	Would change 'not always representative' at end of first paragraph to 'not necessarily prototypical'. Under 'Placebo effect,' what is the basis for the claim that people with borderline personality disorder 'are particularly prone to the placebo effect'? Is there a reference?	On reflection, we agree that the evidence is lacking as to whether people with borderline personality disorder are more susceptible to placebo effects and have amended the wording to reflect this.
John Oldham	6.1.4	Is there a justification cited elsewhere for including unpublished studies?	We try to include as many unpublished studies as we can in order to provide as wide an evidence base as possible. There has been a relatively large number of studies completed, but not yet published, during the development period of the guideline. Since the evidence base is so small we tried to include as many as possible, subject to avoiding prejudicing publication in peer-reviewed journals.
John Oldham	6.1.6	In the first line, 'effect' should be 'affect'	Thank you, we have corrected this.
John Oldham	6.2.1	Is the high co-occurrence referred to in the first sentence established? Reference would be helpful.	Thank you – we have added a reference: Swartz, H. A., Pilkonis, P. A. &

			Frank, E. (2005) Acute treatment outcomes in patients with bipolar I disorder and co-morbid borderline personality disorder receiving medication and psychotherapy. *Bipolar Disorder*, 7, 192–197.*
John Oldham	6.2.2	In the second paragraph, not sure what is meant by the conclusion that the 'theoretical basis for its use in people with borderline personality disorder is weak'.	Thank you, we have deleted this sentence.
John Oldham	6.2.5	Reference is made to the Nickel 2005 study of men with borderline personality disorder. Most borderline personality disorder studies involve predominantly women, and comorbidity patterns and therefore overall clinical patterns are thought to be quite different between males and females with borderline personality disorder. This might be added to the non-generalisable nature of this study.	Thank you.
John Oldham	6.3.5	The last sentence overstates the case, advising against haloperidol 'in the management of BPD', whereas the focus here was on the use of haloperidol as a mood stabiliser.	Thank you, we have amended the sentence.

*This reference was deleted in the final editing of the guideline.

Continued

491

Peer Reviewer	Section	Comments	Developer's Response
John Oldham	6.4.4	Is the last statement under 'Comment' meant to refer to the use of antidepressants as primary therapy for borderline personality disorder versus symptom-targeted adjunctive therapy? Also, many borderline personality disorder patients have comorbid major depressive disorder. Should this be addressed?	Thank you. Yes, we are referring to antidepressants as primary therapy for borderline personality disorder and have amended the paragraph to make our meaning clearer. It has also been amended to consider the issue of comorbid depression, which is an important issue.
John Oldham	6.12.1.1	Again, what about symptom-targeted adjunctive treatment?	We do recommend the use of pharma-cological (and other evidence based) interventions for the treatment of comorbid disorder. We found no evidence to support symptom-targeted adjunctive treatment.
John Oldham	6.14.1	The authors liberally disavow the use of medications based on good careful analysis of the data, then here present recommenda-tions of what staff 'should' do. What is the evidence supporting this advice?	We agree that there is little evidence to support the use of medication in this group, and a little more than that for psychological treatments. However, as a piece of guidance we have to supplement evidence with consensus recommendations where evidence is lacking. We are neverthe-less, cautious in our consensus recom-mendations and follow these with recommendations about minimising harm and reducing drug use.
John Oldham	6.15.2?	Same as above.	As above.

APPENDIX 12:

SEARCH STRATEGIES FOR THE IDENTIFICATION

OF HEALTH ECONOMICS EVIDENCE

Search strategies for the identification of health economics and quality-of-life studies.

1. *Guideline topic search strategies*

A. MEDLINE, EMBASE, PsycINFO, CINAHL – OVID INTERFACE

1. (borderline state or borderline person$).sh.
2. borderline$.mp. and exp personality disorders/
3. (borderline$ adj3 (disorder$ or person$ or PD$1 or state$)).tw. or (borderline$ and personalit$).mp.
4. (borderline$ and cluster b).mp.
5. (emotion$ adj2 (instabil$ or unstable) adj3 (character$ or difficult$ or disorder$ or dysfunction$ or PD or person$1 or personalit$ or state$)).tw.
6. or/1-5
7. (multiple personality disorder$ or personality disorder$).sh.
8. (personalit$ adj (disorder$ or dysfunction$)).tw.
9. (dsm and (axis and II)).mp.
10. or/7-9
11. or/6,10

B. NHS ECONOMIC EVALUATION DATABASE, HEALTH TECHNOLOGY ASSESSMENT DATABASE – WILEY INTERFACE

1. MeSH descriptor Borderline Personality Disorder, this term only
2. (borderline*)
3. MeSH descriptor Personality Disorders explode all trees
4. (#2 AND #3)
5. (borderline* near/3 (disorder* or person* or PD* or state*)) or (borderline* and personalit*)
6. (borderline* and cluster near/1 b)
7. (emotion* near/2 (instabil* or unstable) near/3 (character* or difficult* or disorder* or dysfunction* or PD or person* or state*))
8. (#1 OR #4 OR #5 OR #6 OR #7)
9. MeSH descriptor Multiple Personality Disorder, this term only
10. MeSH descriptor Personality Disorders, this term only
11. (personalit* near/1 (disorder* or dysfunction*))

12. (dsm and (axis and II))
13. (#9 OR #10 OR #11 OR #12)
14. (#8 OR #13)

C. OHE HEED – WILEY INTERFACE

1. ax = borderline*
2. ax = DSM and (Axis and II)
3. ax = emotion* and (instabil* or unstable) and (character* or difficult* or disorder* or dysfunction* or PD or person or persons or personalit* or state*)
4. ax = personalit* and (disorder* or dysfunction*)
5. cs = 1 or 2 or 3 or 4

2. *Health economics and quality-of-life search filters*

A. MEDLINE, EMBASE, PsycINFO, CINAHL – OVID INTERFACE

1. exp "costs and cost analysis"/ or "health care costs"/
2. exp health resource allocation/ or exp health resource utilization/
3. exp economics/ or exp economic aspect/ or exp health economics/
4. exp value of life/
5. (burden adj5 (disease or illness)).tw.
6. (cost or costs or costing or costly or economic$ or or expenditure$ or price or prices or pricing or pharmacoeconomic$).tw.
7. (budget$ or financ$ or fiscal or funds or funding).tw.
8. (resource adj5 (allocation$ or utilit$)).tw.
9. or/1-8
10. (value adj5 money).tw.
11. exp quality of life/
12. (qualit$3 adj5 (life or survival)).tw.
13. (health status or QOL or wellbeing or well being).tw.
14. or/9-13

Details of additional searches undertaken to support the development of this guideline are available on request.

APPENDIX 13:

QUALITY CHECKLIST FOR ECONOMIC STUDIES

Full economic evaluations
Author: **Date:**
Title:

	Study design	Yes	No	NA
1.	The research question is stated	❏	❏	
2.	The viewpoint(s) of the analysis are clearly stated	❏	❏	
3.	The alternatives being compared are relevant	❏	❏	
4.	The rationale for choosing the alternative programmes or interventions compared is stated	❏	❏	
5.	The alternatives being compared are clearly described	❏	❏	
6.	The form of economic evaluation used is justified in relation to the question addressed	❏	❏	
	Data collection			
1.	The source of effectiveness data used is stated	❏	❏	
2.	Details of the design and results of the effectiveness study are given	❏	❏	❏
3.	The primary outcome measure(s) for the economic evaluation are clearly stated	❏	❏	
4.	Methods to value health states and other benefits are stated	❏	❏	
5.	Details of the subjects from whom valuations were obtained are given	❏	❏	
6.	Indirect costs (if included) are reported separately	❏	❏	❏
7.	Quantities of resources are reported separately from their unit costs	❏	❏	
8.	Methods for the estimation of quantities and unit costs are described	❏	❏	
9.	Currency and price data are recorded	❏	❏	

10.	Details of currency of price adjustments for inflation or currency conversion are given	❏	❏	❏
11.	Details of any models used are given	❏	❏	❏
12.	The choice of model used and the key parameters on which it is based are justified	❏	❏	❏
	Analysis and interpretation of results			
1.	Time horizon of costs and benefits is stated	❏	❏	
2.	The discount rate(s) is stated	❏	❏	❏
3.	The choice of rate(s) is justified	❏	❏	❏
4.	An explanation is given if costs or benefits are not discounted	❏	❏	❏
5.	Details of statistical tests and confidence intervals are given for stochastic data	❏	❏	❏
6.	The approach to sensitivity analysis is given	❏	❏	
7.	The choice of variables for sensitivity analysis is given	❏	❏	
8.	The ranges over which the variables are varied are stated	❏	❏	
9.	Relevant alternatives are compared	❏	❏	
10.	Incremental analysis is reported	❏	❏	❏
11.	Major outcomes are presented in a disaggregated as well as aggregated form	❏	❏	
12.	The answer to the study question is given	❏	❏	
13.	Conclusions follow from the data reported	❏	❏	
14.	Conclusions are accompanied by the appropriate caveats	❏	❏	

1.2 Partial economic evaluations
Author: **Date:**
Title:

	Study design	Yes	No	NA
1.	The research question is stated	❑	❑	
2.	The viewpoint(s) of the analysis is clearly stated and justified	❑	❑	
	Data collection			
1.	Details of the subjects from whom valuations were obtained are given	❑	❑	
2.	Indirect costs (if included) are reported separately	❑	❑	❑
3.	Quantities of resources are reported separately from their unit costs	❑	❑	
4.	Methods for the estimation of quantities and unit costs are described	❑	❑	
5.	Currency and price data are recorded	❑	❑	
6.	Details of currency of price adjustments for inflation or currency conversion are given	❑	❑	❑
7.	Details of any model used are given	❑	❑	❑
8.	The choice of model used and the key parameters on which it is based are justified	❑	❑	❑
	Analysis and interpretation of results			
1.	Time horizon of costs is stated	❑	❑	
2.	The discount rate(s) is stated	❑	❑	❑
3.	Details of statistical tests and confidence intervals are given for stochastic data	❑	❑	❑
4.	The choice of variables for sensitivity analysis is given	❑	❑	
5.	The ranges over which the variables are varied are stated	❑	❑	
6.	Appropriate sensitivity analysis is performed	❑	❑	
7.	The answer to the study question is given	❑	❑	
8.	Conclusions follow from the data reported	❑	❑	
9.	Conclusions are accompanied by the appropriate caveats	❑	❑	

APPENDIX 14:
DATA EXTRACTION FORM FOR ECONOMIC STUDIES

Reviewer: **Date of Review:**

Authors:

Publication Date:

Title:

Country:

Language:

Economic study design:

❑ CEA   ❑ CCA

❑ CBA   ❑ CA

❑ CUA   ❑ CMA

Modelling:

❑ No   ❑ Yes

Source of data for effect size measure(s):

❑ RCT   ❑ Meta-analysis

❑ Quasi experimental study   ❑ Expert opinion

❑ Cohort study   ❑ Mirror image (before-after) study

Comments:_____

Primary outcome measure(s) (please list):

_____

Treatment: _____

Comparator: _____

Setting (please describe):

_____

_____

Patient population characteristics (please describe):

_____
_____
_____

Perspective of analysis:

❑ Societal   ❑ Other: _____

❑ Patient and family

❑ Healthcare system

❑ Healthcare provider

❑ Third party payer

Time frame of analysis: _____

Cost data:

❑ Primary   ❑ Secondary

If secondary please specify: _____

Costs included:

Direct medical	Direct non-medical	Lost productivity
❑ direct treatment	❑ social care	❑ income forgone due to illness
❑ inpatient	❑ social benefits	
❑ outpatient	❑ travel costs	❑ income forgone due to death
❑ day care	❑ caregiver out-of-pocket	
❑ community health care	❑ criminal justice	❑ income forgone by caregiver
❑ medication	❑ training of staff	

Or

❑ staff

❑ medication

❑ consumables

❑ overhead

❑ capital equipment

❑ real estate   Others: _____

Currency: _____   **Year of costing:** _____

Was discounting used?

❑ Yes, for benefits and costs ❑ Yes, but only for costs ❑ No

Discount rate used for costs: ⎯⎯⎯⎯⎯⎯⎯⎯⎯⎯⎯⎯⎯⎯⎯

Discount rate used for benefits: ⎯⎯⎯⎯⎯⎯⎯⎯⎯⎯⎯⎯⎯⎯⎯

Result(s):

⎯⎯⎯⎯⎯⎯⎯⎯⎯⎯⎯⎯⎯⎯⎯⎯⎯⎯⎯⎯⎯⎯⎯⎯⎯⎯⎯⎯⎯⎯⎯⎯⎯⎯⎯⎯⎯⎯⎯

⎯⎯⎯⎯⎯⎯⎯⎯⎯⎯⎯⎯⎯⎯⎯⎯⎯⎯⎯⎯⎯⎯⎯⎯⎯⎯⎯⎯⎯⎯⎯⎯⎯⎯⎯⎯⎯⎯⎯

⎯⎯⎯⎯⎯⎯⎯⎯⎯⎯⎯⎯⎯⎯⎯⎯⎯⎯⎯⎯⎯⎯⎯⎯⎯⎯⎯⎯⎯⎯⎯⎯⎯⎯⎯⎯⎯⎯⎯

⎯⎯⎯⎯⎯⎯⎯⎯⎯⎯⎯⎯⎯⎯⎯⎯⎯⎯⎯⎯⎯⎯⎯⎯⎯⎯⎯⎯⎯⎯⎯⎯⎯⎯⎯⎯⎯⎯⎯

Comments, limitations of the study:

⎯⎯⎯⎯⎯⎯⎯⎯⎯⎯⎯⎯⎯⎯⎯⎯⎯⎯⎯⎯⎯⎯⎯⎯⎯⎯⎯⎯⎯⎯⎯⎯⎯⎯⎯⎯⎯⎯⎯

⎯⎯⎯⎯⎯⎯⎯⎯⎯⎯⎯⎯⎯⎯⎯⎯⎯⎯⎯⎯⎯⎯⎯⎯⎯⎯⎯⎯⎯⎯⎯⎯⎯⎯⎯⎯⎯⎯⎯

⎯⎯⎯⎯⎯⎯⎯⎯⎯⎯⎯⎯⎯⎯⎯⎯⎯⎯⎯⎯⎯⎯⎯⎯⎯⎯⎯⎯⎯⎯⎯⎯⎯⎯⎯⎯⎯⎯⎯

Quality checklist score (Yes/NA/All): ...... / ...... / ......

APPENDIX 15:

EVIDENCE TABLES FOR ECONOMIC STUDIES

PSYCHOLOGICAL AND PSYCHOSOCIAL

TREATMENTS IN THE MANAGEMENT OF

BORDERLINE PERSONALITY DISORDER

BRIEF PSYCHOLOGICAL INTERVENTIONS

Please see tables on pages 502–518.

Manual-assisted cognitive therapy (MACT)

Study ID Country Study type	Intervention details	Study population Study design Data sources	Costs: description and values Outcomes: description and values	Results: Cost effectiveness	Comments Quality score (Y/N/NA)
Brazier et al., 2006 (based on TYRER2003) UK Cost-effectivness and cost-utility analysis	Interventions: MACT TAU	People with border-line personality disorder (data from TYRER2003 allowed sub-group analysis on this population) Decision-analytic modelling Source of clinical effectiveness data: RCT (TYRER2003) Source of resource use: RCT (TYRER2003), further assumptions Source of unit costs: national sources	Costs: Healthcare: intervention and staff super-vision costs, inpatient and outpatient care, A&E attendances, day hospital, medication, community services, primary care Social services: day centre, social worker, sheltered workshop, other Criminal justice system, community accommodation Sensitivity analysis for societal perspec-tive: voluntary sector, productivity losses Total cost per person: MACT: £9,580; TAU: £7,563 Measures of outcome: number of para-suicide events, QALYs gained Number of parasuicide events per person: MACT: 4.9 TAU: 1.7 (non-significant difference) Number of QALYs gained per person: MACT: 0.19 TAU: 0.14	For outcome measured as number of parasui-cide events: TAU dominates MACT (TAU more effective and less costly) Probability of TAU being cost effective: 60% at any level of WTP per parasuicide event avoided For outcome measured as QALYs: ICER of MACT versus TAU: £84,032/QALY (MACT more effective and more costly than TAU) Probability of MACT being cost effective: 45% at WTP £20,000 per QALY Results insensitive to adoption of NICE perspective; magnitude of costs in both arms	Perspective: government (NICE and societal in sensitivity analysis) Currency: UK£ Cost year: 2003-2004 Time horizon: 12 months Discounting: not needed EuroQol-5D scores taken directly from the study in order to generate QALYs Quality score: 29/0/6

Byford et al., 2003 (TYRER 2003) UK Cost-effectivness and cost-utility analysis	Interventions: MACT TAU	People with a history of recurrent deliberate self-harm, including people with borderline personality disorder Multicentre RCT (N = 480) Source of clinical effectiveness data: RCT (N = 430) Source of resource use estimates: RCT (N = 397) data based on patient interviews using an adapted version of the Client Service Receipt Inventory (CSRI) Source of unit costs: local data and national sources	Costs: Hospital, community health services, medication, social services, voluntary services, accommodation and living expenses, criminal justice system, productivity losses Total cost per person over 12 months: MACT: £13,450 TAU: £14,288 (non-significant difference) Measures of outcome: proportion of people with a repeat self-harm episode; QALYs Proportion of people with a repeat self-harm episode at 12 months: MACT: 39% TAU: 46% (non-significant difference) Difference in QALYS over 12 months: MACT 0.118 QALYs less than TAU (non-significant difference) [QALYs for each intervention not reported separately]	increased by 75% when adopting a societal perspective For outcome measured as proportion of people with a repeat self-harm: MACT dominant over TAU (MACT more effective and less costly) Probability of MACT being cost-effective: >90% at any level of WTP For outcome measured as QALYs: ICER of TAU versus MACT: £66,000/QALY (MACT less effective and less costly than TAU) Probability of MACT being cost effective: between 44 and 88%; at WTP between 0 and 66,0000/QALY, MACT had higher probability of being cost effective compared with TAU	Perspective: societal Currency: UK£ Cost year: 1999/2000 Time horizon: 12 months Discounting: not needed QALYs generated based on EuroQol-5D scores Quality score: 26/0/9

Individual psychological therapies

Cognitive behavioural therapy (CBT)

Study ID Country Study type	Intervention details	Study population Study design Data sources	Costs: description and values Outcomes: description and values	Results: Cost effectiveness	Comments Quality score (Y/N/NA)
Palmer *et al.*, 2006 (DAVIDSON2006) UK Cost-utility analysis	Interventions: CBT plus treatment as usual (CBT) TAU alone	People with borderline personality disorder Multicentre RCT (N = 106) Source of clinical effectiveness data: RCT (N = 106, ITT analysis) Source of resource use: RCT (N = 106); data derived from hospital records and patient self-reports based on an adapted version of the CSRI Source of unit costs: local data, national sources and patients' reports	Costs: Intervention costs Hospital: inpatient, outpatient, day case, day hospital, A&E Community day services: day care, drop-in centre, sheltered workshop Accommodation Primary and community care: GP, nurses, social worker, occupational therapist, and so on Criminal justice system: arrests, court, prison Patient: travel, childcare, over the counter medication Total cost per person over 2 years: CBT: £12,785 TAU: £18,356 (non-significant difference) Measure of outcome: number of QALYs Number of QALYs over 2 years: CBT: 1.06 TAU: 1.20 (non-significant difference)	ICER of TAU versus CBT: £6,376/QALY (CBT less effective and less costly than TAU) Probability of CBT being cost-effective: 53% at WTP £2,000/QALY; probability falling with increasing levels of WTP	Perspective: NHS, social services, other providers and patients Currency: UK£ Cost year: 2003/2004 Time horizon: 2 years Discounting: 3.5% annually QALYs generated based on EuroQol-5D scores Quality score: 26/0/9

Schema-focused cognitive therapy versus transference-focused psychotherapy

Study ID Country Study type	Intervention details	Study population Study design Data sources	Costs: description and values Outcomes: description and values	Results: Cost effectiveness	Comments Quality score (Y/N/NA)
Van Asselt et al., 2008 (GIESENBLOO2006) The Netherlands Cost-effectiveness and cost-utility analysis	Interventions: Schema-focused cognitive therapy Transference-focused psychotherapy	People with borderline personality disorder Multicentre RCT (N = 86) Source of clinical effectiveness data: RCT (N = 85); Source of resource use: RCT (N = 86); structured interviews with study participants and therapists' records Source of unit costs: national prices and tariffs	Costs Healthcare: intervention, telephone contacts with therapists, other care at treatment centres, other psychological treatment, crisis help, first aid, community care, psychiatric and general hospital, physiotherapy, GP, medication, alternative healers Non-healthcare: paid help, informal care, social services Out-of-pocket expenses, productivity losses Total cost per person over 4 years: Schema-focused cognitive therapy: €37,826 Transference-focused psychotherapy: €46,795 (non-significant difference) Measures of outcome: proportion of people recovered according to the BPDSI version IV; number of QALYs Proportion of people recovered over 4 years: Schema-focused cognitive therapy: 52%	For outcome measured as proportion of people recovered: Schema-focused cognitive therapy dominates transference-focused psychotherapy (schema-focused cognitive therapy more effective and less costly than transference-focused psychotherapy) Probability of schema-focused cognitive therapy being cost effective: over 90% at any level of WTP For outcome measured as QALYs: ICER of transference-focused psychotherapy	Perspective: societal Currency: Euros (€) Cost year: 2000 Time horizon: 4 years Discounting: 4 annually QALYs generated based on EuroQol-5D scores Bootstrap simulations performed to estimate uncertainty around mean costs Quality score: 26/2/7

Continued

Schema-focused cognitive therapy versus transference-focused psychotherapy (*Continued*)

Study ID Country Study type	Intervention details	Study population Study design Data sources	Costs: description and values Outcomes: description and values	Results: Cost effectiveness	Comments Quality score (Y/N/NA)
			Transference-focused psychotherapy: 29% (after regression analysis with treatment group and BPDSI score as covariates: p = 0.035) Number of QALYs over 4 years: Schema-focused cognitive therapy: 2.15 Transference-focused psychotherapy: 2.27 (non-significant difference)	versus schema-focused cognitive therapy: €90,457/QALY (schema-focused cognitive therapy less effective and less costly than transference-focused psychotherapy) Probability of schema-focused cognitive therapy being cost-effective: 84% at WTP €20,000/QALY: probability falling with increasing levels of WTP	

Psychodynamic interpersonal therapy

Study ID Country Study type	Intervention details	Study population Study design Data sources	Costs: description and values Outcomes: description and values	Results: Cost effectiveness	Comments Quality score (Y/N/NA)
Hall *et al.*, 2001 Australia Cost analysis	Intervention: Psychodynamic interpersonal therapy	People with borderline personality disorder Before-after study (N = 30) Source of resource use: before-after study (N = 30); data derived from medical records and interviews with the study participants Source of unit costs: national sources	Costs: Intervention, inpatient care, emergency hospital care, ambulatory care, diagnostic tests, medication Total cost per person: 12 months prior to psychodynamic interpersonal therapy: AUS$25,526 Cost of psychodynamic interpersonal therapy: AUS$4,335 12 months following completion of psychodynamic interpersonal therapy: AUS$2,974 Cost saving per person: AUS$18,217	Non-applicable	Perspective: health service Currency: AUS$ Cost year: 1998 Time horizon: 12 months Discounting: not needed Quality score: 10/3/10

Psychological therapy programmes
Dialectical behaviour therapy (DPT)

Study ID Country Study type	Intervention details	Study population Study design Data sources	Costs: description and values Outcomes: description and values	Results: Cost effectiveness	Comments Quality score (Y/N/NA)
Brazier *et al.*, 2006 (based on TURNER2000) UK Cost-effectiveness and cost-utility analysis	Interventions: DBT Client-centered therapy	People with borderline personality disorder Decision-analytic modelling Source of clinical effectiveness data: RCT (TURNER2000) Source of resource use: RCT (TURNER2000), other published RCT, UK survey of DBT practitioners, further assumptions Source of unit costs: national sources	Costs: Healthcare: intervention and staff supervision costs, inpatient and outpatient care, A&E attendances, day hospital, medication, community services, primary care Social services: day centre, social worker, sheltered workshop, other Criminal justice system, community accommodation Sensitivity analysis for societal perspective: voluntary sector, productivity losses Total cost per person: DBT: £15,743 Client-centered therapy: £20,985 (non-significant difference) Measures of outcome: number of parasuicide events, QALYs gained Number of parasuicide events per person: DBT: 2.92 Client-centered therapy: 12.33 (significant difference)	DBT dominates client-centered therapy (DBT more effective and less costly than client-centered therapy) For outcome measured as reduction in parasuicide events: Probability of DBT being dominant over client-centered therapy: 80%; probability of DBT being cost effective: 85% at WTP £5,000 per parasuicide event avoided For outcome measured as QALYs: Probability of DBT being dominant over client-centered therapy: 85%;	Perspective: government (NICE and societal in sensitivity analysis) Currency: UK£ Cost year: 2003–2004 Time horizon: 12 months Discounting: not needed Regression cost model developed to link length of inpatient stay and parasuicide events with costs BDI scores converted to EuroQol-5D scores in order to generate QALYs Quality score: 29/0/6

			Number of QALYs gained per person: DBT: 0.17 Client-centered therapy: 0.05 (non-significant difference)	probability of DBT being cost effective: 90% at WTP £20,000 per QALY Results insensitive to adoption of NICE perspective; magnitude of costs in both arms increased by 75% when adopting a societal perspective	
Brazier et al., 2006 (based on LINEHAN1991) UK Cost-effectiveness analysis	Interventions: DBT TAU	People with borderline personality disorder Decision-analytic modelling Source of clinical effectiveness data: RCT (LINEHAN1991) Source of resource use: RCT (LINEHAN1991), further assumptions Source of unit costs: national sources	Costs: Healthcare: intervention and staff supervision costs, inpatient and outpatient care, A&E attendances, day hospital, medication, community services, primary care Social services: day centre, social worker, sheltered workshop, other Criminal justice system, community accommodation Sensitivity analysis for societal perspective: voluntary sector, productivity losses Total cost per person: DBT: £15,691 TAU: £16,898 (non-significant difference) Primary outcome: number of parasuicide events Number of parasuicide events per person: DBT: 6.82 TAU: 33.54 (non-significant difference)	DBT dominates TAU (DBT more effective and less costly than TAU) Probability of DBT being dominant over TAU: 53%; probability of DBT being cost effective: 60% at WTP £5,000 per parasuicide event avoided Results insensitive to adoption of NICE perspective; magnitude of costs in both arms increased by 75% when adopting a societal perspective	Perspective: government (NICE and societal in sensitivity analysis) Currency: UK£ Cost year: 2003–2004 Time horizon: 12 months Discounting: not needed Quality score: 27/0/8

Continued

Psychological therapy programmes (*Continued*)

Study ID Country Study type	Intervention details	Study population Study design Data sources	Costs: description and values Outcomes: description and values	Results: Cost effectiveness	Comments Quality score (Y/N/NA)
Brazier *et al.*, 2006 (based on VAN DEN BOSCH2002) UK Cost-effectiveness analysis	Interventions: DBT TAU	People with borderline personality disorder Decision-analytic modelling Source of clinical effectiveness data: RCT (VAN DENBOSCH2002) Source of resource use: RCT (VAN DEN BOSCH2002), other published RCT, UK survey of DBT practitioners, further assumptions Source of unit costs: national sources	Costs: Healthcare: intervention and staff supervision costs, inpatient and outpatient care, A&E attendances, day hospital, medication, community services, primary care Social services: day centre, social worker, sheltered workshop, other Criminal justice system, community accommodation Sensitivity analysis for societal perspective: voluntary sector, productivity losses Total cost per person: DBT: £17,430 TAU: £16,706 (non-significant difference) Primary outcome: number of parasuicide events Number of parasuicide events per person: DBT: 16 TAU: 34.1 (non-significant difference)	ICER of DBT versus TAU: £40 per parasuicide event avoided (DBT more effective and less costly than TAU) Probability of DBT being cost effective: 65% at any level of WTP per parasuicide event avoided Results insensitive to adoption of NICE perspective; DBT dominated TAU when adopting a societal perspective	Perspective: government (NICE and societal in sensitivity analysis) Currency: UK£ Cost year: 2003–2004 Time horizon: 12 months Discounting: not needed Regression cost model developed to link length of inpatient stay and parasuicide events with costs Quality score: 27/0/8

510

Interventions: DBT TAU	People with borderline personality disorder Decision-analytic modelling Source of clinical effectiveness data: RCT (KOONS2001) Source of resource use: RCT (KOONS2001), other published RCT, UK survey of DBT practitioners, further assumptions Source of unit costs: national sources	Costs: Healthcare: intervention and staff supervision costs, inpatient and outpatient care, A&E attendances, day hospital, medication, community services, primary care Social services: day centre, social worker, sheltered workshop, other Criminal justice system, community accommodation Sensitivity analysis for societal perspective: voluntary sector, productivity losses Total cost per person: DBT: £23,439 TAU: £14,815 (significant difference) Primary outcomes: number of parasuicide events, QALYs gained Number of parasuicide events per person: DBT: 4 TAU: 4.2 (non-significant difference) Number of QALYs gained per person: DBT: 0.07 TAU: 0.04 (non-significant difference)	For outcome measured as reduction in para-suicide events: ICER of DBT versus TAU: £43,124 per parasuicide event avoided (DBT more effective and more costly than TAU) Probability of DBT being cost effective: <40% at WTP £5,000 per parasuicide event avoided For outcome measured as QALYs: ICER of DBT versus TAU: £273,801 per QALY (DBT more effective and more costly than TAU) Probability of DBT being cost effective: 5% at WTP £20,000 per QALY Results insensitive to adoption of NICE perspective; magnitude of costs in both arms increased by 75% when adopting a societal perspective	Perspective: government (NICE and societal in sensitivity analysis) Currency: UK£ Cost year: 2003–2004 Time horizon: 12 months Discounting: not needed Regression cost model developed to link parasuicide events with costs BDI scores converted to EuroQol-5D scores in order to generate QALYs Quality score: 29/0/6

Continued

Psychological therapy programmes (*Continued*)

Study ID Country Study type	Intervention details	Study population Study design Data sources	Costs: description and values Outcomes: description and values	Results: Cost effectiveness	Comments Quality score (Y/N/NA)
Brazier *et al.*, 2006 (based on KOONS2001) UK Cost-effectiveness and cost-utility analysis	Interventions: DBT TAU	People with borderline personality disorder Decision-analytic modelling Source of clinical effectiveness data: RCT (KOONS2001) Source of resource use: RCT (KOONS2001), other published RCT, UK survey of DBT practitioners, further assumptions	Costs: Healthcare: intervention and staff supervision costs, inpatient and outpatient care, A&E attendances, day hospital, medication, community services, primary care Social services: day centre, social worker, sheltered workshop, other Criminal justice system, community accommodation Sensitivity analysis for societal perspective: voluntary sector, productivity losses Total cost per person: DBT: £23,439 TAU: £14,815 (significant difference) Primary outcomes: number of parasuicide events, QALYs gained	For outcome measured as reduction in parasuicide events: ICER of DBT versus TAU: £43,124 per parasuicide event avoided (DBT more effective and more costly than TAU) Probability of DBT being cost effective: <40% at WTP £5,000 per parasuicide event avoided For outcome measured as QALYs: ICER of DBT versus TAU:	Perspective: government (NICE and societal in sensitivity analysis) Currency: UK£ Cost year: 2003–2004 Time horizon: 12 months Discounting: not needed Regression cost model developed to link parasuicide events with costs BDI scores converted to EuroQol-5D scores in order to generate QALYs

				Quality score: 29/0/6
	Source of unit costs: national sources	Number of parasuicide events per person: DBT: 4 TAU: 4.2 (non-significant difference) Number of QALYs gained per person: DBT: 0.07 TAU: 0.04 (non-significant difference)	£273,801 per QALY (DBT more effective and more costly than TAU) Probability of DBT being cost effective: 5% at WTP £20,000 per QALY Results insensitive to adoption of NICE perspective; magnitude of costs in both arms increased by 75% when adopting a societal perspective	

Mentalisation-based therapy (MBT) and partial hospitalisation

Study ID Country Study type	Intervention details	Study population Study design Data sources	Costs: description and values Outcomes: description and values	Results: Cost effectiveness	Comments Quality score (Y/N/NA)
Bateman & Fonagy, 2003 (BATEMAN1999) UK Cost-consequence analysis	Interventions: MBT and partial hospitalisation TAU within general psychiatric services	People with borderline personality disorder RCT (N = 44) Source of clinical effectiveness data: N = 38 people from RCT Source of resource use: retrospective collection of resource use data from RCT (N = 41); data taken from case notes and information from service providers Source of unit costs: published local rates	Costs: Psychiatric care: inpatient, outpatient, partial hospitalisation; medication; emergency room visits Costs of community support not included Total estimated annual cost per person – based on data from first 18 months: MBT and partial hospitalisation: $27,303 TAU: $30,976 (non-significant difference) Total estimated annual cost per person – based on data from 18-36 months: MBT and partial hospitalisation: $3,183 TAU: $15,490 (significant difference) Outcomes: number of suicide attempts and acts of self harm; self-reported measures of depression, anxiety, general symptom distress, interpersonal function, social adjustment MBT and partial hospitalisation significantly better than TAU in all outcomes	MBT and partial hospitalisation dominates TAU (MBT and partial hospitalisation more effective and less costly than TAU)	Perspective: NHS Currency: US$ Cost year: not reported Time horizon: 18 and 36 months Discounting: not undertaken Quality score: 19/4/12

514

| Brazier et al., 2006 (based on BATE-MAN1999) UK Cost-effectiveness and cost-utility analysis | Interventions: MBT and partial hospitalisation TAU within general psychiatric services | People with borderline personality disorder Decision-analytic modelling Source of clinical effectiveness data: RCT (BATE-MAN1999) Source of resource use: RCT (BATE-MAN1999), further assumptions | at 18 months; significant superiority of MBT and partial hospitalisation remained at 36 months Costs: Healthcare: intervention and staff supervision costs, inpatient and outpatient care, A&E attendances, day hospital, medication, community services, primary care Social services: day centre, social worker, sheltered workshop, other Criminal justice system, community accommodation Sensitivity analysis for societal perspective: voluntary sector, productivity losses Total cost per person: MBT and partial hospitalisation: £18,174 TAU: £17,743 (non-significant difference) | For outcome measured as reduction in parasuicide events: ICER of MBT and partial hospitalisation versus TAU: £38 per parasuicide event avoided (MBT and partial hospitalisation more effective and less costly than TAU) Probability of MBT and partial hospitalisation being cost effective: 80% at WTP £5,000 per parasuicide event avoided | Perspective: government (NICE and societal in sensitivity analysis) Currency: UK£ Cost year: 2003–2004 Time horizon: 12 months Discounting: not needed BDI scores converted to EuroQol-5D scores in order to generate QALYs Quality score: 29/0/6 |

Continued

515

Mentalisation-based therapy (MBT) and partial hospitalisation (*Continued*)

Study ID Country Study type	Intervention details	Study population Study design Data sources	Costs: description and values Outcomes: description and values	Results: Cost effectiveness	Comments Quality score (Y/N/NA)
		Source of unit costs: national sources	Primary outcomes: number of parasuicide events, QALYs gained Number of parasuicide events per person: MBT and partial hospitalisation: 6.1 TAU: 17.5 (significant difference) Number of QALYs gained per person: MBT and partial hospitalisation: 0.04 TAU: -0.01 (non-significant difference)	For outcome measured as QALYs: ICER of MBT and partial hospitalisation versus TAU: £7,242 per QALY gained Probability of MBT and partial hospitalisation being cost effective: 45% at WTP £20,000 per QALY Results insensitive to adoption of NICE perspective; magnitude of costs in both arms increased by 75% when adopting a societal perspective	

516

Therapeutic communities

Study ID Country Study type	Intervention details	Study population Study design Data sources	Costs: description and values Outcomes: description and values	Results: Cost effectiveness	Comments Quality score (Y/N/NA)
Dolan *et al.*, 1996 UK Cost analysis	Intervention: Therapeutic community (Henderson Hospital)	People with personality disorder Before-after study (N = 24) Source of resource use: before-after study (N = 24); data derived from case notes and questionnaires sent to study participants and their GPs Source of unit costs: local data regarding health-care unit costs; national sources regarding prison unit costs	Costs: Hospital: inpatient care including secure psychiatric bed stays; outpatient assessments and therapy; day hospital Prison Total cost per person: 12 months prior to treatment: £13,966 Treatment period: £25,641 1–12 months after discharge from hospital: £1,308	Non-applicable	Perspective: psychiatric care and prison service Currency: UK£ Cost year: 1992/93 Time horizon: 12 months Discounting: not needed Quality score: 9/4/10

Continued

Therapeutic communities (*Continued*)

Study ID Country Study type	Intervention details	Study population Study design Data sources	Costs: description and values Outcomes: description and values	Results: Cost effectiveness	Comments Quality score (Y/N/NA)
Beecham *et al.*, 2006 (details in Chiesa & Fonagy, 2000) UK Cost-effectiveness analysis	Interventions: Therapeutic community – one-stage programme: 12 months inpatient treatment with no outpatient follow-up in Cassel Hospital Therapeutic community – two-stage programme: 6 months inpatient programme followed by 18 months outpatient psychosocial therapy in Cassel Hospital General psychiatric care	People with personality disorders Prospective cohort study (N = 147) Source of clinical effectiveness data: cohort study (N = 108) Source of resource use: RCT (N = 108); data derived from an adapted version of the CSRI filled in by the study participants Source of unit costs: national sources	Costs: Hospital: inpatient, non-inpatient Mental health care: psychiatrist, psychologist, CPN, private psychotherapist, other counselling services Community-based care: GP, social worker, education classes, employment services, voluntary services Accommodation services Legal services: police, lawyer Total cost per person from initiation of treatment up to 12 months following termination of treatment (endpoint): One-stage programme: £58,241 Two-stage programme: £59,041 General psychiatric care: £29,002 (One-stage programme and two-stage programme significantly less costly than general psychiatric care) Measures of outcome: average change in the GAS, GSI and PST Mean change from baseline to end point: One-stage programme: GAS = 10.44; GSI = 0.40; PST = 9.09 Two-stage programme: GAS = 12.21; GSI = 0.82; PST = 23.45 General psychiatric care: GAS = 5.40; GSI = 0.01; PST = 1.28 (One-stage programme and two-stage programme significantly better than general psychiatric care in all outcomes; two-stage programme significantly better than one-stage programme on the PST and marginally better on GSI	ICER of two-stage programme versus general psychiatric care £3,405 per additional point gained on the GAS, £30,304 per point gained on the GSI and £1,131 per point gained on PST (two-stage programme more effective and more costly than general psychiatric care) One-stage programme dominated by extended dominance; one-stage programme less effective than two-stage programme at a similar cost	Perspective: NHS, social services and criminal justice system Currency: UK£ Cost year: 1998/99 Time horizon: 12 months following termination of treatment Discounting: not undertaken Quality score: 20/4/11

12.   REFERENCES

Abbass, A., Sheldon, A., Gyra, J., *et al.* (2008) Intensive short-term dynamic psychotherapy for DSM-IV personality disorders: a randomized controlled trial. *Journal of Nervous and Mental Disease*, *196*, 211–216.

Aberg, A., Cresswell, T., Lidberg, Y., *et al.* (1995) Two-year outcome of team-based intensive case management for patients with schizophrenia. *Psychiatric Services*, *46*, 1263–1266.

Achenbach, T. M. (1991) *Manual for the Youth Self-Report and 1991 Profile*. Burlington, Vermont: University of Vermont.

Achenbach, T. M. (1997) *Manual for the Young Adult Self-Report and Young Adult Behavior Checklist*. Burlington, Vermont: University of Vermont.

AGREE Collaboration (2003) Development and validation of an international appraisal instrument for assessing the quality of clinical practice guidelines: the AGREE project. *Quality and Safety in Health Care*, *12*, 18–23.

Alden, L. E., Wiggins, J. S. & Pincus, A. L. (1990) Construction of circumplex scales for the Inventory of Interpersonal Problems. *Journal of Personality Assessment*, *55*, 521–536.

Alexander, R. & Cooray, S. (2003) Diagnosis of personality disorders in learning disability. *British Journal of Psychiatry*, *44*, S28–S31.

Alper, G. & Peterson, S. J. (2001) Dialectical behavior therapy for patients with borderline personality disorder. *Journal of Psychosocial Nursing and Mental Health Services*, *39*, 38–45.

Andrea, H., Bales, D. & Smits, M. (2008) Mentalization based treatment in the Netherlands: Preliminary results. Unpublished.

Antikainen, R., Lehtonen, J., Koponen, H., *et al.* (1992) The effect of hospital treatment on depression and anxiety in patients with borderline personality organization. *Nordic Journal of Psychiatry*, *46*, 399–405.

Antikainen, R., Koponen, H., Lehtonen, J., *et al.* (1994) Factors predicting outcome of psychiatric hospital treatment in patients with borderline personality organization. *Nordic Journal of Psychiatry*, *48*, 177–185.

Antikainen, R., Hintikka, J., Lehtonen, J., *et al.* (1995) A prospective three-year follow-up study of borderline personality disorder inpatients. *Acta Psychiatrica Scandinavica*, *92*, 327–335.

APA (1987) *Diagnostic and Statistical Manual of Mental Disorders* (3rd edition, revised) (DSM-III). Washington, DC: APA, 1987.

APA (1994) *Diagnostic and Statistical Manual of Mental Disorders* (4th edn) (DSM-IV). Washington, DC: APA.

APA (2000) *Handbook of Psychiatric Measures*. Washington, DC: APA.

APA (2001) Practice guideline for the treatment of patients with borderline personality disorder. *American Journal of Psychiatry*, *158*, 1–52.

References

Arntz, A., van den Hoorn, M., Cornelis, J., *et al.* (2003) Reliability and validity of the borderline personality disorder severity index. *Journal of Personality Disorders, 17*, 45–59.

Atmaca, M., Kuloglu, M., Tezcan, E., *et al.* (2002) Serum cholesterol and leptin levels in patients with borderline personality disorder. *Neuropsychobiology, 45*, 167–171.

Audini, B., Marks, I. M., Lawrence, R. E., *et al.* (1994) Home-based versus out-patient/in-patient care for people with serious mental illness. Phase II of a controlled study. *British Journal of Psychiatry, 165*, 204–210.

Baldwin, D. S. (2007) Use of licensed medicines for unlicensed applications in psychiatric practice. Royal College of Psychiatrists' Special Interest Group in Psychopharmacology. Available at: http://www.rcpsych.ac.uk

Barber, M., Marzuk, P., Leon, A., *et al.* (1998) Aborted suicide attempts: a new classification of suicidal behavior. *American Journal of Psychiatry, 155*, 385–389.

Barley, W., Buie, S., Peterson, E., *et al.* (1993) Development of an inpatient cognitive-behavioral treatment program for borderline personality disorder. *Journal of Personality Disorders, 7*, 232–240.

Barnes, T. R. E. (1989) A rating scale for drug-induced akathisia. *British Journal of Psychiatry, 154*, 672–676.

Barratt, E. J. (1965) Factor analysis of some psychometric measures of impulsiveness and anxiety. *Psychological Reports, 16*, 547–554.

Bateman, A. & Fonagy, P. (1999) Effectiveness of partial hospitalization in the treatment of borderline personality disorder: a randomized controlled trial. *American Journal of Psychiatry, 156*, 1563–1569.

Bateman, A. & Fonagy, P. (2003) Health service utilization costs for borderline personality disorder patients treated with psychoanalytically oriented partial hospitalization versus general psychiatric care. *American Journal of Psychiatry, 160*, 169–171.

Bateman, A. W. & Tyrer, P. (2004) Services for personality disorder: organisation for inclusion. *Advances in Psychiatric Treatment, 10*, 425–433.

Beck, A. T., Ward, D. M., Mendelson, M., *et al.* (1961) An inventory for measuring depression. *Archives of General Psychiatry, 4*, 561–571

Beck, A. T. (1988) *Beck Hopelessness Scale.* San Antonio, TX: The Psychological Corporation.

Beck, A. T. & Steer, R. A. (1991) *Manual for the Beck Scale for Suicide Ideation.* San Antonio, TX: Psychological Corporation.

Beck, A. T., Epstein, N., Brown, G., *et al.* (1988) An inventory for measuring clinical anxiety: psychometric properties. *Journal of Consulting and Clinical Psychology, 56*, 893–897.

Becker, D. F., Grilo, C. M., Edell, W. S., *et al.* (2002) Diagnostic efficiency of borderline personality disorder criteria in hospitalized adolescents: comparison with hospitalized adults. *American Journal of Psychiatry, 159*, 2042–2047.

Beecham, J., Sleed, M., Knapp, M., *et al.* (2006) The costs and effectiveness of two psychosocial treatment programmes for personality disorder: a controlled study. *European Psychiatry: the Journal of the Association of European Psychiatrists, 21*, 102–109.

Bellino, S., Zizza, M., Di Lorenzo, R., *et al.* (2005) Combined therapy with interpersonal psychotherapy of major depressed patients: comparison between patients with borderline personality disorder and patients with other personality disorders. *Italian Journal of Psychopathology, 11*, 157–164.

Bellino, S., Zizza, M., Rinaldi, C., *et al.* (2006b) Combined treatment of major depression in patients with borderline personality disorder: a comparison with pharmacotherapy. *Canadian Journal of Psychiatry – Revue Canadienne de Psychiatrie, 51*, 453–460.

Bellino, S., Zizza, M., Rinaldi, C., *et al.* (2007) Combined therapy of major depression with concomitant borderline personality disorder: comparison of interpersonal and cognitive psychotherapy. *Canadian Journal of Psychiatry – Revue Canadienne de Psychiatrie, 52*, 718–725.

Bemporad, J., Smith, H., Hanson, G., *et al.* (1982) Borderline syndromes in childhood: criteria for diagnosis. *American Journal of Psychiatry, 139*, 596–602.

Bemporad, J., Smith, H. F. & Hanson, G. (1987) The borderline child. In *Basic Handbook of Child Psychiatry* (ed. J. Noshpitz). New York: Basic Books.

Bender, D. S., Dolan, R. T., Skodol, A. E., *et al.* (2001) Treatment utilization by patients with personality disorders. *American Journal of Psychiatry, 158*, 295–302.

Bender, D. S., Dolan, R. T., Skodol, A. E., *et al.* (2006) Prospective assessment of treatment use by patients with personality disorders. *Psychiatric Services, 57*, 254–257.

Bender, D. S., Skodol, A. E., Dyck, I. R., *et al.* (2007) Ethnicity and mental health treatment utilization by patients with personality disorders. *Journal of Consulting and Clinical Psychology, 75*, 992–999.

Berk, M. S., Jeglic, E., Brown, G. K., *et al.* (2007) Characteristics of recent suicide attempters with and without borderline personality disorder. *Archives of Suicide Research, 11*, 91–104.

Berkowitz, C. B. & Gunderson, J. G. (2002) Multifamily psychoeducational treatment of borderline personality disorder. In *Multifamily Groups in the Treatment of Severe Psychiatric Disorders* (eds W. R. McFarlane), pp. 268–290. New York: Guilford.

Berlin, J. A. (1997) Does blinding of readers affect the results of meta-analyses? *Lancet, 350*, 185–186.

Bernstein, E. M. & Putnam, F. W. (1986) Development, reliability, and validity of a dissociation scale. *Journal of Nervous and Mental Disease, 174*, 727–735.

Bernstein, E. M. & Putnam, F. W. (1993) An update on the Dissociative Experiences Scale. *Dissociation, 6*, 16–27.

Bernstein, D. P., Cohen, P., Velez, C. N., *et al.* (1993) Prevalence and stability of the DSM III-R personality disorders in a community-based survey of adolescents. *American Journal of Psychiatry, 150*, 1237–1243.

Bieling, P. J., Antony, M. M. & Swinson, R. P. (1998) The State-Trait Anxiety Inventory, Trait version: structure and content re-examined. *Behaviour Research and Therapy, 36*, 777–788.

Binks, C. A., Fenton, M., McCarthy, L., *et al.* (2006a) Pharmacological interventions for people with borderline personality disorder. *Cochrane Database Systematic Review*, CD005653.

References

Binks, C. A., Fenton, M., McCarthy, L., *et al.* (2006b) Psychological therapies for people with borderline personality disorder. *Cochrane Database Systematic Review*, CD005652.

Black, D. W., Blum, N., Letuchy, E., *et al.* (2006) Borderline personality disorder and traits in veterans: psychiatric comorbidity, healthcare utilization, and quality of life along a continuum of severity. *CNS Spectrums: The International Journal of Neuropsychiatric Medicine*, *11*, 680–689.

Blum, N., Pfohl, B., St John, D., *et al.* (2002) STEPPS: a cognitive-behavioral systems-based group treatment for outpatients with borderline personality disorder. A preliminary report. *Comprehensive Psychiatry*, *43*, 301–310.

Blum, N., St John, D., Pfohl, B., *et al.* (2008) Systems Training for Emotional Predictability and Problem Solving (STEPPS) for outpatients with borderline personality disorder: a randomized controlled trial and 1-year follow-up. *American Journal of Psychiatry*, *165*, 468–478.

Bogenschutz, M. P. & George, N. (2004) Olanzapine versus placebo in the treatment of borderline personality disorder. *Journal of Clinical Psychiatry*, *65*, 104–109.

Bohus, M. (2007) Health care utilisation of patients with borderline personality disorders in Germany. *Personlichkeitsstorungen Theorie und Therapie*, *11*, 149–153.

Bohus, M., Haaf, B., Simms, T., *et al.* (2004) Effectiveness of inpatient dialectical behavioral therapy for borderline personality disorder: a controlled trial. *Behaviour Research and Therapy*, *42*, 487–499.

Bond, G. R., Miller, L. D., Krumwied, R. D., *et al.* (1988) Assertive case management in three CMHCs: a controlled study. *Hospital Community Psychiatry*, *39*, 411–418.

Bond, G. R., Witheridge, T. F., Dincin, J., *et al.* (1990) Assertive community treatment for frequent users of psychiatric hospitals in a large city: a controlled study. *American Journal of Community Psychology*, *18*, 865–891.

Bradley, R., Conklin, C. & Westen, D. (2005a) The borderline personality diagnosis in adolescents: gender differences and subtypes. *Journal of Child Psychology and Psychiatry*, *46*, 1006–1019.

Bradley, R., Jenei, J. & Westen, D. (2005b) Etiology of borderline personality disorder: disentangling the contributions of intercorrelated antecedents. *Journal of Nervous and Mental Disease*, *193*, 24–31.

Brazier, J., Tumur, I., Holmes, M., *et al.* (2006) Psychological therapies including dialectical behaviour therapy for borderline personality disorder: a systematic review and preliminary economic evaluation. *Health Technology Assessment*, *10*, iii, ix–iii, 117.

Brent, D. A., Johnson, B., Bartle, S., *et al.* (1993) Personality disorder, tendency to impulsive violence, and suicidal behavior in adolescents. *Journal of the American Academy of Child and Adolescent Psychiatry*, *32*, 69–75.

Brodsky, B. S., Malone, K. M., Ellis, S. P., *et al.* (1997) Characteristics of borderline personality disorder associated with suicidal behavior. *American Journal of Psychiatry*, *154*, 1715–1719.

Brown, G. K., Newman, C. F., Charlesworth, S. E., *et al.* (2004) An open clinical trial of cognitive therapy for borderline personality disorder. *Journal of Personality Disorders*, *18*, 257–271.

Brown, G. K., Ten Have, T., Henriques, G. R., *et al.* (2005) Cognitive therapy for the prevention of suicide attempts: a randomized controlled trial. *Journal of the American Medical Association*, *294*, 563–570.

Bruscia, K. E. (1998) *Defining Music Therapy*. Gilsum: Barcelona Publishers.

Buckley, N. A. & McManus, P. R. (2002) Fatal toxicity of serotoninergic and other antidepressant drugs: analysis of United Kingdom mortality data. *British Medical Journal*, *325*, 1332–1333.

Bush, C. T., Langford, M. W., Rosen, P., *et al.* (1990) Operation outreach: intensive case management for severely psychiatrically disabled adults. *Hospital Community Psychiatry*, *41*, 647–649.

Buss, A. H. & Durkee, A. (1957) An inventory for assessing different kinds of hostility. *Journal of Consulting Psychology*, *21*, 343–349.

Buss, A. H. & Perry, M. (1992) The Aggression Questionnaire. *Journal of Personality and Social Psychology*, *63*, 452–459.

Byford, S., Knapp, M., Greenshields, J., *et al.* (2003) Cost-effectiveness of brief cognitive behaviour therapy versus treatment as usual in recurrent deliberate self-harm: a decision-making approach. *Psychological Medicine*, *33*, 977–986.

Calabrese, J. R., Bowden, C. L., Sachs, G. S., *et al.* (1999) A double-blind, placebo-controlled study of lamotrigine monotherapy in outpatients with bipolar 1 depression. Lamictal 602 study group. *Journal of Clinical Psychiatry*, *60*, 79–88.

Campbell, M., Fitzpatrick, R., Haines, A., *et al.* (2000) Framework for design and evaluation of complex interventions to improve health. *British Medical Journal*, *321*, 694–696.

Carter, G. (2008) *Hunter Dialectical Behaviour Therapy Project*. Unpublished report.

Caspi, A., McClay, J., Moffitt, T. E., *et al.* (2002) Role of genotype in the cycle of violence in maltreated children. *Science*, *297*, 851–854.

Caspi, A., Sugden, K., Moffitt, T. E., *et al.* (2003) Influence of life stress on depression: moderation by a polymorphism in the 5-HTT gene. *Science*, *301*, 386–389.

Chabrol, H., Montovany, A., Chouicha, K. (2001) Frequency of borderline personality disorder in a sample of French high school students. *Canadian Journal of Psychiatry*, *46*, 847–849.

Chance, S., Bakeman, R., Kaslow, N., *et al.* (2000) Core conflictual relationship themes in patients diagnosed with borderline personality disorder who attempted, or who did not attempt, suicide. *Psychotherapy Research*, *10*, 337–355.

Chandler, D., Hargreaves, W., Spicer, G., *et al.* (1997) Cost-effectiveness of a capitated assertive community treatment program. *Psychiatric Rehabilitation Journal*, *22*, 327–336.

Chanen, A. M., Jackson, H. J., McGorry, P. D., *et al.* (2004) Two-year stability of personality disorder in older adolescent outpatients. *Journal of Personality Disorders*, *18*, 526–541.

Chanen, A. M., Jovev, M. & Jackson, H. J. (2007a) Adaptive functioning and psychiatric symptoms in adolescents with borderline personality disorder. *Journal of Clinical Psychiatry*, *68*, 297–306.

Chanen, A. M., McCutcheon, L. K., Jovev, M., *et al.* (2007b) Prevention and early intervention for borderline personality disorder. *Medical Journal of Australia*, *187*, S18–S21.

Chanen[21], A. M., Jackson, H. J., McCutcheon, L. K., *et al.* (2008a) Early intervention for adolescents with borderline personality disorder using cognitive analytic therapy: randomised controlled trial. *The British Journal of Psychiatry*, *193*, 477–484.

Chanen, A. M., Jovev, M., Djaja, D., *et al.* (2008b) Screening for borderline personality disorder in outpatient youth. *Journal of Personality Disorders*, *22*, 353–364.

Chanen, A. M., Jovev, M., McCutcheon, L. K., *et al.* (2008c) Borderline personality disorder in young people and the prospects for prevention and early intervention. *Current Psychiatry Reviews*, *4*, 48–57.

Chen, C. K., Shiah I., Yeh, C. B., *et al.* (2005) Combination treatment of clozapine and topiramate in resistant rapid-cycling bipolar disorder. *Clinical Neuropharmacology*, *28*, 136–138.

Cheng, A. T., Mann, A. H. & Chan, K. A. (1997) Personality disorder and suicide: a case-control study. *British Journal of Psychiatry*, *170*, 441–446.

Chiesa, M. (1989) Different origins and meanings of acute acting-out in an inpatient psychotherapeutic setting. *Psychoanalytic Psychotherapy*, *4*, 155–168.

Chiesa, M. & Fonagy, P. (2000) Cassel Personality Disorder Study: methodology and treatment effects. *British Journal of Psychiatry*, *176*, 485–491.

Chiesa, M. & Fonagy, P. (2007) Prediction of medium-term outcome in cluster B personality disorder following residential and outpatient psychosocial treatment. *Psychotherapy and Psychosomatics*, *76*, 347–353.

Chiesa, M., Fonagy, P., Holmes, J., *et al.* (2002) Health service use costs by personality disorder following specialist and nonspecialist treatment: a comparative study. *Journal of Personality Disorders*, *16*, 160–173.

Chiesa, M., Fonagy, P., Holmes, J., *et al.* (2004a) Residential versus community treatment of personality disorders: a comparative study of three treatment programs. *American Journal of Psychiatry*, *161*, 1463–1470.

Chiesa, M., Wright, M. & Leger, D. (2004b) Psychotropic medication and the therapeutic community: a survey of prescribing practices for severe personality disorder. *Therapeutic Communities: International Journal for Therapeutic and Supportive Organisations*, *25*, 131–144.

Chiesa, M., Fonagy, P. & Holmes, J. (2006) Six-year follow-up of three treatment programs to personality disorder. *Journal of Personality Disorders*, *20*, 493–509.

Clarkin, J. F. & Levy, K. N., (2006) Psychotherapy for patients with borderline personality disorder: focusing on the mechanisms of change. *Journal of Clinical Psychology*, *62*, 405–410.

---

[21]This is the reference for study ID CHANEN2008.

Clarkin, J. F., Foelsch, P. A., Levy, K. N., *et al.* (2001) The development of a psychodynamic treatment for patients with borderline personality disorder: a preliminary study of behavioral change. *Journal of Personality Disorders*, *15*, 487–495.

Clarkin, J. F., Levy, K. N., Lenzenweger, M. F., *et al.* (2004) The Personality Disorders Institute/Borderline Personality Disorder Research Foundation randomized control trial for borderline personality disorder: rationale, methods, and patient characteristics. *Journal of Personality Disorders*, *18*, 52–72.

Clarkin, J. F., Yeomans, F. E. & Kernberg, O. F. (2006) *Psychotherapy for Borderline Personality: Focusing on Object Relations*. Washington, D.C.: American Psychiatric Press.

Clarkin, J. F., Levy, K. N., Lenzenweger, M. F., *et al.*, (2007) Evaluating three treatments for borderline personality disorder: a multiwave study. *American Journal of Psychiatry*, *164*, 922–928.

Coccaro, E. F., Harvey, P. D., Kupsaw-Lawrence, E., *et al.* (1991) Development of neuropharmacologically based behavioral assessments of impulsive aggressive behavior. *Journal of Neuropsychiatry and Clinical Neurosciences*, *3*, S44–S51.

Coccaro, E. F., Kavoussi, R. J., Hauger, R. L., *et al.* (1998) Cerebrospinal fluid vasopressin levels: correlates with aggression and serotonin function in personality-disordered subjects. *Archives of General Psychiatry*, *55*, 708–714.

Coccaro, E. F., Lee, R. & McCloskey, M. (2003) Norepinephrine function in personality disorder: plasma free MHPG correlates inversely with life history of aggression. *CNS Spectrums: The International Journal of Neuropsychiatric Medicine*, *8*, 731–736.

Cochrane Collaboration (2005) Review Manager (RevMan). Version 4.2.8 for Windows. Oxford: The Cochrane Collaboration. [Computer programme]

Cohen, P., Crawford, T. N., Johnson, J. G., *et al.* (2005) The children in the community study of developmental course of personality disorder. *Journal of Personality Disorders*, *19*, 466–486.

Cohen, P., Chen, H., Crawford, T., *et al.* (2007) Personality disorders in early adolescence and the development of later substance use disorders in the general population. *Drug and Alcohol Dependence*, *88*, S71–S84.

Coid, J., Yang, M., Tyrer, P., *et al.* (2006) Prevalence and correlates of personality disorder in Great Britain. *British Journal of Psychiatry*, *188*, 423–431.

Comtois, K. A. & Linehan, M. (1999) Lifetime parasuicide count: description and psychometrics. Paper presented at the American Association of Suicidology Annual Conference, Houston, Texas.

Cooper, P., Osborn, M., Gath, D., *et al.* (1982) Evaluation of a modified self-report measure of social adjustment. *British Journal of Psychiatry*, *141*, 68–75.

Copas, J., O'Brien, M., Roberts, J., *et al.* (1984) Treatment outcome in personality disorder: the effect of social, psychological and behavioural variables. *Personality and Individual Differences*, *5*, 565–573.

Corbitt, E. M., Malone, K. M., Haas, G. L., *et al.* (1996) Suicidal behavior in patients with major depression and comorbid personality disorders. *Journal of Affective Disorders*, *39*, 61–72.

Cottraux, J., Note, I. D., Boutitie, F., *et al.* (2008) Cognitive therapy versus rogerian supportive therapy in borderline personality disorder: a two-year follow-up of a controlled study. Unpublished.

Cowdry, R. W. & Gardner, D. L. (1988) Pharmacotherapy of borderline personality disorder. Alprazolam, carbamazepine, trifluoperazine, and tranylcypromine. *Archives of General Psychiatry, 45,* 111–119.

Crawford, M., Rutter, D., Price, K., *et al.* (2007) *Learning the Lessons: a Multi-Method Evaluation of Dedicated Community-Based Services For People With Personality Disorder.* London: National Co-ordinating Centre for NHS Service Delivery and Organisation.

Crawford, T. N., Price, K., Rutter, D., *et al.* (2008) Dedicated community-based services for adults with personality disorder: Delphi study. *The British Journal of Psychiatry, 193,* 342–343.

Creed, F., Black, D., Anthony, P., *et al.* (1990) Randomised controlled trial of day patient versus inpatient psychiatric treatment. *British Medical Journal, 300,* 1033–1037.

Creed, F., Mbaya, P., Lancashire, S., *et al.* (1997) Cost effectiveness of day and inpatient psychiatric treatment: results of a randomised controlled trial. *British Medical Journal, 314,* 1381–1385.

Crumley, F. E. (1981) Adolescent suicide attempts and borderline personality disorder: clinical features. *Southern Medical Journal, 74,* 546–549.

Cunningham, K., Wolbert, R. & Lillie, B. (2004) It's about me solving my problems: clients' assessments of dialectical behavior therapy. *Cognitive and Behavioral Practice, 11,* 248–256.

Curtis, L. & Netten, A. (2003) *Unit Costs of Health and Social Care.* Canterbury: PRSSU, University of Kent.

Daley, S. E., Hammen, C., Burge, D., *et al.* (1999) Depression and axis II symptomatology in an adolescent community sample: concurrent and longitudinal associations. *Journal of Personality Disorders, 13,* 47–59.

Davidson, K. M. (2000) *Cognitive Therapy for Personality Disorders: a Guide for Therapists.* Oxford: Butterworth-Heinemann.

Davidson, K. M. (2008) *Cognitive Therapy for Personality Disorders: a Guide for Clinicians.* (2nd edn). London: Routledge.

Davidson, K., Norrie, J., Tyrer, P., *et al.* (2006) The effectiveness of cognitive behavior therapy for borderline personality disorder: results from the borderline personality disorder study of cognitive therapy (BOSCOT) trial. *Journal of Personality Disorders, 20,* 450–465.

Davidson, K., Tyrer, P., Gumley, A., *et al.* (2006a) A randomized controlled trial of cognitive behavior therapy for borderline personality disorder: rationale for trial, method, and description of sample. *Journal of Personality Disorders, 20,* 431–449.

Davies, S. & Campling, P. (2003) Therapeutic community treatment of personality disorder: service use and mortality over 3 years' follow-up. *British Journal of Psychiatry – Supplementum, 44,* S24–S27.

Davies, S., Campling, P. & Ryan, K. (1999) Therapeutic community provision at regional and district levels. *Psychiatric Bulletin, 23,* 79–83.

Davison, G. C. (2000) Stepped care: doing more with less? *Journal of Consulting and Clinical Psychology*, *68*, 580–585.

De Cangas, J. P. C. (1994) 'Case management' affirmatif: une evaluation complete d'un programme du genre en milieu hospitalier. *Sante mentale au Quebec*, *19*, 75–92.

De la Fuente, J. M. & Lotstra, F. (1994) A trial of carbamazepine in borderline personality disorder. *European Neuropsychopharmacology*, *4*, 479–86.

De la Fuente, J. M., Goldman, S., Stanus, E., *et al.* (1997) Brain glucose metabolism in borderline personality disorder. *Journal of Psychiatric Research*, *31*, 531–541.

Deeks, J. J. (2002) Issues in the selection of a summary statistic for meta-analysis of clinical trials with binary outcomes. *Statistics in Medicine*, *21*, 1575–1600.

Dekker, J., Wijdenes, W., Koning, Y. A., *et al.* (2002) Assertive community treatment in Amsterdam. *Community Mental Health Journal*, *38*, 425–434.

Department of Health (1983) *The Mental Health Act: England and Wales*. London: Department of Health.

Department of Health (1998) *Modernising Social Services: Promoting Independence, Improving Protection, Raising Standards*. London: Department of Health.

Department of Health (1999a) *Modern Standards and Service Models: National Service Framework for Mental Health*. London: Department of Health.

Department of Health (1999b) *The Future Organisation of Prison Health Care. Prison Service and NHS Executive Working Group*. London: Department of Health.

Department of Health (2003) *Personality Disorder. No Longer a Diagnosis Of Exclusion. Policy Implementation Guidance for the Development Of Services For People With Personality Disorder*. London: Department of Health.

Department of Health (2004) *Child and Adolescent Mental Health – National Service Framework for Children, Young People and Maternity Services*. London: Department of Health.

Department of Health (2006) *Personality Disorder Capacity Plans 2005*. London: Department of Health.

Derogatis, L. R. (1993) *Brief Symptom Inventory (BSI): Administration, Scoring and Procedures Manual* (4th edn) Minneapolis, Minnesota: NCS Pearson Incorporation.

Derogatis, L. R. (1994) *Brief Symptom Inventory, and matching clinical rating scales*. In *Psychological Testing, Treatment Planning, and Outcome Assessment* (ed. M. Maruish). New York: Erlbaum.

Derogatis, L. R., Lipman, R. S., Rickels, K., *et al.* (1974) The Hopkins Symptom Checklist (HSCL): a self-report symptom inventory. *Behavioural Science*, *19*, 1–15.

DerSimonian, R. & Laird, N. (1986) Meta-analysis in clinical trials. *Controlled Clinical Trials*, *7*, 177–188.

Dick, P., Ince, A. & Barlow, M. (1985) Day treatment: suitability and referral procedure. *British Journal of Psychiatry*, *147*, 250–253.

Dixon, L., McFarlane, W. R., Lefley, H., *et al.* (2001) Evidence-based practices for services to families of people with psychiatric disabilities. *Psychiatric Services*, *52*, 903–910.

Dolan, B. (1991) *Gender Issues in Impulsive Behaviour.* Paper presented at Perspectives on Women and Violence, London.

Dolan, B. M., Evans, C. & Wilson, J. (1992) Therapeutic community treatment for personality disordered adults: changes in neurotic symptomatology on follow-up. *International Journal of Social Psychiatry, 38,* 243–250.

Dolan, B. M., Warren, F. M., Menzies, D., *et al.* (1996) Cost-offset following specialist treatment of severe personality disorders. *Psychiatric Bulletin, 40,* 413–417.

Dolan, B., Warren, F. & Norton, K. (1997) Change in borderline symptoms one year after therapeutic community treatment for severe personality disorder. *British Journal of Psychiatry, 171,* 274–279.

Donegan, N. H., Sanislow, C. A., Blumberg, H. P., *et al.* (2003) Amygdala hyperreactivity in borderline personality disorder: implications for emotional dysregulation. *Biological Psychiatry, 54,* 1284–1293.

Drake, R. E., McHugo, G. J., Clark, R. E., *et al.* (1998) Assertive community treatment for patients with co-occurring severe mental illness and substance use disorder: a clinical trial. *American Journal of Orthopsychiatry, 68,* 201–215.

Drummond, M. F. & Jefferson, T. O. (1996) Guidelines for authors and peer reviewers of economic submissions to the BMJ. The BMJ Economic Evaluation Working Party. *British Medical Journal, 313,* 275–283.

Dursan, S. M. & Devarajan, S. (2000) Clozapine weight gain, plus topiramate weight loss. *European Neuropsychopharmacology, 4,* 479–486.

D'Zurilla, T. J. & Goldfried, M. R. (1971) Problem solving and behavior modification. *Journal Abnormal Psychology, 78,* 107–126.

Eccles, M., Freemantle, N. & Mason, J. (1998) North of England evidence based guideline development project: methods of developing guidelines for efficient drug use in primary care. *British Medical Journal, 316,* 1232–1235.

Eli Lilly. *Efficacy and Safety of Olanzapine in Patients with Borderline Personality Disorder: a Randomized Double-Blind Comparison with Placebo,* #6253. Unpublished.

Endicott, J., Spitzer, R. L., Fleiss, J. L., *et al.* (1976) The Global Assessment Scale: a procedure for measuring overall severity of psychiatric disturbance. *Archives of General Psychiatry, 33,* 766–771.

Eren, N., Ozdemir, O., Ogunc, N., *et al.* (2000) Borderline hastalarla yapılan dinamik yönelimli sanat psikoterapi grubunda sürecin değerlendirilmesi. [Evaluation of the dynamic oriented art psychotherapy group process in borderline patients.] *Psikiyatri Psikoloji Psikofarmakoloji Dergisi, 8,* 285–294.

Essock, S. M. & Kontos, N. (1995) Implementing assertive community treatment teams. *Psychiatric Services, 46,* 679–683.

Euro-Qol Group (1990) Euro-Qol: a new facility for the measurement of health-related quality of life. *Health Policy, 16,* 199–208.

Evans, K., Tyrer, P., Catalan, J., *et al.* (1999) Manual-assisted cognitive-behaviour therapy (MACT): a randomized controlled trial of a brief intervention with bibliotherapy in the treatment of recurrent deliberate self-harm. *Psychological Medicine, 29,* 19–25.

Fagin, L. (2004) Management of personality disorders in acute in-patient settings. Part 1: borderline personality disorders. *Advances in Psychiatric Treatment, 10*, 93–99.

Fava, M. (2006) Prospective studies of adverse events related to antidepressant discontinuation. *Journal of Clinical Psychiatry, 67, Suppl. 4*, 14–21.

Feigenbaum, J. D., Fonagy, P., Pilling, S., *et al.* (2008) A pilot randomised control trial of the effectiveness of dialectical behavioural therapy (DBT) for Cluster B personality disorder. Unpublished.

Fekete, D. M., Bond, G. R., McDonel, E. C., *et al.* (1998) Rural assertive community treatment: a field experiment. *Psychiatric Rehabilitation Journal, 21*, 371–379.

Fenton, F. R., Tessier, L. & Struening, E. L. (1979) A comparative trial of home and hospital psychiatric care. One-year follow-up. *Archives of General Psychiatry, 36*, 1073–1079.

Fenton, W. S., Mosher, L. R., Herrell, J.M., *et al.* (1998) Randomized trial of general hospital and residential alternative care for patients with severe and persistent mental illness. *American Journal of Psychiatry, 155*, 516–522.

Fenton, W. S., Hibbeln, J. & Knable, M. (2000) Essential fatty acids, lipid membrane abnormalities, and the diagnosis and treatment of schizophrenia. *Biological Psychiatry, 47*, 8–21.

Fenton, W. S., Dickerson, F., Boronow, J., *et al.* (2001) A placebo-controlled trial of omega-3 fatty acid (ethyl-eicosapentaenoic acid) supplementation for residual symptoms and cognitive impairment in schizophrenia. *American Journal of Psychiatry, 158*, 2071–2074.

First, M. B., Gibbon, M., Spitzer, R. L., *et al.* (1997) *The Structured Clinical Interview for DSM-IV Axis II Personality Disorders (SCID-II)*. Washington, DC: American Psychiatric Press.

Fischer, M., Barkley, R. A., Smallish, L., *et al.* (2002) Young adult follow-up of hyperactive children: self-reported psychiatric disorders, comorbidity, and the role of childhood conduct problems and teen CD. *Journal of Abnormal Child Psychology, 30*, 463–475.

Floru, L., Heinrich, K. & Wittek, F. (1975) The problem of post-psychotic schizophrenic depressions and their pharmacological induction. *International Pharmacopsychiatry, 10*, 230–239.

Flynn, A., Matthews, H. & Hollins, S. (2002) Validity of the diagnosis of personality disorder in adults with learning disability and severe behavioural problems. Preliminary study. *British Journal of Psychiatry, 180*, 543–546.

Fonagy, P. & Bateman, A. (2007) Mentalizing and borderline personality disorder. *Journal of Mental Health, 16*, 83–101.

Fonagy, P., Target, M., Gergely, G., *et al.* (2003) The developmental roots of borderline personality disorder in early attachment relationships: a theory and some evidence. *Psychoanalytic Inquiry, 23*, 412–459.

Frankenburg, F. R. & Zanarini, M. C. (2002) Divalproex sodium treatment of women with borderline personality disorder and bipolar II disorder: a double-blind placebo-controlled pilot study. *Journal of Clinical Psychiatry, 63*, 442–446.

Freeman, M. P. (2000) Omega-3 fatty acids in psychiatry: a review. *Annals of Clinical Psychiatry, 12*, 159–165.

Freeman, M. P., Hibbeln, J. R., Wisner, K. L., *et al.* (2006) Omega-3 fatty acids: evidence basis for treatment and future research in psychiatry. *Journal of Clinical Psychiatry, 67*, 1954–1967.

Friedman, R. A. & Leon, A. C. (2007) Expanding the black box – depression, antidepressants, and the risk of suicide. *New England Journal of Medicine, 356*, 2343–2346.

Friedman, R. C. & Corn, R. (1987) Suicide and the borderline depressed adolescent and young adult. *Journal of the American Academy of Psychoanalysis, 15*, 429–448.

Fruzzetti, A. E., Shenk, C., Lowry, K., *et al.* (2003) Emotion regulation. In *Cognitive Behaviour Therapy: Applying Empirically Supported Techniques In Your Practice* (eds W. T. O'Donohue, J. E. Fisher & S. C. Hayes). New York: Wiley.

Fruzzetti, A. E., Shenk, C. & Hoffman, P. D. (2005) Family interaction and the development of borderline personality disorder: a transactional model. *Development and Psychopathology, 17*, 1007–1030.

Furukawa, T. A., Barbui, C. & Cipriani, A., *et al.* (2006) Imputing missing standard deviations in meta-analyses can provide accurate results. *Journal of Clinical Epidemiology, 59*, 7–10.

Fyer, M. R., Frances, A. J., Sullivan, T., *et al.* (1988a) Comorbidity of borderline personality disorder. *Archives of General Psychiatry, 45*, 348–352.

Fyer, M. R., Frances, A. J., Sullivan, T., *et al.* (1988b) Suicide attempts in patients with borderline personality disorder. *American Journal of Psychiatry, 145*, 737–739.

Gabbard, G. O., Coyne, L., Allen, J. G., *et al.* (2000) Evaluation of intensive inpatient treatment of patients with severe personality disorders. *Psychiatric Services, 51*, 893–898.

Garland, M. R., & Hallahan, B. (2006) Essential fatty acids and their role in conditions characterised by impulsivity. *International Review of Psychiatry, 18*, 99–105.

Garnet, K. E., Levy, K. N., Mattanah, J. J., *et al.* (1994) Borderline personality disorder in adolescents: ubiquitous or specific? *American Journal of Psychiatry, 151*, 1380–1382.

George, A. & Soloff, P. H. (1986) Schizotypal symptoms in patients with borderline personality disorder. *American Journal of Psychiatry, 143*, 212–215.

Geraghty, R. & Warren, F. (2003) Ethnic diversity and equality of access to specialist therapeutic community treatment for severe personality disorder. *Psychiatric Bulletin, 27*, 453–456.

Giesen-Bloo, J., van Dyck, R., Spinhoven, P., *et al.* (2006) Outpatient psychotherapy for borderline personality disorder: randomized trial of schema-focused therapy vs transference-focused psychotherapy. *Archives of General Psychiatry, 63*, 649–658.

Gilroy, A. (2006) *Art Therapy, Research and Evidence Based Practice*. London: Sage Publications.

Glick, I. D., Fleming, L., DeChillo, N., *et al.* (1986) A controlled study of transitional day care for non-chronically-ill patients. *American Journal of Psychiatry, 143*, 1551–1556.

Goldberg, S. C., Schulz, S. C., Schulz, P. M., *et al.* (1986) Borderline and schizotypal personality disorders treated with low-dose thiothixene vs placebo. *Archives of General Psychiatry, 43*, 680–686.

Goldman, H. H., Skodol, A. E. & Lave, T. R. (1992) Revising axis V for DSM-IV: a review of measures of social functioning. *American Journal of Psychiatry, 149*, 1148–1156.

Gottschalk, G. & Boekholt, C. (2004) Body-therapeutic work with borderline patients. *PTT: Personlichkeitsstorungen Theorie und Therapie, 8*, 154–160.

GRADE Working Group (2004) Grading quality of evidence and strength of recommendations. *British Medical Journal, 328*, 1490–1497.

Gregory, R. J., Chlebowski, S., Kang, D., *et al.* (2008) A controlled trial of psychodynamic psychotherapy for co-occurring borderline personality disorder and alcohol use disorders. *Psychotherapy: Theory, Research, Practice, Training, 45*, 28–41.

Grilo, C. M., McGlashan, T. H. & Skodol, A. E. (2000) Stability and course of personality disorders: the need to consider comorbidities and continuities between axis I psychiatric disorders and axis II personality disorders. *Psychiatric Quarterly, 71*, 291–307.

Grilo, C. M., Becker D. F., Edell, W. S., *et al.* (2001) Stability and change of DSM-III-R personality disorder dimensions in adolescents followed up 2 years after psychiatric hospitalization. *Comprehensive Psychiatry, 42*, 364–368.

Gross, R., Olfson, M., Gameroff, M., *et al.* (2002) Borderline personality disorder in primary care. *Archives of Internal Medicine, 162*, 53–60.

Gunderson, J. G. & Kolb, J. E. (1978) Discriminating features of borderline patients. *American Journal of Psychiatry, 135*, 792–796.

Gunderson, J. G., Shea, M. T., Skodol, A. E., *et al.* (2000) The Collaborative Longitudinal Personality Disorders Study: development, aims, design, and sample characteristics. *Journal of Personality Disorders, 14*, 300–315.

Gunderson, J. G., Daversa, M. T., Grilo, C. M., *et al.* (2006) Predictors of 2-year outcome for patients with borderline personality disorder. *American Journal of Psychiatry, 163*, 822–826.

Guy, W. (1976) *ECDEU Assessment Manual for Psychopharmacology*. US Department of Health, Education, and Welfare Publication (ADM) 76–338. Rockville, MD: National Institute of Mental Health.

Hafner, R. J. & Holme, G. (1996) The influence of a therapeutic community on psychiatric disorder. *Journal of Clinical Psychology, 52*, 461–468.

Haigh, R. (2002) Services for people with personality disorder: the thoughts of service users. Available at: http://www.dh.gov.uk/en/Publicationsandstatistics/Publications/PublicationsPolicyAndGuidance/DH_4009546 [accessed 10 April 2008]

Haigh, R. (2007) The 16 personality disorder pilot projects. *Mental Health Review Journal, 12*, 29–39.

Haigh, R. & Lees, J. (2008) Fusion therapeutic communities: divergent histories, converging challenges. In *Therapeutic Communities: International Journal for Therapeutic and Supportive Organisations*, in press.

Haigh, R. & Tucker, S. (2004) Democratic development of standards: the community of communities—a quality network of therapeutic communities. *Psychiatric Quarterly, 75*, 263–277.

Haigh, R. & Worrall, A. (2002) *The Principles and Therapeutic Rationale of Therapeutic Communities*. Unpublished.

Hall, J., Caleo, S., Stevenson, J., *et al.* (2001) An economic analysis of psychotherapy for borderline personality disorder patients. *Journal of Mental Health Policy and Economics, 4*, 3–8.

Hallahan, B., Hibbeln, J. R., Davis, J. M., *et al.* (2007) Omega-3 fatty acid supplementation in patients with recurrent self-harm. Single centre double-blind randomised controlled trial. *British Journal of Psychiatry, 190*, 118–122.

Hamilton, C. E. (2000) Continuity and discontinuity of attachment from infancy through adolescence. *Child Development, 71*, 690–694.

Hamilton, M. (1959) The assessment of anxiety states by rating. *British Journal of Medical Psychology, 32*, 50–55.

Hamilton, M. (1960) A rating scale for depression. *Journal of Neurology, Neurosurgery and Psychiatry, 23*, 56–62.

Hammad, T. A., Laughren, T. & Racoosin, J. (2006) Suicidality in pediatric patients treated with antidepressant drugs. *Archives of General Psychiatry, 63*, 332–339.

Hampton, B., Korr, W., Bond, G. R., *et al.* (1992) *Integration Services System Approach to Avert Homelessness, CSP Homeless Prevention Project for HMI Adults*. State of Illinois NIMH Demonstration Grant program, Final report.

Hargreaves, W. A. (1968) Systematic Nurses' Observation of Psychopathology. *Archives of General Psychiatry, 10*, 518–531.

Harley, R. M., Baity, M. R., Blais, M. A., *et al.* (2007) Use of dialectical behavior therapy skills training for borderline personality disorder in a naturalistic setting. *Psychotherapy Research, 17*, 351–358.

Hart, S. D. (2001) Forensic issues. In *Handbook of Personality Disorder* (ed. W. J. Livesley). London: Guilford.

Havsteen-Franklin, D. (2007) Differentiating the ego-personality and internal other in art psychotherapy with patients with borderline personality disorder. *Psychodynamic Practice, 13*, 59–83.

Hawton, K. & Kirk, J. W. (1989) Problem solving. In *Cognitive Behaviour Therapy for Psychiatric Problems: A Practical Guide* (eds K. Hawton, P. M. Salkovskis, J. W. Kirk, *et al.*). Oxford: Oxford Medical Publications.

Helgeland, M. I. & Torgersen, S. (2004) Developmental antecedents of borderline personality disorder. *Comprehensive Psychiatry, 45*, 138–147.

Helgeland, M. I., Kjelsberg, E. & Torgersen, S. (2005) Continuities between emotional and disruptive behavior disorders in adolescence and personality disorders in adulthood. *American Journal of Psychiatry, 162*, 1941–1947.

Hellgren, L., Gillberg, I. C., Bagenholm, A., *et al.* (1994) Children with deficits in attention, motor control and perception (DAMP) almost grown up: psychiatric and personality disorders at age 16 years. *Journal of Child Psychology & Psychiatry & Allied Disciplines, 35*, 1255–1271.

Hengeveld, M. W., Jonker, D. J. L. & Rooijmans, H. G. M. (1996) A pilot study of a short cognitive-behavioral group treatment for female recurrent suicide attempters. *International Journal of Psychiatry in Medicine, 26*, 83–91.

Herinckx, H. A., Kinney, R. F., Clarke, G. N., *et al.* (1997) Assertive community treatment versus usual care in engaging and retaining clients with severe mental illness. *Psychiatric Services*, *48*, 1297–1306.

Herpertz, S. C., Dietrich, T. M., Wenning, B., *et al.* (2001) Evidence of abnormal amygdala functioning in borderline personality disorder: a functional MRI study. *Biological Psychiatry*, *50*, 292–298.

Herpertz, S. C., Zanarini, M., Schulz, C. S., *et al.* (2007) World Federation of Societies of Biological Psychiatry (WFSBP) guidelines for biological treatment of personality disorders. *World Journal of Biological Psychiatry*, *8*, 212–244.

Herz, M. I., Endicott, J., Spitzer, R. L., *et al.* (1971) Day versus inpatient hospitalization: a controlled study. *American Journal of Psychiatry*, *127*, 1371–1382.

Higgins, J. P. T. & Thompson, S. G. (2002) Quantifying heterogeneity in a meta-analysis. *Statistics in Medicine*, *21*, 1539–1558.

HMSO (1989) *Children Act 1989*. London: The Stationery Office. Available at: http://www.opsi.gov.uk/acts/acts1989/Ukpga_19890041_en_1

HMSO (2004) *Children Act 2004*. London: The Stationery Office. Available at: http://www.opsi.gov.uk/acts/acts2004/pdf/ukpga_20040031_en.pdf

HMSO (2005) *The Mental Capacity Act 2005*. London: The Stationery Office. Available at: http://www.opsi.gov.uk/acts/acts2005/ukpga_20050009_en_1

HMSO (2007) *The Mental Health Act 2007*. London: The Stationery Office. Available at: http://www.opsi.gov.uk/acts/acts2007/ukpga_20070012_en_1

Hobson, R. F. (1985) *Forms of Feeling: The Heart of Psychotherapy*. London: Tavistock Publications.

Hodgetts, A., Wright, J. & Gough, A. (2007) Clients with borderline personality disorder: exploring their experiences of dialectical behaviour therapy. *Counselling and Psychotherapy Research*, *7*, 172–177.

Hoffman, P., Buteau, E., Hooley, J., *et al.* (2003) Family members' knowledge about borderline personality disorder: correspondence with their levels of depression, burden, distress, and expressed emotion. *Family Process*, *42*, 469–478.

Hoffman, P. D., Struening, E., Buteau, E., *et al.* (2005) *Family Perspectives Survey*. Unpublished manuscript.

Hoffman, P. D., Buteau, E. & Fruzzetti, A. E. (2007a) Borderline personality disorder: Neo-personality inventory ratings of patients and their family members. *International Journal of Social Psychiatry*, *53*, 204–215.

Hoffman, P. D., Fruzzetti, A. E. & Buteau, E. (2007b) Understanding and engaging families: An education, skills and support programme for relatives impacted by borderline personality disorder. *Journal of Mental Health*, *16*, 69–82.

Hollander, E., Allen, A., Lopez, R. P., *et al.* (2001) A preliminary double-blind, placebo-controlled trial of divalproex sodium in borderline personality disorder. *Journal of Clinical Psychiatry*, *62*, 199–203.

Hollander, E., Tracey, K. A., Swann, A. C., *et al.* (2003) Divalproex in the treatment of impulsive aggression: efficacy in cluster B personality disorders. *Neuropsychopharmacology*, *28*, 1186–1197.

Holmes, J. (1999) Psychotherapeutic approaches to the management of severe personality disorder in general psychiatric settings. *CPD Bulletin Psychiatry*, *1*, 35–41.

Hooley, J. M. & Hoffman, P. D. (1999) Expressed emotion and clinical outcome in borderline personality disorder. *American Journal of Psychiatry*, *156*, 1557–1562.

Horesh, N., Sever, J., & Apter, A. (2003a) A comparison of life events between suicidal adolescents with major depression and borderline personality disorder. *Comprehensive Psychiatry*, *44*, 277–283.

Horesh, N., Orbach, I., Gothelf, D., *et al.* (2003b) Comparison of the suicidal behavior of adolescent inpatients with borderline personality disorder and major depression. *Journal of Nervous and Mental Disease*, *191*, 582–588.

Horn, N., Johnstone, L. & Brooke, S. (2007) Some service user perspectives on the diagnosis of borderline personality disorder. *Journal of Mental Health*, *16*, 255–269.

Horowitz, L. M., Rosenberg, S. E., Baer, B. A., *et al.* (1988) Inventory of interpersonal problems: psychometric properties and clinical applications. *Journal of Consulting and Clinical Psychology*, *56*, 885–892.

Horwitz, A. V., Widom, C. S., McLaughlin, J., *et al.* (2001) The impact of childhood abuse and neglect on adult mental health: a prospective study. *Journal of Health and Social Behaviour*, *42*, 184–201.

Hoult, J., Reynolds, I., Charbonneau-Powis, M., *et al.* (1981) A controlled study of psychiatric hospital versus community treatment – the effect on relatives. *Australian New Zealand Journal of Psychiatry*, *15*, 323–328.

House of Lords (1997) Bolitho v City and Hackney Health Authority. Available at: http://www.publications.parliament.uk/pa/ld199798/ldjudgmt/jd971113/boli01.htm

Huband, N., McMurran, M., Evans, C., *et al.* (2007) Social problem-solving plus psychoeducation for adults with personality disorder: pragmatic randomised controlled trial. *British Journal of Psychiatry*, *190*, 307–313.

Hulbert, C. & Thomas, R. (2007) Public sector group treatment for severe personality disorder: a 12-month follow-up study. *Australasian Psychiatry*, *15*, 226–231.

Hummelen, B., Wilberg, T. & Karterud, S. (2007) Interviews of female patients with borderline personality disorder who dropped out of group psychotherapy. *International Journal of Group Psychotherapy*, *57*, 67–91.

Hyler, S. E. (1994) *PDQ-4 + Personality Questionnaire*. New York: Author.

Isohanni, M. & Nieminen, P. (1989) Predicting immediate outcome on a closed psychiatric ward functioning as a therapeutic community. *Psychiatria Fennica*, *1989*, 13–22.

Isohanni, M. & Nieminen, P. (1990a) Relationship between involuntary admission and the therapeutic process in a closed ward functioning as a therapeutic community. *Acta Psychiatrica Scandinavica*, *81*, 240–244.

Isohanni, M. & Nieminen, P. (1990b) The determinants of therapeutic community activity at an acute patients' psychiatric ward. *International Journal of Therapeutic Communities*, *11*, 140–148.

Jadad, A. R., Moore, R. A. & Carroll, D. (1996) Assessing the quality of reports of randomised clinical trials: is blinding necessary? *Controlled Clinical Trials*, *17*, 1–12.

Jakubczyk, A., Zechowski, C. & Namyslowska, I. (2001) Treatment of adolescent borderline patients in a psychiatric unit. *Archives of Psychiatry and Psychotherapy*, *3*, 65–72.

Jeffrey, W. (1985) Pathology enhancement in the therapeutic community. *International Journal of Social Psychiatry*, *31*, 110–118.

Jerrell, J. M. & Ridgely, M. S. (1995) Comparative effectiveness of three approaches to serving people with severe mental illness and substance abuse disorders. *Journal of Nervous and Mental Disease*, *183*, 566–576.

Johnson, D. A. (1981) Studies of depressive symptoms in schizophrenia: the prevalence of depression and its possible causes. *British Journal of Psychiatry*, *139*, 546–552.

Johnson, J. G., Cohen, P., Brown, J., *et al.* (1999a) Childhood maltreatment increases risk for personality disorders during early adulthood. *Archives of General Psychiatry*, *56*, 600–606.

Johnson, J. G., Cohen, P., Skodol, A. E., *et al.* (1999b) Personality disorders in adolescence and risk of major mental disorders and suicidality during adulthood. *Archives of General Psychiatry*, *56*, 805–811.

Johnson, J. G., Cohen, P., Gould, M. S., *et al.* (2002) Childhood adversities, interpersonal difficulties, and risk for suicide attempts during late adolescence and early adulthood. *Archives of General Psychiatry*, *59*, 741–749.

Johnson, S., Nolan, F., Pilling, S., *et al.* (2005) Randomised controlled trial of acute mental health care by a crisis resolution team: the north Islington crisis study. *British Medical Journal*, *331*, 599.

Jones, J. M., Pearson, G. T. & Dimpero, R. (1989) Long-term treatment of the hospitalized adolescent and his family: an integrated systems-theory approach. *Adolescent Psychiatry*, *16*, 449–472.

Jones, V. & Stafford, C. (2007) How accessible are personality disorder services for black and minority ethnic people? *Therapeutic Communities: the International Journal for Therapeutic and Supportive Organizations*, *28*, 329–332.

Joyce, P. R., McKenzie, J. M., Carter, J. D., *et al.* (2007) Temperament, character and personality disorders as predictors of response to interpersonal psychotherapy and cognitive-behavioural therapy for depression. *British Journal of Psychiatry*, *190*, 503–508.

Karterud, S., Vaglum, S., Friis, S., *et al.* (1992) Day hospital therapeutic community treatment for patients with personality disorders: an empirical evaluation of the containment function. *Journal of Nervous an Mental Disease*, *180*, 238–243.

Kay, S. R., Fiszbein, A. & Opler, L. A. (1987) The Positive and Negative Syndrome Scale (PANSS) for schizophrenia. *Schizophrenia Bulletin*, *13*, 261–276.

Keller, M. B., Lavori, P. W., Friedman, B., *et al.* (1987) The Longitudinal Interval Follow-up Evaluation. A comprehensive method for assessing outcome in prospective longitudinal studies. *Archives of General Psychiatry*, *44*, 540–548.

Kendell, R. E. (2002) The distinction between personality disorder and mental illness. *British Journal of Psychiatry,* *180*, 110–115.

Kennard, D. & Haigh, R. (2009) *Therapeutic Communities*. Oxford: Oxford University Press. In press.

Kernberg, O. (1967) Borderline personality organization. *Journal of the American Psychoanalytic Association*, *15*, 641–685.

Kernberg, O. (1975) *Borderline Conditions and Pathological Narcissism*. New York: Jason Aronson.

Kernberg, O. & Haran, C. (1984) Interview: milieu treatment with borderline patients: the nurse's role. *Journal of Psychosocial Nursing and Mental Health Services*, *22*, 29–36.

Kerr, I. B., Dent-Brown, K. & Parry, G. D. (2007) Psychotherapy and mental health teams. *International Review of Psychiatry*, *19*, 63–80.

Kirsch, I., Deacon, B. J., Huedo-Medina, T. B., *et al.* (2008) Initial severity and antidepressant benefits: a meta-analysis of data submitted to the Food and Drug Administration. *Public Library of Science: Medicine*, *5*, e45.

Koons, C. R., Robins, C. J., Tweed, J. L., *et al.* (2001) Efficacy of dialectical behavior therapy in women veterans with borderline personality disorder. *Behavior Therapy*, *32*, 371–390.

Krawitz, R. & Watson, C. (2000) *Borderline Personality Disorder: A Practical Guide to Treatment*. Oxford: Oxford University Press.

Kris, E. B. (1965) Day hospitals. *Current Therapeutic Research Clinical and Experimental*, *7*, 320–323.

Kunert, H. J., Druecke, H. W., Sass, H., *et al.* (2003) Frontal lobe dysfunctions in borderline personality disorder? Neuropsychological findings. *Journal of Personality Disorders*, *17*, 497–509.

Lafave, H. G., de Souza, H. R. & Gerber, G. J. (1996) Assertive community treatment of severe mental illness: a Canadian experience. *Psychiatric Services*, *47*, 757–759.

Lanius, R. & Tuhan, I. (2003) Stage-oriented trauma treatment using dialectical behaviour therapy. *The Canadian Journal of Psychiatry - La Revue Canadienne de Psychiatrie*, *48*, 126–127.

Lazzaro, T. A., Beggs, D. L. & McNeil, K. A. (1969) The development and validation of the self-report test of impulse control. *Journal of Clinical Psychology*, *25*, 434–438.

Lefley, H. P. (2005) From family trauma to family support system. In *Understanding and Treating Borderline Personality Disorder. A Guide for Professionals and Families.* (eds J. G. Gunderson & P. D. Hoffman), pp. 131–150. Washington DC: American Psychiatric Publishing.

Lehman, A. F., Dixon, L. B., Kernan, E., *et al.* (1997) A randomized trial of assertive community treatment for homeless persons with severe mental illness. *Archives of General Psychiatry*, *54*, 1038–1043.

Leichsenring, F., Masuhr, O., Jaeger, U., *et al.* (2007) The effectiveness of psychoanalytic-interactional therapy in borderline personality disorder: a study of clinical data. *Zeitschrift für Psychosomatische Medizin und Psychotherapie*, *53*, 129–143.

Lenzenweger, M. F. (1999) Stability and change in personality disorder features: the Longitudinal Study of Personality Disorders. *Archives of General Psychiatry*, *56*, 1009–1015.

Leone, N. F. (1982) Response of borderline patients to loxapine and chlorpromazine. *Journal of Clinical Psychiatry*, *43*, 148–150.

Levy, K. N. (2005) The implications of attachment theory and research for understanding borderline personality disorder. *Development and Psychopathology*, *17*, 959–986.

Lewin, J. & Sumners, D. (1992) Successful treatment of episodic dyscontrol with carbamazepine. *British Journal of Psychiatry*, *161*, 261–262.

Lewinsohn, P. M., Rohde, P., Seeley, J. R., *et al.* (1997) Axis II psychopathology as a function of Axis I disorders in childhood and adolescence. *Journal of the American Academy of Child and Adolescent Psychiatry*, *36*, 1752–1759.

Liddel., J., Williamson, M. & Irwig, L. (1996) *Method for Evaluating Research and Guideline Evidence*. Sydney: New South Wales Health Department.

Lindsay, W. R. (2007) Personality disorder. In *Psychiatric and Behavioural Disorders in Intellectual and Developmental Disabilities* (eds N. Bouras & G. Holt), pp. 143–153. Cambridge: Cambridge University Press.

Linehan, M. M. (1993) *Cognitive-Behavioural Treatment of Borderline Personality Disorder*. New York: Guilford.

Linehan, M. M. (1997) Behavioral treatments of suicidal behaviors. Definitional obfuscation and treatment outcomes. *Annals of the New York Academy of Sciences*, *836*, 302–328.

Linehan, M. M. & Heard, H. L. (1987) *Treatment History Interview (THI)*. Seattle, Washington: University of Washington. Unpublished.

Linehan, M. M. & McGhee, D. E. (1994) A cognitive-behavioral model of supervision with individual and group components. In *Clinical Perspectives on Psychotherapy Supervision* (eds S. E. Greben & R. Ruskin). Washington, DC: American Psychiatric Press.

Linehan, M. M. & Nielsen, S. (1981) *Suicidal Behaviors Questionnaire (SBQ)*. Seattle, WA: University of Washington. Unpublished.

Linehan, M. M., Goodstein, J. L., Nielsen, S. L., *et al.* (1983) Reasons for staying alive when you are thinking of killing yourself: The Reasons for Living Inventory. *Journal of Consulting and Clinical Psychology*, *51*, 276–286.

Linehan, M. M., Wagner, A. W., & Cox, G. (1989) *The Parasuicide History Interview: Comprehensive Assessment of Parasuicidal Behaviour*. Seattle, Washington: University of Seattle.

Linehan, M., Heard H. L., Brown, M., *et al.* (1990) *Parasuicide History Interview* (PHI). Seattle, Washington: University of Washington.

Linehan, M. M., Armstrong, H. E., Suarez, A., *et al.* (1991) Cognitive-behavioral treatment of chronically parasuicidal borderline patients. *Archives of General Psychiatry*, *48*, 1060–1064.

Linehan, M. M., Tutek, D. A., Heard, H. L., *et al.* (1994) Interpersonal outcome of cognitive behavioral treatment for chronically suicidal borderline patients. *American Journal of Psychiatry*, *151*, 1771–1776.

Linehan, M. M., Schmidt, H., Dimeff, L. A., *et al.* (1999) Dialectical behavior therapy for patients with borderline personality disorder and drug-dependence. *American Journal on Addictions*, *8*, 279–292.

Linehan, M. M., Dimeff, L. A., Reynolds, S. K., *et al.* (2002) Dialectical behavior therapy versus comprehensive validation therapy plus 12-step for the treatment of opioid dependent women meeting criteria for borderline personality disorder. *Drug and Alcohol Dependence*, *67*, 13–26.

Linehan, M. M., Comtois, K. A., Murray, A. M., *et al.* (2006) Two-year randomized controlled trial and follow-up of dialectical behavior therapy vs therapy by experts for suicidal behaviors and borderline personality disorder. *Archives of General Psychiatry*, *63*, 757–766.

Links, P. S., Steiner, M. & Mitton, J. (1989) Characteristics of psychosis in borderline personality disorder. *Psychopathology*, *22*, 188–193.

Links, P. S., Steiner, M., Bojago, I., *et al.* (1990) Lithium therapy for borderline patients: preliminary findings. *Journal of Personality Disorders*, *4*, 173–181.

Links, P. S., Eynan, R., Heisel, M. J., *et al.* (2007) Affective instability and suicidal ideation and behavior in patients with borderline personality disorder. *Journal of Personality Disorders*, *21*, 72–86.

Linn, M. W., Caffey, E. M., Jr., Klett, C. J., *et al.* (1979) Day treatment and psychotropic drugs in the aftercare of schizophrenic patients. A Veterans Administration cooperative study. *Archives of General Psychiatry*, *36*, 1055–1066.

Loew, T. H., Nickel, M. K., Muehlbacher, M., *et al.* (2006) Topiramate treatment for women with borderline personality disorder: a double-blind, placebo-controlled study. *Journal of Clinical Psychopharmacology*, *26*, 61–66.

Loffler-Stastka, H., Voracek, M., Leithner, K., *et al.* (2003) Predicting psychotherapy utilization for patients with borderline personality disorder. *Psychotherapy Research*, *13*, 255–264.

Lofgren, D. P., Bemporad, J., King, J., *et al.* (1991) A prospective follow-up study of so-called borderline children. *American Journal of Psychiatry*, *148*, 1541–1547.

Lopez, D., Cuevas, P., Gomez, A., *et al.* (2004) Transference-focused psychotherapy for borderline personality disorder. A study with female patients. *Salud Mental*, *27*, 44–54.

Loranger, A. W., Sartorius, N. & Janca, A. (1996) *Assessment and Diagnosis of Personality Disorders: The International Personality Disorder Examination (IPDE)*. New York: Cambridge University Press.

Lorr, M. & Klett, C. J. (1966) *Inpatient Multidimensional Psychiatric Scale: Manual*. Palo Alto, CA: Consulting Psychologists Press.

Luborsky, L., Diguer, L., Seligman, D. A., *et al.* (1999) The researcher's own therapy allegiances: a 'wild card' in comparisons of treatment efficacy. *Clinical Psychology – Science and Practice*, *6*, 95–106.

Lyons-Ruth, K., Yellin, C., Melnick, S., *et al.* (2005) Expanding the concept of unresolved mental states: hostile/helpless states of mind on the Adult Attachment Interview are associated with disrupted mother-infant communication and infant disorganization. *Development and Psychopathology*, *17*, 1–23.

Mackin, P., Watkinson, H. M. & Young, A. H. (2005) Prevalence of obesity, glucose homeostasis disorders and metabolic syndrome in psychiatric patients taking typical or atypical antipsychotic drugs: a cross-sectional study. *Diabetologia*, *48*, 215–221.

Malm, U. & Lewander, T. (2001) Consumer satisfaction in schizophrenia. A 2-year randomized controlled study of two community-based treatment programs. *Nordic Journal of Psychiatry*, 55, 91–96.

Mann, A. H., Raven, P., Pilgrim, J., *et al.* (1999) An assessment of the Standardized Assessment of Personality as a screening instrument for the International Personality Disorder Examination: a comparison of informant and patient assessment for personality disorder. *Psychological Medicine*, 29, 985–989.

Mann, T. (1996) *Clinical Guidelines: Using Clinical Guidelines to Improve Patient Care Within the NHS*, Leeds: NHS Executive.

Markowitz, J. C., Skodol, A. E. & Bleiberg, K. (2006) Interpersonal psychotherapy for borderline personality disorder: possible mechanisms of change. *Journal of Clinical Psychology*, 62, 431–444.

Marx, A. J., Test, M. A. & Stein, L. I. (1973) Extrohospital management of severe mental illness. Feasibility and effects of social functioning. *Archives of General Psychiatry*, 29, 505–511.

Mavromatis, M. (2000) The diagnosis and treatment of borderline personality disorder in persons with developmental disability: three case reports. *Mental Health Aspects of Developmental Disabilities*, 3, 89–97.

McLellan, A. T., Luborsky, L., Woody, G. E., *et al.* (1980) An improved diagnostic evaluation instrument for substance abuse patients. The Addiction Severity Index. *Journal of Nervous and Mental Disease*, 168, 26–33.

McNair, D. M., Lorr, M. & Droppleman, L. F. (1971) *Manual for the Profile of Mood States*. San Diego, California: Educational and Industrial Testing Service.

McQuillan, A., Nicastro, R., Guenot, F., *et al.* (2005) Intensive dialectical behavior therapy for outpatients with borderline personality disorder who are in crisis. *Psychiatric Services*, 56, 193–197.

Meares, R. A. & Hobson, R. F. (1977) The persecutory therapist. *British Journal of Medical Psychology*, 50, 349–359.

Meijer, M., Goedhart, A. W. & Treffers, P. D. (1998) The persistence of borderline personality disorder in adolescence. *Journal of Personality Disorders*, 12, 13–22.

Mellsop, G., Varghese, F., Joshua, S., *et al.* (1982) The reliability of axis II of DSM-III. *American Journal of Psychiatry*, 139, 1360–1361.

Meltzoff, J. & Blumenthal, R. L. (1966) *The Day Treatment Center: Principles, Application and Evaluation*. Springfield, Ill: Charles C Thomas.

Merson, S., Tyrer, P., Onyett, S., *et al.* (1992) Early intervention in psychiatric emergencies: a controlled clinical trial. *Lancet*, 339, 1311–1314.

Mikton, C. & Grounds, A. (2007) Cross-cultural clinical judgment bias in personality disorder diagnosis by forensic psychiatrists in the UK: a case-vignette study. *Journal of Personality Disorders*, 21, 400–417.

Montgomery, S. A. & Asberg, M. (1979) A new depression scale designed to be sensitive to change. *British Journal of Psychiatry*, 134, 382–389.

Montgomery, S. A., Roy, D. & Montgomery, D. B. (1983) The prevention of recurrent suicidal acts. *British Journal of Clinical Pharmacology*, 15, 183–188.

Moran, P., Jenkins, R., Tylee, A., *et al.* (2000) The prevalence of personality disorder among UK primary care attenders. *Acta Psychiatrica Scandinavica*, 102, 52–57.

Moran, P., Rendu, A., Jenkins, R., *et al.* (2001) The impact of personality disorder in UK primary care: a 1-year follow-up of attenders. *Psychological Medicine, 31,* 1447–1454.

Morant, N. & King, J. (2003) A multi-perspective evaluation of a specialist outpatient service for people with personality disorders. *The Journal of Forensic Psychiatry and Psychology, 14,* 44–66.

Moreland, J., Hendy, S. & Brown, F. (2008) The validity of a personality disorder diagnosis for people with an intellectual disability. *Journal of Applied Research in Intellectual Disabilities, 21,* 219–226.

Morrow, J., Russell, A., Guthrie, E., *et al.* (2006) Malformation risks of antiepileptic drugs in pregnancy: a prospective study from the UK Epilepsy and Pregnancy Register. *Journal of Neurology, Neurosurgery and Psychiatry, 77,* 193–198.

Morse, G. A., Calsyn, R. J., Allen, G., *et al.* (1992) Experimental comparison of the effects of three treatment programs for homeless mentally ill people. *Hospital Community Psychiatry, 43,* 1005–1010.

Morse, G. A., Calsyn, R. J., Klinkenberg, W. D., *et al.* (1997) An experimental comparison of three types of case management for homeless mentally ill persons. *Psychiatric Service, 48,* 497–503.

Muijen, M., Marks, I., Connolly, J., *et al.* (1992) Home based care and standard hospital care for patients with severe mental illness: a randomised controlled trial. *British Medical Journal, 304,* 749–754.

Munroe-Blum, H. & Marziali, E. (1995) A controlled trial of short-term group treatment for borderline personality disorder. *Journal of Personality Disorders, 9,* 190.

NCCMH (2002) *Schizophrenia: Core Interventions in the Treatment and Management of Schizophrenia in Primary and Secondary Care.* London: Gaskell.

NCCMH (2004) *Self-harm: The Short-Term Physical and Psychological Management and Secondary Prevention of Self-Harm in Primary and Secondary Care.* Leicester & London: British Psychological Society & Gaskell.

NCCMH (2005) *Depression: Management of Depression in Primary and Secondary Care.* Leicester & London: British Psychological Society & Gaskell.

NCCMH (2006) *Bipolar Disorder: The Management of Bipolar Disorder in Adults, Children and Adolescents, in Primary and Secondary Care.* Leicester and London: British Psychological Society and Gaskell.

Nehls, N. (1999) Borderline personality disorder: the voice of patients. *Research in Nursing and Health, 22,* 285–293.

Nezu, A. M. & Perri, M. G. (1989) Social problem-solving therapy for unipolar depression: an initial dismantling investigation. *Journal of Consulting and Clinical Psychology, 57,* 408–413.

NHS Health Advisory Service (1995) *Child and Adolescent Mental Health Services: Together We Stand: The Commissioning, Role and Management of Child and Adolescent Mental Health Services.* London: HMSO.

NICE (2004a) *Self-harm: The Short-Term Physical and Psychological Management and Secondary Prevention of Self-Harm in Primary and Secondary Care.* NICE Clinical Guideline 16. London: NICE.

NICE (2004b) *Guidance on the Use of Zaleplon, Zolpidem and Zopiclone for the Short-term Management of Insomnia.* Technology Appraisal 77. London: NICE.

NICE (2004c) *Depression: Management of Depression in Primary and Secondary Care.* NICE Clinical Guideline 23. London: NICE.

NICE (2004d) *Guide to the Methods of Technology Appraisal.* London: NICE.

NICE (2006a) *Bipolar Disorder: The Management of Bipolar Disorder in Adults, Children and Adolescents, in Primary and Secondary Care.* London: NICE.

NICE (2006b) *The Guidelines Manual.* London: NICE. Available at: www.nice.org.uk

NICE (2006c) *The Guideline Development Process – An Overview for Stakeholders, the Public and the NHS* (Second Edition). London: NICE.

NICE (2007a) Antenatal and Postnatal Mental Health: Clinical Management and Service Guidance. NICE Clinical Guideline 45. London: NICE.

NICE (2007b) *The Guidelines Manual.* London: NICE. Available at: www.nice.org.uk

NICE (2008) *Guide to the Methods of Technology Appraisal.* London: NICE.

Nickel, M. K., Nickel, C., Mitterlehner, F. O., *et al.* (2004) Topiramate treatment of aggression in female borderline personality disorder patients: a double-blind, placebo-controlled study. *Journal of Clinical Psychiatry, 65,* 1515–1519.

Nickel, M. K., Nickel, C., Kaplan, P., *et al.* (2005) Treatment of aggression with topiramate in male borderline patients: a double-blind, placebo-controlled study. *Biological Psychiatry, 57,* 495–499.

Nickel, C. Lahmann, C., Tritt, K., *et al.* (2005a) Topiramate in treatment of depressive and anger symptoms in female depressive patients: a randomized, double-blind, placebo-controlled study. *Journal of Affective Disorders, 87,* 243–252.

Nickel, M. K., Muehlbacher, M., Nickel, C., *et al.* (2006) Aripiprazole in the treatment of patients with borderline personality disorder: a double-blind, placebo-controlled study. *American Journal of Psychiatry, 163,* 833–838.

NIMHE (2003) *Breaking the Cycle of Rejection: The Personality Disorder Capabilities Framework.* London: Department of Health.

Nordahl, H. M. & Nysaeter, T. E. (2005) Schema therapy for patients with borderline personality disorder: a single case series. *Journal of Behaviour Therapy and Experimental Psychiatry, 36,* 254–264.

O'Brien, M. (1976) The diagnosis of psychopathy: a study of some characteristics in personality and behaviour of psychopaths referred for treatment to a therapeutic community. Doctoral thesis, University of London.

Oldham, J. M. (2006) Borderline personality disorder and suicidality. *American Journal of Psychiatry, 163,* 20–26.

Olsson, P. & Barth, P. (1983) New uses of psychodrama. *Journal of Operational Psychiatry, 14,* 95–101.

Overall, J. E. & Gorham, D. R. (1982) The Brief Psychiatric Rating Scale. *Psychological Reports, 10,* 799–812.

Overall, J. E. & Gorham, D. R. (1988) The Brief Psychiatric Rating Scale. *Psychopharmacology Bulletin, 24,* 97–99.

Palmer, S., Davidson, K., Tyrer, P., *et al.* (2006) The cost-effectiveness of cognitive behavior therapy for borderline personality disorder: results from the BOSCOT trial. *Journal of Personality Disorders, 20,* 466–481.

Paris, J. (2002) Commentary on the American Psychiatric Association guidelines for the treatment of borderline personality disorder: evidence-based psychiatry and the quality of evidence. *Journal of Personality Disorders, 16,* 130–134.

Paris, J. (2004a) Half in love with easeful death: the meaning of chronic suicidality in borderline personality disorder. *Harvard Review of Psychiatry, 12,* 42–48.

Paris, J. (2004b) Is hospitalization useful for suicidal patients with borderline personality disorder? *Journal of Personality Disorders., 18,* 240–247.

Paris, J. & Zweig-Frank, H. (2001) A 27-year follow-up of patients with borderline personality disorder. *Comprehensive Psychiatry, 42,* 482–487.

Paris, J., Nowlis, D. & Brown, R. (1989) Predictors of suicide in borderline personality disorder. *Canadian Journal of Psychiatry-Revue Canadienne de Psychiatrie, 34,* 8–9.

Paris, J., Gunderson, J. & Weinberg, I. (2007) The interface between borderline personality disorder and bipolar spectrum disorders. *Comprehensive Psychiatry, 48,* 145–154.

Pasamanick, B., Scarpitti, F. R., Lefton, M., *et al.* (1964) Home vs hosptial care for schizophrenics. *Journal of American Medical Association, 187,* 177–181.

Pascual, J. C., Soler, J., Puigdemont, D., *et al.* (2008) Ziprasidone in the treatment of borderline personality disorder: a double-blind placebo-controlled randomized study. *Journal of Clinical Psychiatry, 69,* 603–608.

Payne, H. (1993) *Handbook of Inquiry in the Arts Therapies: One River, Many Currents.* London: Jessica Kingsley.

Pearce, S. & Haigh, R. (2008) 'Mini therapeutic communities': a new development in the United Kingdom. *Therapeutic Communities: International Journal for Therapeutic and Supportive Organizations,* in press.

Peet, M., Brind, J., Ramchand, C. N., *et al.* (2001) Two double-blind placebo-controlled pilot studies of eicosapentaenoic acid in the treatment of schizophrenia. *Schizophrenia Research, 49,* 243–251.

Pfohl, B., Coryell, W., Zimmerman, M., *et al.* (1986) DSM-III personality disorders: diagnostic overlap and internal consistency of individual DSM-III criteria. *Comprehensive Psychiatry, 27,* 21–34.

Pfohl, B., Blum, N. & Immerman, M. (1997) *Structured Interview for DSM-IV Personality (SIDP-IV).* Washington, DC: American Psychiatric Press.

Philipsen, A., Schmahl, C., & Lieb, K. (2004a) Naloxone in the treatment of acute dissociative states in female patients with borderline personality disorder. *Pharmacopsychiatry, 37,* 196–199.

Pinto, C., Dhavale, H. S., Nair, S., *et al.* (2000) Borderline personality disorder exists in India. *Journal of Nervous and Mental Disease, 188,* 386–388.

Prendergast, N. & McCausland, J. (2007) Dialectic behaviour therapy: a 12-month collaborative program in a local community setting. *Behaviour Change, 24,* 25–35.

Quinlivan, R., Hough, R., Crowell, A., *et al.* (1995) Service utilization and costs of care for severely mentally ill clients in an intensive case management program. *Psychiatric Services, 46,* 365–371.

Ramklint, M., von Knorring, A-L., von Knorring, L., *et al.* (2003) Child and adolescent psychiatric disorders predicting adult personality disorder: a follow-up study. *Nordic Journal of Psychiatry, 57,* 23–28.

Ramon, S., Castillo, H. & Morant, N. (2001) Experiencing personality disorder: a participative research. *International Journal of Social Psychiatry, 47*, 1–15.

Reichborn-Kjennerud, T., Czajkowski, N., Neale, M. C., *et al.* (2007) Genetic and environmental influences on dimensional representations of DSM-IV cluster C personality disorders: a population-based multivariate twin study. *Psychological Medicine, 37*, 645–653.

Rendu, A., Moran, P., Patel, A., *et al.* (2002) Economic impact of personality disorders in UK primary care attenders. *British Journal of Psychiatry, 181*, 62–66.

Rey, J. M., Morris-Yates, A., Singh, M., *et al.* (1995) Continuities between psychiatric disorders in adolescents and personality disorders in young adults. *American Journal of Psychiatry, 152*, 895–900.

Rinne, T., Westenberg, H. G., den Boer, J. A., *et al.* (2000) Serotonergic blunting to meta-chlorophenylpiperazine (m-CPP) highly correlates with sustained childhood abuse in impulsive and autoaggressive female borderline patients. *Biological Psychiatry, 47*, 548–556.

Rinne, T., Van den Brink, W., Wouters, L., *et al.* (2002) SSRI treatment of borderline personality disorder: a randomized, placebo-controlled clinical trial for female patients with borderline personality disorder. *American Journal of Psychiatry, 159*, 2048–2054.

Rosenheck, R., Neale, M. & Gallup, P. (1993) Community-oriented mental health care: assessing diversity in clinical practice. *Psychosocial Rehabilitation Journal, 16*, 39–50.

Royal College of Psychiatrists (2001) *DC-LD: Diagnostic Criteria For Psychiatric Disorders For Use With Adults With Learning Disabilities/Mental Retardation.* London: Gaskell.

Runeson, B. & Beskow, J. (1991) Borderline personality disorder in young Swedish suicides. *Journal of Nervous and Mental Disease, 179*, 153–156.

Rusch, N., van Elst, L. T., Ludaescher, P., *et al.* (2003) A voxel-based morphometric MRI study in female patients with borderline personality disorder. *Neuroimage, 20*, 385–392.

Ryle, A. (1997) *Cognitive Analytic Therapy of Borderline Personality Disorder: the Model and the Method.* New York: John Wiley & Sons.

Ryle, A. & Golynkina, K. (2000) Effectiveness of time-limited cognitive analytic therapy of borderline personality disorder: factors associated with outcome. *British Journal of Medical Psychology, 73*, 197–210.

Ryle, A. & Kerr, I. B. (2002) *Introducing Cognitive Analytic Therapy: Principles and Practice.* Chichester: John Wiley & Sons.

Salzman, C., Wolfson, A. N., Schatzberg, A., *et al.* (1995) Effect of fluoxetine on anger in symptomatic volunteers with borderline personality disorder. *Journal of Clinical Psychopharmacology, 15*, 23–29.

Sampson, M. J, McCubbin, R. & Tyrer, P. (2006) *Personality Disorder and Community Mental Health Teams: a Practitioner's Guide.* Chichester: John Wiley & Sons.

Samuels, J., Eaton, W. W., Bienvenu, O. J., III, *et al.* (2002) Prevalence and correlates of personality disorders in a community sample. *British Journal of Psychiatry, 180*, 536–542.

Sanderson, C., Swenson, C. & Bohus, M. (2002) A critique of the American psychiatric practice guideline for the treatment of patients with borderline personality disorder. *Journal of Personality Disorders, 16*, 122–129.

Sansone, R. A., Sansone, L. A. & Wiederman, M. W. (1996) Borderline personality disorder and health care utilization in a primary care setting. *Southern Medical Journal, 89*, 1162–1165.

Sansone, R. A., Rytwinski, D. & Gaither, G. A. (2003) Borderline personality and psychotropic medication prescription in an outpatient psychiatry clinic. *Comprehensive Psychiatry*, 44, 454–458.

Schaffer, A. Zuker, P. & Levitt, A. (2006) Randomized double-blind pilot trial comparing lamotrigine versus citalopram for the treatment of bipolar depression. *Journal of Affective Disorders, 96*, 95–99.

Scheirs, J. G. M. & Bok, S. (2007) Psychological distress in caretakers or relatives of patients with borderline personality disorder. *International Journal of Social Psychiatry, 53*, 195–203.

Schmahl, C. G., Vermetten, E., Elzinga, B. M., *et al.* (2003) Magnetic resonance imaging of hippocampal and amygdala volume in women with childhood abuse and borderline personality disorder. *Psychiatry Research, 122*, 193–198.

Schmidt, H. (2002) Music therapy of borderline personality disorder. *PTT: Personlichkeitsstorungen Theorie und Therapie, 6*, 65–74.

Schmidt, U. & Davidson, K. M. (2002) *When Life Is Too Painful: Finding Options after Self Harm*. Hove: Psychology Press.

Schotte, D. E. & Clum, G. A. (1982) Suicide ideation in a consultation. *Journal of Consulting and Clinical Psychology, 50*, 690–696.

Schulz, S. C., Schulz, P. M., Dommisse, C., *et al.* (1985) Amphetamine response in borderline patients. *Psychiatry Research, 15*, 97–108.

Schulz, S. C., Zanarini, M. C., Bateman, A., *et al.* (2008) Olanzapine for the treatment of borderline personality disorder: a variable-dose, 12-week, randomized, double-blind, placebo-controlled study. *British Journal of Psychiatry, 193*, 485–492.

Sellwood, W. Thomas, C. S., Tarrier, N., *et al.* (1999) A randomised controlled trial of home-based rehabilitation versus outpatient-based rehabilitation for patients suffering from chronic schizophrenia. *Social Psychiatry and Psychiatric Epidemiology, 34*, 250–253.

Serban, G. & Siegel, S. (1984) Response of borderline and schizotypal patients to small doses of thiothixene and haloperidol. *American Journal of Psychiatry, 141*, 1455–1458.

Shea, M. T., Stout, R., Gunderson, J., *et al.* (2002) Short-term diagnostic stability of schizotypal, borderline, avoidant, and obsessive-compulsive personality disorders. *American Journal of Psychiatry, 159*, 2036–2041.

Siever, L. J. & Davis, K. L. (1991) A psychobiological perspective on the personality disorders. *American Journal of Psychiatry, 148*, 1647–1658.

SIGN (2001) *SIGN 50: A Guideline Developer's Handbook* (Edinburgh: Scottish Intercollegiate Guidelines Network).

Simpson, E. B., Yen, S., Costello, E., *et al.* (2004) Combined dialectical behavior therapy and fluoxetine in the treatment of borderline personality disorder. *Journal of Clinical Psychiatry, 65*, 379–385.

Simpson, G. M. & Angus, J. W. S. (1970) A rating scale for extrapyramidal side effects. *Acta Psychiatrica Scandinavica, 212,* 11–19.

Singh, M. M. & Kay, S. R. (1975) A comparative study of haloperidol and chlorpromazine in terms of clinical effects and therapeutic reversal; with benztropine in schizophrenia: theoretical implications for potency differences among neuroleptics. *Psychopharmacologia, 43,* 103–113.

Singh, M. M., Kay, S. R., & Opler, L. A. (1987) Anticholinergic-neuroleptic antagonism in terms of positive and negative symptoms of schizophrenia: implications for psychobiological subtyping. *Psychological Medicine, 17,* 39–48.

Singleton, N., Meltzer, H., Gatward, R., *et al.* (1998) *Psychiatric Morbidity Among Prisoners: Summary Report.* London: Government Statistical Service.

Singleton, N., Bumpstead, R., O'Brien, M., *et al.* (2003) Psychiatric morbidity among adults living in private households, 2000. *International Review of Psychiatry, 15,* 65–73.

Skodol, A. E., Stout, R. L., McGlashan, T. H., *et al.* (1999) Co-occurrence of mood and personality disorders: a report from the Collaborative Longitudinal Personality Disorders Study (CLPS). *Depression and Anxiety, 10,* 175–182.

Skodol, A. E., Gunderson, J. G., McGlashan, T. H., *et al.* (2002) Functional impairment in patients with schizotypal, borderline, avoidant, or obsessive-compulsive personality disorder. *American Journal of Psychiatry, 159,* 276–283.

Skodol, A. E., Pagano, M. E., Bender, D. S., *et al.* (2005) Stability of functional impairment in patients with schizotypal, borderline, avoidant, or obsessive-compulsive personality disorder over two years. *Psychological Medicine, 35,* 443–451.

Sledge[22], W. H., Tebes, J., Rakfeldt, J., *et al.* (1996) Day hospital/crisis respite care versus inpatient care, Part I: clinical outcomes. *American Journal of Psychiatry, 153,* 1065–1073.

Smith, K., Shah, A., Wright, K., *et al.* (1995) The prevalence and costs of psychiatric disorders and learning disabilities. *British Journal of Psychiatry, 166,* 9–18.

Soeteman, D.I., Hakkaart-van Roeijn, L., Verheul, R., *et al.* (2008) The economic burden of personality disorders in mental health care. *Journal of Clinical Psychiatry, 69,* 259–265.

Soler, J., Pascual, J. C., Campins, J., *et al.* (2005) Double-blind, placebo-controlled study of dialectical behavior therapy plus olanzapine for borderline personality disorder. *American Journal of Psychiatry, 162,* 1221–1224.

Soloff, P. H., George, A., Nathan, S., *et al.* (1989) Amitriptyline versus haloperidol in borderlines: final outcomes and predictors of response. *Journal of Clinical Psychopharmacology, 9,* 238–246.

Soloff, P. H., Cornelius, J., George, A., *et al.* (1993) Efficacy of phenelzine and haloperidol in borderline personality disorder. *Archives of General Psychiatry, 50,* 377–385.

Soloff, P. H., Lis, J. A., Kelly, T., *et al.* (1994) Self-mutilation and suicidal behavior in borderline personality disorder. *Journal of Personality Disorders, 8,* 257–267.

---

[22]This is the reference for study ID SLEDGE1996A.

Soloff, P. H., Lynch, K. G., Kelly, T. M., *et al.* (2000) Characteristics of suicide attempts of patients with major depressive episode and borderline personality disorder: a comparative study. *American Journal of Psychiatry, 157,* 601–608.

Spielberger, C. D., Gorusch, R. L. & Lushene, R. D. (1970) *STAI Manual.* Palo Alto, CA: Consulting Psychologists Press.

Spielberger, C. D., Jacobs, G. A., Russell, S. *et al.* (1983) Assessment of anger: the State-Trait Anger Scale. In *Advances in Personality Assessment* (eds J. N. Butcher & C. D. Spielberger). Hillsdale, New Jersey: Lawrence Erlbaum Associates.

Springer, T., Lohr, N. A., Buchtel, H. A., *et al.* (1996) A preliminary report of short-term cognitive-behavioural group therapy for inpatients with personality disorders. *Journal of Psychotherapy Practice and Research, 5,* 57–71.

Stalker, K., Ferguson, I. & Barclay, A. (2005) 'It is a horrible term for someone': service user and provider perspectives on 'personality disorder'. *Disability and Society, 20,* 359–373.

Stein, D. J., Hollander, E., Cohen, L., *et al.* (1993) Neuropsychiatric impairment in impulsive personality disorders. *Psychiatry Research, 48,* 257–266.

Stein, L. I. & Test, M. A. (1980) Alternative to mental hospital treatment. I. Conceptual model, treatment program, and clinical evaluation. *Archives of General Psychiatry, 37,* 392–397.

Steinberg, B. J., Trestman, R., Mitropoulou, V., *et al.* (1997) Depressive response to physostigmine challenge in borderline personality disorder patients. *Neuropsychopharmacology, 17,* 264–273.

Stern, A. (1938) Psychoanalytic investigation of and therapy in the borderline group of neuroses. *Psychoanalysis Quarterly, 7,* 467–489.

Stevenson, J. & Meares, R. (1992) An outcome study of psychotherapy for patients with borderline personality disorder. *American Journal of Psychiatry, 149,* 358–362.

Stevenson, J., Meares, R. & D'Angelo, R. (2005) Five-year outcome of outpatient psychotherapy with borderline patients. *Psychological Medicine, 35,* 79–87.

Stone, M. H. (1992) Suicide in borderline and other adolescents. *Adolescent Psychiatry, 18,* 289–305.

Stone, M. H. (1993) Long-term outcome in personality disorders. *British Journal of Psychiatry, 162,* 299–313.

Tebartz van Elst, L., Hesslinger, B., Thiel, T., *et al.* (2003) Frontolimbic brain abnormalities in patients with borderline personality disorder: a volumetric magnetic resonance imaging study. *Biological Psychiatry, 54,* 163–171.

Teicher, M. H., Glod, C. A., Aaronson, S. T., *et al.* (1989) Open assessment of the safety and efficacy of thioridazine in the treatment of patients with borderline personality disorder. *Psychopharmacological Bulletin, 25,* 535–549.

Test, M. A. Knoedler W. H. Allness D. J., *et al.* (1991) Long term community care through an assertive continuous treatment team. In *Advances in Neuropsychiatry and Psychopharmacology.* Volume 1: Schizophrenia Research (eds C. A. Tamminga & S. C. Schulz). New York: Raven.

Theisen, F. M., Linden, A., Geller, F., *et al.* (2001) Prevalence of obesity in adolescent and young adult patients with and without schizophrenia and in relationship to antipsychotic medication. *Journal of Psychiatric Research, 35,* 339–345.

Thompson, A. R., Donnison, J., Warnock-Parkes, E., *et al.* (2008) A multidisciplinary community mental health team (CMHT) staff's experience of a 'skills' level training course in cognitive analytic therapy. *International Journal of Mental Health Nursing*, *17*, 131–137.

Tiihonen, J., Hallikaien, T., Rvvnänen, O. P., *et al.* (2003) Lamotrigine in treatment-resistant schizophrenia: a randomized placebo-controlled crossover trial. *Biological Psychiatry*, *54*, 1241–1248.

Torgersen, S., Lygren, S., Oien, P. A., *et al.* (2000) A twin study of personality disorders. *Comprehensive Psychiatry*, *41*, 416–425.

Torgersen, S., Kringlen, E. & Cramer, V. (2001) The prevalence of personality disorders in a community sample. *Archives of Internal Medicine*, *58*, 590–596.

Torr, J. (2003) Personality disorder in intellectual disability. *Current Opinion in Psychiatry*, *16*, 517–521.

Tritt, K., Nickel, C., Lahmann, C., *et al.* (2003) Lamotrigine treatment of aggression in female borderline-patients: a randomized, double-blind, placebo-controlled study. *Journal of Psychopharmacology*, *19*, 287–291.

Tungaraza, T. & Poole, R. (2007) Influence of drug company authorship and sponsorship on drug trial outcomes. *British Journal of Psychiatry*, *191*, 82–83.

Turner, R. M. (2000) Naturalistic evaluation of dialectical behavior therapy-oriented treatment for borderline personality disorder. *Cognitive and Behavioral Practice*, *7*, 413–419.

Tyrer, P. (1999) Borderline personality disorder: a motley diagnosis in need of reform. *Lancet*, *354*, 2095–2096.

Tyrer, P. (2002) Practice guideline for the treatment of borderline personality disorder: a bridge too far. *Journal of Personality Disorders*, *16*, 113–118.

Tyrer, P. J. & Remington, M. (1979) Controlled comparison of day-hospital and outpatient treatment for neurotic disorders. *Lancet*, *1*, 1014–1016.

Tyrer, P., Alexander, M. S., Cicchetti, D., *et al.* (1979) Reliability of a schedule for rating personality disorders. *British Journal of Psychiatry*, *135*, 168–174.

Tyrer, P., Merson, S., Onyett, S., *et al.* (1994) The effect of personality disorder on clinical outcome, social networks and adjustment: a controlled clinical trial of psychiatric emergencies. *Psychological Medicine*, *24*, 731–740.

Tyrer, P., Gunderson, J., Lyons, M., *et al.* (1997) Extent of comorbidity between mental state and personality disorders. *Journal of Personality Disorders*, *11*, 242–259.

Tyrer, P., Evans, K., Gandhi, N., *et al.* (1998) Randomised controlled trial of two models of care for discharged psychiatric patients. *British Medical Journal*, *316*, 106–109.

Tyrer, P., Jones, V., Thompson, S., *et al.* (2003) Service variation in baseline variables and prediction of risk in a randomised controlled trial of psychological treatment in repeated parasuicide: the POPMACT Study. *International Journal of Social Psychiatry*, *49*, 58–69.

Tyrer, P., Sensky, T., & Mitchard, S. (2003a) Principles of nidotherapy in the treatment of persistent mental and personality disorders. *Psychotherapy and Psychosomatics*, *72*, 350–356.

Tyrer, P., Nur, U., Crawford, M., *et al.* (2005) The Social Functioning Questionnaire: a rapid and robust measure of perceived functioning. *International Journal of Social Psychiatry*, *51*, 265–275.

Vaglum, P., Friis, S., Irion, T., *et al.* (1990) Treatment response of severe and nonsevere personality disorders in a therapeutic community day unit. *Journal of Personality Disorders*, *4*, 161–172.

Van Asselt, A. D. I., Dirksen, C. D., Arntz, A., *et al.* (2007) The cost of borderline personality disorder: societal cost of illness in BPD-patients. *European Psychiatry*, *22*, 354–361.

Van Asselt, A. D. I., Dirksen, C. D., Arntz, A., *et al.* (2008) Out-patient psychotherapy for borderline personality disorder: cost-effectiveness of schema-focused therapy v. transference-focused psychotherapy. *British Journal of Psychiatry*, *192*, 450–457.

Van den Bosch, L. M. C., Verheul, R., Schippers, G. M., *et al.* (2002) Dialectical behavior therapy of borderline patients with and without substance use problems: implementation and long-term effects. *Addictive Behaviors*, *27*, 911–923.

Van Kessel, K., Lambie, I. & Stewart, M. W. (2002) Impact of brief planned admissions on inpatient mental health unit utilisation for people with a diagnosis of borderline personality disorder. *New Zealand Journal of Psychology*, *31*, 93–97.

Vieta, E., Goikolea, J. M., Olivares, J. M., *et al.* (2003) 1-year follow-up of patients treated with risperidone and topiramate for a manic episode. *Journal of Clinical Psychiatry*, *64*, 834–839.

Waller, D. & Gilroy, A. (1992) *Art Therapy: A Handbook*. Buckingham: Open University Press.

Warren, F., Evans, C., Dolan, B., *et al.* (2004) Impulsivity and self-damaging behaviour in severe personality disorder: the impact of democratic therapeutic community treatment. *Therapeutic Communities: the International Journal for Therapeutic and Supportive Organizations*, *25*, 55–71.

Warren, F., Zaman, S., Dolan, B., *et al.* (2006) Eating disturbance and severe personality disorder: outcome of specialist treatment for severe personality disorder. *European Eating Disorders Review*, *14*, 69–78.

Waters, E., Merrick, S., Treboux, D., *et al.* (2000) Attachment security in infancy and early adulthood: a twenty-year longitudinal study. *Child Development*, *71*, 684–689.

Weinberg, I., Gunderson, J. G., Hennen, J., *et al.* (2006) Manual assisted cognitive treatment for deliberate self-harm in borderline personality disorder patients. *Journal of Personality Disorders*, *20*, 482–492.

Weinfield, N. S., Sroufe, L. A. & Egeland, B. (2000) Attachment from infancy to early adulthood in a high-risk sample: continuity, discontinuity, and their correlates. *Child Development*, *71*, 695–702.

Weinstein, W. & Jamison, K. L. (2007) Retrospective case review of lamotrigine use for affective instability of borderline personality disorder. *CNS Spectrums: The International Journal of Neuropsychiatric Medicine*, *12*, 207–210.

Weissman, M. M. & Bothwell, S. (1976) Assessment of social adjustment by patient self-report. *Archives of General Psychiatry, 33*, 1111–1115.

Weldon, E., Clarkin, J. E., Hennessy, J. J., *et al.* (1979) Day hospital versus outpatient treatment: a controlled study. *Psychiatric Quarterly, 51*, 144–150.

Westen, D. (1997) Divergences between clinical and research methods for assessing personality disorders: implications for research and the evolution of axis II. *American Journal of Psychiatry, 154*, 895–903.

Westen, D. & Shedler, J. (2007) Personality diagnosis with the Shedler-Westen assessment procedure (SWAP): integrating clinical and statistical measurement and prediction. *Journal of Abnormal Psychology, 116*, 810–822.

White, C. N., Gunderson, J. G., Zanarini, M. C., *et al.* (2003) Family studies of borderline personality disorder: a review. *Harvard Review of Psychiatry, 11*, 8–19.

Whittington, C. J., Kendall, T., Fonagy, P., *et al.* (2004) Selective serotonin reuptake inhibitors in childhood depression: systematic review of published versus unpublished data. *Lancet, 363*, 1341–1345.

WHOQOL group (1998) The World Health Organization Quality of Life Assessment (WHOQOL): development and general psychometric properties. *Social Sciences and Medicine, 46*, 1569–1585.

Wilberg, T., Friis, S., Karterud, S., *et al.* (1998) Outpatient group psychotherapy: a valuable continuation treatment for patients with borderline personality disorder treated in a day hospital? A 3-year follow-up study. *Nordic Journal of Psychiatry, 52*, 213–222.

Wilson, M. (2001) A four-stage model for management of borderline personality disorder in people with mental retardation. *Mental Health Aspects of Developmental Disabilities, 4*, 68–76.

World Health Organization (1992) *The ICD-10 Classification of Mental and Behavioural Disorders: Clinical Descriptions and Diagnostic Guidelines.* Geneva, Switzerland: World Health Organization.

Wyszynski, D. F., Nambisan, M., Surve, T., *et al.* (2005) Increased rate of major malformations in offspring exposed to valproate during pregnancy. *Neurology, 64*, 961–965.

Yen, S. & Shea, M.T. (2001) Recent developments in research of trauma and personality disorders. *Current Psychiatry Reports, 3*, 52–58.

Yen, S., Shea, M. T., Sanislow, C. A., *et al.* (2004) Borderline personality disorder criteria associated with prospectively observed suicidal behavior. *American Journal of Psychiatry, 161*, 1296–1298.

Yen, S., Pagano, M. E., Shea, M. T., *et al.* (2005) Recent life events preceding suicide attempts in a personality disorder sample: findings from the collaborative longitudinal personality disorders study. *Journal of Consulting and Clinical Psychology, 73*, 99–105.

Young, D. & Gunderson, J. (1995) Family images of borderline adolescents. *Psychiatry: Interpersonal and Biological Processes, 58*, 164–172.

Young, J. (1990) *Cognitive Therapy for Personality Disorders: A Schema-Focused Approach.* Saratosa: Professional Resource Exchange.

Young, J. & Klosko, J. S. (1994) *Reinventing Your Life: the Breakthrough Program to End Negative Behavior . . . and Feel Great Again.* New York: Plume Books.

Young, J. E., Klosko, J. S. & Weishaar, M. E. (2003) *Schema Therapy: A Practitioner's Guide.* New York: Guilford Press.

Young, S. N. & Leyton, M. (2002) The role of serotonin in human mood and social interaction: insight from altered tryptophan levels. *Pharmacology Biochemistry and Behavior, 71*, 857–865.

Yudofsky, S. C., Silver, J. M., Jackson, W., *et al.* (1986) The Overt Aggression Scale for the objective rating of verbal and physical aggression. *American Journal of Psychiatry, 143*, 35–39.

Zanarini, M. (1983) *Diagnostic Interview for Personality Disorders (DIPD).* Belmont, MA: McLean Hospital.

Zanarini, M. C. & Frankenburg, F. R. (2001) Olanzapine treatment of female borderline personality disorder patients: a double-blind, placebo-controlled pilot study. *Journal of Clinical Psychiatry, 62*, 849–854.

Zanarini, M. C. & Frankenburg, F. R. (2003) Omega-3 fatty acid treatment of women with borderline personality disorder: a double-blind, placebo-controlled pilot study. *American Journal of Psychiatry, 160*, 167–169.

Zanarini, M. C., Frankenburg, F. R., Dubo, E. D., *et al.* (1998) Axis I comorbidity of borderline personality disorder. *American Journal of Psychiatry, 155*, 1733–1739.

Zanarini, M. C., Frankenburg, F. R., Reich, D. B., *et al.* (2000) Biparental failure in the childhood experiences of borderline patients. *Journal of Personality Disorders, 14*, 264–273.

Zanarini, M. C., Frankenburg, F. R., Hennen, J., *et al.* (2003) The longitudinal course of borderline psychopathology: 6-year prospective follow-up of the phenomenology of borderline personality disorder. *American Journal of Psychiatry, 160*, 274–283.

Zanarini[23], M. C., Frankenburg, F. R. & Parachini, E. A. (2004) A preliminary, randomized trial of fluoxetine, olanzapine, and the olanzapine-fluoxetine combination in women with borderline personality disorder. *Journal of Clinical Psychiatry, 65*, 903–907.

Zanarini, M. C., Frankenburg, F. R., Hennen, J., *et al.* (2004a) Mental health service utilization by borderline personality disorder patients and Axis II comparison subjects followed prospectively for 6 years. *Journal of Clinical Psychiatry, 65*, 28–36.

Zelkowitz, P., Paris, J., Guzder, J., *et al.* (2007) A five-year follow-up of patients with borderline pathology of childhood. *Journal of Personality Disorders, 21*, 664–674.

Zimmerman, M. (1994) Diagnosing personality disorders: a review of issues and research methods. *Archives of General Psychiatry, 51*, 225–245.

Zigmond, A. S. & Snaith, R. P. (1983) The Hospital Anxiety and Depression Scale. *Acta Psychiatrica Scandinavica, 67*, 361–370.

---

[23]This is the reference for Study ID ZANARINI2004.

Zisook, S., Goff, A., Sledge, P., *et al.* (1994) Reported suicidal behavior and current suicidal ideation in a psychiatric outpatient clinic. *Annals of Clinical Psychiatry*, *6*, 27–31.

Zweig-Frank, H. & Paris, J. (1991) Parents' emotional neglect and overprotection according to the recollections of patients with borderline personality-disorder. *American Journal of Psychiatry*, *148*, 648–651.

13.   ABBREVIATIONS

ADHD	attention deficit hyperactivity disorder
ADI	Atypical Depression Inventory
AIAQ	Anger, Irritability, and Assault Questionnaire
AIMS	Abnormal Involuntary Movement Scale
AMED	Allied and Complementary Medicine Database
AOS	Acting Out Scale
AQ	Aggression Questionnaire
BAI	Beck Anxiety Inventory
BARNES	Barnes Akathisia Scale
BDHI	Buss-Durkee Hostility Inventory
BDI	Beck Depression Inventory
BHS	Beck Hopelessness Scale
BIS	Barratt Impulsiveness Scale
BPD	borderline personality disorder
BPDSI	Borderline Personality Disorder Severity Index
BPQ	Borderline Personality Questionnaire
BPRS	Brief Psychiatric Rating Scale
BSI	Brief Symptom Inventory
BSSI	Beck Scale for Suicide Ideation
CA	cost analysis
CAMHS	child and adolescent mental health services
CAT	cognitive analytic therapy
CBA	cost-benefit analysis
CBT	cognitive behavioural therapy
CCA	cost-consequences analysis
CEA	cost-effectiveness analysis
CGI (-BPD, -I)	Clinical Global Impressions (-borderline personality disorder, -improvement scale)
CI	confidence interval
CINAHL	Cumulative Index to Nursing and Allied Health Literature
CMA	cost-minimisation analysis
CMHT	community mental health team
CNS	central nervous system
CPA	care programme approach
CPN	community psychiatric nurse
CRHTT	crisis resolution and home treatment team
CSRI	Client Service Receipt Inventory
CT	cognitive therapy
CUA	cost-utility analysis

DBT	dialectical behaviour therapy
DES	Dissociative Experiences Scale
DIB	Diagnostic Index for Borderlines
DSM-IV	*Diagnostic and Statistical Manual of Mental Disorders* (4th edition)
EAT-26	Eating Attitudes Test (26 items)
EMBASE	Excerpta Medica database
EQ-5D	Euro-QoL 5-Dimension
EuropASI	European Addiction Severity Index
Euro-QoL	European Quality of Life
5-HT	5-hydroxytryptamine
GAD	generalised anxiety disorder
GAF	Global Assessment of Functioning
GAS	Global Assessment Scale
GDG	Guideline Development Group
GRADE	Grading of Recommendations: Assessment, Development and Evaluation
GRP	Guideline Review Panel
GSA	Global Social Adjustment
GSI	Global Severity Index
HADS	Hospital Anxiety and Depression Scale
HARS	Hamilton Anxiety Rating Scale
HMIC	Health Management Information Consortium
HMSO	Her Majesty's Stationery Office
HRSD	Hamilton Rating Scale for Depression
HTA	Health Technology Assessment
ICD-10	*International Classification of Diseases* (10th revision)
ICER	incremental cost-effectiveness ratio
IIP	Inventory of Interpersonal Problems
IMPS	Inpatient Multidimensional Psychiatric Scale
IPDE	International Personality Disorder Examination
IPT	interpersonal therapy
ITT	intention to treat
K	number of studies
LPC	Lifetime Parasuicide Count
MACT	manual-assisted cognitive therapy
MADRS	Montgomery Asberg Depression Rating Scale

Abbreviations

MBT	mentalisation-based therapy
MEDLINE	Compiled by the US National Library of Medicine and published on the web by Community of Science, MEDLINE is a source of life sciences and biomedical bibliographic information
MIS	Multi-Impulsivity Scale
MOAS	McLean Hospital Overt Aggression Symptom Checklist
N/n	number of participants
NCCMH	National Collaborating Centre for Mental Health
NHS	National Health Service
NHS EED	National Health Service Economic Evaluation Database
NICE	National Institute for Health and Clinical Excellence
NIMHE	National Institute for Mental Health in England
NNTB	number needed to treat – benefit
NNTH	number needed to treat – harm
NSF	National Service Framework
OAS (-M, -R)	Overt Aggression Scale (-modified, -revised)
OCD	obsessive-compulsive disorder
OHE HEED	Office of Health Economics, Health Economics Evaluation Database
PAI	Personality Assessment Inventory
PANAS	Positive and Negative Affect Scale
PANSS	Positive and Negative Syndrome Scale
PAS	Personality Assessment Schedule
PCT	primary care trust
PDRS	Personality Disorder Rating Scale
PHI	Parasuicide History Interview
PI	principal investigator
PILOTS	An electronic index to the worldwide literature on post-traumatic stress disorder
POMS	Profile of Mood States
PST	Positive Symptom Total
PsycINFO	An abstract (not full text) database of psychological literature from the 1800s to the present
PTSD	post-traumatic stress disorder
QALY	quality adjusted life years
RCT	randomised controlled trial
RD	risk difference
RLISC	Reasons for Living Inventory, Survival and Coping Scale
RR	relative risks

554

SAS (-I, -SR, -LIFE)	Social Adjustment Scale (-Interview, -Self-Report, -Longitudinal Interview Follow-up)
SASS	Social Adaptation Self-Evaluation Scale
SAT-P	Satisfaction Profile
SCID (I, II, -NP)	Structured Clinical Interview for DSM-IV Personality Disorders (-non-patient edition)
SCL-90 (-R)	Symptom Check List-90 (-Revised)
SFQ	Social Functioning Questionnaire
SHI	Social History Interview
SIDP-IV	Structured Interview for DSM-IV Personality
SIGLE	System for Information on Grey Literature in Europe
SIGN	Scottish Intercollegiate Guidelines Network
SMD	standardised mean difference
SNOOP	Systematic Nurses' Observation of Psychopathology
SOS	Schwartz Outcome Scale
SSHI	Suicide and Self Harm Inventory
SSI	Scale for Suicide Ideators
STAI (-T)	Spielberger State-Trait Anxiety Inventory (-Trait version)
STAS-T	Spielberger State-Trait Anger Scale
STAXI	Spielberger State-Trait Anger Expression Inventory
STEPPS	systems training for emotional predictability and problem solving
STIC	Self Report Test of Impulse Control
TAU	treatment as usual
THI	Treatment History Interview
UKCP	United Kingdom Council for Psychotherapy
WHO QoL	World Health Organization Quality of Life assessment
WMD	weighted mean difference
WSIAP	Ward Scale of Impulse Action Patterns
WTP	willingness-to-pay
ZAN	Zanarini Rating Scale